OXFORD
UNIVERSITY PRESS

Pemberton
Mathematics
for Cambridge IGCSE®

Third Edition

Extended

Sue Pemberton

Great Clarendon Street, Oxford, OX2 6DP, United Kingdom

Oxford University Press is a department of the University of Oxford.
It furthers the University's objective of excellence in research,
scholarship, and education by publishing worldwide. Oxford is a
registered trade mark of Oxford University Press in the UK and in
certain other countries

British Library Cataloguing in Publication Data
Data available

978-0-19-842480-2

9 10

Paper used in the production of this book is a natural, recyclable
product made from wood grown in sustainable forests.
The manufacturing process conforms to the environmental
regulations of the country of origin.

Printed in India by Gopsons Papers Ltd., Sivakasi

Acknowledgements
The publishers would like to thank the following for permissions
to use copyright material: **Cover image:** Shutterstock
P90: Kuttly/Shutterstock; **P257:** R. Formidable; **P271:** Andreas
Meyer/Shutterstock; **P271:** Jorgen Mcleman/Shutterstock.

® IGCSE is the registered trademark of Cambridge International
Examinations. All examination-style questions and answers within
this publication have been written by the author. In examination,
the way marks are awarded may be different.

Although we have made every effort to trace and contact all
copyright holders before publication this has not been possible
in all cases. If notified, the publisher will rectify any errors or
omissions at the earliest opportunity.

Links to third party websites are provided by Oxford in good faith
and for information only. Oxford disclaims any responsibility for
the materials contained in any third party website referenced in
this work.

Contents

Access your support website for extra exam revision material and presentations www.oxfordsecondary.com/9780198424802

Cambridge IGCSE® Mathematics 0580: Extended

Syllabus topic		Page numbers in student book
E1: Number		
E1.1	Identify and use natural numbers, integers (positive, negative and zero), prime numbers, square numbers, common factors and common multiples, rational and irrational numbers, (e.g. π, $\sqrt{2}$) real numbers, reciprocals.	3–9, 358–359
E1.2	Use language, notation and Venn diagrams to describe sets and represent relationships between sets. Definition of sets e.g. $A = \{x: x \text{ is a natural number}\}$, $B = \{(x,y): y = mx + c\}$, $C = \{x: a \leq x \leq b\}$, $D = \{a, b, c, \dots\}$	256–267
E1.3	Calculate with squares, square roots, cubes and cube roots and other powers and roots of numbers.	Embedded throughout book
E1.4	Use directed numbers in practical situations.	3
E1.5	Use the language and notation of simple vulgar and decimal fractions and percentages in appropriate contexts. Recognise equivalence and convert between these forms.	10–13
E1.6	Order quantities by magnitude and demonstrate familiarity with the symbols =, $\neq$, >, <, $\geq$, $\leq$	62–63
E1.7	Understand the meaning of indices (fractional, negative and zero) and use the rules of indices. Use the standard form $A \times 10^n$ where n is a positive or negative integer, and $1 \leq A < 10$.	58–61, 98–101, 268–271
E1.8	Use the four rules for calculations with whole numbers, decimals and fractions (including mixed numbers and improper fractions), including correct ordering of operations and use of brackets.	2, 10–13
E1.9	Make estimates of numbers, quantities and lengths, give approximations to specified numbers of significant figures and decimal places and round off answers to reasonable accuracy in the context of a given problem.	14–16
E1.10	Give appropriate upper and lower bounds for data given to a specified accuracy. Obtain appropriate upper and lower bounds to solutions of simple problems given data to a specified accuracy.	434–437
E1.11	Demonstrate an understanding of ratio and proportion. Increase and decrease a quantity by a given ratio. Calculate average speed. Use common measures of rate.	52–57, 206–207, 252–255

E1.12	Calculate a given percentage of a quantity. Express one quantity as a percentage of another. Calculate percentage increase or decrease. Carry out calculations involving reverse percentages.	50–51, 162–163, 248–251
E1.13	Use a calculator efficiently. Apply appropriate checks of accuracy.	Embedded throughout the book
E1.14	Calculate times in terms of the 24-hour and 12-hour clock. Read clocks, dials and timetables.	Embedded throughout the book
E1.15	Calculate using money and convert from one currency to another.	204–205
E1.16	Use given data to solve problems on personal and household finance involving earnings, simple interest and compound interest. Extract data from tables and charts.	250–251
E1.17	Use exponential growth and decay in relation to population and finance.	390–393
E2: Algebra and graphs		
E2.1	Use letters to express generalised numbers and express basic arithmetic processes algebraically. Substitute numbers for words and letters in formulae. Construct and transform complicated formulae and equations.	17–27, 112–113, 322–323
E2.2	Manipulate directed numbers. Use brackets and extract common factors. Expand products of algebraic expressions. Factorise where possible expressions of the form: $ax + bx + kay + kby$, $a^2x^2 - b^2y^2$, $a^2 + 2ab + b^2$, $ax^2 + bx + c$.	3–4, 18–21, 108–111, 214–217, 463–468
E2.3	Manipulate algebraic fractions. Factorise and simplify rational expressions.	64–67, 364–365
E2.4	Use and interpret positive, negative and zero indices. Use and interpret fractional indices. Use the rules of indices.	58–61, 268–271
E2.5	Derive and solve simple linear equations in one unknown. Derive and solve simultaneous linear equations in two unknowns. Derive and solve simultaneous equations, involving one linear and one quadratic. Derive and solve quadratic equations by factorisation, completing the square and by use of the formula. Derive and solve simple linear inequalities.	20–23, 62–63, 102–107, 272–275, 360–363, 394–395, 400–403, 438–442
E2.6	Represent inequalities graphically and use this representation in the solution of simple linear programming problems.	72–75, 396–399
E2.7	Continue a given number sequence. Recognise patterns in sequences including the term-to-term rule and relationships between different sequences. Find and use the nth term of sequences.	324–333

E2.8	Express direct and inverse proportion in algebraic terms and use this form of expression to find unknown quantities.	366–373
E2.9	Use function notation, e.g. $f(x) = 3x - 5$, $f: x \rightarrow 3x - 5$, to describe simple functions. Find inverse functions $f^{-1}(x)$. Form composite functions as defined by $gf(x) = g(f(x))$.	208–213
E2.10	Interpret and use graphs in practical situations including travel graphs and conversion graphs. Draw graphs from given data. Apply the idea of rate of change to easy kinematics involving distance–time and speed–time graphs, acceleration and deceleration. Calculate distance travelled as area under a linear speed–time graph.	204–205, 314–321
E2.11	Construct tables of values and draw graphs for functions of the form ax^n (and simple sums of these) and functions of the form $ax^b + c$. Solve associated equations approximately, including finding and determining roots by graphical methods. Draw and interpret graphs representing exponential growth and decay problems. Recognise, sketch and interpret graphs of functions.	168–173, 218–221, 276–277, 334–337, 404–411
E2.12	Estimate gradients of curves by drawing tangents.	170–171
E2.13	Understand the idea of a derived function. Use the derivatives of functions of the form ax^n, and simple sums of not more than three of these. Apply differentiation to gradients and turning points (stationary points). Discriminate between maxima and minima by any method.	443–462
E3: Coordinate geometry		
E3.1	Demonstrate familiarity with Cartesian coordinates in two dimensions.	28–32
E3.2	Find the gradient of a straight line. Calculate the gradient of a straight line from the coordinates of two points on it.	28–32, 68–71
E3.3	Calculate the length and the coordinates of the midpoint of a straight line from the coordinates of its end points.	68–71, 82
E3.4	Interpret and obtain the equation of a straight line graph.	28–32, 68–71
E3.5	Determine the equation of a straight line parallel to a given line.	68–71
E3.6	Find the gradient of parallel and perpendicular lines.	278–281

E4: Geometry		
E4.1	Use and interpret the geometrical terms: point, line, parallel, bearing, right angle, acute, obtuse and reflex angles, perpendicular, similarity and congruence. Use and interpret vocabulary of triangles, quadrilaterals, circles, polygons and simple solid figures including nets.	33–35, 39–40, 84–89, 114–121, 148–149, 222–229
E4.2	Measure and draw lines and angles. Construct a triangle given the three sides using ruler and pair of compasses only.	Embedded throughout the book
E4.3	Read and make scale drawings.	Embedded throughout the book
E4.4	Calculate lengths of similar figures. Use the relationships between areas of similar triangles, with corresponding results for similar figures and extension to volumes and surface areas of similar solids.	230–237
E4.5	Use the basic congruence criteria for triangles (SSS, ASA, SAS, RHS).	114–116
E4.6	Recognise rotational and line symmetry (including order of rotational symmetry) in two dimensions. Recognise symmetry properties of the prism (including cylinder) and the pyramid (including cone). Use the following symmetry properties of circles: • equal chords are equidistant from the centre • the perpendicular bisector of a chord passes through the centre • tangents from an external point are equal in length.	36–38, 282–295
E4.7	Calculate unknown angles using the following geometrical properties: • angles at a point • angles at a point on a straight line and intersecting straight lines • angles formed within parallel lines • angle properties of triangles and quadrilaterals • angle properties of regular polygons • angle in a semicircle • angle between tangent and radius of a circle • angle properties of irregular polygons • angle at the centre of a circle is twice the angle at the circumference • angles in the same segment are equal • angles in opposite segments are supplementary; cyclic quadrilaterals • alternate segment theorem.	33–35, 39–40, 282–295, 374–377

E5: Mensuration		
E5.1	Use current units of mass, length, area, volume and capacity in practical situations and express quantities in terms of larger or smaller units.	76–77, 144
E5.2	Carry out calculations involving the perimeter and area of a rectangle, triangle, parallelogram and trapezium and compound shapes derived from these.	76–77
E5.3	Carry out calculations involving the circumference and area of a circle. Solve problems involving the arc length and sector area as fractions of the circumference and area of a circle.	84–89
E5.4	Carry out calculations involving the surface area and volume of a cuboid, prism and cylinder. Carry out calculations involving the surface area and volume of a sphere, pyramid and cone.	144–149, 222–229
E5.5	Carry out calculations involving the areas and volumes of compound shapes.	144–149, 222–229
E6: Trigonometry		
E6.1	Interpret and use three-figure bearings.	174–177
E6.2	Apply Pythagoras' theorem and the sine, cosine and tangent ratios for acute angles to the calculation of a side or of an angle of a right-angled triangle. Solve trigonometrical problems in two dimensions involving angles of elevation and depression. Know that the perpendicular distance from a point to a line is the shortest distance to the line.	78–83, 178–193, 478–480
E6.3	Recognise, sketch and interpret graphs of simple trigonometric functions. Graph and know the properties of trigonometric functions. Solve simple trigonometric equations for values between 0° and 360°.	338–339, 469–473
E6.4	Solve problems using the sine and cosine rules for any triangle and the formula area of triangle = ½ $ab \sin C$.	338–343
E6.5	Solve simple trigonometrical problems in three dimensions including angle between a line and a plane.	190–193
E7: Vectors and transformations		
E7.1	Describe a translation by using a vector represented by e.g. $\begin{pmatrix} x \\ y \end{pmatrix}$, $\overrightarrow{AB}$ or **a**. Add and subtract vectors. Multiply a vector by a scalar.	130–137, 412–423
E7.2	Reflect simple plane figures. Rotate simple plane figures through multiples of 90°. Construct given translations and enlargements of simple plane figures. Recognise and describe reflections, rotations, translations and enlargements.	122–143

E7.3	Calculate the magnitude of a vector $\begin{pmatrix} x \\ y \end{pmatrix}$ as $\sqrt{x^2+y^2}$. Represent vectors by directed line segments. Use the sum and difference of two vectors to express given vectors in terms of two coplanar vectors. Use position vectors.	412–423
E8: Probability		
E8.1	Calculate the probability of a single event as either a fraction, decimal or percentage.	150–157
E8.2	Understand and use the probability scale from 0 to 1.	150
E8.3	Understand that the probability of an event occurring = 1 – the probability of the event not occurring.	151
E8.4	Understand relative frequency as an estimate of probability. Expected frequency of outcomes.	156–157
E8.5	Calculate the probability of simple combined events, using possibility diagrams, tree diagrams and Venn diagrams.	150–157, 296–303, 424–427
E8.6	Calculate conditional probability using Venn diagrams, tree diagrams and tables.	150–157, 296–303, 424–427
E9: Statistics		
E9.1	Collect, classify and tabulate statistical data.	90–93
E9.2	Read, interpret and draw simple inferences from tables and statistical diagrams. Compare sets of data using tables, graphs and statistical measures. Appreciate restrictions on drawing conclusions from given data.	90–93, 194–197, 344–351, 481–491
E9.3	Construct and interpret bar charts, pie charts, pictograms, stem-and-leaf diagrams simple frequency distributions, histograms with equal and unequal intervals and scatter diagrams.	44–45, 90–93, 194–197, 238–241, 382–385, 481–486
E9.4	Calculate the mean, median, mode and range for individual and discrete data and distinguish between the purposes for which they are used.	41–45
E9.5	Calculate an estimate of the mean for grouped and continuous data. Identify the modal class from a grouped frequency distribution.	238–241
E9.6	Construct and use cumulative frequency diagrams. Estimate and interpret the median, percentiles, quartiles and inter-quartile range. Construct and interpret box-and-whisker plots.	344–351, 487–491
E9.7	Understand what is meant by positive, negative and zero correlation with reference to a scatter diagram.	194–197
E9.8	Draw, interpret and use lines of best fit by eye.	194–197

About this book

This revised edition has been specially prepared to help you achieve your highest potential on the Cambridge IGCSE® Mathematics 0580, extended syllabus. The book is fully up to date and covers the latest syllabus in depth.

The author is an experienced mathematics teacher and an examiner. Packed with carefully chosen examples, helpful tips and plenty of exercises to give you confidence in your abilities, the author's many years of experience ensure that the book is carefully designed to help you succeed.

The contents are organised into ten units and within each unit the sections are grouped into the broad topics: number, algebra, shape and space, and probability and statistics. Each section concludes with a selection of examination-style questions. A unit is intended to be covered in around 20 hours; this should leave ample time for revision and exam practice if the syllabus is being taught over two years.

In all the examination papers it is permissible to use an electronic calculator provided that it is not an algebraic or graphical calculator. Opportunities to practise using a calculator arise throughout the book, though in practice many questions will not require the use of a calculator and candidates should be able to use mental and written methods. Indeed certain questions may require evidence of a written method being used.

Note that because this book is written for the extended syllabus a number of core topics – basic arithmetic, measures, time, money, etc. – are not covered explicitly but are woven into the treatment of more advanced topics.

The support website contains extra exam practice material and presentations, one for each section of the book, that provide many more fully worked examples. All this material can be found online at www.oxfordsecondary.com/9780198424802

Order of operations

> **THIS SECTION WILL SHOW YOU HOW TO**
> - Perform operations in the correct order

 When a calculation involves more than one operation it is important to do the operations in the correct order.
1. Work out the **B**rackets first.
2. Work out the **I**ndices next.
3. Work out the **D**ivisions and **M**ultiplications next.
4. Work out the **A**dditions and **S**ubtractions last.

Memory aid

B I D M A S
- Brackets
- Indices
- Division
- Multiplication
- Addition
- Subtraction

EXAMPLE

Calculate $150 - 3^2 \times (8 + 4) + 6 \div 2$

$150 - 3^2 \times (8 + 4) + 6 \div 2$ *brackets first*
$= 150 - 3^2 \times 12 + 6 \div 2$ *indices next, 3^2 means $3 \times 3 = 9$*
$= 150 - 9 \times 12 + 6 \div 2$ *division and multiplication next*
$= 150 - 108 + 3 = 45$ *addition and subtraction last*

EXERCISE 1.1

Work out:

1. $2 + 3 \times 5$
2. $8 \div 2 + 4$
3. $3 \times 4 - 5 \times 2$
4. $5 \times 6 - 8 \div 2$

5. $7 - 2 \times 3 + 5$
6. $10 - 2 \times 3$
7. $6 + (3 \times 5) - 2$
8. $10 + 3^2 \times 4$

9. $(5 + 4) - 3 \times 2$
10. $(5 \times 4) - (3 \times 2)$
11. $(4 \times 3) \times 2^2$
12. $5 \times (4 - 3) \times 2$

13. $5 \times (16 - 3 \times 2)$
14. $38 \div 2 - 4 \times 3$
15. $56 - (2^3 + 4)$
16. $4 + (3 \times 2)^2$

17. $(4 \times 3 + 2)^2$
18. $(2 \times 3^2) + 4$
19. $4^3 - 5 \times 6$
20. $5 \times (2^3 + 3^2)$

EXERCISE 1.2

Copy these and use brackets (where necessary) to make the statements true.

1. $2 + 3 \times 4 + 5 = 25$
2. $2 \times 3 + 4 \times 5 = 26$

3. $2 + 3 \times 4 + 5 = 29$
4. $2 + 3 \times 4^2 = 80$

5. $2 \times 3 + 4 \times 5 = 46$
6. $5 + 4 \times 3 - 2 = 15$

7. $2 \times 3 + 4 \times 5 = 50$
8. $2 \times 3 + 4 \times 5 = 70$

9. $2 + 3 \times 4 + 5 = 45$
10. $2 + 3 \times 4^2 = 50$

Directed numbers

THIS SECTION WILL SHOW YOU HOW TO
- Perform the four rules on directed numbers

The **positive** and **negative** whole numbers are called **integers**.

They can be shown on a number line.

The number line can be used in practical situations.

To find the difference between a temperature of 5 °C and a temperature of −3 °C, you find the gap between these two numbers on the number line. The difference is 8 °C.

Adding and subtracting directed numbers

The rules for adding and subtracting directed numbers are:

Change	−2 + +5	to	−2 + 5 = 3
Change	−2 + −5	to	−2 − 5 = −7
Change	−2 − +5	to	−2 − 5 = −7
Change	−2 − −5	to	−2 + 5 = 3

EXAMPLE

Work out   **a** $(-9) - (-3)$ **b** $(+8) - (+15)$ **c** $(29) + (-12)$

a   −9 − −3 = −9 + 3 = −6   change − − to +
b   +8 − +15 = +8 − 15 = −7   change − + to −
c   29 + −12 = 29 − 12 = 17   change + − to −

EXERCISE 1.3

Work out:

1 $(-3) + (-5)$

2 $6 - (-4)$

3 $8 + (-10)$

4 $2 + (-5)$

5 $(-4) - (+2)$

6 $(-15) + (-3)$

7 $36 + (-8)$

8 $29 - (+1)$

9 $(-52) - (-38)$

10 $(-54) + (-3)$

11 $(-16) + (-2)$

12 $(-20) - (-20)$

13 $(-57) + (+5)$

14 $41 + (-16)$

15 $52 - (-3)$

16 $(-5) - (+10)$

17 $(-7) - (-14)$

18 $(-42) + (-5)$

19 $(-8) + (-2) + (-5)$

20 $(-6) - (+2) - (-3)$

21 $7 - (-2) + (-3)$

22 $(+9) - (-6) + (-6)$

23 $7 - (+9) + (-3)$

24 $46 - (-12) + (-5)$

Multiplying and dividing directed numbers

The rules for multiplying and dividing directed numbers are:

Multiplication	Division
+ × + = +	+ ÷ + = +
+ × − = −	+ ÷ − = −
− × + = −	− ÷ + = −
− × − = +	− ÷ − = +

If the two signs are the same, the answer will be positive.
If the two signs are different, the answer will be negative.

EXAMPLE

Work out **a** $(-6) \div (-2)$ **b** $5 \times (-8)$ **c** $(-4)^3$

a $(-6) \div (-2) = 3$ *the two signs are the same so the answer is positive*

b $5 \times (-8) = -40$ *the two signs are different so the answer is negative*

c $(-4)^3 = -4 \times -4 \times -4$ *first multiply −4 by −4*
$= 16 \times -4$ *then multiply by −4 again*
$= -64$

EXERCISE 1.4

Work out:

1 $(-12) \times (-5)$ 2 $(-8) \times (+4)$ 3 $(+16) \times (-2)$

4 $(-52) \div (-13)$ 5 $(-55) \div (+5)$ 6 $(-145) \div (-5)$

7 $(+20) \div (-2)$ 8 $(-95) \div (-19)$ 9 $(-11) \times (-11)$

10 $(-3) \times (-4) \times (-5)$ 11 $(-2) \times (+8) \times (-4)$ 12 $(+6) \times (-3) \times (-7)$

13 $(-2) \times (-5) \times (+6)$ 14 $(-9)^2$ 15 $(-15)^2$

16 $(-5)^3$ 17 $(-60)^3$ 18 $(-4)^3 \times (-1)^3$

19 $(-2)^5 \times (-10)^2$ 20 $(-1)^{13}$ 21 $(-1)^{15} \times (-1)^{24}$

22 $\dfrac{-6}{-3}$ 23 $\dfrac{(-10) \times (+3)}{-15}$ 24 $\dfrac{(-12) \times (-5)}{(-2) \times (+10)}$

25 Check your answers to questions 1 to 18 using a calculator.

Find the missing numbers:

26 $\dfrac{\square^2 \times (-12)}{8 \div (-2)} = 48$ 27 $\dfrac{(-5) \times \square}{10} = 3$ 28 $\dfrac{\square \div 3}{(-2) \times (-6)} = -1$

KEY WORDS
positive
negative
integer

Multiples, factors, primes, squares and cubes

THIS SECTION WILL SHOW YOU HOW TO
- Identify and use factors, multiples, primes, squares and cubes

Factors

The whole numbers that divide exactly into 15 are called **factors** of 15.
The factors of 15 are 1, 3, 5 and 15.

EXAMPLE

List all the factors of 24.

$24 = 1 \times 24$ *write 24 as the product of two factors*
$24 = 2 \times 12$ *repeat until all pairs have been found*
$24 = 3 \times 8$
$24 = 4 \times 6$
Factors of 24 = 1, 2, 3, 4, 6, 8, 12 and 24.

EXAMPLE

Find the **highest common factor (HCF)** of 20 and 36.

Factors of 20 = ①, ②, ④, 5, 10, 20   *list the factors of both 20 and 36*
Factors of 36 = ①, ②, 3, ④, 6, 9, 12, 18, 36
Common factors of 20 and 36 are 1, 2, and 4.   *find the numbers that are in both lists*
Highest common factor of 20 and 36 is 4.   *select the highest number*

Multiples

The **multiples** of 6 are the numbers 6, 12, 18, 24, 30 …

EXAMPLE

Find the **lowest common multiple (LCM)** of 12 and 9.

Multiples of 12 = 12, 24, ㊱, 48, 60, ㊲, 84 …   *list the multiples of 12 and 9*
Multiples of 9 = 9, 18, 27, ㊱, 45, 54, 63, ㊲, 81 …
Common multiples of 12 and 9 are 36, 72 …   *find the numbers that are in both lists*
Lowest common multiple of 12 and 9 is 36.   *select the lowest number*

EXERCISE 1.5

1   Write down all the factors of:
    a   10   b   15   c   9   d   17   e   60
    f   80   g   100   h   64   i   125   j   90

2   Find the common factors of:
    a   6 and 8   b   10 and 15   c   9 and 18
    d   16 and 20   e   20 and 25   f   12 and 30
    g   80 and 100   h   42 and 48   i   6, 12 and 42

3   Find the highest common factor (HCF) of:
    a   6 and 8   b   10 and 15   c   90 and 18
    d   36 and 45   e   23 and 46   f   20 and 24
    g   30 and 45   h   42 and 48   i   8, 32 and 44

4   List the first six multiples of each of the following numbers.
    a   10   b   6   c   9   d   18   e   25
    f   40   g   100   h   12   i   27   j   121

5   Find the lowest common multiple (LCM) of:
    a   6 and 8   b   5 and 15   c   6 and 9
    d   7 and 8   e   4 and 6   f   12 and 8
    g   14 and 21   h   11 and 5   i   8, 10 and 12

6   A piece of rope can be cut into an exact number of 6 m lengths.
    The rope could also be cut into an exact number of 8 m lengths.
    What is the shortest possible length of the rope?

7   A light flashes every 15 minutes.
    A second light flashes every 18 minutes.
    Both lights flash together at 2 a.m.
    What will be the time when they next flash together?

8   A bell rings every 20 seconds. A second bell rings every 25 seconds.
    A third bell rings every 30 seconds. They all ring together at 8 p.m.
    How long will it be before all three bells ring together again?

Primes

A **prime** number is a number that has exactly two factors.
5 is a prime number because it has exactly two factors (1 and 5)

List the first ten prime numbers

The prime numbers are: 2, 3, 5, 7, 11, 13, 17, 19, 23 and 29

A **prime factor** is a factor that is also a prime number.

EXAMPLE

List the prime factors of 30.

The factors of 30 are: 1, ②, ③, ⑤, 6, 10, 15 and 30   *select the factors that are prime*
The prime factors of 30 are: 2, 3 and 5.

Numbers can be written as the **product of prime factors**.
For example $120 = 2 \times 60$

$$= 2 \times 2 \times 30$$
$$= 2 \times 2 \times 2 \times 15$$
$$= 2 \times 2 \times 2 \times 3 \times 5$$
$$= 2^3 \times 3 \times 5$$

The next example shows how a factor tree can be used.

EXAMPLE

Write 84 as the product of prime factors.

$$84 = 2 \times 2 \times 3 \times 7 = 2^2 \times 3 \times 7$$

Expressing numbers as the product of prime factors can help you to
find highest common factors (HCF) and lowest common multiples (LCM).

EXAMPLE

Find the HCF and the LCM of 270 and 420.

First write 270 and 420 as the product of prime factors.
$270 = 2 \times 3 \times 3 \times 3 \times 5$ and $420 = 2 \times 2 \times 3 \times 5 \times 7$
Write the prime factors on a diagram.

Prime factors   Prime factors
of 270   of 420

3   3 (2   3   5) 2   7

The HCF is the product of the numbers in the intersection = $2 \times 3 \times 5 = 30$.
The LCM is the product of all the numbers in the diagram = $3 \times 3 \times 2 \times 3 \times 5 \times 2 \times 7 = 3780$.

EXERCISE 1.6

1 Which of the following numbers are prime numbers?
11, 17, 21, 35, 47, 69, 72, 81.

2 Which of the following numbers are prime numbers?
3, 13, 23, 33, 43, 53, 63, 73.

3 Calculate the value of the following.

   a $2 \times 5 \times 5$ b $2 \times 3 \times 11$ c $3 \times 3 \times 3 \times 7$ d $2 \times 5 \times 7$

   e $2 \times 3 \times 3 \times 13$ f $2 \times 2 \times 3 \times 11$ g $3^3 \times 5^2 \times 7$ h $2^5 \times 3^2 \times 5 \times 11$

4 Write each of the numbers as the product of prime factors.

   a 10   b 150   c 81   d 60

   e 74   f 100   g 98   h 250

   i 1110   j 275   k 2004   l 2210

5 3, 7, 10, 15, 19, 21, 35

   a Which of these numbers are prime numbers?

   b Which of these numbers are multiples of 3?

   c Which of these numbers are multiples of 5?

   d Which of these numbers are factors of 30?

   e Which of these numbers are factors of 380?

6 List the prime numbers between 80 and 100.

7 Sanjit thinks that 713 is a prime number. Explain why he is wrong.

8 The number 12 can be written as the sum of two prime numbers.

    $12 = 5 + 7$

 Write each of the following numbers as the sum of two prime numbers.

   a 10   b 14   c 25   d 49   e 30

   f 20   g 38   h 82   i 36   j 48

9 Find the HCF and LCM of:

   a 24 and 42   b 45 and 105   c 70 and 42   d 40 and 75

10 Find the HCF and LCM of:

   a 30, 36 and 42   b 28, 35 and 56   c 60, 90 and 210

Square and cube numbers

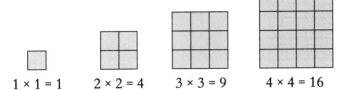

$1 \times 1 = 1$ $2 \times 2 = 4$ $3 \times 3 = 9$ $4 \times 4 = 16$

The numbers 1, 4, 9 and 16 are called **square numbers**.
The number 169 is also a square number because $13 \times 13 = 169$
13×13 can be written as 13^2

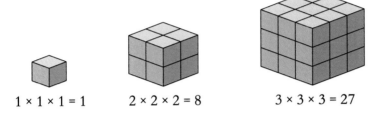

$1 \times 1 \times 1 = 1$ $2 \times 2 \times 2 = 8$ $3 \times 3 \times 3 = 27$

The numbers 1, 8 and 27 are called **cube numbers**.
The number 8000 is a cube number because $20 \times 20 \times 20 = 8000$.
$20 \times 20 \times 20$ can also be written as 20^3.

EXERCISE 1.7

1   Which is biggest 2^3 or 3^2?

2   1, 5, 9, 20, 27, 56, 48, 49, 52, 64, 275, 289, 343, 436, 512.
    a   Write down the numbers that are square numbers.
    b   Write down the numbers that are cube numbers.

3   The number 64 is a square number because $8 \times 8 = 64$.
    It is also a cube number because $4 \times 4 \times 4 = 64$.
    Can you find another number (bigger than 1) that is both
    a square and a cube number?

> **KEY WORDS**
> factor
> highest common
> factor (HCF)
> multiple
> lowest common
> multiple (LCM)
> prime
> prime factor
> product of prime factors
> square numbers
> cube numbers

Four rules for fractions

 The language of fractions

In the fraction $\frac{3}{7}$, the top part is called the **numerator** and the bottom part is called the **denominator**.

The fraction $\frac{8}{3}$ is called an **improper fraction** because the numerator is bigger than the denominator.

The number $2\frac{2}{3}$ is called a **mixed number** because it is made up of a whole number and a fraction.

To simplify a fraction you divide the numerator and denominator by a common factor.

EXERCISE 1.8

Simplify:

1 $\frac{6}{12}$ **2** $\frac{35}{49}$ **3** $\frac{18}{24}$ **4** $\frac{6}{15}$ **5** $\frac{80}{128}$ **6** $\frac{150}{175}$

7 $\frac{36}{63}$ **8** $\frac{60}{75}$ **9** $\frac{42}{48}$ **10** $\frac{36}{132}$ **11** $\frac{51}{60}$ **12** $\frac{84}{144}$

Change to mixed numbers:

13 $\frac{8}{5}$ **14** $\frac{7}{3}$ **15** $\frac{15}{7}$ **16** $\frac{20}{17}$ **17** $\frac{13}{2}$ **18** $\frac{19}{4}$

19 $\frac{17}{12}$ **20** $\frac{47}{15}$ **21** $\frac{15}{8}$ **22** $\frac{22}{21}$ **23** $\frac{17}{5}$ **24** $\frac{30}{9}$

Adding and subtracting fractions

To add or subtract fractions a common denominator is needed as shown below.

EXAMPLE

Calculate **a** $2\frac{3}{4} + 1\frac{2}{5}$ **b** $3\frac{1}{5} - 1\frac{2}{3}$

a $2\frac{3}{4} + 1\frac{2}{5}$ *write both fractions with a common denominator of 20*

$= 2\frac{15}{20} + 1\frac{8}{20}$

$= 3\frac{23}{20}$

$= 4\frac{3}{20}$

b $3\frac{1}{5} - 1\frac{2}{3}$ *write both fractions with a common denominator of 15*

$= 3\frac{3}{15} - 1\frac{10}{15}$

$= 2\frac{18}{15} - 1\frac{10}{15} = 1\frac{8}{15}$ $3\frac{3}{15} = 2 + 1\frac{3}{15} = 2\frac{18}{15}$

EXERCISE 1.9

Calculate:

1 $1\frac{1}{2} + 2\frac{1}{3}$ **2** $3\frac{1}{4} + 2\frac{1}{5}$ **3** $5\frac{1}{6} + 2\frac{3}{7}$ **4** $3\frac{2}{3} + 3\frac{4}{5}$

5 $1\frac{5}{6} + 2\frac{3}{4}$ **6** $2\frac{5}{6} + 1\frac{2}{5}$ **7** $2\frac{3}{8} + 1\frac{4}{5}$ **8** $5\frac{2}{3} + 9\frac{7}{9}$

9 $3\frac{4}{5} - 1\frac{1}{2}$ **10** $2\frac{5}{8} - 2\frac{1}{3}$ **11** $6\frac{4}{7} - 3\frac{2}{9}$ **12** $4\frac{7}{8} - 2\frac{3}{5}$

13 $5\frac{7}{8} - 2\frac{3}{5}$ **14** $2\frac{2}{5} - 1\frac{5}{6}$ **15** $6\frac{1}{6} - 2\frac{3}{4}$ **16** $7\frac{2}{5} - 3\frac{4}{7}$

17 $-3\frac{4}{5} + 1\frac{1}{2}$ **18** $4\frac{2}{3} - \left(-2\frac{1}{5}\right)$ **19** $2\frac{1}{2} + 3\frac{1}{3} - 1\frac{3}{4}$ **20** $\frac{1}{2} - 2\frac{1}{3} + \frac{5}{6}$

21 $2\frac{1}{5} - 1\frac{4}{5} - 1\frac{2}{3}$ **22** $5 - \left(2\frac{1}{3} + 1\frac{1}{5}\right)$

23 Use a calculator to check your answers to questions **1** to **22**.

24 Omar has some money. He spends $\frac{1}{5}$ of the money on a book, $\frac{3}{7}$ of the money on a CD and he puts the rest of the money in a bank. What fraction of the money does he put in the bank?

25 Fatimah has 3 kg of flour. She uses $1\frac{3}{5}$ kg to make some bread and $\frac{3}{4}$ kg to make a cake. How much flour does she have left?

26 The sum of two fractions is $6\frac{4}{5}$. One of the fractions is $4\frac{9}{10}$. Find the other fraction.

27 The difference of two fractions is $4\frac{2}{7}$. One of the fractions is $2\frac{3}{5}$. Find the other fraction.

28 Find the fraction that is halfway between $-\frac{1}{2}$ and $\frac{1}{3}$.

29 Arrange these fractions in order of size starting with the smallest:

a $\quad\frac{3}{5}, \frac{2}{3}, \frac{13}{30}$ b $\quad\frac{7}{12}, \frac{11}{18}, \frac{5}{9}$

c $\quad\frac{4}{5}, \frac{3}{4}, \frac{7}{10}$ d $\quad\frac{5}{6}, \frac{8}{9}, \frac{11}{12}$

TOP TIP

Change the fractions so they have the same common denominators.

Multiplying and dividing fractions

EXAMPLE

Calculate   a $2\frac{1}{5} \times 1\frac{3}{4}$ b $3\frac{1}{3} \div 3\frac{1}{2}$

a $2\frac{1}{5} \times 1\frac{3}{4} = \frac{11}{5} \times \frac{7}{4}$ *change to improper fractions*

$\quad\quad\quad\quad = \frac{77}{20}$ *multiply the numerators, multiply the denominators*

$\quad\quad\quad\quad = 3\frac{17}{20}$ *change to a mixed number*

b $3\frac{1}{3} \div 3\frac{1}{2} = \frac{10}{3} \div \frac{7}{2}$ *change to improper fractions*

$\quad\quad\quad\quad = \frac{10}{3} \times \frac{2}{7}$ *dividing by $\frac{7}{2}$ is the same as multiplying by $\frac{2}{7}$*

$\quad\quad\quad\quad = \frac{20}{21}$ *multiply the numerators, multiply the denominators*

The reciprocal of a number

A number multiplied by its **reciprocal** is always equal to 1.

$$5 \times \frac{1}{5} = 1$$

number × reciprocal = 1

To obtain the reciprocal of a number, you divide 1 by the number.

The reciprocal of 5 is $\frac{1}{5}$ and the reciprocal of $\frac{2}{3}$ is $\frac{3}{2}$.

EXERCISE 1.10

Calculate:

1 $1\frac{2}{3} \times 2\frac{1}{5}$

2 $2\frac{1}{4} \times 2\frac{1}{4}$

3 $3\frac{2}{5} \times 1\frac{1}{6}$

4 $5\frac{2}{7} \times 3\frac{3}{4}$

5 $4\frac{5}{6} \times 2\frac{1}{3}$

6 $7\frac{3}{10} \times 2\frac{4}{5}$

7 $1\frac{1}{2} \div 2\frac{1}{3}$

8 $3\frac{3}{4} \div 1\frac{1}{2}$

9 $2\frac{5}{6} \div 1\frac{2}{3}$

10 $3\frac{1}{8} \div \frac{4}{5}$

11 $\frac{5}{9} \div 1\frac{1}{2}$

12 $2\frac{4}{5} \div 2\frac{2}{3}$

13 $\left(\frac{3}{5}\right)^2$

14 $\left(2\frac{1}{2}\right)^2$

15 $\left(\frac{3}{20}\right)^3$

16 $\left(1\frac{1}{3}\right)^3$

TOP TIP

$\left(2\frac{1}{2}\right)^2$ means $2\frac{1}{2} \times 2\frac{1}{2}$

17 $\frac{1}{4} + \frac{2}{5} \times \frac{3}{8}$

18 $2\frac{1}{4} - \frac{3}{8} \div \frac{3}{5}$

19 Check your answers to questions **1** to **18** using a calculator.

Find the missing numbers:

20 $\frac{3}{5} \times \square = 1$

21 $\square \times \frac{2}{3} = 1$

22 $\square \div \frac{3}{7} = \frac{5}{8}$

23 $\square \times 2\frac{1}{5} = 5$

24 Tom has six bottles of juice. Each bottle contains $\frac{5}{8}$ of a litre. How many litres of juice does he have altogether?

25 Write down the reciprocal of each of these numbers.

a 3

b 7

c $\frac{1}{2}$

d $\frac{1}{8}$

e $\frac{3}{5}$

f $\frac{6}{7}$

g $2\frac{1}{3}$

h $1\frac{3}{4}$

> **KEY WORDS**
> numerator
> denominator
> improper fraction
> mixed number
> reciprocal

Significant figures and decimal places

 It is often useful to give an answer to a number of **decimal places (d.p.)**.
If you are asked to **round** a number to 2 decimal places you must have exactly 2 digits after the decimal point. The following rules are used.

> 1 Count along the digits to the required number of decimal places.
> 2 Look at the next digit.
>   If it is less than 5, leave the digit before it as it is.
>   If it is 5 or more, you must round up the digit before it.

EXAMPLE

a   Write 6.34296 correct to 3 decimal places.
b   Write 31.3027 correct to 2 decimal places.

a   6.34296 = 6.342⦙96   *the next digit is 9 so you must round up*

    = 6.343 (to 3 d.p.)
b   31.3027 = 31.30⦙27   *the next digit is 2 so the digit before it will not change*

    = 31.30 (to 2 d.p.)   *you **must** keep the 0 in your answer*

You may also be asked to round to a number of **significant figures (s.f.)**.
To round a number to a given number of significant figures use the following rules.

> 1 Count along the digits to the required number of significant figures.
>   (The most significant figure is the first non-zero figure.)
> 2 Look at the next digit.
>   If it is less than 5, leave the digit before it as it is.
>   If it is 5 or more, you must round up the digit before it.

EXAMPLE

a   Write 62934 correct to 3 significant figures.
b   Write 0.00047928 correct to 2 significant figures.
c   Write 0.08702 correct to 3 significant figures.

a   62934 = 629⦙34   *the next digit is 3 so the digit before does not change*

    = 62900 (to 3 s.f.)
b   0.00047928 = 0.00047⦙928   *the next digit is 9 so the digit before it must round up*

    = 0.00048 (to 2 s.f.)
c   0.08702 = 0.0870⦙2   *the next digit is 2 so the digit before does not change*

    = 0.0870 (to 3.s.f.)   *you must keep the 0 after the 7 in your answer*

EXERCISE 1.11

1 Round each of these correct to 1 decimal place (1 d.p.).

   a 5.347   **b** 8.75   **c** 5.99   **d** 30.021   **e** 0.06

   f 8.88   **g** 4.2067   **h** 16.255   **i** 643.991   **j** 7.006

2 Round each of these correct to 2 decimal places (2 d.p.).

   a 6.352   **b** 8.388   **c** 16.1555   **d** 4.2081   **e** 5.6999

   f 0.0384   **g** 0.0666   **h** 2.994   **i** 3.056   **j** 7.1025

3 Round each of these correct to 3 decimal places (3 d.p.).

   a 7.2222   **b** 6.1616   **c** 35.6855   **d** 82.0089   **e** 24.7894

   f 3.00002   **g** 6.0091   **h** 6.66666   **i** 102.1028   **j** 5.0096

4 Round each of these correct to 1 significant figure (1 s.f.).

   a 2.56   **b** 8.09   **c** 9.7   **d** 48.26   **e** 352

   f 26700   **g** 51000   **h** 0.0022   **i** 0.087   **j** 0.308

5 Round each of these correct to 2 significant figures (2 s.f.).

   a 1.7328   **b** 3.094   **c** 5680   **d** 61300   **e** 15.93

   f 20.07   **g** 103.24   **h** 0.00633   **i** 0.0577   **j** 0.000399

6 Round each of these correct to 3 significant figures (3 s.f.).

   a 27.348   **b** 6.5137   **c** 2587   **d** 148.8   **e** 16.745

   f 0.3492   **g** 0.07175   **h** 0.008076   **i** 10.066   **j** 39992

7 In 2010 the population of the world was estimated to be 6 831 000 000.
Round this number to 1 s.f.

8 The total area of the Atlantic Ocean is about 106 400 000 square kilometres.
Round this number to

   a 1 s.f.   **b** 2 s.f.   **c** 3 s.f.

9 Mount Everest is the highest mountain in the world.
The summit is 8848 metres above sea level. Round this number to

   a 1 s.f.   **b** 2 s.f.   **c** 3 s.f.

10 An egg has mass of 0.06395 kg. Round this number to

   a 1 s.f.   **b** 2 s.f.   **c** 3 s.f.

   d 1 d.p.   **e** 2 d.p.   **f** 3 d.p.

11 The length of the Earth's equator is 40 008.629 km.
Round this number to

   a 1 s.f.   **b** 2 s.f.   **c** 3 s.f.

   d 4 s.f   **e** 1 d.p.   **f** 2 d.p.

Estimating

It is important that you know how to check if your answer to a calculation is a sensible answer. To do this you need to **estimate** the answer.
To estimate the answer to a calculation use the following steps.

> 1 Round each of the numbers to 1 significant figure.
> 2 Do the calculation using your rounded numbers.

EXAMPLE

Estimate the answers to these calculations.

a $5.94591 \div 2.0738$

b $\dfrac{(19.719)^2 - 2.9513 \times 22.628}{685 \div (5.16 + 1.7694)}$

---

a $5.94591 \div 2.0738$ *first round each of the numbers to 1 s.f.*

$\approx 6 \div 2$

$= 3$ *[the answer using a calculator is 2.86715….]*

b $\dfrac{(19.719)^2 - 2.9513 \times 22.628}{685 \div (5.16 + 1.7694)}$ *first round each of the numbers to 1 s.f.*

$\approx \dfrac{(20)^2 - 3 \times 20}{700 \div (5 + 2)}$ *remember to do the operations in the correct order (BIDMAS)*

$= \dfrac{400 - 60}{700 \div 7} = \dfrac{340}{100} = 3.4$ *[the answer using a calculator is 3.257899….]*

EXERCISE 1.12

1 Estimate the answers to these calculations.

   a 6.4×9.8 **b** 2.16×7.79 **c** 289×12.3

   d 49.3×52.1 **e** 218×372.9 **f** $17.94 \div 3.15$

   g $22.8 \div 3.89$ **h** $188.3 \div 42.76$ **i** $5.76 + 4.73 \times 2.28$

2 Estimate the answers to these calculations.

   a $\dfrac{84.3 + 17.8}{7.16 + 2.947}$ **b** $\dfrac{8.26 - 1.99}{1.207 + 1.806}$ **c** $\dfrac{5.16 + (1.94)^2}{7.26 - 3.78}$

3 Use a calculator to find the answers to questions **1** and **2**, give your answers correct to four significant figures. Comment on whether your estimate is either an over- or an under-estimate.

4 Estimate the cost of 2.16 kg of bananas at $3.84 per kg.

5 A theatre sells tickets for a show. They sell 103 tickets at $18.99 per ticket, 321 tickets at $21.50 per ticket and 48 tickets at $27.99 per ticket. Estimate the total amount of money obtained from the sale of the tickets.

> **KEY WORDS**
> round
> decimal places (d.p.)
> significant figures (s.f.)
> estimate

Simplifying algebraic expressions

THIS SECTION WILL SHOW YOU HOW TO
- Collect like terms
- Expand single brackets

 You can simplify **expressions** by collecting **like terms**.

Simplify these expressions.

a $9x + 5y - 3x - 8y$ **b** $4x^2 - 3x - 7 - 2x^2 - 5x + 1$ **c** $7x^2y - 3xy - 7xy - 2x^2y$

a $9x + 5y - 3x - 8y$ *find the like terms*
$= 9x + 5y - 3x - 8y$ *put the like terms next to each other*
$= 9x - 3x + 5y - 8y$ $9 - 3 = 6$ and $+5 - 8 = -3$
$= 6x - 3y$

b $4x^2 - 3x - 7 - 2x^2 - 5x + 1$ *find the like terms*
$= 4x^2 - 3x - 7 - 2x^2 - 5x + 1$ *put the like terms next to each other*
$= 4x^2 - 2x^2 - 3x - 5x - 7 + 1$ $4 - 2 = 2$ $-3 - 5 = -8$ $-7 + 1 = -6$
$= 2x^2 - 8x - 6$

c $7x^2y - 3xy - 7xy - 2x^2y$ *find the like terms*
$= 7x^2y - 3xy - 7xy - 2x^2y$ *put the like terms next to each other*
$= 7x^2y - 2x^2y - 3xy - 7xy$ $7 - 2 = 5$ and $-3 - 7 = -10$
$= 5x^2y - 10xy$

EXERCISE 1.13

Simplify these expressions.

1   $5x - 8x + 2x$

2   $3y - 4y - 2y$

3   $8xy - 2xy$

4   $6xy - 9yx$

5   $6x - 4y + x - 5y$

6   $3p + 9q + 2p - 4q$

7   $3xy + 5x + 2xy - 8x$

8   $5x^2 - 9x - 6x + 2x^2$

9   $9 - 4x - 2 + 8x$

10   $4xy - 3yx + 2xy - 10yx$

11   $x^2 - 6 - 4x^2 + 15$

12   $7y^2 - 2y^2 + 3y - 5y - 11y^2$

13   $6xy - x + 2xy$

14   $a + 8ab - 12ab$

15   $7ab - 4bc + 3ab - 2bc$

16   $x^2 + x^4 + x^2 - 5 + 3x^2$

17   $6x^2 + 5x^3 - 7x^2 + x$

18   $7fg + 2gh - 5fg - 6gh - 4fg$

19   $6a^2b - 4ab^2 - 12ab^2 - 2a^2b$

20   $8cd^2 - 5c^2d - 4c^2d - 3cd^2$

21   $x + \dfrac{3}{x} + 5x + \dfrac{7}{x}$

22   $\dfrac{8}{x} - \dfrac{2}{y} + \dfrac{3}{x} - \dfrac{5}{y} - \dfrac{2}{x}$

23   $3xy^2 + 7xy - 6x^2y - 5y^2x - 4x^2y + x^2 + 5xy - y^2$

24   $7xy - 5x^2 + 3y^2 - 2x^2 - 9xy + 7x^2 - 15y^2 + 3 + 2xy + 12y^2$

Expressions involving brackets

$2(x + 3)$ means the same as $2 \times (x + 3)$
The diagram below helps to show that $2(x + 3) = 2x + 6$

The area of rectangle A is $2x$
The area of rectangle B is 6
The area of the whole rectangle is $2x + 6$

When you multiply out the brackets you must multiply each term inside the bracket by the term outside the bracket.

$5(2x + 3y)$ means $5 \times 2x + 5 \times 3y = 10x + 15y$

EXAMPLE

Expand   **a** $7(2a - 5b)$ **b** $9x(3x - 4y + 8)$

a $7(2a - 5b)$ $= 7 \times 2a - 7 \times 5b$
                          $= 14a - 35b$

b $9x(3x - 4y + 8) = 9x \times 3x - 9x \times 4y + 9x \times 8$
                          $= 27x^2 - 36xy + 72x$

You need to be very careful when multiplying by a negative number
To expand $-2(x - 6)$ you multiply both terms in the bracket by -2.
$$-2(x - 6) = (-2 \times x) + (-2 \times -6) = -2x + 12$$

EXAMPLE

Expand   **a** $-5(3x + 6)$ **b** $-8(7 - 5y)$

a $-5(3x + 6) = (-5 \times 3x) + (-5 \times 6)$
                   $= -15x + -30$
                   $= -15x - 30$

b $-8(7 - 5y) = (-8 \times 7) + (-8 \times -5y)$
                   $= -56 + 40y$

EXAMPLE

Expand and simplify
a $6(2x - 3) + 5(3x - 1)$ **b** $7(2x - 3) - 5(3x - 2)$

a $6(2x - 3) = 12x - 18$ and $+5(3x - 1) = +15x - 5$ *expand each set of brackets*
         $6(2x - 3) + 5(3x - 1) = 12x - 18 + 15x - 5$ *collect like terms*
                          $= 27x - 23$

b $7(2x - 3) = 14x - 21$ and $-5(3x - 2) = -15x + 10$ *expand each set of brackets*
         $7(2x - 3) - 5(3x - 2) = 14x - 21 - 15x + 10$ *collect like terms*
                          $= -x - 11$

EXERCISE 1.14

1   Freda says that $7(2x + 3) = 14x + 3$.
    Explain why she is wrong.

2   Expand these expressions.
    a $4(x + 3)$ b $6(y + 2)$ c $4(x + 5)$
    d $2(3 - a)$ e $7(y - 4)$ f $8(x - 9)$
    g $5(2x + 3)$ h $6(3y + 4)$ i $7(5a + 6)$
    j $3(2x + 2y - 1)$ k $5(4a + 5b - 3)$ l $8(3p - 4q + 7r)$
    m $\frac{1}{2}(8x - 2)$ n $\frac{1}{4}(12x + 8)$ o $\frac{1}{3}(15y - 6)$

3   Expand these expressions.
    a $-3(x + 4)$ b $-2(x - 6)$ c $-5(6 - 4x)$
    d $-8(2x + 5)$ e $-7(3x - 8)$ f $-8(x - 9)$
    g $-(5x + 4)$ h $-(2x - 7)$ i $-(3x + 8)$
    j $-6(3x - 3y + 5)$ k $-4(3p + 4q - 5)$ l $-3(9x^2 + 3x - 2)$

4   Expand these expressions.
    a $x(x + 3)$ b $y(y - 5)$ c $a(7 - a)$
    d $2x(5 - 3x)$ e $5y(y + 8)$ f $3x(2x + 4y)$

5   Expand and simplify.
    a $2(x + 3) + 3(x + 8)$ b $5(x - 2) + 6(x + 7)$ c $6(y + 1) + 3(y - 2)$
    d $4(x - 8) + 7(x - 6)$ e $6(5x - 2y) + 2(3x + 4y)$ f $7(2x^2 - 3x) + 2(5x - 6x^2)$
    g $x(x + 4) + x(x + 2)$ h $x(x - 3) + x(x + 7)$ i $2x(3x + 4) + 5x(6 - 3x)$
    j $2x(3y - 4) + 3y(2x - 5)$ k $2x(3x - 5y) + 3y(2x + 7y) + 5x(3y - 2x)$

6   Joe says that $5(2x - 3) - 4(x - 6) = 10x - 15 - 4x - 24 = 6x - 39$.
    Explain why he is wrong.

7   Expand and simplify.
    a $3(x - 4) - 2(x - 6)$ b $5(y + 2) - 3(y + 7)$ c $7(a + 2) - 8(3 - 2a)$
    d $6(7x - 2) - 2(3x + 4)$ e $3(x + 4) - (x - 5)$ f $7(2 - y) - (y + 3)$
    g $4(2h - 3g) - 3(3h - 2g)$ h $3x(2x + 1) - x(5x + 8)$ i $5p(p - 6) - 2p(7 - 3p)$
    j $2a(3b - 5a + 7) - 5a(7a + 3b - 5) - 3a(2a - 5b - 8)$

8   Expand and simplify.
    a $10 + 2(x + 3)$ b $15 - 3(x - 4)$
    c $20 - 2(3x - 4y + 6)$ d $9 - 5(y + 2)$
    e $8 - 7(x - 2)$ f $17x - 3(x + 5)$
    g $10y - (2y - x)$ h $5x - 2x(x - 3)$

┌ ─ ─ ─ ─ ─ ─ ─ ─ ─ ┐
│   **KEY WORDS**   │
│   expression   │
│   like terms   │
│   expand   │
└ ─ ─ ─ ─ ─ ─ ─ ─ ─ ┘

Solving linear equations

THIS SECTION WILL SHOW YOU HOW TO
- Set up simple equations
- Solve linear equations

EXAMPLE

Solve **a** $6x - 5 = 11$ **b** $9 - 5x = 2$

a $6x - 5 = 11$

$6x - 5 + 5 = 11 + 5$ *add 5 to both sides*

$6x = 16$

$\dfrac{6x}{6} = \dfrac{16}{6}$ *divide both sides by 6*

$x = 2\dfrac{2}{3}$ *change to a mixed number*

b $9 - 5x = 2$

$9 - 5x + 5x = 2 + 5x$ *add 5x to both sides*

$9 = 2 + 5x$

$9 - 2 = 2 + 5x - 2$ *subtract 2 from both sides*

$7 = 5x$ *divide both sides by 5*

$\dfrac{7}{5} = \dfrac{5x}{5}$ *divide both sides by 5*

$x = 1\dfrac{2}{5}$ *change to a mixed number*

EXAMPLE

Solve **a** $3(x - 4) = 5(2x + 3)$ **b** $5 - 6y = 2 - 4y$

a $3(x - 4) = 5(2x + 3)$ *expand the brackets*

$3x - 12 = 10x + 15$

$3x - 12 - 3x = 10x + 15 - 3x$ *take 3x from both sides*

$-12 = 7x + 15$

$-12 - 15 = 7x + 15 - 15$ *take 15 from both sides*

$-27 = 7x$ *divide both sides by 7*

$\dfrac{-27}{7} = \dfrac{7x}{7}$

$x = -3\dfrac{6}{7}$ *change to a mixed number*

b $5 - 6y = 2 - 4y$

$5 - 6y + 6y = 2 - 4y + 6y$ *add 6y to both sides*

$5 = 2 + 2y$

$5 - 2 = 2 + 2y - 2$ *take 2 from both sides*

$3 = 2y$

$\dfrac{3}{2} = \dfrac{2y}{2}$ *divide both sides by 2*

$y = 1\dfrac{1}{2}$ *change to a mixed number*

EXERCISE 1.15

1 Solve these equations.

a $2x + 3 = 15$	b $7x - 1 = 62$	c $5x + 2 = 37$	d $6x - 2 = 5$
e $8x + 3 = 15$	f $4x - 1 = 52$	g $18 - 2x = 12$	h $6 - 3x = 8$
i $10 - 4x = 7$	j $30 - 8x = 15$	k $10 - 2x = 15$	l $6 - 5x = 20$
m $3x + 4 = 27$	n $4(y - 5) = 14$	o $2(x + 3) = 7$	p $3(2x + 5) = 26$
q $4(3x - 1) = 80$	r $5(3x + 8) = 4$	s $2(13 - x) = 22$	t $5(10 - 3x) = 8$

2 Solve these equations.

a $12x + 5 = 8x + 13$	b $7x + 2 = 3x + 22$	c $6x - 3 = 5x + 4$	d $2x - 3 = 6x - 17$
e $3x + 1 = 2 - 5x$	f $7x - 9 = 10 + 2x$	g $3x + 7 = 8 - 2x$	h $7x - 3 = 9x + 10$
i $3 - 2x = 8 - x$	j $10 - 3x = 5 + 2x$	k $6 - 7x = 3 - 5x$	l $5 - 2x = 10 - 7x$

3 Solve these equations.

a $2(x - 3) + 4(2x - 7) = 6$	b $3x + 11 = 5(x + 1)$	c $7 - x = 3(5 - x)$
d $5(2x + 2) = 6(x + 5)$	e $3(2x + 5) - 2(x - 5) = 51$	f $3(3x - 2) - 7(x - 2) = 0$
g $4(1 - 2x) - 2(3 - x) = 0$	h $6(2x - 5) - 4(x - 2) = 14$	i $37 - 2(3x + 1) = 30 - 3x$

4 The sum of three consecutive numbers is 171.
Find the numbers.

● ● ● ● ● ● ● ● ● ● ● ● ● ● ● ●
TOP TIP
Let the numbers be x, $x + 1$
and $x + 2$.
● ● ● ● ● ● ● ● ● ● ● ● ● ● ● ●

5 AB is a straight line. Find the value of x.

● ● ● ● ● ● ● ● ● ● ● ● ● ● ● ●
TOP TIP
The angles on a straight line add
up to 180°.
● ● ● ● ● ● ● ● ● ● ● ● ● ● ● ●

6 ABCD is a rectangle.
Find the value of x.

● ● ● ● ● ● ● ● ● ● ● ● ● ● ● ●
TOP TIP
Opposite sides of a rectangle
are equal.
● ● ● ● ● ● ● ● ● ● ● ● ● ● ● ●

7 The perimeter of the triangle is 10 cm.
Find the value of x.

8 Expression A is 18 more than expression B.
Find the value of x.

Solving linear equations involving fractions

EXAMPLE

Solve   **a** $\frac{x}{2} + 4 = 12$ **b** $\frac{x-3}{4} = 5$ **c** $\frac{3}{x} - 2 = 8$

a $\frac{x}{2} + 4 = 12$ *subtract 4 from both sides*

$\frac{x}{2} = 8$ *multiply both sides by 2*

$2 \times \frac{x}{2} = 2 \times 8$ ➡ **NOTE:** $2 \times \frac{x}{2} = x$

$x = 16$

b $\frac{x-3}{4} = 5$ *multiply both sides by 4*

$4 \times \frac{(x-3)}{4} = 4 \times 5$ ➡ **NOTE:** $4 \times \frac{(x-3)}{4} = x - 3$

$x - 3 = 20$ *add 3 to both sides*

$x = 23$

c $\frac{3}{x} - 2 = 8$ *add 2 to both sides*

$\frac{3}{x} = 10$ *multiply both sides by x*

$x \times \frac{3}{x} = 10 \times x$ ➡ **NOTE:** $x \times \frac{3}{x} = 3$

$3 = 10x$ *divide both sides by 10*

$x = \frac{3}{10}$

The next example shows how to solve an equation when there is a single fraction on both sides of the equation.

You multiply both fractions by the lowest common multiple (LCM) of the two denominators.

EXAMPLE

Solve $\frac{x-4}{5} = \frac{x-2}{6}$

$\frac{x-4}{5} = \frac{x-2}{6}$ *multiply both sides by 30*

$30 \times \frac{(x-4)}{5} = 30 \times \frac{(x-2)}{6}$ *30 ÷ 5 = 6 and 30 ÷ 6 = 5*

$6(x-4) = 5(x-2)$ *expand the brackets*

$6x - 24 = 5x - 10$ *add 24 to both sides*

$6x = 5x + 14$ *subtract 5x from both sides*

$x = 14$

TOP TIP

You can simplify an equation with a single fraction on each side by 'cross-multiplying'.

$\frac{x-4}{5} = \frac{x-2}{6}$

$6(x-4) = 5(x-2)$

EXERCISE 1.16

1 Solve these equations.

a $\dfrac{x}{4} = 5$

b $\dfrac{x}{3} = 20$

c $\dfrac{2x}{5} = 30$

d $\dfrac{3x}{4} = 5$

e $\dfrac{x}{3} + 2 = 17$

f $\dfrac{x}{4} - 1 = -8$

g $\dfrac{2x}{5} - 3 = 7$

h $\dfrac{3x}{7} + 2 = 6$

i $\dfrac{x}{2} + 10 = 3$

j $16 - \dfrac{x}{2} = 5$

k $18 - \dfrac{x}{3} = 10$

l $19 - \dfrac{4x}{5} = 3$

2 Solve these equations.

a $\dfrac{2x+1}{3} = 5$

b $\dfrac{3x+2}{5} = 7$

c $\dfrac{4x-1}{3} = 4$

d $\dfrac{6-2x}{3} = 1$

e $\dfrac{10-4x}{5} = 4$

f $\dfrac{2(x+4)}{3} = 6$

g $\dfrac{3(2x-1)}{4} = 6$

h $\dfrac{5(2-3x)}{4} = -3$

3 Solve these equations.

a $\dfrac{24}{x} = 8$

b $24 = \dfrac{12}{x}$

c $4 = \dfrac{7}{x}$

d $5 = \dfrac{3}{2x}$

e $\dfrac{5}{x} - 2 = 8$

f $\dfrac{2}{x} + 4 = 5$

g $\dfrac{30}{x} - 2 = 4$

h $\dfrac{8}{x} - 7 = -11$

i $5 - \dfrac{3}{x} = 3$

j $24 - \dfrac{12}{x} = 30$

k $18 - \dfrac{15}{2x} = 15$

l $9 - \dfrac{36}{x} = 18$

m $\dfrac{8}{x+1} = 2$

n $\dfrac{6}{x-1} = 3$

o $\dfrac{10}{3x+2} = 2$

p $\dfrac{8}{2-5x} = 4$

4 Solve these equations.

a $\dfrac{3-x}{3} = \dfrac{2+x}{2}$

b $\dfrac{x+1}{4} = \dfrac{8-x}{5}$

c $\dfrac{2x+2}{5} = \dfrac{8-x}{2}$

d $\dfrac{3x-1}{4} = \dfrac{x}{2}$

e $\dfrac{5x+2}{3} = \dfrac{3x}{4}$

f $\dfrac{x+1}{3} = \dfrac{x-1}{4}$

g $\dfrac{x+5}{4} = \dfrac{3x+1}{5}$

h $\dfrac{6x-3}{5} = \dfrac{4x+5}{2}$

5 Explain why you cannot solve the equation $\dfrac{6x+2}{3} = \dfrac{4x-5}{2}$

6 The perimeter of the equilateral triangle is 15 cm. Find the value of x.

Constructing formulae

 A **formula** is a rule that shows how **variables** are connected.

EXAMPLE

A chocolate has a mass of 15 grams and a sweet has a mass of 22 grams.
I have x chocolates and $x + 7$ sweets.
Write down a formula for the total mass M, in grams, of the chocolates and sweets.

mass of x chocolates = $15x$
mass of $x + 7$ sweets = $22(x + 7)$
$M = 15x + 22(x + 7)$ *expand brackets*
$M = 15x + 22x + 154$ *collect like terms*
$M = 37x + 154$

➡ **NOTE:** the two variables in this question are x and M.

EXERCISE 1.17

1   A theatre sells 135 tickets at $10 each and n tickets at $13 each
    Write down a formula for the total cost P, in $, of the tickets.

2   I have $100 to spend. I buy n books at $9 each.
    Write down a formula for the amount of money Q, in $, that
    I have left after buying the books.

3   Light bulbs cost b each and candles cost c each.
    Write down a formula for the total cost C, in $, of 4 light bulbs and 7 candles.

4   Rulers cost r cents each, pencils cost p cents each and files cost f each.
    Write down a formula for the total cost T, in $, of 5 rulers, 6 pencils and 4 files.

5   The cost of hiring a tent is made up of two parts. There is a fixed charge of $30
    and then an extra charge of $4 for each day that the tent is rented.
    Write down a formula for the total cost T, in $, when a tent is rented for n days.

6   The instructions for calculating the roasting time for a chicken
    are given below.

    Allow 45 minutes per kg plus 20 minutes.

    Write down a formula for the total cooking time T,
    in minutes, to cook a chicken that has a mass of m kg.

KEY WORDS
formula
variable

Substitution into formulae

THIS SECTION WILL SHOW YOU HOW TO
- Replace letters by numbers in an expression
- Replace letters by numbers in a formula

Substitution into an **expression** means replacing the letters in an expression by the given numbers.

If $a = 2$, $b = 3$ and $c = -5$ find the value of these expressions.

a $a^2 - bc$ **b** $ac + bc$ **c** $\dfrac{4bc^2 + 5a^2}{2c}$

---

a $a^2 - bc = 2^2 - (3 \times -5)$
$= 4 - -15 = 19$

replace the letters with the given numbers
$4 - -15 = 4 + 15$

b $ac + bc = (2 \times -5) + (3 \times -5)$
$= -10 + -15 = -25$

replace the letters with the given numbers
$-10 + -15 = -10 - 15$

c $\dfrac{4bc^2 + 5a^2}{2c} = \dfrac{4 \times 3 \times (-5)^2 + 5 \times 2^2}{2 \times -5}$

replace the letters with the given numbers

$= \dfrac{300 + 20}{-10}$

$4 \times 3 \times (-5)^2 = 4 \times 3 \times 25 \text{ because} - 5 \times - 5 = 25$

$= \dfrac{320}{-10}$

remember that $+ \div - = -$

$= -32$

EXERCISE 1.18

If $a = -4$, $b = 2$ and $c = -3$ find the value of these expressions.

1 $3a + 2b$ 2 $5c - 4b$ 3 $6a - 3b + 2c$ 4 $-5c - 2b$

5 $a^2 + b^2$ 6 $c^2 - 3b$ 7 $a(b + c)$ 8 $7c(2a - b)$

9 $ab + bc + ac$ 10 $abc + ab$ 11 $3ab^2$ 12 $5a^2 bc$

13 $a - (2c)^2$ 14 $(3a)^2 - (2b)^2$ 15 $b^2 + 5b - 2$ 16 $c^2 - 4c + 7$

17 $\dfrac{ac}{b}$ 18 $\dfrac{a^2}{b}$ 19 $5 - \dfrac{ac}{b}$ 20 $\dfrac{b^2 c^2}{a}$

21 $\dfrac{a + b + c}{2}$ 22 $\dfrac{2a + 7b}{b}$ 23 $\dfrac{a + c}{a + b}$ 24 $\dfrac{4ac - 1}{c}$

25 $\dfrac{3b + 2c}{a^2 + b^2}$ 26 $\dfrac{a^2 + b^2 + c^2}{a + b + c}$ 27 $\dfrac{3a}{b} + \dfrac{4c}{a}$ 28 $8 - \dfrac{ac^2}{b}$

Substitution into a formula means replacing the letters in a formula by the given numbers.

EXAMPLE

The formula $v = u + at$ is used in physics.
Work out the value of v when $u = 20$, $a = 3$ and $t = 5$.

$v = u + at$	*replace the letters with the given numbers*
$v = 20 + 3 \times 5$	*remember to do the operations in the correct order (BIDMAS)*
$v = 20 + 15$	
$v = 35$	

EXAMPLE

The formula $s = ut + \dfrac{1}{2}at^2$ is also used in physics.

Work out the value of s when $u = 40$, $t = 10$ and $a = -5$.

$s = ut + \dfrac{1}{2}at^2$	*replace the letters with the given numbers*
$s = 40 \times 10 + \dfrac{1}{2} \times -5 \times 10^2$	$40 \times 10 = 400$ and $\dfrac{1}{2} \times -5 \times 100 = -250$
$s = 400 + \dfrac{1}{2} \times -5 \times 100$	
$s = 400 + -250$	$400 + -250 = 400 - 250$
$s = 150$	

You may need to solve an equation after substituting the numbers into the formula.

EXAMPLE

The formula $\dfrac{1}{f} = \dfrac{1}{u} + \dfrac{1}{v}$ is used in physics.

Work out the value of u when $f = 3$ and $v = 4$.

$\dfrac{1}{f} = \dfrac{1}{u} + \dfrac{1}{v}$	*replace the letters with the given numbers*
$\dfrac{1}{3} = \dfrac{1}{u} + \dfrac{1}{4}$	*take $\dfrac{1}{4}$ from both sides*
$\dfrac{1}{u} = \dfrac{1}{3} - \dfrac{1}{4}$	$\dfrac{1}{3} - \dfrac{1}{4} = \dfrac{4}{12} - \dfrac{3}{12}$
$\dfrac{1}{u} = \dfrac{1}{12}$	
$u = 12$	

EXERCISE 1.19

1 Use the formula $C = \dfrac{5(F-32)}{9}$ to work out the value of C when

   a $F = 14$ b $F = 41$ c $F = -4$ d $F = 212$

2 Use the formula $s = \dfrac{1}{2}(u + v)t$ to work out the value of s when

   a $u = 3, v = 7, t = 5$ b $u = -2, v = 5, t = 6$ c $u = 8, v = -3, t = 4$

3 Use the formula $f = \dfrac{uv}{u+v}$ to work out the value of f when

   a $u = 10, v = 15$ b $u = 3, v = 7$ c $u = 3.8, v = 1.2$

4 Use the formula $A = \sqrt{\dfrac{hm}{3600}}$ to work out the value of A when

   a $h = 180, m = 20$ b $h = 120, m = 43.2$ c $h = 150, m = 77.76$

5 The cost C, in \$, of hiring a car for n days is given by the formula
   $C = 120 + 45n$
   a Find C when $n = 7$ b Find n when $C = 840$

6 The formula for the area A of a trapezium is
   $A = \dfrac{1}{2}(a + b)h$
   a Find h when $a = 3, b = 7, A = 25$
   b Find b when $a = 5, h = 4, A = 26$

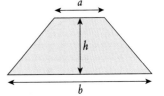

7 The formula for the total surface area A of a cuboid is
   $A = 2lw + 2hw + 2hl$

   where l is the length, w is the width and h is the height.
   a Find h when $A = 310, w = 5, l = 10$
   b Find w when $A = 164, l = 3, h = 4$

8 The formula for the volume V of a square based pyramid is
   $V = \dfrac{1}{3}x^2h$

   where x is the length of the sides of the square base and h is the height of the pyramid.
   a Find h when $V = 300, x = 10$
   b Find x when $h = 12, V = 256$.

> **KEY WORDS**
> substitution
> expression

Gradients and straight line graphs

THIS SECTION WILL SHOW YOU HOW TO
- Find the gradient of a straight line
- Draw straight line graphs

 The **gradient** of a straight line is a measure of how steep the line is.

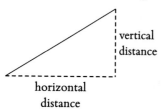

$$\text{gradient} = \frac{\text{vertical distance}}{\text{horizontal distance}}$$

Gradients can be either positive or negative.
This line has positive gradient.　　　　This line has negative gradient.

EXAMPLE

On a graph draw the line joining the points $(-2, 6)$ and $(6, 2)$ and find its gradient.

$$\text{gradient} = \frac{\text{vertical distance}}{\text{horizontal distance}}$$

$$\text{gradient} = -\frac{4}{8} = -\frac{1}{2}$$　➡ NOTE: the gradient is negative

The gradient of a line passing through two points can also be calculated using a formula.

The gradient, m, of the line passing through the points (x_1, y_1) and (x_2, y_2) is given by $m = \dfrac{y_2 - y_1}{x_2 - x_1}$

EXAMPLE

Find the gradient of the line joining $(-2, -3)$ and $(6, -1)$.

$(-2, -3)$　　　$(6, -1)$　　　　*first decide which values to use for x_1, y_1, x_2 and y_2.*
　↑　↑　　　　　↑　↑
(x_1, y_1)　　　(x_2, y_2)

$$\text{gradient} = \frac{y_2 - y_1}{x_2 - x_1} = \frac{-1 - -3}{6 - -2}$$

$$= \frac{2}{8} = \frac{1}{4}$$　　　　*simplify the fraction*

EXERCISE 1.20

1

(Grid with labelled points A–T and line segments.)

Find the gradient of the lines.

a AB   b CD   c EF   d GH   e IJ
f KL   g MN   h OP   i QR   j ST

2 Use a graph to help you work out the gradient of the line joining these pairs of points.

a $(5, 3), (6, 4)$ b $(-2, 4), (6, -5)$ c $(-1, 1), (3, 7)$
d $(2, -4), (5, -3)$ e $(1, 9), (4, -3)$ f $(5, 6), (-2, -3)$
g $(6, 4), (8, 4)$ h $(6, -3), (5, 8)$ i $(2, -4), (5, 8)$
j $(14, 0), (10, 4)$ k $(-7, -8), (-2, -6)$ l $(0, -6), (4, -5)$

3 Calculate the gradient of the line joining these pairs of points using
the formula: gradient $= \dfrac{y_2 - y_1}{x_2 - x_1}$.

a $(2, 3), (5, 6)$ b $(-2, 4), (1, 10)$ c $(4, 2), (6, 3)$
d $(2, -3), (6, 5)$ e $(2, 5), (6, 3)$ f $(1, 4), (1, -2)$
g $(-3, -1), (-6, -4)$ h $(6, -3), (5, -3)$

4 The line joining $(2, 1)$ to $(7, a)$ has a gradient of 1. Find the value of a.

5 The line joining $(4, 2)$ to $(6, b)$ has a gradient of 3. Find the value of b.

6 The line joining $(0, 3)$ to $(6, c)$ has a gradient of $\dfrac{2}{3}$. Find the value of c.

7 The line joining $(3, 6)$ to $(7, d)$ has a gradient of $\dfrac{1}{2}$. Find the value of d.

8 The line joining $(-4, -1)$ to $(-1, e)$ has a gradient of 2. Find the value of e.

9 The line joining $(-2, 1)$ to $(6, 3)$ is parallel to the line
joining $(2, -4)$ to $(6, f)$.
Find the value of f.

10 The line joining $(8, 6)$ to $(2g, -g)$ has a gradient of 2.
Find the value of g.

11 A steep road has gradient $\dfrac{4}{15}$.
The road rises by 3 meters. Calculate the horizontal distance x.

The graphs of $x = c$, $y = c$, and $y = x$

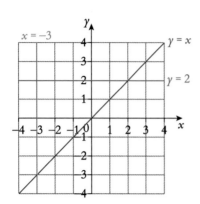

The x and y coordinates are the same at every point on the line $y = x$

eg $(1, 1)$, $(-3, -3)$, $(2, 2)$ …

The y coordinate is 2 at every point on the line $y = 2$

eg $(4, 2)$, $(0, 2)$, $(-3, 2)$ …

The x coordinate is -3 at every point on the line $x = -3$

eg $(-3, 2)$, $(-3, -1)$, $(-3, 4)$ …

➡ **NOTE:** these are important graphs that you should remember

Straight line graphs of the form $y = ax + b$

EXAMPLE

Plot the graph of $y = \dfrac{1}{2}x + 1$

Choose 3 values of x and work out the corresponding y values.

when $x = 0$, $y = \left(\dfrac{1}{2} \times 0\right) + 1 = 1$

when $x = 2$, $y = \left(\dfrac{1}{2} \times 2\right) + 1 = 2$

when $x = 4$, $y = \left(\dfrac{1}{2} \times 4\right) + 1 = 3$

x	0	2	4
y	1	2	3

➡ **NOTE:** to find each y value you halve the x value and then add 1

EXAMPLE

The line $y = ax - 5$ passes through the point $(4, 11)$
Find the value of a.

$y = ax - 5$ substitute $x = 4$ and $y = 11$ into the equation
$11 = 4a - 5$ add 5 to both sides
$4a = 16$ divide both sides by 4
$a = 4$

EXERCISE 1.21

1 Write down the equations of each of these lines.

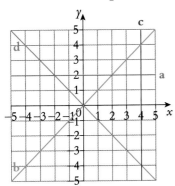

2 For each of the following copy and complete the table of values and then draw
a graph of the function. Use coordinate axes with values from −6 to 6.

a $y = x + 2$

x	0	1	2
y			

b $y = x - 5$

x	0	1	2
y			

c $y = 2x - 2$

x	0	1	2
y			

d $y = 3x - 4$

x	0	1	2
y			

e $y = \frac{1}{2}x - 1$

x	-2	0	2
y			

f $y = \frac{1}{3}x - 4$

x	-3	0	3
y			

g $y = 3 - 2x$

x	0	1	2
y			

h $y = 5 - 3x$

x	0	1	2
y			

3 Plot these graphs on the same set of axes.

$y = 3x$ $\qquad$ $y = 3x + 2$ $\qquad$ $y = 3x - 5$

What do you notice about the graphs?

4 Plot these graphs on the same set of axes.

$y = 3x - 2$ $\qquad$ $y = 2x + 1$

Write down the coordinates of the point where the two lines inersect.

5 Plot these graphs on the same set of axes.

$y = 2x - 3$ $\qquad$ $y = \frac{1}{2}x + 3$

Write down the coordinates of the point where the two lines inersect.

6 The graph $y = ax + 4$ passes through the point (2, 8). Find the value of a.

7 The graph $y = bx - 3$ passes through the point (−2, 6). Find the value of b.

8 The graph $y = 3x + c$ passes through the point (3, −5). Find the value of c.

Graphs of the form $ax + by = c$

An easy method to draw or sketch a graph of this form is to find the axis crossing points.
Putting $x = 0$ into the equation will tell you where the graph crosses the y-axis.
Putting $y = 0$ into the equation will tell you where the graph crosses the x-axis.

EXAMPLE

Sketch the graph of $3x + 4y = 12$.

when $x = 0$, $4y = 12$

$\quad\quad\quad\quad y = 3$ *the graph crosses the y-axis at (0,3)*

when $y = 0$, $3x = 12$

$\quad\quad\quad\quad x = 4$ *the graph crosses the x-axis at (4,0)*

EXERCISE 1.22

Copy and complete the table for each of the following functions
and sketch the graph.

1 $2x + y = 4$

x	0	
y		0

2 $3x + 2y = 6$

x	0	
y		0

3 $2x + 5y = 10$

x	0	
y		0

4 $y + 3x = 9$

x	0	
y		0

5 $2x + 3y = -12$

x	0	
y		0

6 $6x + 5y = -30$

x	0	
y		0

7 $x - 2y = 6$

x	0	
y		0

8 $4x - 5y = 20$

x	0	
y		0

9 $2x - 3y = 12$

x	0	
y		0

10 $y - 3x = 15$

x	0	
y		0

11 $5x - 3y = -30$

x	0	
y		0

12 $2x - \dfrac{1}{3}y = -4$

x	0	
y		0

Angle properties

You should already know the following facts.

Isosceles triangle

Equilateral triangle

Names of angles

acute angles   between 0° and 90°
right angle   90°
obtuse angle   between 90° and 180°
reflex angle   more than 180°

Angle properties

Angles on a straight line

$a + b = 180°$

Angles at a point

$a + b + c = 360°$

Vertically opposite angles

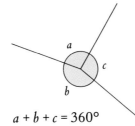

$a = b$

Angles in a triangle

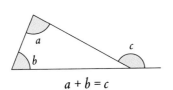

$a + b + c = 180°$

Exterior angles of a triangle

$a + b = c$

Angles in a quadrilateral

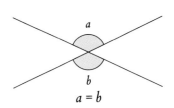

$a + b + c + d = 360°$

Parallel lines

Perpendicular lines

Corresponding angles

$a = b$

Alternate angles

$a = b$

Find the lettered angles giving reasons for your answers.

AD̂E = DB̂C	$a = 64°$	*corresponding angles*
AÊD = EĈB = 48°		
CÊD + AÊD = 180°	$b = 132°$	*angles on a straight line*
DÂE + AÊD + ED̂A = 180°	$c = 68°$	*angles in a triangle*

EXERCISE 1.23

Calculate the size of each lettered angle.

1

2

3

4

5

6

7

8

9

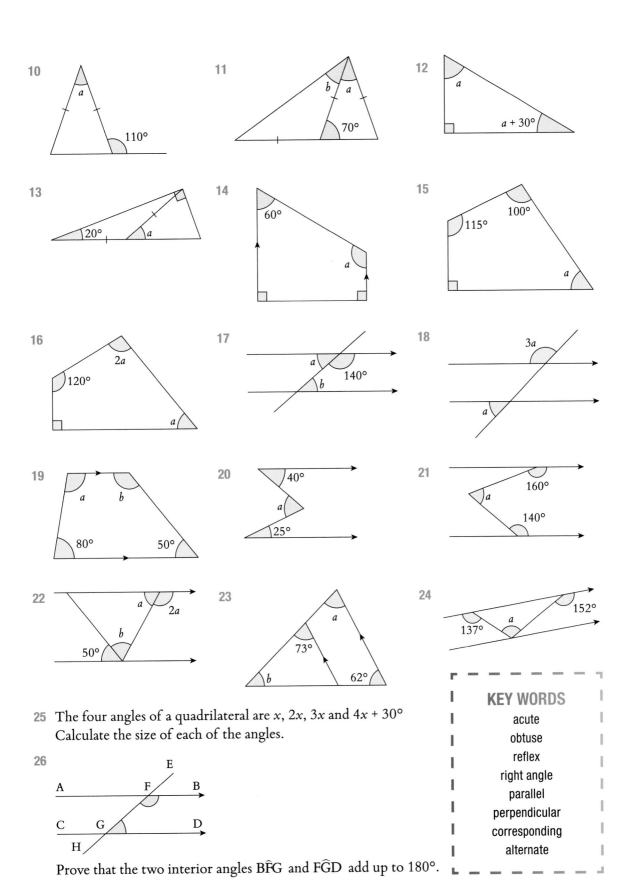

10
a
$110°$

11
b a
$70°$

12
a
$a + 30°$

13
$20°$ a

14
$60°$
a

15
$100°$
$115°$
a

16
$2a$
$120°$
a

17
a
$140°$
b

18
$3a$
a

19
a b
$80°$ $50°$

20
$40°$
a
$25°$

21
$160°$
a
$140°$

22
a $2a$
b
$50°$

23
a
$73°$
b $62°$

24
$152°$
$137°$ a

25 The four angles of a quadrilateral are x, $2x$, $3x$ and $4x + 30°$
Calculate the size of each of the angles.

26

Prove that the two interior angles BF̂G and FĜD add up to 180°.

KEY WORDS
acute
obtuse
reflex
right angle
parallel
perpendicular
corresponding
alternate

Symmetry

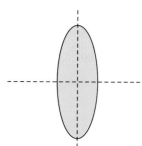

This shape has 2 **lines of symmetry**.

A line of symmetry divides a shape into two identical parts.

It also has **rotational symmetry** of order 2.

Rotational symmetry of order 2 means that if you rotate the shape about its centre through one complete turn, it will fit onto itself twice.

EXAMPLE

Describe the symmetry of these two shapes.

This shape has 0 lines of symmetry and rotational symmetry of order 4.

This shape has 1 (vertical) line of symmetry and rotational symmetry of order 1.

EXERCISE 1.24

1   For each quadrilateral write down the number of lines of symmetry and the order of rotational symmetry.

a

square

b

rectangle

c

parallelogram

d

trapezium

e

rhombus

f

kite

2 For each shape write down the number of lines of symmetry and the
   order of rotational symmetry.

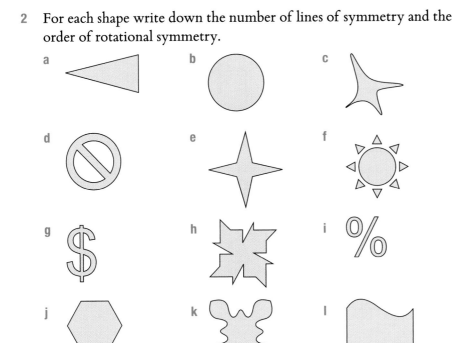

a   b   c

d   e   f

g   h   i

j   k   l

3 For each pattern write down the number of lines of symmetry and
   the order of rotational symmetry.

a   b   c

4 Make three copies of this grid. Colour each grid so that it has
   a One line of symmetry and rotational symmetry of order 1
   b Two lines of symmetry and rotational symmetry of order 2
   c No lines of symmetry and rotational symmetry of order 2

5 For each of the following curves write down the number of lines
   of symmetry and the order of rotational symmetry.

a   b   c   d

6 For an unknown quadrilateral you are told how many lines of
   symmetry it has, its order of rotational symmetry, whether its
   diagonals cross at right angles and whether the diagonals bisect
   one another. Given this information can you always identify the
   quadrilateral.

TOP TIP

Start by constructing a table of
properties of quadrilaterals.

Planes of symmetry

This cuboid has 3 **planes of symmetry**.

A plane of symmetry cuts a solid into two equal parts.
Each part is a mirror image of the other.

EXAMPLE

How many planes of symmetry does a square based pyramid have?

A square based pyramid has 4 planes of symmetry.

EXERCISE 1.25

1   The end face of this prism is an equilateral triangle.
    A plane of symmetry is shown.
    The prism has three more planes of symmetry.
    Draw three diagrams to show these planes of symmetry.

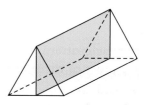

2   How many planes of symmetry are there for each of these solid objects.

   a   b   c   d   e

    cube   cylinder   sphere   cone   hexagonal prism

3   These solids are made from small cubes.
    How many planes of symmetry does each solid have?

    a   b   c   d

4   Draw a prism whose cross section is an isosceles trapezium.
    How many planes of symmetry does the prism have?

KEY WORDS
line of symmetry
order of rotational symmetry
plane of symmetry

Polygons

THIS SECTION WILL SHOW YOU HOW TO
- Find the sum of the interior angles in a polygon
- Find the size of exterior and interior angles in a regular polygon

A **polygon** is a shape enclosed by straight lines.
An n-sided polygon can be divided into $(n - 2)$ triangles.

Number of sides	Name of polygon	Sum of interior angles
3	triangle	$(3 - 2) \times 180° = 180°$
4	quadrilateral	$(4 - 2) \times 180° = 360°$
5	pentagon	$(5 - 2) \times 180° = 540°$
6	hexagon	$(6 - 2) \times 180° = 720°$

the sum of the **interior angles** in an n-sided polygon $= (n - 2) \times 180°$

interior angle + exterior angle $= 180°$

the exterior angles of any polygon always add up to $360°$

A **regular polygon** has all sides equal and all angles the same.

In a regular n-sided polygon

exterior angle $= \dfrac{360°}{n°}$

interior angle $= 180° - \dfrac{360°}{n°}$

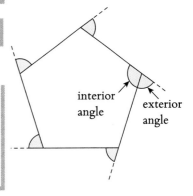

interior angle   exterior angle

EXAMPLE

ABCDE is a regular pentagon.
The lines BA and DE are extended to meet at F.
Calculate the size of angle AFE.

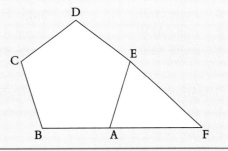

Angle FAE $= \dfrac{360}{5} = 72°$ *angle FAE is an exterior angle of the pentagon*

Angle FEA is also $72°$

Angle AFE $= 180 - (72 + 72)$ *angles in a triangle add up to $180°$*

$\qquad = 180 - 144 = 36°$

EXERCISE 1.26

1 Jay says that the sum of the interior angles of a six-sided polygon is 6 × 180° = 1080°.
   Is he correct? Explain your answer.

2 Four of the angles of a pentagon are 123°, 84°, 113° and 96°. Calculate the fifth angle.

3 A regular polygon has nine sides. Calculate the size of the interior angle.

4 The exterior angle of a regular polygon is 30°. How many sides does the polygon have?

5 The interior angle of a regular polygon is 162°. How many sides does it have?

6 A polygon has 10 sides. Find the sum of the interior angles.

7 Calculate the size of *x* for each of the diagrams.

a

b

c

d

e

f

8 The diagram shows a regular octagon and a regular pentagon.
   Calculate:
   a angle AED   b angle DEF
   c angle HDE   d angle HDG
   e angle ADE   f angle ADG
   g angle AEF   h angle BDA

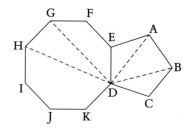

9 The interior angle of a regular polygon is eight times
   the size of the exterior angle. How many sides does the
   polygon have?

> **KEY WORDS**
> polygon
> regular polygon
> interior angle
> exterior angle

Averages and range

The three types of **average** that you need to know are

mean	the total of all the values divided by the number of values
median	the middle value when the data are arranged in order
mode	the value (or item) that occurs most often

The **range** is a measure of spread.

range = highest value – smallest value

EXAMPLE

The list shows the times taken by six students to solve a puzzle.

55 sec   48 sec   36 sec   55 sec   29 sec   41 sec

Work out
a   the mean
b   the median
c   the mode
d   the range for the times taken.

a $\text{mean} = \dfrac{55+48+36+55+29+41}{6}$

$= \dfrac{264}{6}$

$= 44$ sec

b   29   36   (41)   (48)   55   55   *arrange in order of size first*
There are two middle values.
The median is the number half-way between these values.
$\text{median} = \dfrac{41+48}{2}$
$= 44.5$ sec

c   mode = 55 sec   *the value that occurs most often*
d   range = 55 – 29   *highest value – smallest value*
          = 26 sec

Sometimes you might be asked to choose which type of average is most representative for a data set.

The list shows the test results of eight students.

1   17   18   19   19   20   20   20

Find the mean, mode and median.

Comment on each of your averages.

$$\text{mean} = \frac{1+17+18+19+19+20+20+20}{8} = \frac{134}{8} = 16.75$$

The mean is not a representative average because only one student scored less than this.

mode = 20
The mode is not a representative average to use because everyone scored 20 or less.

median = 19
This is the most representative (best) average to use.

EXERCISE 1.27

1   7, 3, 5, 6, 2, 1, 5

Raju says that the median of the numbers is 6. Is he correct?
Explain your answer.

2   Find the mean, median, mode and range for each list of numbers.

  a   8, 10, 11, 10, 6   b   3, −6, −10, 5, −1, −3   c   50, 63, 54, 65

  d   3, 1, 6, 5, 2, 3, 5, 4, 3, 1, 2, 3, 1   e $1\frac{2}{3}, \frac{5}{6}, \frac{1}{2}, 1\frac{1}{3}$

3   The table shows the number of cars sold each month by a car salesman in one year.

Month	Jan	Feb	Mar	Apr	May	Jun	July	Aug	Sept	Oct	Nov	Dec
Number of cars	13	13	12	10	13	12	13	15	14	13	6	10

Find the mean, median, mode and range for the data.

4   The times (in seconds) for 10 runners in a 100 metre race were

10.35   10.28   10.05   10.25   10.28   10.65   10.47   10.33   10.28   10.42

Find the mean, median, mode and range for the data.

5   For the following data sets explain, with reasons, which average you would
use to describe them.

  a   0, 0, 1, 2, 4, 6, 7, 8, 8, 9   b   6, 7, 7, 8, 29
  c   1, 2, 3, 4, 5, 11, 12, 13, 14, 15   d   −5, −3, 2, 3, 3

6   a   The mean mass of 8 men is 82.4 kg. What is the total mass of the 8 men?

  b   The mean length of 7 sticks is 1.02 m. What is the total length of the 7 sticks?

7 The mean height of six women is 1.64 m.
The heights of five of the women are
1.60 m, 1.62 m, 1.64 m, 1.61 m and 1.62 m.
Find the height of the sixth woman.

● ● ● ● ● ● ● ● ● ● ● ● ● ●

TOP TIP
First find the total height of the
six women.
● ● ● ● ● ● ● ● ● ● ● ● ● ●

UNIT 1

8 a The mean of four numbers is 59.
The numbers are 52, 57, 58 and p.
Find the value of p.

 b The mean of six numbers is 9.
The numbers are 5, 7, 7, x, 12 and 16.
Find the value of x.

 c The mean of five numbers is 14.
The numbers are 9, y, 15, 15 and 18.
Find the value of y.

 d The mean of seven numbers is 19.
The numbers are 6, 10, 11, 13, 17, 20 and w.
Find the value of w.

9 There are six women and four men in a group of ten people.
The mean age of the six women is 65.
The mean age of the four men is 73.
Find the mean age of the group of ten people.

10 Students from two different schools do an examination paper.
There are 150 students at School A and the mean mark for
School A is 66.
There are 250 students at School B and the mean mark for
School B is 58.
Calculate the mean mark of the 400 students.

11 A sample of fish is taken from two different lakes.
Seventy fish are taken from Lake A and the mean length of the
fish is 35 cm.
Thirty fish are taken from Lake B and the mean length of the
fish is 42 cm.
Calculate the mean length of the 100 fish.

KEY WORDS
average
mean
median
mode
range

Frequency tables

THIS SECTION WILL SHOW YOU HOW TO

- Find the mean, median, mode and range for a frequency distribution

 Large data sets are usually recorded in a **frequency table**.

EXAMPLE

The list shows the number of absences from a class over a period of 25 days.

```
0   3   2   2   0   2   2   0   2   2   2   1   0
1   2   1   2   0   1   3   2   1   1   2   2
```

Arrange the data into a frequency table.

Use your frequency table to work out the

a mode   **b** median   **c** range   **d** mean.

Number of absences (x)	Frequency (f)
0	5
1	6
2	12
3	2

a   Mode = 2 absences

the mode is the number of absences with the highest frequency

b   Median = 2 absences

the median is the (25 + 1) ÷ 2 = 13th number. There are 11 numbers up to the end of the 1's, so the 13th number must be a 2.

c   Range = 3 absences

highest value – lowest value = 3 – 0

d

Number of absences (x)	Frequency (f)	x × f
0	5	0 × 5 = 0
1	6	1 × 6 = 6
2	12	2 × 12 = 24
3	2	3 × 2 = 6
Total	**25**	**36**

A third column is used to find the total number of absences for each row

$$\text{Mean} = \frac{\text{total number of absences}}{\text{total number of days}}$$

$$= \frac{36}{25} = 1.44 \text{ absences}$$

EXERCISE 1.28

1 a   Gina says the mode for the number of fish is 6.
       Is she correct? Explain your answer.
   b   Gregor says that the median number of fish is 2.
       Is he correct? Explain your answer.

Number of fish	Frequency
0	5
1	6
2	5
3	3
4	1

2 The table shows the number of people in each car passing
   a checkpoint.
   a   Find the mode for the number of people in a car.
   b   Find the median number of people in a car.
   c   Copy and complete the table.
       Calculate the mean number of people in a car.

Number of people	Frequency
1	52
2	38
3	8
4	2

Number of people (x)	Frequency (f)	$f \times x$
1	52	1 × 52 =
2	38	
3	8	
4	2	
Total		

3 Twenty children were asked how many pets they own. The table shows the results.

Number of pets	0	1	2	3	4
Frequency	5	9	4	1	1

Find the mode, median and mean number of pets.

4 The table shows the number of suitcases belonging to each of 100 air passengers.

Number of suitcases	0	1	2	3
Frequency	3	55	38	4

Find the mode, median and mean number of suitcases.

5 The table shows the scores in a quiz for 40 students.

Quiz score	5	6	7	8	9
Frequency	3	7	17	12	1

Find the mode, median and mean quiz score.

6 The table shows the test marks for n students. The mean test mark is 4.

Test mark	1	2	3	4	5
Frequency	3	5	6	2	x

   a   Find the values of x and n.
   b   Find the median test mark.

┌ ─ ─ ─ ─ ─ ─ ─ ─ ┐
│ **KEY WORDS** │
│ frequency table │
└ ─ ─ ─ ─ ─ ─ ─ ─ ┘

Unit 1 Examination-style questions

1 Use brackets to make the following statement correct.

$$15 - 2 \times 3 + 4 \div 2 = 2.5$$ [1]

2 The lowest recorded temperature in Alaska is $-62.2\,°C$.
   The highest recorded temperature in Alaska is $37.8\,°C$.

   Find the difference between these temperatures. [1]

3 Find the highest common factor (HCF) of 240 and 336. [2]

4 **(a)** Write 140 as a product of prime factors. [2]
   (b) Find the lowest common multiple (LCM) of 84 and 140. [2]

5 Write down the prime numbers between 50 and 60. [1]

6 **Without using a calculator**, work out $5\frac{2}{7} - 3\frac{5}{6}$.

   You must show all your working and give your answer as a mixed number
   in its simplest form. [3]

7 **Without using a calculator**, work out $2\frac{5}{6} \div 1\frac{1}{3}$.

   You must show all your working and give your answer as a mixed number
   in its simplest form. [3]

8 **(a)** Write the number 302.658 correct to 2 decimal places, [1]
   (b) Write the number 302.658 correct to 2 significant figures. [1]

9 Write each number correct to 1 significant figure and estimate the value of
   the calculation. You must show your working.

   $$\frac{27.8^2}{6.85 + 2.34}$$ [2]

10 Expand the brackets and simplify.

    $$3(2x - 1) - 2(x + 4)$$ [2]

11 Solve.

    $$2 - \frac{x}{5} = 6$$ [2]

12 Solve.

(a) $5(2x - 1) = 7$ [3]

(b) $\dfrac{12 - 5x}{6} = 3 - 2x$ [3]

13 Solve.

(a) $10 - 2(x - 4) = 5(3x + 2)$ [3]

(b) $\dfrac{2x - 3}{5} = \dfrac{1 - 4x}{3}$ [3]

14 Ali hires a car.
There is a fixed charge of $170 and then an extra charge of $40 for each day that the car is hired.

Write down a formula for the total cost T, in dollars, when the car is hired for n days. [2]

15 Peaches cost 80 cents each and apples cost 65 cents each.
Anna buys x peaches and 14 apples and spends a total of $17.90

(a) Write down an equation, in terms of x, for the total cost of this fruit. [2]
(b) Solve your equation in **part (a)**. [2]

16 $e = 2f + 5g^3$

Find the value of e when $f = 4$ and $g = -5$. [2]

17 The equation of a straight line is $3x + 2y = 6$.

(a) Write down the gradient of this line, [1]
(b) Write down the coordinates of the point where the line crosses the y-axis. [1]

18 A is the point $(5, -3)$ and B is the point $(-9, 4)$.

Find the gradient of the line AB. [2]

19 P is the point $(-4, 5)$ and Q is the point $(2a, -3a)$.
The gradient of the line PQ is -2.

Find the value of a. [2]

20 P is the point $(p, 15)$ and Q is the point $(-4, q)$.
The line PQ has gradient -2.

Find an expression for q in terms of p. [3]

21 The line $y = mx + 4$ passes through the point $(5, -6)$.

Find the value of m. [2]

22

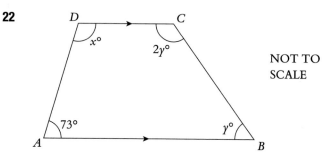

ABCD is a trapezium with *AB* parallel to *CD*.

Find the value of *x* and the value of *γ*.   [2]

23

For the diagram above, write down

(a) the order of rotational symmetry,   [1]
(b) the number of lines of symmetry.   [1]

24

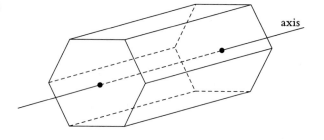

The diagram shows a prism.
The cross-section of the prism is a regular hexagon.

(a) Write down the order of rotational symmetry of this prism about
the axis shown.   [1]
(b) Write down the number of planes of symmetry for this prism.   [1]

25 The interior angle of a regular polygon is 162°.

Find the number of sides for this polygon.   [2]

26 The interior angle of a regular polygon is seven times the size of
the exterior angle.

How many sides does this polygon have?   [3]

27

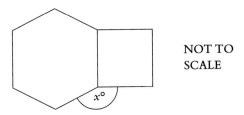

NOT TO SCALE

The diagram shows a regular hexagon joined to a square.

Find the value of x. [3]

28 Alan counts the number of sweets in each of 8 packets.
The results are shown below.

22   28   25   29   24   28   26   23

(a) (i) Find the range. [1]
(ii) Write down the mode. [1]
(iii) Find the median. [2]
(iv) Calculate the mean. [2]

(b) Alan buys another n packets of sweets.
The mean for these n packets is 26.

Find, in terms of n, an expression for the mean number of
sweets in the $(n + 8)$ packets. [2]

29 A six-sided dice, numbered 1 to 6, is rolled 40 times.

The frequency table shows the results.

Score	1	2	3	4	5	6
Frequency	10	3	5	7	8	7

(a) Write down the modal score. [1]
(b) Find the median score. [1]
(c) Calculate the mean score. [3]
(d) The dice is then rolled another 10 times.
The mean score for these 10 rolls is 3.4

Calculate the mean score for all 50 rolls. [3]

30 The table shows information about the number of text messages received, in
one hour, by each student in a class.

Number of text messages	0	1	2	3	4	7
Frequency	7	12	15	x	2	1

The mean number of text messages is 1.8

Calculate the value of x. [3]

Percentages 1

 Percentage means parts of 100 so 37% = $\frac{37}{100}$ (= 0.37)

Percentages are often used to compare quantities.

You should know how to convert fractions and decimals to percentages.

> To change a fraction or decimal to a percentage, multiply by 100

$\frac{1}{4} = \frac{1}{4} \times 100\% = 25\%$ $0.03 = 0.03 \times 100\% = 3\%$

> To change a percentage to a fraction or a decimal, divide by 100.

$29\% = 29 \div 100 = \frac{29}{100}$ or 0.29

EXAMPLE

a Find 27% of 540 m   **b** Find 8% of $350

a 27% of 540 m = $\frac{27}{100} \times 540$

       = 145.8 m

Alternative method:
0.27 × 540 = 145.8 m

b 8% of $350 = $\frac{8}{100} \times 350$

       = $28

Alternative method:
0.08 × 350 = $28

EXAMPLE

An airline increases its ticket prices by 15%.
Calculate the new price of a ticket costing $1300.

Increase in price = 15% of $1300

       = $\frac{15}{100} \times 1300$

       = $195

New price = $1300 + $195

       = $1495

Quicker method:
multiplying factor is 1.15 (= 1 + 0.15)
1.15 × 1300 = $1495

EXAMPLE

A coat costing $180 is reduced by 12% in a sale.
Calculate the price of the coat in the sale.

Decrease in price = 12% of $180

       = $\frac{12}{100} \times 180$

       = $21.60

New price = $180 − $21.60 = $158.40

Quicker method:
multiplying factor is 0.88 (= 1 − 0.12)
0.88 × 180 = $158.40

EXERCISE 2.1

1 Write these percentages as fractions in their simplest form.
   a 24%   b 80%   c 58%   d 65%   e 30%

2 Write these fractions as percentages.
   a $\dfrac{3}{5}$ b $\dfrac{7}{20}$ c $\dfrac{18}{25}$ d $\dfrac{37}{50}$ e $\dfrac{7}{8}$

3 Write these percentages as decimals.
   a 18%   b 70%   c 6%   d 47%   e 2.5%

4 Write these decimals as percentages.
   a 0.28   b 0.8   c 0.08   d 1.2   e 0.755

5 Calculate the following.
   a 15% of $80   b 52% of 600 km   c 27% of 500 kg

6 Which is bigger: 35% of $50 or 30% of $60?

7 a Increase $58 by 12%   b Increase $72 by 24%
   c Increase $136 by 40%   d Increase $230 by 18%
   e Increase $440 by 2.5%   f Increase $90 by 120%

8 a Decrease $64 by 15%   b Decrease $400 by 32%
   c Decrease $250 by 8%   d Decrease $128 by 12.5%
   e Decrease $500 by 3.5%   f Decrease $360 by 0.2%

9 Nadia is paid $700 dollars a week. Her pay is increased by 5%.
   Calculate her new weekly pay.

10 A holiday is advertised as costing $950.
    Raju is given a 7% discount for booking online.
    Calculate how much he pays for the holiday.

11 A new car costs $1750.
    The car depreciates in value by 27% in its first year.
    Find the value of the car after one year.

12 A rare book is bought for $3250. It increases in value by 8%.
    Calculate the new value of the book.

13 Rukhusana and Shahida invested $300 each in company shares.
    Rukhusana's investment increased in value by 5.2% in the first year.
    Shahida's investment decreased in value by 0.8% in the first year.
    At the end of the first year, find how much more Rukhusana's
    investment is worth than Shahida's.

> **KEY WORDS**
> percentage

UNIT 2

Ratio

THIS SECTION WILL SHOW YOU HOW TO
- Simplify ratios
- Divide a quantity in a given ratio
- Solve problems using ratios

Simplifying ratios

You can use **ratios** to compare one quantity with another quantity.
If there are 4 teachers and 18 students on a school trip then the ratio
of teachers to students can be written as

teachers : students = 4 : 18

Ratios are simplified in a similar way to fractions.

$\div 2$ $\qquad$ $\div 2$

$\longrightarrow$ 2 : 9 $\longleftarrow$

➡ **NOTE:** divide both sides of
the ratio by the common
factor 2.

This means that for every 2 teachers there are 9 students.

> A ratio in its simplest form (lowest terms) has integer values that
> cannot be cancelled further.

EXAMPLE

Write these ratios in their simplest form.

a 44 : 36 **b** 1.7 : 0.4 **c** $\frac{1}{2} : \frac{2}{3}$

a 44 : 36

$\div 4$ $\qquad$ $\div 4$

= 11 : 9

b 1.7 : 0.4

$\times 10$ $\qquad$ $\times 10$

= 17 : 4

c $\frac{1}{2} : \frac{2}{3}$

$\times 6$ $\qquad$ $\times 6$

= 3 : 4

Writing a ratio in the form 1 : n

Map scales are often written as ratios in the form 1 : n

EXAMPLE

Write the ratio 2 cm : 5 km in the form 1 : n.

2 cm : 5 km   *change 5 km to m*
= 2 cm : 5000 m   *change 5000 m to cm*
= 2 cm : 500 000 cm   *divide both sides of the ratio by 2*
= 1 : 250 000

EXERCISE 2.2

1 Write these ratios in their simplest form.

   a 20 : 30   b 18 : 24   c 6 : 30   d 40 : 25

   e 29 : 36   f 55 : 33   g 48 : 42   h 63 : 99

2 Write these ratios in their simplest form.

   a 200 g : 1 kg   b 10 cm : 2 m   c 5 mm : 2 cm

   d 1 cm : 50 km   e 5 m : 20 cm   f 60 g : 3 kg

   g 80 mm : 2 m   h 0.5 kg : 800 g   i 6 hours : 1 day

> **TOP TIP**
>
> Change to the same units before simplifying.

3 Write these ratios in their simplest form.

   a 5.6 : 2.4   b 0.8 : 0.6   c 1.2 : 0.4   d 1.5 : 7.5

   e 0.08 : 0.2   f 1.04 : 0.44   g 4.9 : 0.7   h 3 : 0.02

4 Write these ratios in their lowest terms.

   a $\frac{1}{2} : \frac{1}{4}$ b $\frac{2}{6} : \frac{5}{6}$ c $\frac{3}{4} : \frac{2}{3}$ d $\frac{1}{5} : \frac{1}{3}$

   e $\frac{1}{10} : \frac{2}{5}$ f $\frac{3}{10} : \frac{1}{3}$ g $\frac{3}{8} : \frac{1}{4}$ h $2\frac{1}{2} : 1\frac{2}{3}$

5 Write these ratios in their simplest form.

   a 10 : 40 : 50   b 6 : 10 : 8   c 5 : 15 : 25   d 64 : 24 : 56

   e 21 : 45 : 77   f 0.5 : 2 : 3.5   g 1.6 : 2.4 : 0.2   h $\frac{1}{2} : \frac{3}{4} : \frac{1}{5}$

6 Write these ratios in the form 1 : n

   a 2 : 8   b 6 : 4   c 25 : 4   d 8 : 5

   e 1 cm : 5 km   f 5 cm : 20 m   g 2 cm : 15 km   h 3 mm : 1 km

7 Concrete is made from sand and cement.
   20 kg of concrete contains 15 kg of sand.
   Find the ratio of sand to cement in its simplest form.

8 There are 24 men, 60 women and 44 children on a bus.
   Write the ratio   men : women : children   in its simplest form.

9 Tickets are sold for a school concert.
   72 student tickets and 168 adult tickets are sold.
   Write the ratio   number of student tickets : number of adult tickets
   in its simplest form.

UNIT 2

10   1   1   2   3   5   8   13   21   34   …

The rule to find the next term in this sequence is 'add together the two previous terms'.
So the next term = 21 + 34 = 55.

Suri investigates the ratio of adjacent numbers. She writes each ratio in the form 1 : *n*.

Ratio of 1st number to 2nd number   = 1 : 1
Ratio of 2nd number to 3rd number   = 1 : 2
Ratio of 3rd number to 4th number   = 2 : 3 = 1 : 1.5
Ratio of 4th number to 5th number   = 3 : 5 = 1 : 1.666…

➡ **NOTE:** you can find out more about the golden ratio on the internet.

Write down the next six ratios and describe what happens to the ratio.

Dividing quantities in a given ratio
You can use ratios to share quantities.

Marla wants to share $36 between her two friends Lesley and Barbara in the ratio 3 : 1.
This means that Lesley receives three times as much as Barbara.
The diagram shows how the money is split.

To divide a quantity in a given ratio

- first find the total number of equal parts
- find the value of one part
- multiply to find each share

Lesley ($27)   Barbara ($9)

EXAMPLE

Share $42 between Kurt and Anna in the ratio 5 : 1.

Total number of parts = 5 + 1 = 6
Value of one part = $42 ÷ 6 = $7

Kurt receives 5 parts = 5 × $7 = $35
Anna receives 1 part = 1 × $7 = $7

➡ **CHECK:**
$35 + $7 = $42 ✓

EXAMPLE

Share $2000 between Adam, Jason and Omar in the ratio 1 : 2 : 5.

Total number of parts = 1 + 2 + 5 = 8
Value of one part = $2000 ÷ 8 = $250

Adam receives 1 part = 1 × $250 = $250
Jason receives 2 parts = 2 × $250 = $500
Adam receives 5 parts = 5 × $250 = $1250

➡ **CHECK:**
$250 + $500 + $1250 = $2000 ✓

Antonio and Filippo do a sponsored swim to raise money for charity.
The amounts they raise are in the ratio 3 : 7.
Antonio raised $177. How much did Filippo raise?

Antonio raised 3 parts.
Value of one part = $177 ÷ 3 = $59.
Filippo raised 7 parts = 7 × $59 = $413.

➡ **CHECK:** ÷59

177 : 413

3 : 7

÷59

EXERCISE 2.3

1 Divide each amount in the ratio given.
   a $84 in the ratio 2 : 1   **b** 280 m in the ratio 3 : 5
   c $2100 in the ratio 4 : 3   **d** 624 km in the ratio 3 : 7
   e 182 kg in the ratio 8 : 5   **f** $52.20 in the ratio 4 : 5

2 Divide each amount in the ratio given.
   a $420 in the ratio 1 : 2 : 3   **b** 360 m in the ratio 5 : 1 : 2
   c $220 in the ratio 7 : 3 : 1   **d** 2850 km in the ratio 6 : 5 : 8
   e 24 000 kg in the ratio 4 : 3 : 5 **f** $1078.40 in the ratio 5 : 7 : 8

3 Jenny and Chris share some prize money in the ratio 5 : 3
   Jenny receives $52.25
   How much does Chris receive?

4 The three angles of a triangle are in the ratio 3 : 5 : 7
   Find the largest angle in the triangle.

5 The four angles of a quadrilateral are in the ratio 2 : 5 : 6 : 7
   Find the smallest angle in the quadrilateral.

6 The ratio of boys to girls in a class is 4 : 5
   What fraction of the class are boys?

7 $\frac{4}{7}$ of the children at a swimming club are girls.
   What is the ratio of girls to boys?

8 A bag contains orange sweets and yellow sweets.
   The ratio of orange sweets to yellow sweets is 3 : 2
   There are 51 orange sweets in the bag.
   Find the total number of sweets in the bag.

9 The ratio of adults to children on a train is 7 : 2
   There are 245 adults on the train.
   Find the total number of people on the train.

10 At a football match, the ratio of male spectators to female spectators is 11 : 3.
    There are 4257 male spectators.
    Find the number of female spectators.

11 A length of rope is cut into two pieces in the ratio 4 : 5.
    The shortest piece is 92 cm long.
    Find the length of the longest piece.

12 Paul is exactly 6 years older than Jane.
    The ratio of their ages is 5 : 3.
    How old is Paul?

Map scales

Map scales are written as ratios in the form 1: n
A scale of 1 : 2 000 000 means that 1 cm on the map represents 2 000 000 cm on land.
You can convert the units of length as follows

   1 cm : 2 000 000 cm   *divide by 100 to change cm to m*
= 1 cm : 20 000 m   *divide by 1000 to change m to km*
= 1 cm : 20 km

So a map scale of 1 : 2 000 000 means that 1 cm on the map represents 20 km on the land.

EXAMPLE

This map has a scale of 1 : 5 000 000.
Use the map to calculate the actual distance
between Buenos Aires and Montevideo.

Distance on map = 4.4 cm.
    1 cm : 5 000 000 cm
= 1 cm : 50 000 m
= 1 cm : 50 km
So 1 cm on the map represents 50 km
on land.
Actual distance = 4.4 × 50 = 220 km.

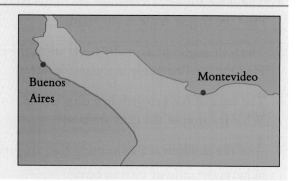

EXAMPLE

The distance between two villages is 16 km.
How far apart will they be on a map of scale 1 : 200 000?

   1 : 200 000 = 1 cm : 200 000 cm
            = 1 cm : 2000 m
            = 1 cm : 2 km
So each centimetre on the map represents 2 km on land.
Distance between villages on the map = $\frac{16}{2}$ = 8 cm.

EXERCISE 2.4

1 The map has a scale of 1 : 2 000 000.
   a Use a ruler to measure the distance on the map between
      i A and B,   ii B and C,   iii A and C.
   b Find the actual distance (in km) between
      i A and B,   ii B and C,   iii A and C.

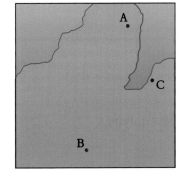

2 A map has a scale of 1 : 1 000 000
   The distance between two lighthouses on the map is 4 cm.
   What is the actual distance, in kilometres, between the
   two lighthouses?

3 The scale of a map is 1 : 500 000
   Find the actual distance, in kilometres, represented by these
   distances on the map.
   a 3 cm   b 6.5 cm   c 4.2 cm   d 9 mm

4 The scale of a map is 1 : 200 000
   Find the actual distance, in kilometres, represented by these
   distances on the map.
   a 4 cm   b 2.5 cm   c 3.8 cm   d 7 mm

5 A map has a scale of 1 : 50 000
   Find the distance on the map that would represent an actual distance of
   a 1 km   b 5 km   c 2.5 km   d 4.3 km

6 The scale of a map is 1 : 100 000
   The distance between two houses on the map is 3.2 cm.
   Find the actual distance, in kilometres, between the two houses.

7 A map has a scale of 1 : 50 000. A river is 6 cm long on the map.
   Find the actual length, in kilometres, of the river.

8 A map has a scale of 1 : 500 000. The actual distance between two
   villages is 30 km.
   Find the distance between the two villages on the map.

9 A map has a scale of 1 : 400 000. Two towns are 6.8 cm apart on the map.
   Find the actual distance between the two towns.

10 A map has a scale of 1 : 10 000 000. The actual distance between two
   cities is 480 km.
   Find the distance between the two cities on the map.

11 The length of a section of motorway is 39 km. How long will
   the section of motorway be on a map whose scale is 1 : 500 000?

┌ ─ ─ ─ ─ ─ ─ ─ ┐
│   **KEY WORDS**   │
│   ratio   │
└ ─ ─ ─ ─ ─ ─ ─ ┘

Indices 1

- Use simple laws of indices

$6 \times 6 \times 6 \times 6 = 6^4$ ← index or power

← base

Multiplying: $\quad 2^3 \times 2^4 = (2 \times 2 \times 2) \times (2 \times 2 \times 2 \times 2) = 2^7$

RULE 1 $\quad a^m \times a^n = a^{m+n}$

Dividing: $\quad 4^5 \div 4^2 = \dfrac{4 \times 4 \times 4 \times \cancel{4} \times \cancel{4}}{\cancel{4} \times \cancel{4}} = 4^3$

RULE 2 $\quad a^m \div a^n = a^{m-n}$

Raising to a power: $\quad (3^2)^4 = (3 \times 3) \times (3 \times 3) \times (3 \times 3) \times (3 \times 3) = 3^8$

RULE 3 $\quad (a^m)^n = a^{mn}$

EXAMPLE

Simplify $\quad$ **a** $x^3 \times x^4$ $\quad$ **b** $p^9 \div p^3$ $\quad$ **c** $(q^4)^5$

a $x^3 \times x^4 = x^{3+4}$ $\qquad$ *add the powers*
$\qquad\qquad = x^7$

b $p^9 \div p^3 = p^{9-3}$ $\qquad$ *subtract the powers*
$\qquad\qquad = p^6$

c $\quad (q^4)^5 = q^{4 \times 5}$ $\qquad$ *multiply the powers*
$\qquad\qquad = q^{20}$

EXAMPLE

Simplify $\quad$ **a** $5x^3 \times 2x^4 y^2 \times 3y^5$ $\qquad$ **b** $\dfrac{6x^5 y^8}{3x^2 y^4}$

a $5x^3 \times 2x^4 y^2 \times 3y^5 = 5 \times 2 \times 3 \times x^3 \times x^4 \times y^2 \times y^5$
$\qquad\qquad\qquad\qquad = 30 \times x^{3+4} \times y^{2+5}$
$\qquad\qquad\qquad\qquad = 30x^7 y^7$

b $\dfrac{6x^5 y^8}{3x^2 y^4} = \dfrac{6}{3} \times (x^5 \div x^2) \times (y^8 \div y^4)$
$\qquad\qquad = 2 \times x^{5-2} \times y^{8-4}$
$\qquad\qquad = 2x^3 y^4$

EXERCISE 2.5

1 Sarah says that $3^x \times 3^y = 9^{x+y}$. Is she correct? Explain your answer.

2 Simplify these expressions.

TOP TIP

$a = a^1$

  a $x^2 \times x^7$ b $b^4 \times b^4$ c $y^8 \times y^2$ d $c^3 \times c^9$

  e $a^4 \times a^2 \times a^5$ f $p^2 \times p^2 \times p^4$ g $y^3 \times y^5 \times y$ h $a^2 \times a \times a^4$

3 a $5x^2 \times 3x^4$ b $2b \times 4b^3$ c $7y^8 \times 2y^6$ d $5c^3 \times 5c^3$

     e $2a^2 \times 3a$ f $7p^4 \times 2p^3 \times 5p$ g $3y \times 4y^2 \times 5y^3$ h $3a^2 \times 3a^2 \times 3a^2$

4 a $2x^2 \times 3y^2 \times x^4$ b $3x^4 \times 2y \times 5y^2$ c $5y^2 \times x^2 \times 2y$ d $x^3 \times 2y^2 \times 3x$

     e $5xy^2 \times 3x^2y$ f $7xy \times 5x^2$ g $4x^3y \times xy$ h $3a^5b^2 \times 2a^3b^2$

5 a $x^8 \div x^3$ b $b^7 \div b^6$ c $a^6 \div a^3$ d $x^6 \div x$

     e $6x^5 \div x^2$ f $8y^7 \div 4y^5$ g $15b^9 \div 3b^2$ h $21c^8 \div 7c^7$

6 a $\dfrac{5y^4}{y^2}$ b $\dfrac{12a^2b}{a}$ c $\dfrac{2x^2}{8x}$ d $\dfrac{5y^2}{10y}$

     e $\dfrac{6a^4}{3a^3}$ f $\dfrac{16a^2b^2c^2}{4abc}$ g $\dfrac{a^3b^4c^2}{ab^2c}$ h $\dfrac{\left(5x^2\right)^2}{5x^2}$

TOP TIP

Simplify the numerator first.

     i $\dfrac{x^3 \times x^6}{x^4}$ j $\dfrac{y^8 \times y^2}{y^3}$ k $\dfrac{3a^4 \times 2a^5}{a^2}$ l $\dfrac{6x^4 \times 2x^4}{4x^2}$

7 a $\left(x^3\right)^2$ b $\left(a^2\right)^5$ c $\left(b^4\right)^4$ d $\left(y^7\right)^3$

     e $3\left(a^2\right)^3$ f $5\left(x^5\right)^4$ g $\left(2x^3\right)^3$ h $\left(3y^2\right)^4$

     i $\left(2a^2\right)^3$ j $\left(3y^4\right)^2$ k $2y^2\left(3x^2\right)^2$ l $5x\left(2x^2\right)^3$

8 a $\left(3xy^2\right)^3$ b $\left(2a^2b^3\right)^5$ c $\left(5x^4y^3\right)^2$ d $\left(10x^5y^7\right)^3$

9 a $\dfrac{3x^2 + 5x^2}{2x^2}$ b $\dfrac{15x^{10}}{3x^4} + 8x^6$ c $\dfrac{\left(2x^2\right)^3 \times \left(3x\right)^2}{2x^5}$ d $\dfrac{5a^2b^4}{3c} \times \dfrac{abc}{15a^2b^2}$

     e $\dfrac{4a^5b}{cd} \div \dfrac{a}{c^2d^3}$ f $\dfrac{\left(4x^8y^3\right)^3}{2x^5y^2}$ g $\dfrac{\left(2x^2y\right)^6}{\left(2xy^2\right)^3}$ h $\left(\left(2xy^2\right)^2\right)^2$

Negative powers: $\quad 4^3 \div 4^5 = \dfrac{\cancel{4} \times \cancel{4} \times \cancel{4}}{4 \times 4 \times \cancel{4} \times \cancel{4} \times \cancel{4}} = \dfrac{1}{4^2}$

and $\quad 4^3 \div 4^5 = 4^{3-5} = 4^{-2}$

so $\quad 4^{-2} = \dfrac{1}{4^2}$

RULE 4 $\quad a^{-m} = \dfrac{1}{a^m}$

Zero powers: $\quad 5^4 \div 5^4 = \dfrac{\cancel{5} \times \cancel{5} \times \cancel{5} \times \cancel{5}}{\cancel{5} \times \cancel{5} \times \cancel{5} \times \cancel{5}} = 1$

and $\quad 5^4 \div 5^4 = 5^{4-4} = 5^0$

so $\quad 5^0 = 1$

RULE 5 $\quad a^0 = 1$

Any number raised to the power zero is equal to 1.

EXAMPLE

Work out the value of $\quad$ **a** 5^{-2} $\qquad$ **b** 8^0 $\qquad$ **c** $(-3)^{-5}$ $\qquad$ **d** $\left(\dfrac{3}{5}\right)^{-1}$

a $\quad 5^{-2} = \dfrac{1}{5^2} = \dfrac{1}{5 \times 5} = \dfrac{1}{25}$ $\qquad$ **b** $\quad 8^0 = 1$

c $\quad (-3)^{-5} = \dfrac{1}{(-3)^5} = \dfrac{1}{(-3) \times (-3) \times (-3) \times (-3) \times (-3)} = \dfrac{1}{-243} = -\dfrac{1}{243}$

d $\quad \left(\dfrac{3}{5}\right)^{-1} = \dfrac{1}{\left(\dfrac{3}{5}\right)^1} = 1 \div \dfrac{3}{5} = 1 \times \dfrac{5}{3} = \dfrac{5}{3}$

➡ **NOTE:** it is very useful to know that $\left(\dfrac{3}{5}\right)^{-1}$ is the same as $\left(\dfrac{5}{3}\right)$.

EXAMPLE

Simplify

a $x^9 \times x^{-3} \times x^{-4}$ $\quad$ **b** $5x^{-5} \times 4x^2$ $\qquad$ **c** $x^6 \div x^{-8}$ $\qquad$ **d** $\left(x^{-2}\right)^3$ $\qquad$ **e** $\left(5x^2\right)^{-3}$

a $\quad x^9 \times x^{-3} \times x^{-4} = x^{9+-3+-4}$ $\quad$ *add the powers*
$\qquad\qquad\qquad\qquad\quad = x^{9-3-4}$
$\qquad\qquad\qquad\qquad\quad = x^2$

b $\quad 5x^{-5} \times 4x^2 = 5 \times 4 \times x^{-5} \times x^2$
$\qquad\qquad\qquad\quad = 20 \times x^{-5+2}$
$\qquad\qquad\qquad\quad = 20x^{-3}$

c $\quad x^6 \div x^{-8} = x^{6--8}$ $\qquad$ *subtract the powers*
$\qquad\qquad\quad = x^{6+8}$
$\qquad\qquad\quad = x^{14}$

d $\quad \left(x^{-2}\right)^3 = x^{-2 \times 3}$ $\quad$ *multiply the powers*
$\qquad\qquad\quad = x^{-6}$

e $\quad \left(5x^2\right)^{-3} = \dfrac{1}{\left(5x^2\right)^3} = \dfrac{1}{5x^2 \times 5x^2 \times 5x^2}$ $\qquad$ or $\quad \left(5x^2\right)^{-3} = (5)^{-3}\left(x^2\right)^{-3}$

$\qquad\qquad\qquad = \dfrac{1}{5 \times 5 \times 5 \times x^2 \times x^2 \times x^2}$ $\qquad\qquad\qquad = 5^{-3}x^{-6}$

$\qquad\qquad\qquad = \dfrac{1}{125x^6}$ or $\dfrac{1}{125}x^{-6}$ $\qquad\qquad\qquad = \dfrac{1}{125}x^{-6}$ or $\dfrac{1}{125x^6}$

EXERCISE 2.6

Work out the value of these.

1 a 3^{-1} b 5^0 c 2^{-3} d 3^{-3} e 7^0 f 10^{-3}
   g 4^{-2} h 7^{-1} i 10^{-4} j 5^{-3} k 2^{-5} l 3^{-4}

2 a $(-3)^{-2}$ b $(-2)^{-3}$ c $(-6)^{-2}$ d $(-9)^{-1}$ e $(-2)^{-4}$ f $(-10)^{-3}$

3 a $\left(\dfrac{2}{3}\right)^{-1}$ b $\left(\dfrac{2}{5}\right)^{-1}$ c $\left(\dfrac{3}{4}\right)^{-1}$ d $\left(\dfrac{5}{6}\right)^{-1}$ e $\left(\dfrac{2}{7}\right)^{-1}$ f $\left(\dfrac{4}{5}\right)^{-1}$

4 a $\left(\dfrac{2}{3}\right)^{-2}$ b $\left(\dfrac{2}{5}\right)^{-2}$ c $\left(\dfrac{3}{4}\right)^{-2}$ d $\left(\dfrac{5}{6}\right)^{-2}$

   e $\left(\dfrac{2}{7}\right)^{-2}$ f $\left(\dfrac{4}{5}\right)^{-2}$ g $\left(\dfrac{1}{2}\right)^{-3}$ h $\left(\dfrac{1}{10}\right)^{-3}$

> • • • • • • • • • • • • • • •
> **TOP TIP**
>
> $\left(\dfrac{2}{3}\right)^{-2} = \left(\dfrac{3}{2}\right)^{2}$
> • • • • • • • • • • • • • • •

Simplify the following expressions. Give your answers in index form.

5 a $a^6 \times a^{-2}$ b $b^{-5} \times b^{-4}$ c $c^{-3} \times c$ d $d^{-6} \times d^{-7}$
   e $d^{-3} \times d^{-4} \times d^{10}$ f $x^2 \times x^5 \times x^{-4}$ g $y^4 \times y^2 \times y^{-2}$ h $d^{-3} \times d^{-4} \times d^{10}$
   i $a^{-3} \times a^3 \div a^{-5}$ j $b^6 \times b^{-3} \div b^2$ k $c^4 \times c^{-7} \div c^{-3}$ l $d^{-3} \times d^{-2} \div d^{-1}$

6 a $\dfrac{x^2 \times x^4}{x^8}$ b $\dfrac{x^{-3} \times x^5}{x^{-3}}$ c $\dfrac{4x^5 \times 3x^2}{2x^{-2}}$ d $\dfrac{8x^2}{4x^3 \times 2x^4}$

7 a $2x^{-2} \times 4x^3$ b $5x^{-1} \times 3x^{-2}$ c $2x^{-2} \times 3x^5$ d $7x^{-1} \times 4x^{-4}$

8 a $(x^2)^{-1}$ b $(y^3)^{-2}$ c $(a^{-4})^5$ d $(b^{-2})^4$
   e $(a^{-3})^{-2}$ f $(y^{-1})^{-2}$ g $(a^{-2})^{-5}$ h $(a^{-1})^{-1}$

9 a $(3a^{-1})^2$ b $(5b^{-1})^3$ c $(2c^{-2})^4$ d $(4d^{-2})^2$
   e $(2x^2)^{-2}$ f $(3y^2)^{-3}$ g $(5x^3)^{-2}$ h $(2x^{-2})^{-2}$

10 a $x^{-1} \div \dfrac{1}{x^2}$ b $x^3 \div \dfrac{2}{x^4}$ c $y \div \dfrac{1}{y^{-2}}$ d $\dfrac{4}{x^2} + 3x^{-2}$

11 Find the odd one out in these three expressions.

| $5a^3b^{-4} \times a^{-1}b$ | $2a^2 + 3b^{-3}$ | $\dfrac{5a^{-2}b^{-2}}{a^{-4}b}$ |

> **KEY WORDS**
> index
> power
> base

Solving linear inequalities

> **THIS SECTION WILL SHOW YOU HOW TO**
> - Solve linear inequalities
> - Represent solutions to linear inequalities on a number line.

 You need to know these **inequality** signs:

> means 'is greater than'   ≥ means 'is greater than or equal to'
< means 'is less than'   ≤ means 'is less than or equal to'

You solve a linear inequality in a similar way to solving linear equations.

$$2x - 3 < 10 \quad \textit{add 3 to both sides}$$
$$2x < 13 \quad \textit{divide both sides by 2}$$
$$x < 6.5$$

You must be careful if you multiply or divide an inequality by a negative number. You must reverse the inequality sign.
(For example $-3 < 7$, multiplying both sides by -1 gives $3 > -7$)

EXAMPLE

Solve $7 - 2x > 1$ and show your answer on a number line.

Method 1		**Method 2**	
$7 - 2x > 1$	*add 2x to both sides*	$7 - 2x > 1$	*take 7 from both sides*
$7 > 1 + 2x$	*take 1 from both sides*	$-2x > -6$	*divide both sides by -2*
$6 > 2x$	*divide both sides by 2*	$x < 3$	*and reverse the sign*
$3 > x \quad$ so $\quad x < 3$			

number line from -4 to 4 with hollow circle at 3, arrow to left

➡ **NOTE:** a hollow circle is used for < or >.

EXAMPLE

Solve $4(x + 1) \le 4 - 2(x + 3)$ and show your answer on a number line.

$4(x + 1) \le 4 - 2(x + 3)$	*multiply out the brackets*
$4x + 4 \le 4 - 2x - 6$	
$4x + 4 \le -2 - 2x$	*add 2x to both sides*
$6x + 4 \le -2$	*take 4 from both sides*
$6x \le -6$	*divide both sides by 6*
$x \le -1$	

number line from -4 to 4 with solid circle at -1, arrow to left

➡ **NOTE:** a solid circle is used for ≤ or ≥.

EXAMPLE

Solve $-1 \le 2x + 1 < 5$ and show your answer on a number line.

$-1 \le 2x + 1 < 5$	*subtract 1 throughout*
$-2 \le 2x < 4$	*divide by 2*
$-1 \le x < 2$	

number line from -4 to 4 with solid circle at -1 and hollow circle at 2

➡ **NOTE:** if a question asks for the integer values that satisfy the inequality $-1 \le 2x + 1 < 5$ the final answer will be -1, 0 and 1. (An integer is a whole number.)

EXERCISE 2.7

Write the inequalities shown on these diagrams.

1
```
  ●——→
-3 -2 -1  0  1  2  3
```

2
```
  ←————○
-3 -2 -1  0  1  2  3
```

3
```
     ●———●
-3 -2 -1  0  1  2  3
```

4
```
  ●————○
-3 -2 -1  0  1  2  3
```

Solve these inequalities.

5 $2x - 5 \le 7$

6 $3x + 2 \ge 14$

7 $5x + 4 < 39$

8 $6x - 2 > 10$

9 $8x + 3 \ge 15$

10 $4x - 5 < 19$

11 $2x + 6 \le 4$

12 $6 > 3x - 15$

13 $10 - 4x \le 6$

14 $30 - 2x > 15$

15 $4 - 2x \ge 16$

16 $6 - 5x > -4$

17 $27 - 3x \le 6$

18 $1 - 10x > 3$

19 $7 - 2x < 12$

20 $16 \le 8 - 2x$

21 $3(2x + 5) \le 21$

22 $4(y - 5) > 12$

23 $3(2x + 5) \ge 27$

24 $4(3x - 1) < 80$

25 $7 > 2(x + 3)$

26 $-25 \le 5(3x + 4)$

27 $3(2 - x) \ge -6$

28 $2(13 - x) < 22$

29 $5x - 2 \ge 3x + 4$

30 $8x + 4 < 3x - 31$

31 $2x + 1 \le 5x - 26$

32 $5 - 2x > 3 - x$

33 $3(x + 1) \le 4(x - 1)$

34 $2(x + 2) \ge 5(x - 1)$

35 $3(x + 2) - 2(x - 4) \ge 4(x + 2)$

36 $2(3x - 1) - 5(x + 2) > 3(x - 5)$

37 $\dfrac{x - 1}{8} \le 1 - x$

38 $x - 3 \ge \dfrac{x + 12}{2}$

39 $\dfrac{x - 3}{3} > \dfrac{x - 2}{5}$

40 $\dfrac{x + 2}{2} \le \dfrac{x - 1}{7}$

41 $\dfrac{x - 5}{3} > \dfrac{4 - x}{2}$

42 $\dfrac{x - 1}{2} > \dfrac{x + 2}{5}$

43 $\dfrac{x - 3}{5} \ge \dfrac{x + 3}{2}$

44 $\dfrac{2x - 3}{4} < \dfrac{3x - 1}{5}$

45 $5 \le 3 - \dfrac{2x + 1}{5}$

Solve these inequalities and then list the integer solutions.

46 $-6 \le 2x \le 10$

47 $-9 \le 3x < 12$

48 $8 < 4x \le 36$

49 $-1 < \dfrac{x}{2} \le 2$

50 $0 < \dfrac{x}{2} - 1 < 1$

51 $-8 \le 2n - 3 < 8$

52 $3 < 2x + 3 \le 11$

53 $-2 \le 2(x - 4) \le 6$

54 $-3 < 3(x - 4) \le 15$

55 Write down the smallest integer that satisfies the inequality $3x + 2 \ge 12$

56 Find the largest integer that satisfies $5(3x - 7) < 28$

57 $3x + 2y \le 6$ and x and y are both positive integers (not including 0).
List all the possible pairs of values
for x and y.

Manipulating algebraic fractions

THIS SECTION WILL SHOW YOU HOW TO
- Add and subtract algebraic fractions
- Solve equations involving algebraic fractions

Adding and subtracting algebraic fractions
Reminder

$\dfrac{2}{3}+\dfrac{1}{4}$ Similarly

$=\dfrac{8}{12}+\dfrac{3}{12}$

$=\dfrac{8+3}{12}$

$=\dfrac{11}{12}$

$\dfrac{2x}{3}+\dfrac{x}{4}$

$=\dfrac{8x}{12}+\dfrac{3x}{12}$

$=\dfrac{8x+3x}{12}$

$=\dfrac{11x}{12}$

the common denominator is $3 \times 4 = 12$

$\dfrac{2}{3}=\dfrac{8}{12}$ *and* $\dfrac{1}{4}=\dfrac{3}{12}$

EXAMPLE

Simplify $\dfrac{2x}{3}+\dfrac{x}{4}-\dfrac{3x}{5}$.

$\dfrac{2x}{3}+\dfrac{x}{4}-\dfrac{3x}{5}$

$=\dfrac{40x}{60}+\dfrac{15x}{60}-\dfrac{36x}{60}$

$=\dfrac{40x+15x-36x}{60}$

$=\dfrac{19x}{60}$

the common denominator is $3 \times 4 \times 5 = 60$

$\dfrac{2}{3}=\dfrac{40}{60},\ \dfrac{1}{4}=\dfrac{15}{60}$ *and* $\dfrac{3}{5}=\dfrac{36}{60}$

EXAMPLE

Simplify $\dfrac{5(2x-1)}{6}-\dfrac{2(2x-3)}{5}$.

$\dfrac{5(2x-1)}{6}-\dfrac{2(2x-3)}{5}$

$=\dfrac{25(2x-1)}{30}-\dfrac{12(2x-3)}{30}$

$=\dfrac{25(2x-1)-12(2x-3)}{30}$

$=\dfrac{50x-25-24x+36}{30}$

$=\dfrac{26x+11}{30}$

the common denominator is $6 \times 5 = 30$

$\dfrac{5}{6}=\dfrac{25}{30}$ *and* $\dfrac{2}{5}=\dfrac{12}{30}$

remove the brackets and be careful with the signs

collect like terms in the numerator

EXERCISE 2.8

1 Simplify the following algebraic fractions.

a $\dfrac{3x}{5}+\dfrac{x}{5}$

b $\dfrac{2x}{7}+\dfrac{3x}{7}$

c $\dfrac{x}{4}+\dfrac{x}{4}$

d $\dfrac{x}{8}+\dfrac{3x}{8}$

e $\dfrac{5x}{6}-\dfrac{x}{6}$

f $\dfrac{5x}{8}-\dfrac{x}{8}$

g $\dfrac{7x}{10}-\dfrac{3x}{10}$

h $\dfrac{4x}{5}-\dfrac{2x}{5}$

i $\dfrac{4x}{7}+\dfrac{2x}{7}-\dfrac{x}{7}$

2 Pedro says that $\dfrac{y}{3}+\dfrac{2y}{5}=\dfrac{3y}{8}$.

Explain why he is wrong.

Simplify the following algebraic fractions.

3 a $\dfrac{x}{2}+\dfrac{x}{4}$

b $\dfrac{x}{3}+\dfrac{x}{4}$

c $\dfrac{2x}{5}+\dfrac{x}{3}$

d $\dfrac{3x}{5}+\dfrac{x}{4}$

e $\dfrac{x}{2}-\dfrac{x}{3}$

f $\dfrac{2x}{3}-\dfrac{x}{5}$

g $\dfrac{9x}{10}-\dfrac{2x}{5}$

h $\dfrac{8x}{9}-\dfrac{3x}{4}$

i $\dfrac{x}{2}-\dfrac{3x}{10}+\dfrac{2x}{5}$

4 a $\dfrac{x}{3}+\dfrac{x+2}{4}$

b $\dfrac{x-3}{5}+\dfrac{x+1}{6}$

c $\dfrac{2x-3}{7}+\dfrac{x+4}{5}$

d $\dfrac{6x-3}{7}+\dfrac{x+4}{5}$

e $\dfrac{3(x+1)}{4}+\dfrac{2(x+3)}{3}$

f $\dfrac{8(x-1)}{11}+\dfrac{2(x+4)}{3}$

5 a $\dfrac{6x+1}{3}-\dfrac{x+2}{4}$

b $\dfrac{3x-2}{5}-\dfrac{x-3}{8}$

c $\dfrac{4x+2}{5}-\dfrac{3x+4}{6}$

d $\dfrac{2x+3}{9}-\dfrac{5x-1}{4}$

e $\dfrac{2(3x+4)}{3}-\dfrac{3(2x-1)}{5}$

f $\dfrac{3(x-1)}{4}-\dfrac{2(x+6)}{9}$

6 $\dfrac{2x+1}{4}-\dfrac{3(x-2)}{5}+\dfrac{2(x+1)}{3}$

7 Find the odd one out.

$\dfrac{2x}{3}-\dfrac{x}{4}$ $\qquad$ $\dfrac{x}{4}+\dfrac{x}{3}-\dfrac{x}{6}$ $\qquad$ $\dfrac{x}{2}-\dfrac{x}{12}$ $\qquad$ $\dfrac{3x}{4}-\dfrac{2x}{3}$ $\qquad$ $\dfrac{x}{4}+\dfrac{x}{6}$

Solving equations

EXAMPLE

Solve $\dfrac{2x}{5} + \dfrac{3x}{2} = 38$

There are two methods for solving this type of equation. Use the method that you prefer.

Method 1

$$\dfrac{2x}{5} + \dfrac{3x}{2} = 38 \qquad \text{\textit{common denominator is 10}}$$

$$\dfrac{4x}{10} + \dfrac{15x}{10} = 38$$

$$\dfrac{19x}{10} = 38 \qquad \text{\textit{multiply by 10}}$$

$$19x = 380 \qquad \text{\textit{divide by 19}}$$

$$x = 20$$

Method 2

$$\dfrac{2x}{5} + \dfrac{3x}{2} = 38 \qquad \text{\textit{multiply by 10}}$$

$$^2\cancel{10} \times \dfrac{2x}{\cancel{5}} + {}^5\cancel{10} \times \dfrac{3x}{\cancel{2}} = 10 \times 38 \qquad \text{\textit{cancel}}$$

$$4x + 15x = 380$$

$$19x = 380 \qquad \text{\textit{divide by 19}}$$

$$x = 20$$

EXAMPLE

Solve $\dfrac{2x+8}{3} - \dfrac{x-1}{2} = 4$

Method 1

$$\dfrac{2x+8}{3} - \dfrac{x-1}{2} = 4 \qquad \text{\textit{change fractions to a common denominator of 6}}$$

$$\dfrac{2(2x+8)}{6} - \dfrac{3(x-1)}{6} = 4$$

$$\dfrac{2(2x+8) - 3(x-1)}{6} = 4 \qquad \text{\textit{remove the brackets and be careful with the signs!}}$$

$$\dfrac{4x + 16 - 3x + 3}{6} = 4 \qquad \text{\textit{collect like terms in the numerator}}$$

$$\dfrac{x+19}{6} = 4 \qquad \text{\textit{multiply both sides by 6}}$$

$$x + 19 = 24 \qquad \text{\textit{subtract 19 from both sides}}$$

$$x = 5$$

Method 2

$$\dfrac{2x+8}{3} - \dfrac{x-1}{2} = 4 \qquad \text{\textit{multiply both sides by 6}}$$

$$^2\cancel{6} \times \dfrac{(2x+8)}{\cancel{3}} - {}^3\cancel{6} \times \dfrac{(x+1)}{\cancel{2}} \qquad \text{\textit{cancel}}$$

$$= 6 \times 4$$

$$2(2x + 8) - 3(x - 1) = 24 \qquad \text{\textit{remove the brackets and be careful with the signs!}}$$

$$4x + 16 - 3x + 3 = 24 \qquad \text{\textit{collect like terms}}$$

$$x + 19 = 24 \qquad \text{\textit{take 19 from both sides}}$$

$$x = 5$$

EXERCISE 2.9

Solve these equations.

1 a $\dfrac{x}{3} - \dfrac{x}{4} = 3$ b $\dfrac{2x}{3} - \dfrac{x}{2} = 3$ c $\dfrac{x}{4} + \dfrac{x}{5} = 18$ d $\dfrac{2x}{3} + \dfrac{3x}{2} = 26$

   e $\dfrac{3x}{5} + \dfrac{x}{4} = 34$ f $\dfrac{2x}{9} - \dfrac{x}{2} = 10$ g $\dfrac{4x}{5} + \dfrac{3x}{2} = 23$ h $\dfrac{6x}{7} - \dfrac{x}{3} = 22$

2 a $\dfrac{x}{5} - \dfrac{x}{6} = \dfrac{1}{2}$ b $\dfrac{3x}{4} - \dfrac{2x}{3} = \dfrac{1}{3}$ c $\dfrac{2x}{5} + \dfrac{x}{4} = 2\dfrac{3}{5}$ d $\dfrac{2x}{9} - \dfrac{x}{8} = \dfrac{7}{12}$

   e $\dfrac{x}{8} - \dfrac{2x}{5} = 1\dfrac{1}{10}$ f $\dfrac{3x}{5} - \dfrac{3x}{8} = \dfrac{3}{20}$ g $\dfrac{x}{4} - \dfrac{x}{7} = \dfrac{9}{14}$ h $\dfrac{x}{8} + \dfrac{3x}{5} = -1\dfrac{9}{20}$

3 a $\dfrac{3x+4}{2} + \dfrac{8-x}{3} = 7$ b $\dfrac{x+1}{4} + \dfrac{2x+1}{5} = 5$ c $\dfrac{4x}{5} + \dfrac{3x-7}{2} = 8$

   d $\dfrac{x+9}{6} + \dfrac{5x-3}{3} = 6$ e $\dfrac{11x+5}{4} + \dfrac{4x-3}{3} = -12$ f $\dfrac{3x+2}{2} + \dfrac{x+6}{3} = 14$

   g $\dfrac{4x-1}{5} + \dfrac{5x-16}{2} = 5$ h $\dfrac{x}{4} + \dfrac{x-5}{3} = 3$ i $\dfrac{3-x}{6} + \dfrac{x+8}{5} = 2$

   j $\dfrac{3x+10}{8} + \dfrac{4x+11}{6} = 1$ k $\dfrac{2x+1}{2} + \dfrac{6x-3}{4} = 6$ l $\dfrac{6x-1}{3} + \dfrac{15x+7}{9} = 1\dfrac{2}{3}$

4 a $\dfrac{x+8}{5} - \dfrac{x+1}{4} = 1$ b $\dfrac{19x+5}{6} - \dfrac{2(x+4)}{5} = 2$ c $\dfrac{5x+6}{3} - \dfrac{5x-1}{7} = 5$

   d $\dfrac{5x-2}{4} - \dfrac{x+6}{3} = 3$ e $\dfrac{4x-1}{3} - \dfrac{20-x}{8} = 3$ f $\dfrac{11x+5}{4} - \dfrac{3x-5}{2} = 5$

   g $\dfrac{2(x-2)}{3} - \dfrac{6x-5}{5} = -3$ h $\dfrac{3x-5}{4} - \dfrac{5(x-4)}{3} = -1$ i $\dfrac{3(3-x)}{2} - \dfrac{2(x+6)}{3} = 7$

   j $\dfrac{3(5-x)}{5} - \dfrac{4(2-x)}{7} = 2$ k $\dfrac{3(4x+1)}{7} - \dfrac{14x-5}{8} = 1$ l $\dfrac{21x+11}{6} - \dfrac{9x-1}{3} = 2\dfrac{1}{3}$

5 $\dfrac{5x-4}{6} - \dfrac{2x+1}{5} = \dfrac{3x-2}{4} - \dfrac{x+1}{3}$

6 The perimeter of this rectangle is 20 cm.
   a Show that $17x + 31 = 150$
   b Hence, or otherwise, find the sides of the rectangle.

7 The perimeter of this isosceles triangle is 22 cm. Find the value of x.

┌ ─ ─ ─ ─ ─ ─ ─ ┐
│   **KEY WORDS**   │
│   algebraic fraction   │
└ ─ ─ ─ ─ ─ ─ ─ ┘

The general equation of a straight line

THIS SECTION WILL SHOW YOU HOW TO
- Use the equation $y = mx + c$
- Find the midpoint of a line segment

The diagram shows the graph of $y = 2x + 1$
From the graph you can see that the
- gradient = 2
- **y-intercept** = 1

This important result can be written as

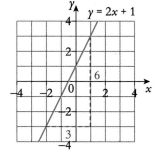

> The graph of $y = mx + c$ is a straight line where m is the gradient and c is the y-intercept.

EXAMPLE

Find the gradient and y-intercept for these lines.

  a $y = 3x - 5$ b $2y - x = 8$

  a $y = 3x - 5$ *compare with $y = mx + c$*

           $m = 3$ and $c = -5$

      gradient = 3 y-intercept = -5

  b $2y - x = 8$ *add x to both sides*

       $2y = x + 8$ *divide both sides by 2*

       $y = \dfrac{1}{2}x + 4$ *compare with $y = mx + c$*

          $m = \dfrac{1}{2}$ and $c = 4$

      gradient = $\dfrac{1}{2}$ y-intercept = 4

Parallel lines

> Parallel lines have the same gradient.

EXAMPLE

A line is parallel to the line $4y = 2x + 8$ and passes through the point $(4, 5)$.
Find the equation of the line.

$4y = 2x + 8$ *divide both sides by 4*

$y = \dfrac{1}{2}x + 2$ *compare with $y = mx + c$*

This line has a gradient of $\dfrac{1}{2}$ so the line parallel to it will also have gradient $\dfrac{1}{2}$

The equation of the parallel line is $y = \dfrac{1}{2}x + c$

The line passes through $(4, 5)$ so substitute $x = 4$ and $y = 5$ into $y = \dfrac{1}{2}x + c$

$5 = \dfrac{1}{2} \times 4 + c$

$5 = 2 + c$

$c = 3$

The equation of the parallel line is $y = \dfrac{1}{2}x + 3$

EXERCISE 2.10

1   Write down the gradient and y-intercept for these lines.

   a $y = 3x + 2$ b $y = 2x - 5$ c $y = \frac{1}{2}x + 3$ d $y = \frac{2}{3}x - 1$

   e $y = 3 + 2x$ f $y = 4 - 5x$ g $y = 7 - \frac{1}{2}x$ h $y = \frac{1}{2} + 3x$

2   Find the gradient and y-intercept for these lines.

   a $2y = 3x + 4$ b $3y = 6x - 2$ c $5y = 2x - 3$ d $2x + 3y = 5$

   e $3x + 2x = 6$ f $x - 3y = 6$ g $4x - 2y = 3$ h $3x + 7y = 2$

3   For each of the lines a, b, c and d write down
   i   the gradient
   ii   the y-intercept
   iii   the equation of the line.

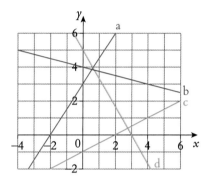

4   Write down the equation of each of these lines.

Line A	**Line B**	**Line C**
Gradient = 0	Gradient = 2	Gradient = 3
Passes through (5, −2)	Passes through (0, 0)	Passes through (0, −2)

Line D	**Line E**	**Line F**
Parallel to $y = \frac{1}{2}x + 4$	Parallel to $3x + 4y = 12$	Parallel to $2y - x = 6$
Passes through (0, 6)	Passes through (2, 5)	Passes through (−6, 1)

5   Sketch each of these graphs, labelling the point where the graph crosses the y-axis.

   a $y = x + 4$ b $y = 3x - 5$ c $y = \frac{1}{2}x - 3$ d $y = 5 - 2x$

   e $y + 2x = -4$ f $2x + 3y = 12$ g $2x - y = 3$ h $5x - 2y = 10$

6

   A $2y = (x + 8)$ **B** $y = 3x + 2$ **C** $x = y + 2$ **D** $3x + y = 2$ **E** $x = 2y$

   From the list above write down the lines that
   a   pass through (0, 0)
   b   are parallel
   c   pass through the point (−2, −4)
   d   have negative gradient
   e   are reflections of each other in the y-axis.

UNIT 2

Finding the equation of a line passing through two given points
Some questions give you the y-intercept and another point on the line.

EXAMPLE

Find the equation of the line passing through (0, −2) and (4, 1).

Using a sketch graph:
gradient $= \dfrac{3}{4}$ so $m = \dfrac{3}{4}$ or   gradient $= \dfrac{y_2 - y_1}{x_2 - x_1} = \dfrac{1 - -2}{4 - 0} = \dfrac{3}{4}$

y-intercept $= -2$ so $c = -2$

Using $y = mx + c$, $m = \dfrac{3}{4}$ and $c = -2$

The equation of the line is $y = \dfrac{3}{4}x - 2$

When the two points given do not include the y-intercept it can be more difficult.

EXAMPLE

Find the equation of the line passing through (−3, 5) and (5, −3).

Using a sketch graph: gradient $= -\dfrac{8}{8} = -1$ so $m = -1$

Using $y = mx + c$ and $m = -1$
$\qquad y = -x + c$
The line passes through (−3, 5) so substitute $x = -3$ and $y = 5$
into $y = -x + c$
$\qquad 5 = 3 + c$
$\qquad c = 2$
The equation of the line is $y = -x + 2$.

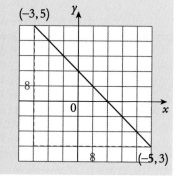

EXERCISE 2.11

Find the equations of the lines passing through these points.

1 a (0, 6) and (8, 10)   b (0, −3) and (−2, 1)   c (0, 1) and (9, 10)
   d (0, −4) and (3, 8)   e (0, −2) and (−6, 10)   f (0, 5) and (9, 11)
   g (0, −10) and (5, −13)   h (0, 8) and (10, 12)   i (0, 5) and (−4, 2)

2 a (2, 3) and (6, 5)   b (−1, −1) and (1, −7)   c (−3, 2) and (1, 6)
   d (1, 0) and (−2, 6)   e (4, −1) and (1, −4)   f (2, 1) and (5, 3)
   g (−4, 4) and (1, 3)   h (−4, −6) and (4, −4)   i (−5, −4) and (−1, −2)

Finding the midpoint of a line

The **midpoint** of a line segment can be found using a diagram or using the rule
midpoint = (mean of x coordinates, mean of y coordinates)

This rule can be written more formally as

> The midpoint of the line segment joining the points (x_1, y_1) and (x_2, y_2) is given by $\qquad$ midpoint $= \left(\dfrac{x_1 + x_2}{2}, \dfrac{y_1 + y_2}{2} \right)$

EXAMPLE

Find the midpoint of the line joining the points $(1, 2)$ and $(9, 5)$.

From the graph the midpoint is $(5, 3.5)$.
This answer can also be found using the formula.
First decide which values to use for x_1, y_1, x_2 and y_2.

$$(1, 2) \qquad\qquad (9, 5)$$
$$\uparrow \uparrow \qquad\qquad \uparrow \uparrow$$
$$(x_1, y_1) \qquad\qquad (x_2, y_2)$$

$$\text{midpoint} = \left(\frac{x_1 + x_2}{2}, \frac{y_1 + y_2}{2} \right) = \left(\frac{1+9}{2}, \frac{2+5}{2} \right) = \left(\frac{10}{2}, \frac{7}{2} \right) = \left(5, 3\frac{1}{2} \right)$$

EXAMPLE

Without drawing the line segment find the midpoint of $(-5, -2)$ and $(-2, 2\frac{1}{2})$.

$$(-5, -2) \qquad (-2, 2\frac{1}{2})$$
$$\uparrow \uparrow \qquad\quad \uparrow \uparrow$$
$$(x_1, y_1) \qquad (x_2, y_2)$$
$$\text{midpoint} = \left(\frac{x_1 + x_2}{2}, \frac{y_1 + y_2}{2} \right) = \left(\frac{-5 + -2}{2}, \frac{-2 + 2\frac{1}{2}}{2} \right) = \left(\frac{-7}{2}, \frac{\frac{1}{2}}{2} \right) = \left(-3\frac{1}{2}, \frac{1}{4} \right)$$

EXERCISE 2.12

1 Write down the midpoints of the following lines.
   a   AB   b   CD   c   EF
   d   GH   e   IJ

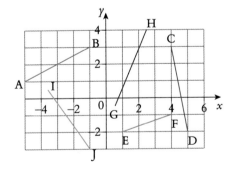

2 Use the formula to find the midpoint of the lines
joining the following points.
   a $(2, 3)$ and $(6, 4)$ b $(-4, 2)$ and $(0, -2)$
   c $(1, -4)$ and $(4, 2)$ d $(-6, 4)$ and $(-2, 6)$
   e $(-2, 2)$ and $(-1, 5)$ f $(4, -2)$ and $(5, -6)$
   g $(-6, -6)$ and $(-1, -3)$ h $(-5.5, -2.5)$ and $(-2, -2)$
   i $(1, -1.5)$ and $(4, 3)$

> **KEY WORDS**
> y-intercept
> midpoint

Representing linear inequalities on graphs

THIS SECTION WILL SHOW YOU HOW TO
• Represent linear inequalities on a graph

 You can represent an inequality by a **region** on a graph.
There are some important rules that you must follow.

If the inequality is ≥ or ≤ the **boundary line** for the region is shown by a <u>solid</u> line.
If the inequality is > or < the boundary line for the region is shown by a <u>broken</u> (dashed) line.
You are usually expected to shade the <u>unwanted</u> region.

EXAMPLE

Show the region $x + y \geq 3$ on a graph. Leave the required region unshaded.

First draw the boundary line $x + y = 3$.

x	0	3
y	3	0

The line will be solid because of the ≥ symbol.
The line divides the graph into two regions.
Find the required region using a trial point that is not on the line.
Using a trial point of (3, 2), substitute $x = 3$ and $y = 2$ into $x + y \geq 3$ to see if the inequality is true for the trial point.
$3 + 2 \geq 3$ is true. So (3, 2) is in the required region.

EXAMPLE

Show the region $y < \dfrac{1}{2} x + 1$ on a graph. Leave the required region unshaded.

x	0	2	4
y	1	2	3

Draw the boundary line $y = \dfrac{1}{2}x + 1$

The line is broken because of the < symbol.

Using a trial point of (0, 0): $0 < \dfrac{1}{2} \times 0 + 1$ is true.

So (0, 0) is in the required region.

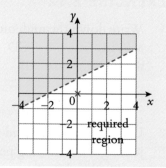

A region, R, contains points whose coordinates satisfy the following inequalities:

$-2 < x \leq 1$ $\qquad y > -3 \qquad y \leq x + 1$

On a graph, draw suitable lines and label the region R.

For $-2 < x \leq 1$: draw the lines $x = -2$ (broken) and $x = 1$ (solid)
The required region is between the two lines so shade outside the lines.
For $y > -3$: draw the line $y = -3$ (broken)
The required region is above the line so shade below the line.
For $y \leq x + 1$: draw the line $y = x + 1$ (solid)
The required region is below the line so shade above the line.

EXERCISE 2.13

1 Write down the inequality that describes the unshaded region for each of these graphs.

a

b

c

d

e

f

g

h

i
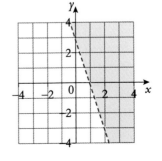

2   Draw a graph to represent each of these inequalities. Leave the equired region <u>unshaded</u>.

   a $y < 2$ b $x \geq 1$ c $-2 < x \leq 3$ d $1 < y < 3$

   e $y \leq 2x$ f $y > \frac{1}{2}x$ g $y \geq x + 1$ h $y < x - 2$

   i $x + y \geq 0$ j $x + y < 4$ k $x - 2y \geq 4$ l $x - y < 3$

3   Draw a graph to show the regions defined by each of these inequalities.
   Leave the required region unshaded.

   a $-2 < y \leq 3$ and $1 < x \leq 2$
   b $-3 < x \leq -1$ and $-2 \leq y \leq 2$

4   The red lines divide the graph into four regions A, B, C and D.

   The region D is described by the inequalities:

   $y \geq 2$ and $y \geq 2x$

   Write down the inequalities that describe

   a   Region A
   b   Region B
   c   Region C.

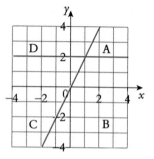

5   Match the regions P, Q and R to the inequality cards A, B and C.

A $y \leq 3, x < 2, 3x + 2y > 6$	B $y < 2, x \leq 3, 2x + 3y > 6$	C $x < 3, y < 2, 2x + 3y < 6$

6   Find the three inequalities which define the unshaded region on each of the graphs.

   a   b   c

d

e

f

g

h

i

7   A region, R, contains points whose coordinates satisfy the inequalities:
    $-3 < y \leq 2$ $x > -4$ $y \geq 2x$
    On a graph, draw suitable lines and label the region R.

8   A region, R, contains points whose coordinates satisfy the inequalities:
    $x + y \leq 2$ $y < 2x + 2$ $y \geq 0.5x - 1$
    On a graph, draw suitable lines and label the region R.

9   A region, R, contains points whose coordinates satisfy the inequalities:
    $y \leq 4$ $x \geq -2$ $y \geq x$ $2x + y < 4$
    On a graph, draw suitable lines and label the region R.

10 a   Plot the points (0, 3), (4, 3) and (4, 0) on a graph and join the points
        to make a triangle.
    b   Write down the three inequalities that define the region <u>inside</u>
        the triangle.
    c   List all the points <u>inside</u> the triangle that have integer
        coordinates.

UNIT 2

Perimeter and area

The distance around an enclosed shape is called the **perimeter**.
The amount of space enclosed inside a shape is called the **area**.
You should already know these area formulae:

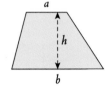

Area of rectangle = base × height

Area of parallelogram = base × height

Area of triangle $= \frac{1}{2} \times$ base × height

Area of trapezium $= \frac{1}{2}(a + b)h$

EXAMPLE

Find the perimeter and area of this shape.

Perimeter = AB + BC + CD + DE + EF + FA
$$= 7 + 5 + 3 + 3 + 4 + 2 = 24 \text{ cm}$$
Area = area of large rectangle + area of small rectangle
$$= (3 \times 5) + (4 \times 2) = 23 \text{ cm}^2$$

EXAMPLE

Find the area of this trapezium.

$a = 4$, $b = 10$ and $h = 2$

Area $= \frac{1}{2}(a + b)h$

$= \frac{1}{2} \times (4 + 10) \times 2$

$= 14 \text{ cm}^2$

To find the area of this rhombus divide it into 2 triangles.

Area of triangle
$= \frac{1}{2} \times 6 \times 2.5 = 7.5$

Area of rhombus
$= 2 \times 7.5 = 15 \text{ cm}^2$

To find the area of this kite divide it into 2 triangles.

Area of triangle
$= \frac{1}{2} \times 5 \times 2 = 5$

Area of kite
$= 2 \times 5 = 10 \text{ cm}^2$

To convert an area in cm² to an area in mm² you need to remember that:

$1\,cm^2 =$ 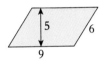 $= 10 \times 10 = 100\,mm^2$ $1\,cm^2 = 100\,mm^2$
$1\,m^2 = 10\,000\,cm^2$
$1\,km^2 = 1\,000\,000\,m^2$

EXERCISE 2.14

1   Find the perimeter and area of these shapes. All lengths are in cm.

a

b

c

d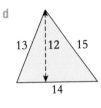

2   Find the area of these parallelograms. All lengths are in cm.

a

b

c

3   Find the area of these trapeziums.

a

b

c

d

4   Find the area of these shapes. All lengths are in cm.

a

b

c

d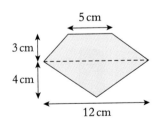

5   A trapezium has an area of 36 cm². The two parallel sides are 3 cm and 6 cm. Find the distance between the two parallel sides.

6   The trapezium has two parallel sides of length x cm and $3x + 2$ cm.
The distance between the parallel sides is 6 cm.
The area of the trapezium is 108 cm².
Find the value of x.

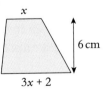

┌ ─ ─ ─ ─ ─ ─ ─ ┐
│   **KEY WORDS**   │
│   area   │
│   perimeter   │
└ ─ ─ ─ ─ ─ ─ ─ ┘

UNIT 2

Pythagoras

 You can use **Pythagoras' theorem** when you know the length of two sides in a right-angled triangle and you want to find the length of the third side.

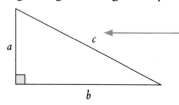

the longest side in a right-angled triangle is called the **hypotenuse**

Pythagoras' theorem for right-angled triangles says that:

The sum of the squares of the lengths of the two shorter sides is equal to the square of the length of the hypotenuse.

$$a^2 + b^2 = c^2$$

EXAMPLE

Find the length of x.

The two shorter sides are 6 cm and 8 cm. The hypotenuse is x cm.

$6^2 + 8^2 = x^2$	*square 6 and 8*
$36 + 64 = x^2$	$6 \times 6 = 36$ *and* $8 \times 8 = 64$
$100 = x^2$	*square root both sides*
$x = \sqrt{100} = 10$ cm	

EXAMPLE

Find the length of x.

The two shorter sides are x cm and 5 cm. The hypotenuse is 12 cm.

$x^2 + 5^2 = 12^2$	*square 5 and 12*
$x^2 + 25 = 144$	*take 25 from both sides*
$x^2 = 119$	*square root both sides*
$x = \sqrt{119}$	
$x = 10.908712\ldots$	*round to a suitable degree of accuracy*
$x = 10.9$ cm (to 3 s.f.)	

EXERCISE 2.15

1 Calculate x for each of these triangles.

a

4 cm
x
7 cm

b

x
3 cm
10 cm

c

8 cm
2 cm
x

d

x
3.2 m
5.8 m

e

6.5 m
2 m
x

f

x
3.7 cm
5.9 cm

2 Manuel is trying to calculate the value of x for this triangle.
This is what he writes

$6^2 + 4^2 = x^2$
$36 + 16 = x^2$
$x^2 = 52$
$x = \sqrt{52}$
$x = 7.21$ cm

He has made a mistake. Correct his working.

x
6 cm
4 cm

3 Calculate x for each of these triangles.

a

x
8 cm
4 cm

b

6 cm
2 cm
x

c

7 cm
15 cm
x

d

8.4 cm
2.3 cm
x

e

16.3 cm
x
25 cm

f

19.8 cm
x
13.6 cm

4 A boat sails 15 km due south and then 35 km due east.
How far is the boat from its starting position?

5 A ladder is 5 m long. It rests against a vertical wall with the bottom of the
ladder 1.5 m from the base of the wall. How far up the wall does the ladder reach?

UNIT 2

6 Calculate x for these right-angled triangles.

a

b

c

7 Calculate AD.

8 Calculate AB.

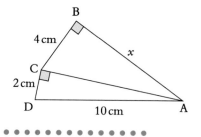

TOP TIP

Calculate the length of AC first.

9 Find the length of DB.

TOP TIP

Calculate the length of CD first.

10 Calculate
  a   the length of AD
  b   the perimeter of ABCD
  c   the area of ABCD
  d   the area of triangle ADC.

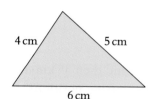

11 An equilateral triangle has sides of length 5 cm.
   Calculate
   a   the height of the triangle
   b   the area of the triangle.

12 A rhombus has a perimeter of 24 cm. The longest diagonal
   is 10 cm. Calculate the length of the shortest diagonal.

13 Sungu says this triangle is a
   right-angled triangle
   is he correct?

TOP TIP

Is $4^2 + 5^2 = 6^2$?

14 A triangle has sides of length 48 cm, 55 cm and 73 cm.
   Is it a right-angled triangle? Explain your answer.

UNIT 2

15 Suri travels 5 miles west, then 4 miles north, then 8 miles east.
How far is she from her starting point?

16 The circle has radius 4 cm.
The vertices of the rectangle lie on the circumference of the circle.
The rectangle has width 6 cm.
Calculate the height of the rectangle.

17 A hollow circular cylinder is used for storing thin metal rods.
The cylinder has a height of 15 cm and a base radius 4 cm.
Calculate the length of the longest rod that will fit exactly
inside the cylinder.

18 The perpendicular height of a circular cone is twice the length
of the diameter of the circular base.
The slant height is 10 cm.
Calculate the diameter of the circular base.

10 cm

19 The diagram shows a square with sides of length 8 cm.
Inside the square there are four touching circles of radius 2 cm
and a smaller circle of radius r cm.
Calculate the radius r.

Distance between two points on a graph

You can use Pythagoras' theorem to find the length of a line joining two points on a graph.

To do this you

- Plot the points on a graph
- Make a right-angled triangle
- Mark the horizontal distance and vertical distance on the triangle
- Apply Pythagoras' theorem to the triangle.

EXAMPLE

Find the length of the line joining A $(-3, 2)$ and B $(4, 6)$.

$AB^2 = 7^2 + 4^2$

$AB^2 = 49 + 16$

$AB^2 = 65$

$AB = \sqrt{65}$

$AB = 8.062\ldots$

$AB = 8.06$ (to 3 s.f.)

EXERCISE 2.16

1 Work out the length of the following lines.

    a   AB   b   CD

    c   EF   d   GH

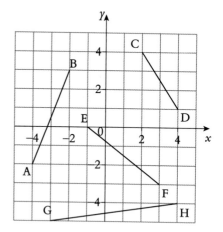

2 Calculate the length of the lines joining the following pairs of points.

    a $(2, -4)$ and $(6, 3)$ b $(5, 8)$ and $(2, -7)$

    c $(3, -6)$ and $(-8, 5)$ d $(0, -4)$ and $(-3, 4)$

    e $(-9, 2)$ and $(1, -4)$ f $(6, -2)$ and $(-6, 5)$

    g $(5, -1)$ and $(-4, -4)$ h $(-2, -2)$ and $(-5, -1)$

    i $(-2, -4)$ and $(-6, -3)$

Pythagoras in 3-D

To find the length of AG you need to look at triangle AGC.

Before you can calculate AG you need to calculate AC using Pythagoras on triangle ABC.

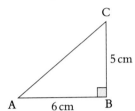

$AC^2 = 6^2 + 5^2$
$AC^2 = 36 + 25$
$AC^2 = 61$
$AC = \sqrt{61}$

Now use Pythagoras on triangle ACG.

$AC^2 + 4^2 = AG^2$
$61 + 16 = AG^2$
$AG^2 = 77$
$AG = 8.77 \text{ cm (to 3 s.f.)}$

It is useful to remember that AG can be calculated directly using

$AG^2 = 6^2 + 5^2 + 4^2$
$AG^2 = 36 + 25 + 16$
$AG^2 = 77$
$AG = 8.77 \text{ cm}$

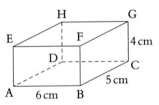

EXERCISE 2.17

1   Find the length of AG for each of these cuboids.

a

b

c

d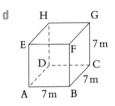

2   Find the length of AC in this triangular prism.

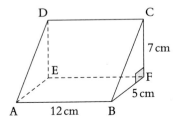

3   ABCDEFGH is a cuboid.
P is the midpoint of GC.
Calculate the length of AP.

┌ ─ ─ ─ ─ ─ ─ ─ ─ ┐
 KEY WORDS
 Pythagoras' theorem
 hypotenuse
└ ─ ─ ─ ─ ─ ─ ─ ─ ┘

UNIT 2

Area and circumference of a circle

THIS SECTION WILL SHOW YOU HOW TO

- Find the circumference of a circle
- Find the area of a circle
- Find the length of an arc
- Find the area of a sector

 The perimeter of a circle is called the **circumference** (C).
The **diameter** (d) of a circle is twice the **radius** (r).

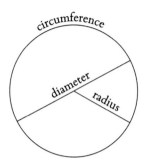

circumference

diameter

radius

Circumference = $2\pi r$ (or πd)

Area = πr^2

EXAMPLE

A circular window has a diameter of 1.2 m
Calculate

a the circumference   **b** the area of the window.

a $C = 2\pi r$	**b** $A = \pi r^2$
$C = 2 \times \pi \times 0.6$	$A = \pi \times 0.6^2$
$C = 3.77$ cm (to 3 s.f.)	$A = 1.13$ cm^2 (to 3 s.f.)

➡ **NOTE:** use $\pi = 3.142$ or the π key on your calculator.

EXAMPLE

The distance round a CD is 38 cm.
Calculate the diameter of the CD.

$C = 2\pi r$ *substitute $C = 38$ in formula*

$38 = 2\pi \times r$ *divide both sides by 2π*

$\dfrac{38}{2\pi} = r$

$r = 6.04788...$ $d = 2r$

$d = 12.1$ cm   *give your answer to 3 s.f.*

EXAMPLE

A circular clock face has an area of 50 cm^2.
Calculate the radius of the clock face.

$A = \pi r^2$ *substitute $A = 50$ into the formula*

$50 = \pi \times r^2$ *divide both sides by π*

$\dfrac{50}{\pi} = r^2$ *square root both sides*

$r = \sqrt{\dfrac{50}{\pi}}$

$r = 3.99$ cm   *give your answer to 3 s.f.*

EXERCISE 2.18

1 Find the circumference and area of these circles. All lengths are in cm.

a

b

c

d

e

f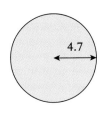

2 The wheels on a car have a diameter of 52 cm.
   a Calculate the distance travelled by the car when the wheels rotate once.
   b How many km does the car travel if the wheels rotate 5000 times?

3 A circular table has an area of 1.25 m².
   Calculate   a the radius   b the circumference of the table.

4 The length of the sides of each square is 12 cm.
   The circles fit tightly inside the square.
   Calculate the shaded area for each diagram.

a

b

c

   d What do you notice about your answers? Can you explain why?

5 The radius of the large circle is 5 cm.
   The radius of the small circle is 3 cm.
   Calculate the shaded area.

6 The radius of the circle is 10 cm.
   The vertices of the square lie on the circumference of the circle.
   Calculate the shaded area.

Semicircles and quadrants

A **semicircle** is half a circle. A **quadrant** is quarter of a circle.

EXAMPLE

Find the perimeter and area of the shape.

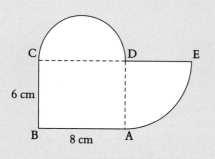

The radius of the semicircle is 4 cm.
The radius of the quadrant is 6 cm.
Perimeter = AB + BC + arc CD + DE + arc EA

$$= 8 + 6 + \frac{2 \times \pi \times 4}{2} + 6 + \frac{2 \times \pi \times 6}{4}$$

$$= 8 + 6 + 4\pi + 6 + 3\pi$$

$$= 41.99114\ldots$$

$$= 42.0 \text{ cm} \quad \text{(to 3 s.f.)}$$

Area = area of rectangle + area of semicircle
+ area of quadrant

$$= (8 \times 6) + \frac{\pi \times 4^2}{2} + \frac{\pi \times 6^2}{4}$$

$$= 48 + 8\pi + 9\pi$$

$$= 101.407\ldots$$

$$= 101 \text{ cm}^2 \quad \text{(to 3 s.f.)}$$

EXERCISE 2.19

Calculate the perimeter and area of each of these shaded shapes. All lengths are in cm.

1

2

3

4

5

6

7

8

9

10

11

12 The diagram shows four rods of radius 2 cm.
The rods are held tightly together by a piece of wire.
Calculate the length of the wire.

13 **a** The area of a semicircle is 6 cm². Find the radius and perimeter.
   b The area of a semicircle is 24 cm². Find the radius and perimeter.
   c Compare your answers to parts **a** and **b**. What do you notice?

14 **a** The area of a quadrant is 5 cm². Find the radius and perimeter.
   b The area of a quadrant is 45 cm². Find the radius and perimeter.
   c Compare your answers to parts **a** and **b**. What do you notice?

15 The perimeter of a quadrant is 24 cm.
Calculate the area of the quadrant.

16 This shape is made from two identical quadrants.
The perimeter of the shape is 40 cm.
Calculate the radius of the quadrants.

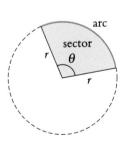

17 A circle has a circumference of x cm and an area of $2x$ cm².
Calculate the radius of the circle.

Arcs and sectors
An **arc** is part of the circumference of a circle.
A **sector** of a circle is a region bounded by an arc and two radii.

Arc length = $\dfrac{\theta}{360} \times 2\pi r$ Sector area = $\dfrac{\theta}{360} \times \pi r^2$

UNIT 2

EXAMPLE

Find
a the area of the sector OAB
b the length of the arc AB
c the perimeter of the sector AOB.

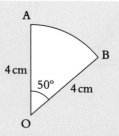

a area of sector OAB $= \dfrac{50}{360} \times \pi r^2$

$\qquad = \dfrac{50}{360} \times \pi \times 4^2$

$\qquad = 6.98\,\text{cm}^2$ (to 3 s.f.)

b arc length AB $= \dfrac{50}{360} \times 2\pi r$

$\qquad = \dfrac{50}{360} \times 2 \times \pi \times 4$

$\qquad = 3.49\,\text{cm}$ (to 3 s.f.)

c perimeter of sector OAB = OA + OB + arc AB
$\qquad = 4 + 4 + 3.49$
$\qquad = 11.5\,\text{cm}$ (to 3 s.f.)

EXAMPLE

a Arc AB = 7 cm.
Find the value of θ

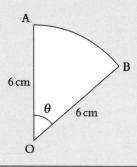

b Area of sector AOB = 50 cm².
Find the value of r.

a Arc length $= \dfrac{\theta}{360} \times 2\pi r$

$\qquad 7 = \dfrac{\theta}{360} \times 2 \times \pi \times r$

$\qquad 7 = \dfrac{\theta}{360} \times 12\pi$

$\qquad \theta = \dfrac{7 \times 360}{12\pi}$

$\qquad \theta = 66.8°$ (to 3 s.f.)

b Area of sector $= \dfrac{\theta}{360} \times \pi r^2$

$\qquad 50 = \dfrac{115}{360} \times \pi r^2$

$\qquad 50 \times 360 = 115\pi \times r^2$

$\qquad r = \sqrt{\dfrac{50 \times 360}{115\pi}}$

$\qquad r = 7.06\,\text{cm}$ (to 3 s.f.)

EXERCISE 2.20

1 Find the length of the arc AB for each of these.

a

b

c

d

2 Find the area of the sector for each of these.

a

b

c

d

3 Find the perimeter and area of these shapes.

a

b

c

d

4 The area of the sector is 6 cm².
   Calculate the value of θ.

5

The length of arc AB is 10 cm.
Calculate the value of r.

6 This shape is made from a square of length 5 cm and four
   identical sectors of a circle of radius 5 cm and angle 60°.
   Calculate   a   the perimeter
                b   the area of the shape.

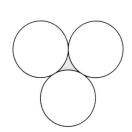

7 The diagram shows three identical coins of
   radius 1 cm.
   Calculate the shaded area in the middle
   of the diagram.

UNIT 2

Displaying data

THIS SECTION WILL SHOW YOU HOW TO

- Display data and interpret data

Types of data

Discrete Data	Continuous Data
• marks in a test	• height of students
• number of people in a boat	• mass of sand
• number of coins	• time to complete a puzzle
• shoe size	• speed of a car

> Discrete data can only have exact numbers.

> Continuous data can take any value in a particular range.

Bar charts, pictograms and pie charts

A **pictogram** is similar to a **bar chart**, except that the frequencies are represented by a number of identical pictures.

In a **pie chart** the frequency is represented by the angle of the sector of a circle.

EXAMPLE

The table shows the grades obtained by 30 students in an examination. Show this information on
a a bar chart   **b** a pictogram   **c** a pie chart.

Grade	A★	A	B	C	D
Number of students	3	12	10	3	2

a

b

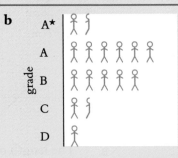

Key: represents 2 students

c   The pie chart represents 30 students. Each student is represented by 360° ÷ 30 = 12°

Grade	Frequency	Angle
A★	3	3 × 12° = 36°
A	12	12 × 12° = 144°
B	10	10 × 12° = 120°
C	3	3 × 12° = 36°
D	2	2 × 12° = 24°
		360°

Examination grades

Displaying continuous data

Continuous data is often put into a grouped frequency table with equal class widths. A **frequency diagram** can then be drawn to represent the data.

EXAMPLE

2.83	3.22	3.79	2.95	3.88	3.08	4.23	1.74	3.47	2.77
3.56	2.03	3.14	4.11	2.51	2.38	3.98	3.37	3.66	3.33

The table shows the mass (m), in kilograms of 20 newborn babies.
a   Arrange the data into a grouped frequency table using class intervals of $1.5 < m \leq 2.0$, $2.0 < m \leq 2.5$, $2.5 < m \leq 3.0$, $3.0 < m \leq 3.5$, $3.5 < m \leq 4.0$ and $4.0 < m \leq 4.5$.
b   Use the grouped frequency table in part **a** to draw a frequency diagram to represent the data.

a

mass (m) kg	tally	frequency
$1.5 < m \leq 2.0$	|	1
$2.0 < m \leq 2.5$	||	2
$2.5 < m \leq 3.0$	||||	4
$3.0 < m \leq 3.5$	ЖҢ |	6
$3.5 < m \leq 4.0$	ЖҢ	5
$4.0 < m \leq 4.5$	||	2

b

➡ **NOTE:** for continuous data
- there are no gaps between the bars
- the horizontal axis is written as a continuous number line

EXERCISE 2.21

1   The table shows the colour of 60 students' mobile phones.

black	silver	blue	other
25	20	10	5

Show this information on
a   a bar chart   b   a pictogram   c   a pie chart.

2   The table shows the sales of four different flavour packs of crisps.

plain	vinegar	chicken	cheese
16	8	12	4

Show this information on
a   a bar chart   b   a pictogram   c   a pie chart.

3   The table shows how 50 adults travel to work.

walk	cycle	bus	car	train
15	5	10	18	2

Show this information on
a   a bar chart   b   a pictogram   c   a pie chart.

4   The pie chart shows the ingredients used to make a cake.
The cake mixture has a total mass of 900 g.
Measure each of the angles on the pie chart and then
calculate the mass of each of the ingredients used to
make the cake.

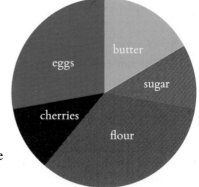

5   Two dice are thrown 40 times and the scores on each dice are
added together to give a total score. These are the results.

5	7	4	8	10	6	7	3	9	6
6	9	8	7	5	2	11	10	11	9
7	3	8	5	12	6	7	4	8	6
10	6	4	11	7	7	8	5	9	4

a   Construct a frequency table to show the total scores.
b   Draw a bar chart to show the total scores.

6   The table shows information about the ages of people in
a swimming pool.
a   Draw a frequency diagram to show the information in
the table.
b   Find the percentage of people that are over
30 years old.

Age (x years)	Number of people
$0 < x \le 10$	4
$10 < x \le 20$	20
$20 < x \le 30$	15
$30 < x \le 40$	6
$40 < x \le 50$	4
$50 < x \le 60$	1

7   The table shows information about the times taken
by 32 teachers to travel to work.
a   Draw a frequency diagram to show the information
in the table.
b   Find the percentage of teachers that take more than
5 minutes.

Time (t minutes)	Frequency
$0 < t \le 5$	8
$5 < t \le 10$	12
$10 < t \le 15$	6
$15 < t \le 20$	4
$20 < t \le 25$	2

Two-way tables

A **two-way table** shows two or more sets of data at the same time.

EXERCISE 2.22

1   The table shows information about the number
    of boys and girls in Class 5A who did and did not
    do their homework.

    a   How many boys are in Class 5A?

    b   How many students did not do their homework?

    c   How many students are there altogether in Class 5A?

	Boys	Girls
Homework	13	15
No homework	4	1

2   In a survey 100 students are asked if they are
    left-handed or right-handed.
    The table shows the results.
    Copy and complete the table.

	Boys	Girls	Total
Left-handed	7		18
Right-handed		41	
Total			100

3   Students in a small school must attend one lunchtime club.
    They have a choice of Athletics Club, Drama Club or Music Club.
    The table shows information about the number of students attending each club.

	Boys	Girls	Total
Athletics	56	42	
Drama	58	37	
Music	16		
Total			250

    a   Copy and complete the table.

    b   What percentage of the students attend the Music Club?

4   The table shows information about the times taken by a group of people
    to solve a puzzle.

		TIME (*t* minutes)		
		$0 < t \le 10$	$10 < t \le 20$	$20 < t \le 30$
	$10 < x \le 20$	5	9	23
AGE	$20 < x \le 30$	15	10	7
(*x* years)	$30 < x \le 40$	13	12	15
	$40 < x \le 50$	10	15	16

    a   How many people are there altogether?

    b   How many people took more than 10 minutes?

    c   What percentage of the people took 10 minutes or less?

> **KEY WORDS**
> discrete data
> continuous data
> bar chart
> pictogram
> pie chart
> frequency diagram
> two-way table

Unit 2 Examination-style questions

1 The normal selling price of a car is $18 000.
This price is reduced by 14% in a sale.

Calculate the sale price of the car. [2]

2 At noon, the number of bacteria in a culture was 25 500.
One hour later this number had increased by 8%.

Calculate the number of bacteria at 1 p.m. [2]

3 Raju was paid $800 each week.
His pay is increased by x% to $828 each week.

Find the value of x. [3]

4 Alan and Barbara share $500 in the ratio 13 : 7.

Calculate the amount that each receives. [2]

5 Edward, Fred and George share some money in the ratio 5 : 7 : 3.
George receives $237.

Find the total amount of money that was shared. [2]

6 A map has a scale of 1 : 20 000.
A road is 16 cm long on the map.

Find the actual length, in kilometres, of the road. [2]

7 Simplify.

   (a) $x^{10} \div x^2$ [1]
   (b) $(x^3)^4$ [1]

8 **(a)** Work out $\left(\dfrac{2}{3}\right)^{-3}$. [1]

   (b) Simplify.

      (i) $7x^0$ [1]
      (ii) $8x^5 \times 4x^{-3}$ [2]

9 $5^x = \dfrac{1}{625}$

Find the value of x. [1]

10 Solve the inequality.

   $5x - 2 > 7x + 3$ [2]

11 $\dfrac{2x-5}{3} \le \dfrac{x+2}{5}$

    (a) Solve the inequality.   [3]

    (b) Using your answer to **part (a)**, write down the positive integer values
of x that satisfy the inequality.   [1]

12 Simplify.

    $\dfrac{2x}{3} - \dfrac{x}{8}$ [2]

13 Solve.

    $\dfrac{5-x}{6} + \dfrac{2x+3}{4} = 5$ [4]

14 E is the point $(5, 7)$ and F is the point $(0, -3)$.

    Find the equation of the line EF.   [3]

15 P is the point $(-2, 9)$ and Q is the point $(4, -3)$.

    (a) Find the coordinates of the midpoint of the line PQ.   [2]

    (b) Calculate the length of the line PQ.   [3]

    (c) Find the equation of the line through P and Q.
Write your answer in the form $y = mx + c$.   [3]

    (d) Another line is parallel to PQ and passes through the point $(4, -9)$.
Write down the equation of this line.   [2]

16 Change $925\,000\,\text{cm}^2$ to m^2.   [1]

17 In this diagram all lengths are in centimetres.

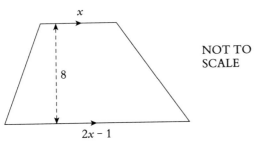

NOT TO
SCALE

The trapezium has two parallel sides of length x cm and $(2x-1)$ cm.
The perpendicular distance between the two parallel sides is 8 cm.
The area of the trapezium is $110\,\text{cm}^2$.

Find the value of x.   [3]

18

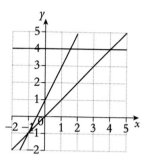

By shading the **unwanted** regions on the grid, find and label the region R that satisfies the following three inequalities.

$y \leq 4$ $y \leq 2x + 1$ $y \leq x$

[3]

19

NOT TO SCALE

The circle has radius 5 cm.
The vertices of the square lie on the circumference of the circle.

Calculate the length of the sides of the square.

[2]

20

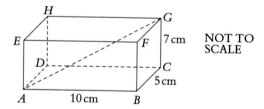

NOT TO SCALE

The diagram shows a cuboid $ABCDEFGH$.
$AB = 10$ cm, $BC = 5$ cm and $CG = 7$ cm.

Calculate the length of the line AG.

[4]

21

NOT TO SCALE

10 cm   10 cm

Two semicircles with diameter 10 cm are removed from a semicircle with diameter 20 cm.

(a) Calculate the area of the shaded shape. [3]

(b) Calculate the perimeter of the shaded shape. [3]

22

NOT TO SCALE

42°

The diagram shows the sector of a circle with sector angle 42°.
The perimeter of the sector is 45 cm.

Calculate the radius of the circle. [3]

23

Grade	A★	A	B	C	D	E
Frequency	5	11	15	8	4	2

The table shows the results of a group of students in an examination.

(a) Write down the modal grade. [1]

(b) Paul draws a pie chart to represent the results.
Calculate the sector angle for grade A. [2]

24 In a survey, 54 students were asked how they travelled to school.
The table shows some of the results.

	Walked	Cycled	Bus	Total
Boys	8	10		25
Girls		7	5	
Total				54

(a) Complete the table. [2]

(b) Find the percentage of students who cycled to school. [1]

Standard form

 A number in standard form must be written as

$A \times 10^n$ where $1 \le A < 10$ and n is an integer

It is a very useful way of writing very large and very small numbers.

Large numbers

> **EXAMPLE**
>
> Write these numbers in standard form
> a 8 000 000   b 30 500
>
> ---
>
> a $8\,000\,000 = 8 \times 10^6$ b $30\,500 = 3.05 \times 10^4$

➡ **NOTE:**
$10^1 = 10$
$10^2 = 100$
$10^3 = 1000$
$10^4 = 10\,000$
$10^5 = 100\,000$
$10^6 = 1\,000\,000$

> **EXAMPLE**
>
> Write these as ordinary numbers
> a 1.36×10^5 b 7×10^8
>
> ---
>
> a $1.36 \times 10^5 = 136\,000$ b $7 \times 10^8 = 700\,000\,000$

> **EXAMPLE**
>
> $a = 4.5 \times 10^8$ and $b = 3 \times 10^5$
> Calculate the following giving your answers in standard form.
> a $a + b$ b $a \times b$ c $a \div b$
>
> ---
>
> a $a + b = (4.5 \times 10^8) + (3 \times 10^5)$ *change so they are both $\times 10^5$*
> $\quad = (4500 \times 10^5) + (3 \times 10^5)$
> $\quad = 4503 \times 10^5$ *this is not in standard form so replace 4503 by 4.503×10^3*
> $\quad = 4.503 \times 10^3 \times 10^5$ *$10^3 \times 10^5 = 10^{3+5} = 10^8$*
> $\quad = 4.503 \times 10^8$
>
> b $a \times b = (4.5 \times 10^8) \times (3 \times 10^5)$ *multiply 4.5 by 3 and 10^8 by 10^5*
> $\quad = 13.5 \times 10^{8+5}$
> $\quad = 13.5 \times 10^{13}$ *this is not in standard form so replace 13.5 by 1.35×10^1*
> $\quad = 1.35 \times 10^1 \times 10^{13}$
> $\quad = 1.35 \times 10^{14}$
>
> c $a \div b = (4.5 \times 10^8) \div (3 \times 10^5)$ *divide 4.5 by 3 and 10^8 by 10^5*
> $\quad = 1.5 \times 10^{8-5}$
> $\quad = 1.5 \times 10^3$

EXERCISE 3.1

1 Which of these numbers are written in standard form?

   a 4×10^2 b 15×10^6 c 9.5×10^4 d 10×10^3
   e 23.4×10^7 f 1×10^8 g 7.07×10^5 h 50.03×10^8

2 Write these numbers in standard form.

   a $54\,000$ b 200 c $700\,000$ d 5330
   e $82\,000\,000$ f 3020 g $666\,000$ h 36.36

3 Write these as ordinary numbers.

   a 4.8×10^5 b 3.7×10^2 c 5.64×10^8 d 7.06×10^7
   e 2×10^4 f 1.1×10^6 g 3.001×10^2 h 9.5×10^9

4 Calculate the following, giving your answer in standard form.

   a $(4 \times 10^3) + (2 \times 10^3)$ b $(4 \times 10^5) + (5 \times 10^4)$ c $(8 \times 10^4) - (5 \times 10^4)$
   d $(4.3 \times 10^6) - (2 \times 10^5)$ e $(4 \times 10^3) \times (8 \times 10^5)$ f $(2.1 \times 10^5) \times (3 \times 10^2)$
   g $(8 \times 10^7) \div (2 \times 10^4)$ h $(7.5 \times 10^9) \div (3 \times 10^2)$ i $(4 \times 10^6)^2$
   j $\dfrac{(4 \times 10^8) + (5 \times 10^7)}{9 \times 10^3}$ k $\dfrac{(2.1 \times 10^3) \times (4 \times 10^5)}{2 \times 10^6}$ l $\dfrac{(4.9 \times 10^8) - (3 \times 10^6)}{(7 \times 10^5) + (3 \times 10^5)}$

5 Check your answers to question 4 using a calculator.

6 $p = 6 \times 10^9$ and $q = 2 \times 10^8$

   Calculate the following giving your answers in standard form.

   a $p + q$ b $p - q$ c $2p - 5q$ d $p \times q$
   e $p \div q$ f p^2 g $\dfrac{p + q}{q}$ h $\dfrac{p^2}{2q}$

7 Simplify the ratios.

   a $6 \times 10^5 : 2 \times 10^4$ b $2.5 \times 10^6 : 1 \times 10^8$ c $5.6 \times 10^7 : 11.2 \times 10^4$

8 Solve the equations.

   a $5x + 3 \times 10^4 = 5.1 \times 10^5$ b $2(x - 6 \times 10^3) = 3 \times 10^4$ c $3(x - 2 \times 10^4) = 2(x + 7 \times 10^5)$

9 Simplify, giving your answer in standard form.

   a $\sqrt{4 \times 10^8}$ b $\sqrt{9 \times 10^4}$ c $\sqrt{3.6 \times 10^7}$ d $\sqrt{4.9 \times 10^9}$

10 Write these in order of size, smallest first.

   2.2×10^{14} 2.04×10^{14} 5.8×10^{13} 2.13×10^4

11 The distance between the Earth and the Sun is 149 million kilometres.
   Write this number in standard form.

12 The area of land on the Earth is 1.5×10^8.
   The area of ocean on the Earth is 3.6×10^8.
   Write the ratio of land to ocean in its simplest form.

13 The population of China is approximately 1.34×10^9.
   The population of Argentina is approximately 4.05×10^7.
   Calculate the difference in population, giving your answer in standard form.

Small numbers

UNIT 3

EXAMPLE

Write these numbers in standard form
a 0.000 7   b 0.000 0061

a $0.000\,7 = 7 \times 10^{-4}$ b $0.000\,0061 = 6.1 \times 10^{-6}$

➡ **NOTE:**
$10^{-1} = 0.1$
$10^{-2} = 0.01$
$10^{-3} = 0.001$
$10^{-4} = 0.000\,1$
$10^{-5} = 0.000\,01$
$10^{-6} = 0.000\,001$

EXAMPLE

Write these as ordinary numbers
a 4.23×10^{-2} b 9×10^{-4}

a $4.23 \times 10^{-2} = 0.0423$ b $9 \times 10^{-4} = 0.0009$

EXAMPLE

$a = 3 \times 10^5$ $b = 4 \times 10^{-3}$ $c = 2 \times 10^{-4}$
Calculate the following giving your answers in standard form.
a $a \times b$ b $b \times c$ c $a \div c$ d $c \div b$ e $b - c$

a $a \times b = (3 \times 10^5) \times (4 \times 10^{-3})$ *multiply 3 by 4 and 10^5 by 10^{-3}*
$\quad = 12 \times 10^2$ *this is not in standard form so replace 12 by 1.2×10^1*
$\quad = 1.2 \times 10^1 \times 10^2$ *$10^1 \times 10^2 = 10^{1+2} = 10^3$*
$\quad = 1.2 \times 10^3$

b $b \times c = (4 \times 10^{-3}) \times (2 \times 10^{-4})$ *multiply 4 by 2 and 10^{-3} by 10^{-4}, $10^{-3} \times 10^{-4} = 10^{-3+-4} = 10^{-7}$*
$\quad = 8 \times 10^{-7}$

c $a \div c = (3 \times 10^5) \div (2 \times 10^{-4})$ *divide 3 by 2 and 10^5 by 10^{-4}, $10^5 \div 10^{-4} = 10^{5--4} = 10^9$*
$\quad = 1.5 \times 10^9$

d $c \div b = (2 \times 10^{-4}) \div (4 \times 10^{-3})$ *divide 2 by 4 and 10^{-4} by 10^{-3}, $10^{-4} \div 10^{-3} = 10^{-4--3} = 10^{-1}$*
$\quad = 0.5 \times 10^{-1}$ *this is not in standard form so replace 0.5 by 5×10^{-1}*
$\quad = 5 \times 10^{-1} \times 10^{-1}$ *$10^{-1} \times 10^{-1} = 10^{-1+-1} = 10^{-2}$*
$\quad = 5 \times 10^{-2}$

e **Method 1**
$b - c = (4 \times 10^{-3}) - (2 \times 10^{-4})$
$\quad = (4 \times 10^{-3}) - (0.2 \times 10^{-3})$
$\quad = 3.8 \times 10^{-3}$

Method 2
$b - c = (4 \times 10^{-3}) - (2 \times 10^{-4})$
$\quad = 0.004 - 0.0002$
$\quad = 0.0038$
$\quad = 3.8 \times 10^{-3}$

EXERCISE 3.2

1 Write these numbers in standard form.

a 0.015	b 0.000 67	c 0.000 9
d 0.000 606	e 3 200 000	f 0.000 52
g 0.44	h 53 080 000	i 0.000 000 057
j 0.000 613	k 700 200	l 0.000 89

2 Write these as ordinary numbers.
   a 8.8×10^{-5} b 2.3×10^{-7} c 6×10^{-3}
   d 5.11×10^{-2} e 9.9×10^{4} f 1.04×10^{-6}
   g 6.8×10^{-4} h 6×10^{8} i 3.8×10^{-1}
   j 2.2×10^{1} k 4.08×10^{5} l 9.5×10^{-6}

3 Calculate the following, giving your answer in standard form.
   a $(4 \times 10^{-2}) + (2 \times 10^{-2})$ b $(7 \times 10^{-5}) + (2 \times 10^{-6})$
   c $(8 \times 10^{-8}) - (3 \times 10^{-8})$ d $(6.2 \times 10^{-4}) - (2 \times 10^{-5})$
   e $(5 \times 10^{-5}) \times (6 \times 10^{-5})$ f $(3.2 \times 10^{-3}) \times (2 \times 10^{-4})$
   g $(9 \times 10^{7}) \times (3 \times 10^{-5})$ h $(4.8 \times 10^{-6}) \div (2 \times 10^{-4})$

   i $(3 \times 10^{-5})^2$ j $\dfrac{\left(5 \times 10^{4}\right) + \left(2 \times 10^{4}\right)}{3.5 \times 10^{-2}}$

   k $\dfrac{\left(1.8 \times 10^{-2}\right) \times \left(3 \times 10^{8}\right)}{2 \times 10^{3}}$ l $\dfrac{\left(9 \times 10^{-4}\right) + \left(7 \times 10^{-4}\right)}{\left(4 \times 10^{-5}\right) \times \left(2 \times 10^{9}\right)}$

4 Check your answers to question 3 using a calculator.

5 Simplify, giving your answer in standard form.

   a $\sqrt{9 \times 10^{-6}}$ b $\sqrt{4 \times 10^{-10}}$
   c $\sqrt{6.4 \times 10^{-5}}$ d $\sqrt{8.1 \times 10^{-13}}$

6 $p = 6 \times 10^{-8}$ and $q = 3 \times 10^{-9}$
   Calculate the following, giving your answers in standard form.
   a $p + q$ b $p - q$ c $3p + 2q$ d $p \times q$
   e $p \div q$ f p^2 g q^2 h $\dfrac{5p^2}{4q}$

7 The mass, in grams, of a single hydrogen atom is $1.67 \times 10^{-24}\,\text{g}$.
   Find the total mass of 500 hydrogen atoms.
   Give your answer in standard form.

8 The mass, in grams, of a single oxygen atom is 2.67×10^{-23} g.
   Calculate the number of oxygen atoms in 5 grams of oxygen.
   Give your answer in standard form.

9 The time taken by light to travel one metre is approximately 3×10^{-9} seconds.
   How long does it take light to travel 5 kilometres?
   Give your answer in standard form.

10 The mass, in kilograms, of a grain of sand is $3.5 \times 10^{-10}\,\text{kg}$.
   Find the total mass of 75 000 grains of sand.
   Give your answer in standard form.

KEY WORDS
standard form

Simultaneous equations 1

THIS SECTION WILL SHOW YOU HOW TO
- Solve simultaneous equations using a graph
- Solve simultaneous equations using the elimination method

 Simultaneous equations are a set of equations that are all satisfied by the same values of the variables. Simultaneous equations can be solved using a graph or by using algebra.

EXAMPLE

Solve these simultaneous equations using a graph.
$$x + 2y = 4$$
$$x - y = 1$$

First, make a table of values for each equation.

$x + 2y = 4$

x	0	4
y	2	0

$x - y = 1$

x	0	1
y	-1	0

Then draw both lines on one set of axes.

The lines intersect at the point (2, 1).

The solution to the simultaneous equations is $x = 2$, $y = 1$

➡ **CHECK:** substitute the values for x and y into the original equations:
$$2 + (2 \times 1) = 4 \checkmark$$
$$2 - 1 = 1 \checkmark$$

EXERCISE 3.3

1 Copy and complete these tables for the given equations.

$y = x + 2$

x	0	2	4
y			

$y = 4 - x$

x	0	2	4
y			

Draw both graphs on one set of axes.

Use your graph to solve the simultaneous equations $y = x + 2$ and $y = 4 - x$

2 Copy and complete these tables for the given equations.

$y = \dfrac{1}{2}x + 1$

x	0	2	4
y			

$5x + 4y = 20$

x	0	
y		0

Draw both graphs on one set of axes.

Use your graph to solve the simultaneous equations $y = \dfrac{1}{2}x + 1$ and $5x + 4y = 20$

Solving simultaneous equations using a graph takes time and can be inaccurate if the coordinates of the point of intersection are not integers. It is quicker and easier to use an algebraic method.

Elimination method

The elimination method involves adding or subtracting the equations (or multiples of them) to **eliminate** one of the variables.

UNIT 3

EXAMPLE

Solve these simultaneous equations. $3x + 2y = 19$
$x + 2y = 13$

$$3x + 2y = 19 \quad (1)$$
$$x + 2y = 13 \quad (2)$$

Subtracting equation (2) from equation (1) will eliminate the y terms.

$$2x = 6$$
$$x = 3$$

To find y substitute $x = 3$ in equation (1) and then solve.

$$9 + 2y = 19$$
$$2y = 10$$
$$y = 5$$

The solution is $x = 3$, $y = 5$.

➡ **CHECK:**

$$(3 \times 3) + (2 \times 5) = 19 \checkmark$$
$$3 + (2 \times 5) = 13 \checkmark$$

EXAMPLE

Solve these simultaneous equations. $4x + 3y = 1$
$2x - 3y = 14$

$$4x + 3y = 1 \quad (1)$$
$$2x - 3y = 14 \quad (2)$$

Adding equations (1) and (2) will eliminate the y terms.

$$6x = 15$$
$$x = 2\frac{1}{2}$$

Substitute $x = 2\frac{1}{2}$ in equation (1) and then solve to find y:

$$10 + 3y = 1$$
$$3y = -9$$
$$y = -3$$

The solution is $x = 2\frac{1}{2}$, $y = -3$.

➡ **CHECK:**

$$\left(4 \times 2\frac{1}{2}\right) + (3 \times -3) = 10 - 9 = 1 \checkmark$$

$$\left(2 \times 2\frac{1}{2}\right) - (3 \times -3) = 5 - -9 = 14 \checkmark$$

EXERCISE 3.4

Solve these simultaneous equations.

1
a $2x + y = 10$
$x + y = 9$

b $3x + 2y = 19$
$x + 2y = 9$

c $2x + y = 19$
$2x + 3y = 15$

d $4x + 3y = 28$
$4x + y = 20$

e $5x + 2y = 8$
$3x + 2y = 4$

f $7x + y = -17$
$5x + y = -11$

g $4x + 5y = -34$
$4x + 2y = -28$

h $3x + 8y = -1$
$5x + 8y = 9$

2
a $5x - 2y = 2$
$3x + 2y = 14$

b $3x + 5y = 52$
$4x - 5y = 11$

c $4x - 3y = -22$
$5x + 3y = 40$

d $2x - 9y = -13$
$2x + 9y = 41$

e $4x + 9y = 2$
$3x - 9y = 33$

f $5x - 4y = -31$
$2x + 4y = 10$

g $7x + 2y = 39$
$3x - 2y = 31$

h $6x + y = -21$
$10x - y = -19$

3
a $3x - 7y = 4$
$x - 7y = -8$

b $-2x + 5y = 9$
$-2x + 3y = 3$

c $8x - y = 42$
$6x - y = 32$

d $4x - 3y = -3$
$8x - 3y = 3$

e $-3x + 2y = 17$
$-3x + 4y = 22$

f $2x - 3y = 0$
$5x - 3y = 6$

g $8x - 4y = 1$
$3x - 4y = 6$

h $7x - 2y = -35$
$3x - 2y = -19$

4 The sum of two numbers is 15 and the difference is 4. Let the two numbers be x and y.
Write down a pair of simultaneous equations involving x and y. Solve the equations.

5 Find two numbers with
a a mean of 27 and a difference of 24
b a mean of 4 and a difference of 22.

6 Find the values of x and y.

7 Find the values of x and y.

8 Seven pens and two pencils cost $6.59. Seven pens and 5 pencils cost $7.55
Find the cost of a pencil and the cost of a pen.

9 The line $y = mx + c$ passes through the points $(-2, 1)$ and $(4, 4)$.
Write down a pair of simultaneous equations involving m and c.
Solve the simultaneous equations.

10 The cost of a taxi journey is made of two parts.
There is a fixed charge of x and then an extra charge of y per km.
The total cost for a 5 km journey is $14.60. The total cost for a 12 km journey is $23.84
Find the total cost of a 24 km journey.

To eliminate one of the variables you might first need to multiply one or both of the equations by a suitable number before adding or subtracting.

UNIT 3

EXAMPLE

Solve these simultaneous equations. $8x + 3y = 7$
$3x + 5y = -9$

$8x + 3y = 7$ (1)
$3x + 5y = -9$ (2)

Multiply equation (1) by 5 and equation (2) by 3.

$40x + 15y = 35$
$9x + 15y = -27$

Subtracting these two equations will eliminate the y terms.

$31x = 62$
$x = 2$

Substitute $x = 2$ in equation (1) and then solve to find y:

$16 + 3y = 7$
$3y = -9$
$y = -3$.

The solution is $x = 2$, $y = -3$.

➡ CHECK:

$(8 \times 2) + (3 \times -3) = 16 + -9 = 7$ ✓
$(3 \times 2) + (5 \times -3) = 6 + -15 = -9$ ✓

Some simultaneous equations need to be re-arranged before solving them.

EXAMPLE

Solve these simultaneous equations. $5x + 2y - 25 = 0$
$2x - 1 = y$

First re-arrange the equations into the form $ax + by = c$

$5x + 2y = 25$ (1)
$2x - y = 1$ (2)

Multiply equation (2) by 2.

$5x + 2y = 25$
$4x - 2y = 2$

Adding the equations will eliminate the y terms

$9x = 27$
$x = 3$

Substitute $x = 3$ in equation (1) and then solve to find y:

$15 + 2y = 25$
$2y = 10$
$y = 5$

The solution is $x = 3$, $y = 5$.

➡ CHECK:

$(5 \times 3) + (2 \times 5) = 25$ ✓
$(2 \times 3) - 5 = 1$ ✓

EXERCISE 3.5

Solve these simultaneous equations.

1
a $\begin{aligned} 2x + 3y &= 21 \\ 5x - y &= 10 \end{aligned}$
b $\begin{aligned} 8x + 2y &= 34 \\ 3x + y &= 13 \end{aligned}$
c $\begin{aligned} 4x + 3y &= 36 \\ 2x - y &= 8 \end{aligned}$
d $\begin{aligned} 3x + 7y &= 58 \\ x + 2y &= 17 \end{aligned}$

e $\begin{aligned} 5x + 2y &= 21 \\ x + y &= 3 \end{aligned}$
f $\begin{aligned} 6x + 5y &= 45 \\ 2x - 3y &= 29 \end{aligned}$
g $\begin{aligned} 4x + 2y &= 22 \\ 6x - y &= 2 \end{aligned}$
h $\begin{aligned} 7x + 8y &= 1 \\ x + 4y &= -7 \end{aligned}$

2
a $\begin{aligned} 3x + 8y &= 68 \\ 5x - 6y &= -22 \end{aligned}$
b $\begin{aligned} 4x + 3y &= 18 \\ 3x - 2y &= 5 \end{aligned}$
c $\begin{aligned} 5x - 2y &= 19 \\ 2x - 3y &= 1 \end{aligned}$
d $\begin{aligned} 4x + 5y &= 18 \\ 6x + 2y &= 16 \end{aligned}$

e $\begin{aligned} 3x - 4y &= 0 \\ 2x + 5y &= 46 \end{aligned}$
f $\begin{aligned} 9x + 7y &= 127 \\ 3x + 2y &= 41 \end{aligned}$
g $\begin{aligned} 2x + 3y &= 33 \\ 6x - 5y &= -27 \end{aligned}$
h $\begin{aligned} 8x + 5y &= 43 \\ 5x + 3y &= 26 \end{aligned}$

3
a $\begin{aligned} 10x - 2y &= -13 \\ 4x - 3y &= -14 \end{aligned}$
b $\begin{aligned} 2x + 7y &= -29 \\ 3x - 4y &= 29 \end{aligned}$
c $\begin{aligned} 5x + 6y &= 32 \\ 3x + 9y &= 57 \end{aligned}$
d $\begin{aligned} 8x - 5y &= -14 \\ 3x - 4y &= -1 \end{aligned}$

e $\begin{aligned} 6x - 7y &= -6 \\ 8x + 2y &= 26 \end{aligned}$
f $\begin{aligned} 2x - 8y &= 0 \\ 3x + 12y &= 36 \end{aligned}$
g $\begin{aligned} 8x + 7y &= -7 \\ 6x + 5y &= -4 \end{aligned}$
h $\begin{aligned} 2x - 3y &= -30 \\ 3x - 2y &= -35 \end{aligned}$

4
a $\begin{aligned} x &= 10 - 3y \\ 2x - 3y &= 2 \end{aligned}$
b $\begin{aligned} y &= x - 1 \\ 3x - y &= 5 \end{aligned}$
c $\begin{aligned} x + 2y - 8 &= 0 \\ 2x - 3y - 14 &= 0 \end{aligned}$
d $\begin{aligned} 3x + 2y &= 11 \\ y - 2x &= 3 \end{aligned}$

e $\begin{aligned} y - 3x &= -9 \\ x + 2y &= -4 \end{aligned}$
f $\begin{aligned} y &= x + 3 \\ 3y + x &= 5 \end{aligned}$
g $\begin{aligned} 3y - 5x &= 13 \\ 3x + y + 5 &= 0 \end{aligned}$
h $\begin{aligned} 3y &= 2x + 4 \\ 2y &= 7 - 3x \end{aligned}$

5
a $\begin{aligned} \frac{x}{4} + \frac{y}{3} &= 8 \\ \frac{x}{2} - \frac{y}{5} &= 3 \end{aligned}$
b $\begin{aligned} \frac{x}{2} + \frac{y}{4} &= 6 \\ \frac{x}{5} - \frac{y}{2} &= 12 \end{aligned}$
c $\begin{aligned} \frac{x}{6} - \frac{y}{2} &= -8 \\ \frac{x}{3} - \frac{y}{5} &= -8 \end{aligned}$
d $\begin{aligned} \frac{x}{8} + \frac{y}{3} &= 1 \\ \frac{x}{12} + \frac{y}{2} &= -1 \end{aligned}$

6 Four times one number added to three times another number gives 33.
The sum of the two numbers is 10. Find the two numbers.

7 Five times one number take away two times another number gives 15.
The sum of the two numbers is 6.5. Find the two numbers.

8 A bag contains 36 coins. The coins are a mixture of one-dollar coins
and 50-cent coins. The total value of the coins in the bag is $26.50.
How many one-dollar coins are there?

9 Cinema tickets cost $8.50 per child and $14 per adult.
One evening the cinema sells 201 tickets for a total of $2550.
How many adult tickets were sold?

10 Eight bottles of fruit juice and three bottles of water cost $17.89
Five bottles of fruit juice and four bottles of water cost $13.37
Find the cost of a bottle of fruit juice.

11 Four lemons and three oranges cost $5.45
Seven lemons and four oranges cost $9.30
Find the cost of an orange.

12 The straight line $ax + by = 15$ passes through the points $(-5, 6)$ and $(15, -6)$.
Find the values of a and b.

13 The straight line $ax + by = 9$ passes through the points $(12, 5)$ and $(-6, -7)$.
Find the values of a and b.

14 For the rectangle ABCD, find
  a the values of x and y
  b the perimeter of the rectangle
  c the area of the rectangle.

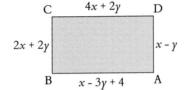

15 For the square ABCD, find
  a the values of x and y
  b the perimeter of the square
  c the area of the square.

16 For the equilateral triangle ABC, find
  a the values of x and y
  b the perimeter of the triangle
  c the area of the triangle.

> **KEY WORDS**
> simultaneous equations
> eliminate

Factorising 1

THIS SECTION WILL SHOW YOU HOW TO
- Factorise simple expressions
- Use factorisation to simplify fractions

 Expanding $3x(5x + 4)$ gives $15x^2 + 12x$.
Factorising is the reverse of expanding.
So factorising $15x^2 + 12x$ gives $3x(5x + 4)$.

EXAMPLE

Factorise $6x + 8$

$6x + 8$
$= 2(3x + 4)$

2 is the highest common factor (HCF) of the two terms
$6x = 2 \times 3x$ *and* $8 = 2 \times 4$
It is sensible to check your answer by expanding the brackets.
$2(3x + 4) = 2 \times 3x + 2 \times 4 = 6x + 8$ ✓

EXAMPLE

Factorise $5x^2 + 10xy$

$5x^2 + 10xy$
$= 5x(x + 2y)$

5x is the HCF of the two terms
$5x^2 = 5x \times x$ *and* $10xy = 5x \times 2y$

EXAMPLE

Factorise $xy^2 + x^3y^4$

$xy^2 + x^3y^4$
$= xy^2(1 + x^2y^2)$

xy^2 is the HCF of the two terms
$xy^2 = xy^2 \times 1$ *and* $x^3y^4 = xy^2 \times x^2y^2$

EXAMPLE

Factorise $x(x + 2) + 5(x + 2)$

$x(x + 2) + 5(x + 2)$
$= (x + 2)(x + 5)$

$x + 2$ is the HCF of the two terms
➡ NOTE: $(x + 5)(x + 2)$ is also correct

EXAMPLE

Factorise $xy - 2x + 3y - 6$

$xy - 2x + 3y - 6$
$= x(y - 2) + 3(y - 2)$
$= (y - 2)(x + 3)$

factorise the first two terms and the last two terms
$y - 2$ is the HCF of these two terms
➡ NOTE: $(x + 3)(y - 2)$ is also correct

EXERCISE 3.6

1 Abdullah has got his factorising homework wrong.
Copy out each question and correct his mistakes.

a) $6x + 12y$ b) $5xy - 10xy^3$ c) $4x + 6y$

$= 2(3x + 6y)$ $= 5x(y - y^2)$ $= 4\left(x + 1\frac{1}{2}y\right)$

Factorise these expressions completely.

2 a $4x + 8$ b $3x - 6$ c $8x + 2$
   d $10x - 15$ e $7y - 14$ f $9y + 12$
   g $20 - 8x$ h $36 - 12y$ i $42 - 7x$
   j $18y - 4$ k $24x + 16$ l $22y - 55$

3 a $x^2 + 5x$ b $x^2 - 8x$ c $y^2 - 4y$
   d $a^2 + 9a$ e $4x^2 - 8x$ f $3y^2 - 9y$
   g $10x^2 - 4x$ h $8y - 2y^2$ i $15y^2 + 5y$
   j $14x - 7x^2$ k $6x - 4x^2$ l $12y^2 - 9y$

4 a $8\pi + 4$ b $15 - 9\pi$
   c $\pi r^2 + \pi r l$ d $2\pi r^2 + 2\pi r h$

5 a $6x^2y - 3xy$ b $10x^4y^2 - 5x^4y$ c $8xy^3 - 32x^3y$
   d $15x^3y^2 - 12x^2y^4$ e $12x^2y - 15xy$ f $28pq^2 - 35p^2q$
   g $6a^2b + 9ab$ h $21x^5y - 28x^2y$ i $56a^4b^7 - 35ab^5$

6 a $3a + 3b - 3c$ b $5x + 5y + 5x^2$ c $2ax - ay - 3ay^2$
   d $x^3 + 4x^2 - 2x$ e $y^4 + 6y^3 - 6y^2$ f $p^2q^2r + pqr + pq^2r$
   g $20a^2b^2c^2 - 8a^2b^2 + 16abc^2$ h $15x^3y^2 - 27x^2y + 21x^2y^2$
   i $8p^7q^5r^3 + 6p^4q^3r^2 - 4p^3q^3r^3$

7 a $x(y + 2) + 3(y + 2)$ b $a(b - 4) + 2(b - 4)$ c $p(q + 3) - 5(q + 3)$
   d $x(y - 5) - 3(y - 5)$ e $x(x + y)^2 + y(x + y)^2$ f $(a + b)^3 - (a + b)^2$
   g $(x - y)^2 - (x - y)^3$ h $5(x + y) + (x + y)^2$ i $(x - y)^3 - 4(x - y)^2$

8 a $xy + y + 3x + 3$ b $5y - 10 + xy - 2x$ c $4a + 4b + ac + bc$
   d $pq + 2pr + 3q + 6r$ e $3x + 12 - xy - 4y$ f $xy - 3x - 4y + 12$

UNIT 3

You can use factorisation to simplify algebraic fractions.

EXAMPLE

Simplify $\dfrac{x^2 + 4x}{x}$

$\dfrac{x^2 + 4x}{x}$ *factorise the numerator*

$= \dfrac{{}^{1}\cancel{x}\,(x+4)}{\cancel{x}_{1}}$ *cancel*

$= x + 4$

EXAMPLE

Simplify $\dfrac{6x - 12}{18}$

$\dfrac{6x - 12}{18}$ *factorise the numerator*

$= \dfrac{{}^{1}\cancel{6}\,(x-2)}{\cancel{18}_{3}}$ *cancel*

$= \dfrac{x-2}{3}$

EXAMPLE

Simplify $\dfrac{x^2 - xy}{7x^2 - 7xy}$

$\dfrac{x^2 - xy}{7x^2 - 7xy}$ *factorise the numerator and denominator*

$= \dfrac{{}^{1}\cancel{x}\left(\cancel{x-y}\right)^{1}}{7\cancel{x}_{1}\left(\cancel{x-y}\right)_{1}}$ *cancel*

$= \dfrac{1}{7}$

EXAMPLE

Simplify $\dfrac{3x + 3y}{x^2 - xy} \times \dfrac{5x - 5y}{2x + 2y}$

$= \dfrac{3(x+y)}{x(x-y)} \times \dfrac{5(x-y)}{2(x+y)}$ *factorise both numerators and denominators*

$= \dfrac{3\left(\cancel{x+y}\right)^{1}}{x\left(\cancel{x-y}\right)_{1}} \times \dfrac{5\left(\cancel{x-y}\right)^{1}}{2\left(\cancel{x+y}\right)_{1}}$ *cancel*

$= \dfrac{15}{2x}$

EXERCISE 3.7

1 Sheeba has got her simplifying algebraic fractions homework wrong.
Copy out each question and correct her mistakes.

a) $\dfrac{4x-8}{4}$ b) $\dfrac{x^2+2x}{4x}$ c) $\dfrac{6x+8}{10}$

$= 4x - 2$ $= \dfrac{x^2+2}{4}$ $= \dfrac{2(3x+8)}{10} = \dfrac{(3x+8)}{5}$

Simplify these algebraic fractions.

2 a $\dfrac{3x+6}{3}$ b $\dfrac{8y+4}{2}$ c $\dfrac{5x+10}{5}$ d $\dfrac{12y+8}{4}$

    e $\dfrac{6x-12}{8}$ f $\dfrac{9x+6}{12}$ g $\dfrac{15-20y}{10}$ h $\dfrac{24-16a}{20}$

3 a $\dfrac{x^2+9x}{x}$ b $\dfrac{y^2-8y}{y}$ c $\dfrac{x^2-3x}{x^2}$ d $\dfrac{x-x^3}{x}$

    e $\dfrac{8x+4y}{4z}$ f $\dfrac{5x+5y}{5z}$ g $\dfrac{x^2+xy}{xy}$ h $\dfrac{x^2-2x}{xy}$

4 a $\dfrac{3x+3y}{x+y}$ b $\dfrac{5a-5b}{a-b}$ c $\dfrac{x-y}{6x-6y}$ d $\dfrac{2x+2y}{10x+10y}$

    e $\dfrac{2-2y}{5-5y}$ f $\dfrac{3x+3xy}{7+7y}$ g $\dfrac{xy+x}{yz+z}$ h $\dfrac{10x-10y}{15x-15y}$

5 a $\dfrac{x^2+x}{x+1}$ b $\dfrac{5x}{x^2-5x}$ c $\dfrac{x^2-3x}{5x-15}$ d $\dfrac{4y-6y^2}{10-15y}$

    e $\dfrac{x^2-x}{(x-1)^2}$ f $\dfrac{3y-6}{(y-2)^3}$ g $\dfrac{x^2+3x}{x+3}$ h $\dfrac{3x^2y-6xy}{6x-12}$

6 a $\dfrac{4p+4q}{2p-2q} \times \dfrac{5p-5q}{3p+3q}$ b $\dfrac{7a+14b}{a-b} \times \dfrac{2a-2b}{3a+6b}$ c $\dfrac{x^2-3x}{y} \times \dfrac{x}{xy-3y}$

    d $\dfrac{x^2+x}{y^2+y} \times \dfrac{y}{x}$ e $\dfrac{7x-7y}{xy} \times \dfrac{x^2+xy}{x-y}$ f $\dfrac{f^2-6f}{2g} \times \dfrac{4g}{fg-6g}$

7 a $\dfrac{2x-4y}{6xy} \div \dfrac{4x-8y}{5x^2y^2}$ b $\dfrac{3x^2-6x}{6y-2y^2} \div \dfrac{5x^2-10x}{9y-3y^2}$

┌─ ─ ─ ─ ─ ─ ─ ─ ─ ┐
│   **KEY WORDS**   │
│   factorise   │
└─ ─ ─ ─ ─ ─ ─ ─ ─ ┘

Rearranging formulae 1

In the formula $P = 2x + 2y$, P is called the **subject** of the formula. The formula can be rearranged to make x the subject as follows:

$P = 2x + 2y$ *take 2y from both sides*

$P - 2y = 2x$ *divide both sides by 2*

$\dfrac{P - 2y}{2} = x$

EXAMPLE

Rearrange the formula $y = \dfrac{m - n}{2}$ to make m the subject.

$y = \dfrac{m - n}{2}$ *multiply both sides by 2*

$2y = m - n$ *add n to both sides*

$2y + n = m$

EXAMPLE

Rearrange the formula $x = \dfrac{y^2}{3} + z$ to make y the subject.

$x = \dfrac{y^2}{3} + z$ *take z from both sides*

$x - z = \dfrac{y^2}{3}$ *multiply both sides by 3*

$3(x - z) = y^2$ *square root both sides*

$y = \pm\sqrt{3(x - z)}$

➡ **NOTE:** remember for example that both $5^2 = 25$ and $(-5)^2 = 25$

EXAMPLE

Rearrange the formula $T = 2\pi\sqrt{\dfrac{l}{g}}$ to make l the subject.

$T = 2\pi\sqrt{\dfrac{l}{g}}$ *divide both sides by 2π*

$\dfrac{T}{2\pi} = \sqrt{\dfrac{l}{g}}$ *square both sides*

$\dfrac{T^2}{4\pi^2} = \dfrac{l}{g}$ *multiply both sides by g*

$\dfrac{T^2 g}{4\pi^2} = l$

EXERCISE 3.8

1 Hassan has got his rearranging formulae homework wrong.
Copy out each question and correct his mistakes.

a)
$$p = 3x - q$$
$$p - q = 3x$$
$$\frac{p - q}{3} = 3$$

b)
$$2x + a = 8b$$
$$x + a = 4b$$
$$x = 4b - a$$

c)
$$y = \sqrt{x} + b$$
$$y^2 = x + b^2$$
$$y^2 - b^2 = x$$

Make x the subject of these formulae.

2 a $x + 3 = y$ b $x - 6 = 5y$ c $x + y = 4$ d $x - a = b$
   e $y = x - 8$ f $x + 2y - 5 = 0$ g $x - 4y + 8 = 2y$ h $y - x = 10$

3 a $6x = y$ b $9x = 3y$ c $3x = y - 4$ d $ax = 7 - 5y$
   e $\dfrac{x}{2} = p$ f $\dfrac{x}{5} = 3 + d$ g $\dfrac{x}{2} = y - 8$ h $\dfrac{x}{a} = 10 - 4y$
   i $\dfrac{2x}{3} = y$ j $\dfrac{4x}{5} = 3y$ k $\dfrac{3x}{7} = a + b$ l $\dfrac{ax}{b} = c + d$

4 a $2x + c = d$ b $5x - y = 2z$ c $4x + 3y = 6$ d $8x - 3b = c + d$
   e $ax + b = d$ f $bx - c = cd$ g $px - q = a + b$ h $y - xy = 8$

5 a $x(y + z) = 2$ b $p = (2q + 3)x$ c $a = 3(2x + y)$ d $p = q(x - r)$

6 a $\dfrac{x + a}{b} = c$ b $\dfrac{x - 2f}{3g} = h$ c $\dfrac{ax + by}{c} = d$ d $\dfrac{p - qx}{r} = m$
   e $\dfrac{p}{x} = q$ f $f = \dfrac{g}{x}$ g $\dfrac{p + q}{x} = r$ h $5 = \dfrac{p - q}{x}$

7 a $ax^2 = b$ b $px^2 = q$ c $abx^2 = c$ d $ax^2 = bc$
   e $x^2 + a = b$ f $x^2 - d = e$ g $ax^2 + b = c$ h $px^2 - 5q = 4r$
   i $\dfrac{x^2}{4} - a = b$ j $\dfrac{x^2}{a} + bc = d$ k $f - \dfrac{x^2}{g} = 3h$ l $3fg - \dfrac{x^2}{2} = g$

8 a $\sqrt{x + a} = b$ b $\sqrt{x - p} = qr$ c $\sqrt{2x - y} = 4$ d $2\sqrt{x - y} = z$

9 Sofia and Karl are asked to make h the subject of the formula $A = 2\pi r(r + h)$

Sofia writes:
$$A = 2\pi r(r + h)$$
$$A = 2\pi r^2 + 2\pi rh$$
$$A - 2\pi r^2 = 2\pi rh$$
$$\frac{A - 2\pi r^2}{2\pi r} = h$$

Karl writes:
$$A = 2\pi r(r + h)$$
$$\frac{A}{2\pi r} = r + h$$
$$\frac{A}{2\pi r} - r = h$$

> **KEY WORDS**
> subject

Who is correct? Explain your answer.

Similar triangles

Congruency

Two shapes are **congruent** if one of the shapes fits exactly on top of the other shape.

These three triangles are all congruent.

In congruent shapes

- corresponding angles are equal
- corresponding lengths are equal.

To prove that two triangles are congruent you must show that they satisfy one of the following four sets of conditions.

SSS three sides are equal.

SAS two sides and the included angle are the same.

ASA two angles and the included side are the same.

RHS right-angled triangles with hypotenuse and one other side the same.

Explain why the following pairs of triangles are congruent.

a

6 cm   3 cm
30°
3 cm   6 cm

b

2 cm   9 cm   2 cm
9 cm

a   Two sides and the included angle are the same. (SAS)
b   The triangle is right-angled (R), the hypotenuses (H) are the same and one other side (S) is the same. (RHS)

EXERCISE 3.9

1 Using axes from 0 to 10, draw each pair of triangles.
   Which pairs of triangles are congruent?

a	Triangle A: (0, 5) (0, 9) (1, 6)	Triangle B: (3, 10) (7, 10) (5, 9)
b	Triangle C: (0, 2) (1, 0) (3, 2)	Triangle D: (1, 7) (1, 10) (3, 8)
c	Triangle E: (4, 4) (6, 6) (3, 7)	Triangle F: (7, 7) (10, 8) (8, 10)
d	Triangle G: (2, 3) (6, 3) (7, 4)	Triangle H: (6, 5) (9, 5) (10, 6)
e	Triangle I: (0, 4) (1, 3) (2, 7)	Triangle J: (9, 0) (10, 1) (8, 3)
f	Triangle K: (3, 9) (6, 8) (7, 6)	Triangle L: (5, 0) (7, 1) (8, 4)

2 Explain why each of the following pairs of triangles are congruent.

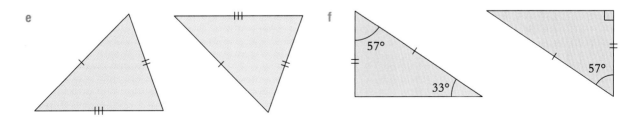

3 ABCD is a parallelogram.
Explain why triangles ABC and ACD are congruent.

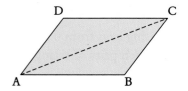

4 PQRS is a rectangle.
Explain why triangles PQS and QSR are congruent.

5 Explain why triangles ABC and PQR are congruent.

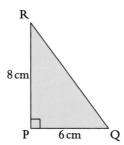

Similar shapes

These two quadrilaterals are **similar**.

$$\frac{PQ}{AB} = \frac{QR}{BC} = \frac{RS}{CD} = \frac{SP}{DA} = 2$$

In similar shapes

- Corresponding angles are equal
- Corresponding sides are in the same ratio.

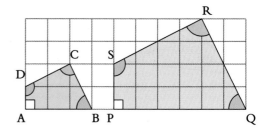

Similar triangles

To show that two triangles are similar it is sufficient to show that just
one of the above conditions is satisfied.

Are these triangles similar?

For the triangles to be similar, corresponding angles must be equal.

Triangle A: third angle = $180 - (58 + 78)$

= 44   *Angles are: 58° 78° 44°.*

Triangle B: third angle = $180 - (78 + 44)$

= 58   *Angles are: 58° 78° 44°.*

Triangles A and B are similar.

Are these triangles similar?

For the triangles to be similar, corresponding sides must be in the same ratio.

Ratio of longest sides = $\dfrac{9}{2} = 4.5$

Ratio of shortest sides = $\dfrac{4.5}{1} = 4.5$

Ratio of remaining sides = $\dfrac{7.5}{1.5} = 5$

Triangles A and B are not similar.

Find x and y.

 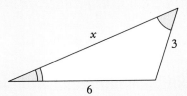

Using ratios of corresponding sides $\dfrac{3}{2} = \dfrac{x}{5} = \dfrac{6}{y}$

separating gives $\dfrac{3}{2} = \dfrac{x}{5}$ and $\dfrac{3}{2} = \dfrac{6}{y}$

'cross multiply' $15 = 2x$ $3y = 12$

$x = 7.5$ $y = 4$

Alternative method:

using scale factors

$3 = 2 \times 1.5$

So $x = 5 \times 1.5 = 7.5$

and $y = 6 \div 1.5 = 4$

EXERCISE 3.10

1 Which of these triangles are similar in shape?

2 Which of these triangles are similar in shape?

  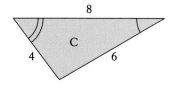

3 The following pairs of shapes are similar. Find the unknown lengths.

a

b

c

d

e

f

Triangles ABC and PQR are similar. Find the values of x and y.

Rotating the second triangle makes it easier to see which are the corresponding sides.

Using ratios of corresponding sides:

$$\frac{12}{6} = \frac{x}{4} = \frac{10}{y}$$

so $\dfrac{12}{6} = \dfrac{x}{4}$ and $\dfrac{12}{6} = \dfrac{10}{y}$

$\quad\quad 2 = \dfrac{x}{4} \quad\quad\quad\quad 2 = \dfrac{10}{y}$

$\quad\quad x = 8 \quad\quad\quad\quad\quad y = 5$

Alternative method:
using scale factors

$\quad\quad 12 = 6 \times 2$

So $x = 4 \times 2 = 8$

and $y = 10 \div 2 = 5$

AB is parallel to DE.
AB = 14 cm, AD = 6 cm, CD = 18 cm and CE = 12 cm.
BE = x cm and DE = y cm.
Find the values of x and y.

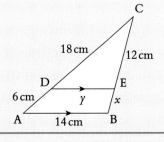

Triangles ABC and DEC are similar because:
∠DCE = ∠ACB (common angle)
∠CDE = ∠CAB (corresponding angles)
∠CED = ∠CBA (corresponding angles)
(Draw the two triangles separately to help
you to identify the corresponding sides.)
Using ratios of corresponding sides:

$$\frac{24}{18} = \frac{x+12}{12} = \frac{14}{y}$$

so $\dfrac{24}{18} = \dfrac{x+12}{12}$ and $\dfrac{24}{18} = \dfrac{14}{y}$

$\quad 288 = 18x + 216 \quad 24y = 252$ 'cross multiplying'

$\quad 18x = 72 \quad\quad\quad\quad y = 10.5$

$\quad\quad x = 4$

Similar triangles   119

EXERCISE 3.11

1 Find the values of x and y for each of the following diagrams.

a

b

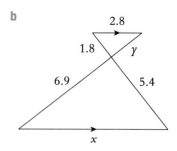

2 The width of a river can be estimated without having to cross over the river. Use the diagram below to calculate the width (w) of this river.

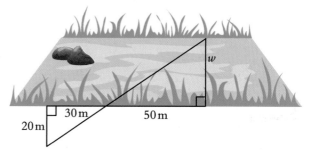

3 Find the value of x for each of the following diagrams.

a

b

c

d

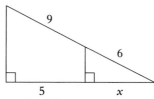

4 At midday the length of the shadow from a building is 50 m and the length of the shadow from a man is 1.65 m.
The height of the man is 1.8 m.
Calculate the height of the building.

5 Find the values of x and y for each of the following diagrams.

a

b

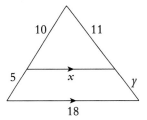

6 DE is parallel to AC.

$AD = \frac{1}{4} AB$.

a Find the coordinates of D and E.

b Find the coordinates of the midpoint of the line DE.

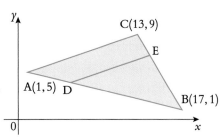

7 A is the point $(3, -7)$ and B is the point $(13, -2)$.

P and Q are points that lie on the line segment joining A to B.

a Find the coordinates of the midpoint of the line AB.

b AP : PB = 3 : 2. Find the coordinates of the point P.

c AQ : AB = 1 : 5. Find the coordinates of the point Q.

8 Find the values of x and y for each of the following diagrams.

a

b

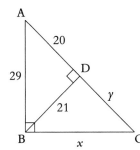

TOP TIP

$\angle BCD = \angle ABD$
in each of these triangles.

9 Find the values of x and y for each of the following diagrams.

a $\angle CAD = \angle DCB$

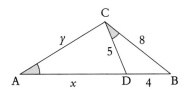

b $\angle DAB = \angle CBD$

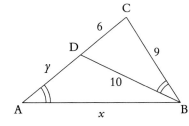

KEY WORDS
congruent
similar

UNIT 3

Reflections, rotations and translations

A **transformation** changes the position or size of a shape.
The original shape is called the **object** and the final shape is called the **image**.
Reflections, **rotations** and **translations** are transformations that change only the position of a shape.
The object and image are congruent for reflections, rotations and translations.

Reflections

A reflection is a transformation that involves a mirror line.

In the diagram, triangle A′B′C′ is the image of triangle ABC after a reflection in the line $x = 4$.

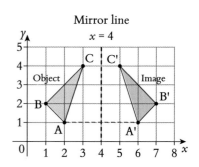

The line joining the point A to its image A′ is at right angles to the mirror line **and** A is the same distance in front of the mirror line as A′ is behind the mirror line.

On a graph plot the points P(3, 1), Q(7, 3) and R(7, 7).
Reflect triangle PQR in the line $y = x$. Label the image P′Q′R′.

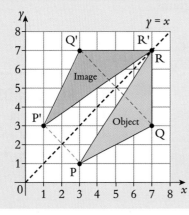

The point R lies on the line $y = x$ so it does not move when reflected in the line. It is called an **invariant** point.

The lines PP′ and QQ′ are at right angles to the mirror line $y = x$.

EXERCISE 3.12

1 Copy the diagrams and draw the image of each shape when reflected in the mirror line.

a

b

c

d

e

f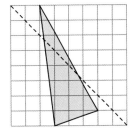

2 Write the equation of the mirror line for each of these reflections.

a A onto B   b B onto C
c B onto D   d E onto F
e E onto G   f E onto I
g F onto H   h G onto H

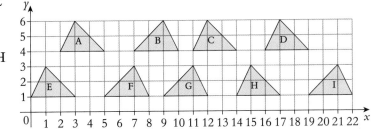

3 Name the mirror line for each of these reflections.

a A onto B
b A onto C
c D onto F
d E onto F
e G onto H
f H onto I

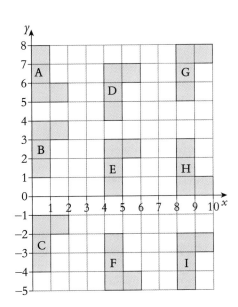

4 Name the mirror line for each of these reflections.

  a A onto B

  b A onto D

  c B onto C

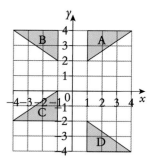

5 Name the mirror line for each of these reflections.

  a A onto B

  b A onto C

  c C onto E

  d B onto E

  e D onto E

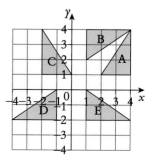

6 Name the mirror line for each of these reflections.

  a A onto D   b F onto G

  c C onto E   d B onto H

  e C onto D   f C onto H

  g D onto G   h A onto E

  i H onto G   j F onto B

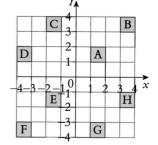

7 Copy the diagram onto graph paper.

  a Reflect shape A in the line $x = 0$ and label the image B.

  b Reflect shape A in the line $y = 1$ and label the image C.

  c Reflect shape A in the line $y = x$ and label the image D.

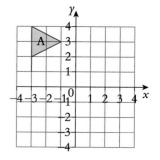

8 Copy the diagram onto graph paper.

  a Reflect shape A in the line $y = 2$ and label the image B.

  b Reflect shape A in the line $y = -1$ and label the image C.

  c Reflect shape A in the line $x = 0$ and label the image D.

  d Reflect shape A in the line $y = -x$ and label the image E.

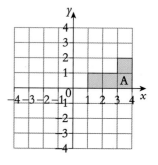

9 Copy the diagram onto graph paper.
   a   Reflect shape A in the line $y = 1$ and label the image B.
   b   Reflect shape A in the line $x = -1$ and label the image C.
   c   Reflect shape A in the line $x = 2$ and label the image D.
   d   Reflect shape A in the line $y = x$ and label the image E.
   e   Reflect shape A in the line $y = x + 2$ and label the image F.
   f   Reflect shape A in the line $x + y = 1$ and label the image G.

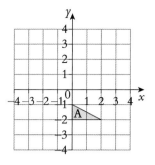

10 Copy the diagram onto graph paper.
   a   Reflect shape A in the x-axis and label the image B.
   b   Reflect shape A in the line $x = 0.5$ and label the image C.
   c   Reflect shape A in the line $y = x$ and label the image D.
   d   Reflect shape A in the line $y = x + 3$ and label the image E.

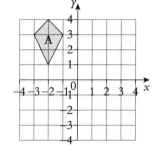

11 Use axes from −4 to 4.
   Draw the pentagon whose vertices are $(-1, -1)$, $(2, 3)$,
   $(1, 4)$, $(-2, 3)$ and $(-3, 1)$.
   Reflect the pentagon in the line $y = x$.
   The object and image are congruent.
   Mark the sides and angles to
   show which are equal to each other.

12 Copy the diagram onto graph paper.
   a   Reflect shape A in the line $x = 4$
       and label the image B.
   b   Reflect shape B in the line $x = 8$
       and label the image C.
   c   Reflect shape C in the line $x = 10.5$
       and label the image D.
   d   Shape A can be transformed onto
       shape D by a **single** reflection.
       Name the mirror line for this single reflection.

13 Copy the diagram onto graph paper.
   a   Reflect shape A in the line $y = x$ and label the image B.
   b   Reflect shape B in the line $x + y = 4$ and label the image C.
   c   Reflect shape C in the line $x = 2$ and label the image D.
   d   Shape A can be transformed onto shape D by a **single**
       reflection. Name the mirror line for this single reflection.

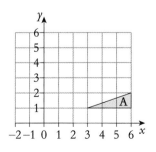

Rotations

A **rotation** is a transformation that turns a shape about a fixed point.

The fixed point is called the **centre of rotation**.

The shape can be rotated in a clockwise (↻) or anticlockwise (↺) direction.

To describe a rotation fully, you need to give
- the angle of rotation
- the direction of rotation
- the centre of rotation.

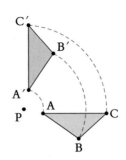

➡ **NOTE:** you can use tracing paper to help you to do rotations.

➡ **NOTE:** you can use compasses to check the paths traced out by the points.

In the diagram above, triangle A′B′C′ is the image of triangle ABC after a rotation of 90° anticlockwise about the point P.

EXAMPLE

Rotate shape A 180° about the point (8, 2).

A rotation of 180° clockwise is the same as a rotation of 180° anticlockwise so the direction does not need to be given.

EXERCISE 3.13

1 Copy these shapes on graph paper.
   Draw the image of each shape for the given rotations.
   Use the marked point as the centre of rotation.

a

180°

b

90° anticlockwise

c

90° clockwise

d

90° anticlockwise

e

180°

f

90° clockwise

2   Use axes from −4 to 4.
    a   Draw the triangle with vertices (−4, 1), (−4, 4) and (−3, 1).
        Label the triangle A.
    b   Rotate A through 90° clockwise about the origin.
        Label the image B.
    c   Rotate A through 180° about the origin.
        Label the image C.
    d   Rotate A through 90° anticlockwise about the origin.
        Label the image D.

3   Use axes from −4 to 4.
    a   Draw the triangle with vertices (3, 1), (3, 4) and (2, 3).
        Label the triangle A.
    b   Rotate A through 180° about the point (2, 0).
        Label the image B.
    c   Rotate A through 180° about the point (0, 1).
        Label the image C.
    d   Rotate A through 90° clockwise about the point (1, 3).
        Label the image D.

4   Use axes from −4 to 4.
    a   Draw the kite with vertices (1, 0), (2, 2), (1, 3) and (0, 2).
        Label the kite A.
    b   Rotate A through 90° anticlockwise about the point (−1, 1).
        Label the image B.
    c   Rotate A through 180° about the point (−1, 1).
        Label the image C.
    d   Rotate A through 90° clockwise about the point (−1, 1).
        Label the image D.

5   Use axes from −6 to 6.
    a   Draw the triangle with vertices (3, −4), (6, −1) and (5, 1).
        Label the triangle A.
    b   Rotate A through 180° about the point (2, −1).
        Label the image B.
    c   Rotate B through 90° clockwise about the point (0, 3).
        Label the image C.
    d   Rotate C through 90° anticlockwise about the point (−2, 1).
        Label the image D.

Describing a rotation

EXAMPLE

Describe fully the single transformation that takes triangle ABC onto triangle A'B'C'.

The line AB is vertical and the line A'B' is horizontal so the angle of rotation is 90°.
The shape has been rotated clockwise.
There are two methods for finding the centre of rotation.

Method 1 (By trial and error)

Use tracing paper to try to find the centre of rotation.
Through trial and error you should find that the centre of rotation is at the point (4, 1).

Method 2 (By construction)

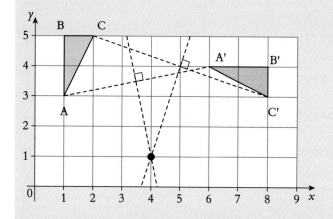

➡ **NOTE:** only two perpendicular bisectors need to be drawn to locate the centre of rotation.

Join A to A' and draw the perpendicular bisector of the line AA'
Join C to C' and draw the perpendicular bisector of the line CC'
The point where the two perpendicular bisectors meet is the centre of rotation.
The transformation that takes triangle ABC onto triangle A'B'C' is a rotation 90° clockwise about the point (4, 1).

EXERCISE 3.14

1 Describe fully the single transformation that takes shape A onto shape B for each of the following diagrams.

a

b

c

d

e

f

2
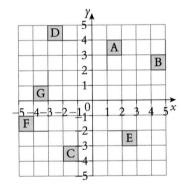

Describe fully the single transformation that moves shape:
a A onto B   b A onto C   c A onto D
d A onto E   e A onto F   f A onto G
g C onto D   h C onto E   i C onto F
j D onto E   k D onto G   l E onto G.

Translations

A **translation** is a transformation that 'slides' a shape from one place to another. In a translation every point on the original shape moves the same distance and in the same direction.

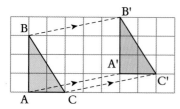

This is a translation of 5 squares to the right and 1 square up.
The translation can be described using a **column vector**:

This is a translation of $\begin{pmatrix} 5 \\ 1 \end{pmatrix}$
← The top number is the movement in the x direction.
← The bottom number is the movement in the y direction.

For the top number: a movement to the right is positive
                       a movement to the left is negative.

For the bottom number: a movement up is positive
                        a movement down is negative.

         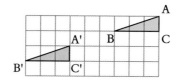

This is a translation of $\begin{pmatrix} 4 \\ -3 \end{pmatrix}$.   This is a translation of $\begin{pmatrix} -6 \\ -2 \end{pmatrix}$.

EXAMPLE

Translate this shape by the vector $\begin{pmatrix} -6 \\ 1 \end{pmatrix}$.

$\begin{pmatrix} -6 \\ 1 \end{pmatrix}$ means:

- move 6 squares to the left and
- move 1 square up.

EXERCISE 3.15

1 Write down the vector for the translation that maps shape A onto shape B.

a   b   c

d   e   f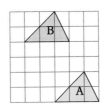

2 Copy these shapes onto squared paper. Translate each shape by the given vector.

a $\begin{pmatrix} 5 \\ 2 \end{pmatrix}$ b 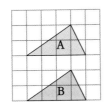 $\begin{pmatrix} -4 \\ 3 \end{pmatrix}$ c 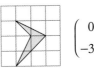 $\begin{pmatrix} 0 \\ -3 \end{pmatrix}$

d $\begin{pmatrix} 3 \\ -4 \end{pmatrix}$ e $\begin{pmatrix} -3 \\ -4 \end{pmatrix}$ f 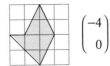 $\begin{pmatrix} -4 \\ 0 \end{pmatrix}$

3 Copy and complete the following table.

	Point	Transformation	Image
a	(3, 6)	Translation of $\begin{pmatrix} 5 \\ 2 \end{pmatrix}$	
b	(1, 0)	Translation of $\begin{pmatrix} 4 \\ -2 \end{pmatrix}$	
c	(2, −5)	Translation of $\begin{pmatrix} -6 \\ 4 \end{pmatrix}$	
d	(−2, 8)	Translation of $\begin{pmatrix} -7 \\ -2 \end{pmatrix}$	
e	(−10, −4)	Translation of $\begin{pmatrix} 6 \\ -8 \end{pmatrix}$	
f	(0, −3)	Translation of $\begin{pmatrix} 7 \\ -5 \end{pmatrix}$	

4

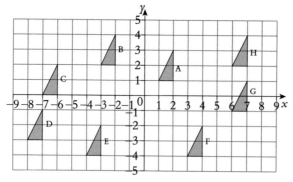

Describe fully the single transformation that moves triangle:

a   A onto B   b   A onto C   c   A onto D   d   A onto E
e   A onto F   f   A onto G   g   A onto H   h   H onto G
i   F onto E   j   B onto H   k   C onto F   l   G onto D.

5 a   Translate shape A by the vector $\begin{pmatrix} 3 \\ 3 \end{pmatrix}$
       Label the image B.

   b   Translate shape B by the vector $\begin{pmatrix} 4 \\ -1 \end{pmatrix}$
       Label the image C.

   c   Describe the single transformation that
       moves shape A onto shape C.

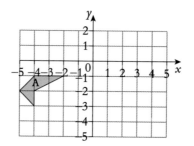

6 a   Translate shape A by the vector $\begin{pmatrix} 4 \\ 1 \end{pmatrix}$
       Label the image B.

   b   Translate shape B by the vector $\begin{pmatrix} -8 \\ -3 \end{pmatrix}$
       Label the image C.

   c   Describe the single transformation that
       moves shape A onto shape C.

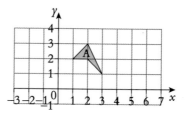

7   Triangle ABC is translated onto triangle A′B′C′.
    Copy and complete the table.

A = (1, 1)	B = (3, 2)	C = (…, …)
A′ = (4, −4)	B′ = (…, …)	C′ = (4, −1)

8   Quadrilateral ABCD is translated onto quadrilateral A′B′C′D′.
    Copy and complete the table.

A = (…, …)	B = (2, 2)	C = (…, …)	D = (1, 2)
A′ = (2, −3)	B′ = (0, −2)	C′ = (−3, −1)	D′ = (…, …)

EXERCISE 3.16

1

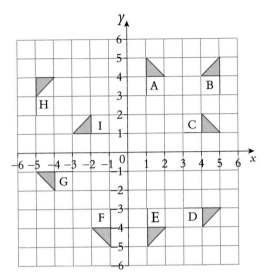

Describe fully the single transformation that moves shape:

a A onto B	b A onto C	c A onto E	d A onto F
e A onto G	f A onto H	g A onto I	h G onto F
i E onto G	j C onto D	k E onto F	l C onto I.

2

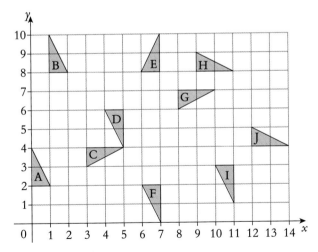

Describe fully the single transformation that moves triangle:

a A onto B	b A onto F	c B onto E	d B onto D
e C onto D	f C onto G	g D onto I	h E onto F
i I onto J	j J onto H	k E onto H	l F onto C.

Combined transformations

Transformations can be applied one after another. A combination of transformations can sometimes be described using a single transformation.

EXAMPLE

a Draw triangle A whose vertices are (2, 1), (4, 1) and (2, 2).
b Reflect triangle A in the line $y = x$. Label the image B.
c Rotate triangle B 90° anticlockwise about the point (0, 0). Label the image C.
d Describe fully the single transformation that maps triangle A onto triangle C.

The single transformation that maps triangle A onto triangle C is a reflection in the y-axis.

EXAMPLE

a Draw triangle A whose vertices are (−6, 1), (−2, 1) and (−5, 3).
b Reflect triangle A in the line $x = -1$. Label the image B.
c Reflect triangle B in the line $y = -1$. Label the image C.
d Describe fully the single transformation that maps triangle A onto triangle C.

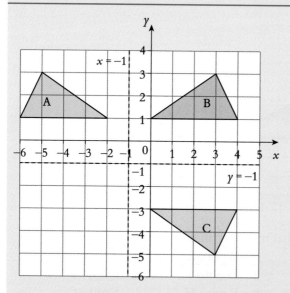

The single transformation that maps triangle A onto triangle C is a rotation of 180° about the point (−1, −1).

a Draw triangle P whose vertices are (1, 0), (0, 1) and (2, 3).
b Reflect triangle P in the line $x = 3$. Label the image Q.
c Reflect triangle Q in the line $x = 9$. Label the image R.
d Describe fully the single transformation that maps triangle P onto triangle R.

The single transformation that maps triangle P onto triangle R

is a translation of $\begin{pmatrix} 12 \\ 0 \end{pmatrix}$.

EXERCISE 3.17

1 Draw axes from −6 to 6.
   a Draw triangle P whose vertices are (6, 1), (1, 1) and (2, 5).
   b Reflect triangle P in the x-axis. Label the image Q.
   c Reflect triangle Q in the y-axis. Label the image R.
   d Describe fully the single transformation that maps triangle P onto triangle R.

2 Draw axes from −6 to 6.
   a Draw triangle P whose vertices are (1, 1), (1, 6) and (3, 6).
   b Rotate triangle P 180° about the point (0, 0). Label the image Q.
   c Translate triangle Q by the vector $\begin{pmatrix} 6 \\ 3 \end{pmatrix}$. Label the image R.
   d Describe fully the single transformation that maps triangle P onto triangle R.

3 Draw axes from −6 to 6.
   a Draw triangle P whose vertices are (4, 1), (2, 2) and (4, 5).
   b Reflect triangle P in the line $y = 0$. Label the image Q.
   c Rotate triangle Q 180° about the point (−1, 0). Label the image R.
   d Describe fully the single transformation that maps triangle P onto triangle R.

4 Draw axes from −6 to 6.

   a Draw triangle P whose vertices are (1, 3), (2, 6) and (4, 6).

   b Reflect triangle P in the line $y = 2$.
      Label the image Q.

   c Reflect triangle Q in the line $y = -1$.
      Label the image R.

   d Describe fully the single transformation that maps triangle P onto triangle R.

5 Draw axes from −6 to 6.

   a Draw triangle P whose vertices are (1, 3), (2, 6) and (4, 6).

   b Reflect triangle P in the line $y = 0$.
      Label the image Q.

   c Rotate triangle Q 90° clockwise about the point (0, 0).
      Label the image R.

   d Describe fully the single transformation that maps triangle P onto triangle R.

6 Draw axes from −6 to 6.

   a Draw triangle P whose vertices are (2, 3), (5, 3) and (5, 5).

   b Rotate triangle P 180° about the point (4, 1).
      Label the image Q.

   c Rotate triangle Q 180° about the point (1, −3).
      Label the image R.

   d Describe fully the single transformation that maps triangle P onto triangle R.

7 Which single transformation is the same as:

   a A translation of $\begin{pmatrix} 4 \\ 3 \end{pmatrix}$ followed by a translation of $\begin{pmatrix} 2 \\ 7 \end{pmatrix}$

   b A translation of $\begin{pmatrix} -5 \\ 6 \end{pmatrix}$ followed by a translation of $\begin{pmatrix} 8 \\ 4 \end{pmatrix}$.

8 Which single transformation is the same as:

   a A reflection in $y = 2$ followed by a reflection in $x = 3$

   b A reflection in $y = 2$ followed by a reflection in $y = 5$

9 Which single transformation is the same as:

   a A rotation of 180° about the point (1, 2) followed by a rotation of 180° about the point (3, 4).

   b A rotation of 180° about the point (5, 0) followed by a rotation of 180° about the point (2, 5).

If you translate an object by the vector $\begin{pmatrix} 5 \\ 2 \end{pmatrix}$ and then translate the image by the vector $\begin{pmatrix} -5 \\ -2 \end{pmatrix}$, the image will be transformed back to the original object.

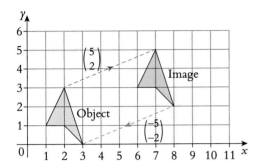

A translation of $\begin{pmatrix} 5 \\ 2 \end{pmatrix}$ and a translation of $\begin{pmatrix} -5 \\ -2 \end{pmatrix}$ are called **inverse transformations**.

EXERCISE 3.18

Write down the inverse of each of these transformations.

1 A translation of $\begin{pmatrix} 2 \\ -4 \end{pmatrix}$

2 A translation of $\begin{pmatrix} 0 \\ 6 \end{pmatrix}$

3 A translation of $\begin{pmatrix} -5 \\ 7 \end{pmatrix}$

4 A translation of $\begin{pmatrix} -8 \\ 0 \end{pmatrix}$

5 A reflection in the x-axis.

6 A reflection in the y-axis.

7 A reflection in the line $y = 3$

8 A reflection in the line $x = -5$

9 A reflection in the line $x + y = 4$

10 A rotation of 90° clockwise about the point (0, 0).

11 A rotation of 90° anticlockwise about the point (0, 0).

12 A rotation of 180° about the point (0, 0).

13 A rotation of 90° clockwise about the point (5, −2).

14 A rotation of 90° anticlockwise about the point (−4, 7).

KEY WORDS

transformation
object
image
reflection
invariant
rotation
translation
centre of rotation
column vector
inverse transformation

UNIT 3

Enlargements

An **enlargement** is a transformation where
- Corresponding angles are the same
- Lengths of corresponding sides are in the same ratio.

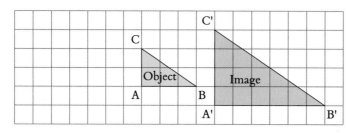

➡ **NOTE:** the object and image are similar in shape.

Triangle ABC has been enlarged with **scale factor** 2 to give triangle A'B'C'.
(The scale factor is 2 because the lengths of the sides of the triangle have doubled.)

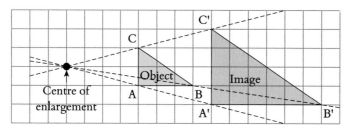

The position of the centre of enlargement is found by drawing lines through A and A', B and B' and C and C'. The point where these lines intersect is called the **centre of enlargement**.

EXAMPLE

Describe fully the transformation that maps triangle PQR onto triangle P'Q'R'.

The lengths of all the sides of the triangle have trebled so the scale factor of the enlargement is 3.
To find the centre of enlargement draw the lines through P and P', Q and Q' and R and R'. These lines intersect at the point (1, 6).
The transformation is an enlargement scale factor 3, centre (1, 6).

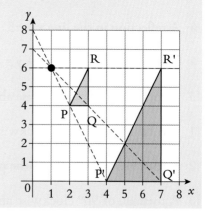

To describe an enlargement fully you must state the scale factor and the centre of enlargement.

EXERCISE 3.19

1 In each diagram shape A has been enlarged to make shape B.
State the scale factor and the centre of enlargement for each diagram.

a

b

c

d

e

f
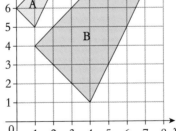

2 Describe fully the single
transformation that maps shape:

  a A onto C   b A onto D

  c D onto F   d B onto E

  e B onto C   f B onto D

EXAMPLE

Enlarge triangle ABC using a scale factor of 2 and centre of enlargement P(1, 2).

PA′ = 2 × PA
PB′ = 2 × PB
PC′ = 2 × PC

EXAMPLE

Enlarge quadrilateral ABCD using a scale factor of $\frac{1}{2}$ and centre of enlargement P(11, 3).

$PA' = \frac{1}{2} \times PA$

$PB' = \frac{1}{2} \times PB$

$PC' = \frac{1}{2} \times PC$

$PD' = \frac{1}{2} \times PD$

> An enlargement scale factor $\frac{1}{2}$ makes the shape smaller.

EXAMPLE

Enlarge triangle ABC using a scale factor of −2 and centre of enlargement P(4, 2).

PA′ = 2 × PA
PB′ = 2 × PB
PC′ = 2 × PC

> For a negative enlargement the object and image are on opposite sides of the centre of enlargement.

EXERCISE 3.20

1 Copy each diagram and enlarge with scale factor 2. Use point P as the centre of enlargement.

a

b

c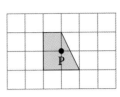

2 Copy each diagram and enlarge with scale factor $\frac{1}{2}$. Use point P as the centre of enlargement.

a

b

c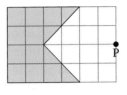

3 Copy each diagram and enlarge with scale factor −2. Use point P as the centre of enlargement.

a

b

c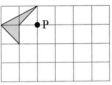

4 Copy the following diagrams. Enlarge each shape using the given scale factor and the point P as the centre of enlargement.

a

scale factor 3

b

scale factor 2

c

scale factor $\frac{1}{2}$

d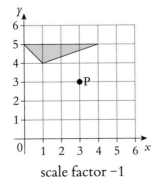

scale factor −2

e

scale factor −1

f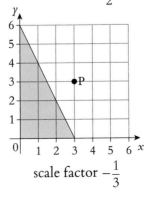

scale factor $-\frac{1}{3}$

UNIT 3

5 Draw axes from −7 to 7.
Draw triangle T whose vertices are
(2, 0), (0, 2) and (−2, 2).
Draw the image of triangle T after each
of these enlargements.
Label your images A, B, C, and D.

Scale factor	Centre of enlargement	Image
2	(−2, 0)	A
$\frac{1}{2}$	(0, −4)	B
−1	(−2, 1)	C
−2	(0, −1)	D

6 Draw axes from −6 to 6.
Draw triangle T whose vertices are
(4, 2), (6, 2) and (4, 6).
Draw the image of triangle T after each
of these enlargements.
Label your images P, Q, R and S.

Scale factor	Centre of enlargement	Image
$\frac{1}{2}$	(0, 0)	P
$\frac{1}{2}$	(−6, 4)	Q
−1	(4, 0)	R
−2	(2, 3)	S

7 Draw axes from −6 to 6.
Draw triangle T whose vertices are (−6, −2),
(−4, −4) and (−2, −4).
Enlarge triangle T with scale factor $2\frac{1}{2}$, centre (−6, −6).

8 Draw axes from −6 to 6.
Draw triangle T whose vertices are (1, 0), (−3, 4) and (0, −2).
Enlarge triangle T with scale factor $1\frac{1}{3}$, centre (6, 1).

9 Draw axes from −7 to 7.
Draw triangle T whose vertices are (5, −2), (5, 2) and (−3, 2).
Enlarge triangle T with scale factor $−1\frac{1}{2}$, centre (1, 0).

Enlarge triangle P with scale factor 3, centre (0, 0).
Label the image Q.
Enlarge triangle Q with scale factor $\frac{1}{3}$, centre (−9, 6).
Label the image R.
Describe fully the single transformation
that maps triangle P onto triangle R.

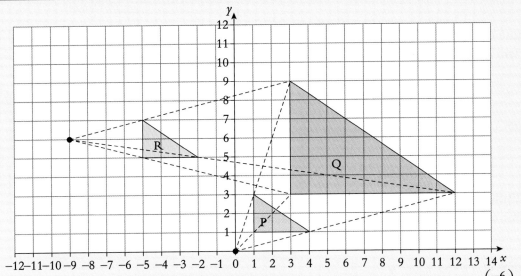

The single transformation that maps triangle P onto triangle R is a translation of $\begin{pmatrix} -6 \\ 4 \end{pmatrix}$.

EXERCISE 3.21

1   Draw axes from −6 to 6.
   a   Draw triangle P with vertices (1, 0), (0, 1) and (−2, −1).
   b   Enlarge triangle P with scale factor 2, centre (2, −2). Label the image Q.
   c   Enlarge triangle Q with scale factor $\frac{1}{2}$, centre (−6, −6). Label the image R.
   d   Describe fully the single transformation that maps triangle P onto triangle R.

2   Draw axes from −6 to 6.
   a   Draw triangle P with vertices (−3, 0), (−6, 0) and (−5, −1).
   b   Enlarge triangle P with scale factor −2, centre (−3, −2). Label the image Q.
   c   Enlarge triangle Q with scale factor −2, centre (0, −2). Label the image R.
   d   Describe fully the single transformation that maps triangle P onto triangle R.

3   Draw axes from −6 to 6.
   a   Draw triangle P with vertices (−4, 1), (−4, 3) and (−3, 1).
   b   Enlarge triangle P with scale factor 4, centre (−6, 2).
       Label the image Q.
   c   Enlarge triangle Q with scale factor $\frac{1}{2}$, centre (−6, −2).
       Label the image R.
   d   Describe fully the single transformation that maps triangle P
       onto triangle R.

```
┌ ─ ─ ─ ─ ─ ─ ─ ─ ┐
I      KEY WORDS      I
I      enlargement     I
I       scale factor     I
I  centre of enlargement  I
└ ─ ─ ─ ─ ─ ─ ─ ─ ┘
```

UNIT 3

Surface area and volume 1

Volume of a cuboid

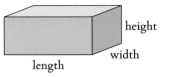

Volume of a cuboid = length × width × height

Volume of a prism

A **prism** is a three-dimensional shape with a uniform **cross-section**.

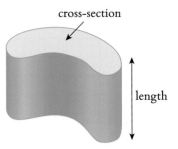

Volume of a prism = area of cross-section × length

➡ **NOTE:** a cuboid is a prism with a rectangular cross-section.

A **cylinder** is a prism with a circular cross-section.

Volume of cylinder = area of cross-section × length
$$= \pi r^2 \times h$$

Volume of cylinder = $\pi r^2 h$

Converting units of volume

$1\ \text{cm}^3 = 10 \times 10 \times 10\ \text{mm}^3$

Similarly,
$1\ \text{m}^3 = 100 \times 100 \times 100\ \text{cm}^3$

$1\ \text{cm}^3 = 1000\ \text{mm}^3$

$1\ \text{m}^3 = 1\,000\,000\ \text{cm}^3$

Capacity

The **capacity** is the amount that a container can hold.
Units for capacity are litres (ℓ) and millilitres ($\text{m}\ell$).

1 litre = 1000 millilitres

$1\ \text{cm}^3$ contains $1\ \text{m}\ell$

'The bottle has a capacity of 200 mℓ' means that the bottle has a volume of 200 cm³.

EXAMPLE

Find the volume of the prism.

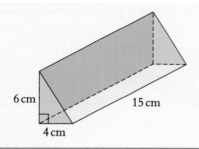

6 cm

15 cm

4 cm

Area of cross-section = $\frac{1}{2} \times 4 \times 6 = 12$ cm².
Volume of prism = area of cross-section × length
$$= 12 \times 15$$
$$= 180 \text{ cm}^3$$

EXAMPLE

a Find the volume of the cylinder.
b Find the capacity of the
   cylinder in litres.

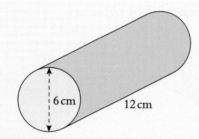

6 cm

12 cm

a Volume of cylinder = $\pi r^2 h$
$$= \pi \times 3^2 \times 12$$
$$= 339 \text{ cm}^3 \text{ (to 3 s.f.)}$$

Remember: 1 cm³ = 1 mℓ   and
                1000 mℓ = 1 litre

b Capacity = 339 mℓ
$$= 0.339 \text{ litres}$$

EXERCISE 3.22

1   Find the volume of these cuboids.

a

5 cm

5 cm   5 cm

b

2 cm

8 cm   6 cm

c

40 cm

30 cm   1 m

2   Find the volume of these prisms.

a

12 cm

A = 15 cm²

b

20 cm

A = 9.6 cm²

c

5 cm

A = 3.2 cm²

3 Find the volume of these prisms. (All lengths are in cm.)

a

b

c

d

e

f

4 Find the volumes of these cylinders.

a

2 m
1 m

b

6 cm
8 cm

c

5 cm
12 cm

5 Find the volume of these hollow cylinders.

a

outer diameter = 10 cm
inner diameter = 6 cm
length = 3 cm

b

outer diameter = 8 cm
inner diameter = 5 cm
length = 16 cm

c

outer diameter = 50 cm
inner diameter = 30 cm
length = 20 cm

6 A carton contains 1 litre of mango juice.
The length of the carton is 10 cm and the width is 5 cm.
Calculate the height of the carton.

5 cm   10 cm

7   This container is a prism.
    The cross-section of the prism is a trapezium.
    a   Find the volume of the container in m³.
    b   Find the volume of the container in cm³.
    c   How many litres of water does the container hold
        when it is full?

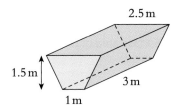

8   This piece of cheese is a prism.
    The cross-section is a sector of a circle of radius 14 cm and angle 25°.
    The height of the piece of cheese is 6 cm.
    Calculate the volume.

9   A cylindrical can contains 1.5 litres of coconut milk.
    The height of the can is 15 cm.
    Calculate the radius of the can.

10 This water trough is a prism.
    The cross-section is a semi-circle of diameter 50 cm.
    When full the water trough holds 300 litres of water.
    Calculate the length of the water trough.

11 The diagram shows a cube with a circular hole.
    The cube has sides of length 5 cm.
    The circular hole has radius 1 cm.
    Calculate the volume of the solid.

12 The cross-section of this solid prism is a
    regular hexagon with sides of length 8 cm.
    The length of the prism is 25 cm.

    a   Find the area of the regular hexagon.
    b   Find the volume of the prism.
    The prism is made of wood.
    1 cm³ of wood has a mass of 0.65 g.
    c   Find the mass of the hexagonal prism.

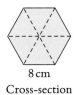

Prism   Cross-section

· · · · · · · · · · · · · · · · · ·

TOP TIP

The hexagon is made from six
equilateral triangles. Find the
area of one of the triangles and
multiply by six.

· · · · · · · · · · · · · · · · · ·

Surface area of a prism

> **Surface area** of prism = sum of area of all the faces

Net of prism

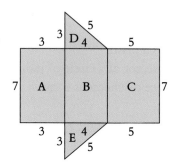

Area of rectangle A = 3 × 7 = 21 cm²
Area of rectangle B = 4 × 7 = 28 cm²
Area of rectangle C = 5 × 7 = 35 cm²
Area of triangle D = $\frac{1}{2}$ × 3 × 4 = 6 cm²

Area of triangle E = $\frac{1}{2}$ × 3 × 4 = 6 cm²

Total surface area = 96 cm²

Surface area of a cylinder
The surface of a solid cylinder consists of two circles and a rectangle.

The two circles are flat surfaces.
The rectangle is made from the **curved surface** of the cylinder.

> Curved surface area of cylinder = $2\pi rh$

> Total surface area of cylinder = $2\pi rh + 2\pi r^2$

EXAMPLE

A solid cylinder has radius 3 cm and length 10 cm.
Calculate the total surface area of the cylinder.

Total surface area of cylinder = $2\pi rh + 2\pi r^2$
$\qquad\qquad = 2 \times \pi \times 3 \times 10 + 2 \times \pi \times 3^2$
$\qquad\qquad = 60\pi + 18\pi$
$\qquad\qquad = 78\pi$
$\qquad\qquad = 245$ cm² (to 3 s.f.)

EXERCISE 3.23

1 Calculate the surface area of these prisms.

a
6 cm
6 cm 6 cm

b
4 cm
8 cm 5 cm

c
12 cm
7 cm 20 cm

2 Find the surface area of these prisms. (All lengths are in cm.)

a
10
6 8
8

b
1
1 2
1
8

c
2
2 2
2
6 7

3 Find the surface area of these prisms. (All lengths are in cm.)

a
5 15
12

b
6 3
4 10

TOP TIP

You will need to use Pythagoras to find the length of the sloping edges.

4 Find the **curved** surface areas of these cylinders.

a
8 cm
4 cm

b
9 cm
9 cm

c
4 cm
14 cm

5 Find the **total** surface area of these solid cylinders.

a
4 cm
4 cm

b
3 cm
8 cm

c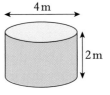
4 m
2 m

6 This piece of cheese is a prism.
The cross-section is a sector of a circle of radius 12 cm and angle 32°.
The height of the piece of cheese is 5 cm.
Calculate the total surface area.

12 cm
32°
5 cm

KEY WORDS

prism, cross-section
cylinder, capacity
volume, surface area
curved surface

Surface area and volume 1   149

UNIT 3

Probability 1

THIS SECTION WILL SHOW YOU HOW TO
- Understand and use the probability scale from 0 to 1
- Calculate the probability of a single event
- Use relative frequency
- Use possibility diagrams to calculate the probability of simple combined events

 Probability is a measure of how likely an **event** is to happen.
An event can be made up of one or more possible **outcomes**.
For example, when a dice is rolled then the possible outcomes are 1, 2, 3, 4, 5 and 6.
If the event A is 'the number on the dice is greater than 4' then there are two desired outcomes for event A which are 5 and 6.

Probability is measured on a scale from 0 to 1

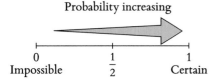

Probability increasing

0 — Impossible $\frac{1}{2}$ 1 — Certain

➡ **NOTE:** you can write probability as a fraction, decimal or a percentage.

If all possible outcomes are equally likely, you can calculate the theoretical probability, P(A), of the event happening.

$$P(A) = \frac{\text{number of desirable outcomes}}{\text{total number of possible outcomes}}$$

So, when a **fair** dice is rolled the probability the number on the dice is greater than $4 = \frac{2}{6} = \frac{1}{3}$

A fair (or **unbiased**) dice means the possible outcomes are equally likely.
A **biased** dice means the possible outcomes are not equally likely.

EXAMPLE

The spinner has eight coloured sections. When the spinner is spun it is equally likely that it stops on any one of the sections.
Find the probability that it stops on
  a a green section,   **b** a yellow section,
  c a blue section,   **d** a red section,
  e a section that is not green, **f** a blue or green section.

  a $P(\text{green}) = \frac{1}{8}$ **b** $P(\text{yellow}) = \frac{3}{8}$ **c** $P(\text{blue}) = \frac{4}{8} = \frac{1}{2}$

  d $P(\text{red}) = 0$ **e** $P(\text{not green}) = \frac{7}{8}$ **f** $P(\text{blue or green}) = \frac{4+1}{8} = \frac{5}{8}$

In the last example $P(\text{green}) = \dfrac{1}{8}$ and $P(\text{not green}) = \dfrac{7}{8}$

This is an example of the rule $\boxed{P(\bar{A}) = 1 - P(A)}$ where $\bar{A}$ means 'not A'.

> **EXAMPLE**
>
> The probability that Omar is late for school is 0.17.
> Find is the probability that he is not late to school.
>
> $P(\text{not late}) = 1 - P(\text{late}) = 1 - 0.17 = 0.83$

EXERCISE 3.24

1   An unbiased eight-sided dice is thrown. Find the probability that the dice
   a   lands on a 5   b   lands on an even number
   c   lands on a square number   d   lands on a number greater than 4
   e   lands on a 6 or a 7   f   lands on a number smaller than 9

2   One of the five cards is chosen at random.
   Find the probability of choosing a card with
   a number that is

   | 3 | 6 | 6 | 8 | 9 |

   a   a six   b   an odd number
   c   not prime   d   square
   e   a multiple of 3   f   a factor of 72

3   A box contains 5 orange balls, 4 yellow balls and 1 green ball.
   A ball is picked out of the box at random. Find the probability that it is
   a   green   b   orange
   c   yellow   d   not green
   e   orange or green   f   green or yellow
   g   blue   h   not blue

4 | A | C | B | C | B | A | B | C | A |

   One of the nine cards is chosen at random. Find the probability that
   a   the letter on the card is an A   b   the letter on the card is not an A
   c   a green card is chosen   d   the card is orange with a letter B

5   The table shows the number of boys and girls in Years 8
   and 9 at a school.
   a   A student is chosen at random from Year 8.
       Find the probability that the student is a girl.
   b   A student is chosen at random from Year 9.
       Find the probability that the student is a boy.

	Year 8	Year 9
Boys	52	48
Girls	68	52

EXAMPLE

One of these six cards is chosen at random.
The first card is **not** replaced before a second card is
chosen at random.

a Find the probability that the first card chosen is a
   i 7   **ii** 8   **iii** 9

b If the first card chosen is a 8, find the probability that the second card chosen is a
   i 7   **ii** 8   **iii** 9

---

a **i** $P(7) = \dfrac{3}{6} = \dfrac{1}{2}$ *because there are **three** cards with a number 7 and **six** cards to chose from*

    ii $P(8) = \dfrac{2}{6} = \dfrac{1}{3}$ *because there are **two** cards with a number 8 and **six** cards to chose from*

    iii $P(9) = \dfrac{1}{6}$ *because there is **one** card with a number 9 and **six** cards to chose from*

b If the first card chosen was a 8 then the cards remaining are

    i $P(7) = \dfrac{3}{5}$ *because there are **three** cards with a number 7 and **five** cards to chose from*

    ii $P(8) = \dfrac{1}{5}$ *because there is now only **one** card with a number 8 and **five** cards to chose from*

    iii $P(9) = \dfrac{1}{5}$ *because there is **one** card with a number 9 and **five** cards to chose from*

Sometimes the probabilities of all the outcomes are put into a table.
The probabilities for part **a** in the example above could be displayed as:

Number	7	8	9
Probability	$\dfrac{1}{2}$	$\dfrac{1}{3}$	$\dfrac{1}{6}$

➡ **NOTE:** the bottom row of the table will always add up to 1.

EXAMPLE

Score	1	2	3	4	5
Probability	0.1	x	0.2	0.3	0.15

The table shows the probabilities of getting scores on
a biased 5-sided spinner.
a Find the value of x.
b Find the probability of a score greater than 2.
c Find the probability of not scoring a 3.

---

a The probabilities of all the possible outcomes add up to give 1.
    So $0.1 + x + 0.2 + 0.3 + 0.15 = 1$
              $x + 0.75 = 1 \Rightarrow x = 0.25$
b $P(\text{score} > 2) = P(3) + P(4) + P(5)$
                 $= 0.2 + 0.3 + 0.15 = 0.65$
c $P(\text{not } 3) = 1 - P(3)$
            $= 1 - 0.2 = 0.8$

UNIT 3

EXERCISE 3.25

1 The circular board is divided into eight numbered sections. When the arrow is spun it is equally likely to stop in any of the eight sections.

a Copy and complete the table which shows the probability of the arrow stopping at each number.

b The arrow is spun once. Find
   i the probability of a number smaller than 3
   ii the probability of an odd number
   iii the probability of a prime number
   iv the probability the number is a 4.

Number	1	2	3
Probability		$\frac{1}{8}$	

2 There are five red sweets and three yellow sweets in a bag. Rosa takes a sweet at random from the bag and eats it. Rosa then takes a second sweet at random from the bag.

a Find the probability that the first sweet that Rosa took from the bag was
   i red   ii yellow.

b If the first sweet that Rosa took from the bag was red, find the probability that the second sweet she takes from the bag is
   i red   ii yellow.

c If the first sweet that Rosa took from the bag was yellow, find the probability that the second sweet she takes from the bag is
   i red   ii yellow.

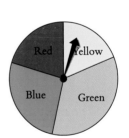

3 The table shows the probability of the spinner landing on each of the four colours.

Colour	Red	Yellow	Green	Blue
Probability	$\frac{1}{6}$	$\frac{1}{4}$	$\frac{1}{3}$	x

a Find the value of x.
b What is the most likely colour?
c Find the probability of not getting a red.

4

Number	1	2	3	4	5	6
Probability	0.1	0.15	0.05	0.1	$2x$	x

The table shows the probabilities of getting scores on a biased 6-sided dice.

a Find the value of x.
b What is the most likely score?
c Find the probability of a score greater than 2.

Possibility diagrams

When a dice is rolled and a one-dollar coin is tossed,
the possible outcomes can be recorded in a possibility diagram.
Let H mean heads and T mean tails

Dice

		1	2	3	4	5	6
Coin	**H**	H1	H2	H3	H4	H5	H6
	T	T1	T2	T3	T4	T5	T6

The possibility diagram shows that there are 12 equally likely outcomes.

The probability of each of the outcomes = $\frac{1}{12}$.

There are three places on the diagram where you can get a head and an even number; they are H2, H4 and H6.

So, the probability of getting a head and an even number = $\frac{3}{12} = \frac{1}{4}$

UNIT 3

EXAMPLE

Two unbiased six-sided dice are rolled. The scores are added together.
a Draw a possibility diagram to show all the outcomes.
b What is the most likely total score?
c Use the diagram in part **a** to find the probability of
   i a total score of 9 **ii** a total score less than 4.

a

Red dice

Blue dice	1	2	3	4	5	6
1	2	3	4	5	6	7
2	3	4	5	6	7	8
3	4	5	6	7	8	9
4	5	6	7	8	9	10
5	6	7	8	9	10	11
6	7	8	9	10	11	12

➡ **NOTE:** there are 36 possible outcomes.

The probability of each outcome = $\frac{1}{36}$

b The most likely total score is 7   *there are more outcomes with a total of 7 than any other number*

c **i**   P(total score of 9) = $\frac{4}{36} = \frac{1}{9}$ *there are 4 scores of 9 on the diagram*

    ii   P(total score less than 4) = $\frac{3}{36} = \frac{1}{12}$ *there are 3 scores less than 4 on the diagram*

EXERCISE 3.26

1

	1	2	3	4	5
1					
2				6	
3					
4					
5			8		

An unbiased five-sided spinner is spun twice and the scores are added.
a   Copy and complete the possibility diagram.
b   Use the diagram to find the probability that the total score is
  i   9   ii   3   iii   1
  iv   an odd number   v   a square number,   vi   a prime number.

2

	1	2	3	4
1	2	3		
2				
3				
4			7	

Two unbiased four-sided dice are thrown and their scores are added together.
a   Copy and complete the possibility diagram.
b   Use the diagram to find the probability the total score is
  i   7   ii   5   iii   even   iv   less than 5.

3

	2	4	6	8
1	2			
2		8		
3				24

An unbiased three-sided spinner numbered 1, 2, 3 and an unbiased
four-sided spinner numbered 2, 4, 6, 8 are spun.
The scores are multiplied together.
a   Copy and complete the possibility diagram.
b   Use the diagram to find the probability the product of the scores is
  i   8   ii   odd   iii   even   iv   smaller than 7.

Experimental probability

You can use data from a survey or experiment to estimate **experimental probability**.
The more trials that are done, then the more reliable the estimate will be.
Relative frequency is an estimate of experimental probability.

$$\text{Relative frequency} = \frac{\text{number of times an event occurs}}{\text{total number of trials}}$$

Sami thinks that a particular spinner is biased.
To test his theory he spins it 100 times.
The results are shown in the table.

Score	1	2	3	4	5
Frequency	13	15	16	42	14

a Calculate the relative frequency for each number on the spinner.
b Compare the relative frequencies with the theoretical probabilities to
   decide if the spinner is biased.
c How could the experiment be improved?

a

Score	1	2	3	4	5
Frequency	13	15	16	42	14
Relative frequency	$\frac{13}{100}$ $= 0.13$	$\frac{15}{100}$ $= 0.15$	$\frac{16}{100}$ $= 0.16$	$\frac{42}{100}$ $= 0.42$	$\frac{14}{100}$ $= 0.14$

b The theoretical probability for obtaining each number is $\frac{1}{5} = 0.2$.

   The figures suggest that the spinner is biased towards landing on the number 4.
c The experiment could be improved by doing more trials.

You may need to work out the **expected number** of times that an event might happen.

Expected number = total number × probability

A biased coin is tossed 150 times. It lands on heads 51 times.
a Estimate the probability that the coin lands on a head on the next throw.
b Estimate the number of heads you would expect when you toss the coin 650 times.

a P(Head) $= \frac{51}{150} = \frac{17}{50}$

b Expected number of heads = total number × probability
$$= 650 \times \frac{17}{50} = 221$$

EXERCISE 3.27

1   The probability that a biased coin will land on heads is 0.72
    The coin is tossed 400 times.
    Estimate the number of times the coin will land on a head.

2   The probability that a biased dice will land on a five is 0.29
    The dice is rolled 500 times.
    Estimate the number of times the dice will land on a five.

3   A fair dice is rolled 900 times.
    Estimate the number of times the dice will land on a five.

4   The probability that a light bulb is defective is 0.015
    Find the number of defective light bulbs that you would expect
    to find in a batch of 2000 light bulbs.

5   The probability that a drawing pin lands point down when
    it is dropped is 0.82
    The drawing pin is dropped 600 times.
    Estimate the number of times it will land point down.

Point up   Point down

6   The table shows the results when the three-sided spinner is spun 200 times.

Score	1	2	3
Frequency	51	84	65

    a   Copy and complete the table.

Score	1	2	3
Relative frequency			

    b   Estimate the number of times the spinner will land on
        the number 3 if the spinner is spun 720 times.

7   The table shows the results when the circular
    spinner is spun 200 times.

Colour	Red	Yellow	Green	Blue
Frequency	36	72	54	38

    a   Copy and complete the table.

Colour	Red	Yellow	Green	Blue
Relative frequency				

    b   Estimate the number of times the spinner will land on each
        of the four colours if the spinner is spun 900 times.

> **KEY WORDS**
> probability
> event
> outcome
> fair
> unbiased
> biased
> possibility diagram
> experimental probability
> relative frequency
> expected number

1 **(a)** Write 562 000 000 in standard form. [1]

    (b) Calculate $2.4 \times 10^5 + 1.3 \times 10^4$, giving your answer in standard form. [2]

2 **(a)** Write 0.000 000 78 correct to 1 significant figure. [1]

    (b) Write 0.000 000 78 in standard form. [1]

3 Solve the simultaneous equations.
You must show all your working.
$$5x + 2y = 8$$
$$3x - 2y = 8$$
[2]

4 Solve the simultaneous equations.
You must show all your working.
$$7x + 3y = 16$$
$$2x + 9y = 29$$
[3]

5 Solve the simultaneous equations.
You must show all your working.
$$4x - 5y + 4 = 0$$
$$6x - 14y - 7 = 0$$
[4]

6 Factorise.
$$x^2 - 7x$$
[1]

7 Factorise.

    (a) $5x^3y^2 - 10x^2y$ [2]

    (b) $2xy + 3y - 8x - 12$ [2]

8 Simplify.
$$\frac{5x^2}{x - 3x^2}$$
[2]

9 Make a the subject of the formula.
$$c = \frac{a}{5} - b$$
[2]

10 Make x the subject of the formula.
$$5(x + 2y) = 7x - 4$$
[2]

11 Make h the subject of the formula.
$$A = 2\pi rh + \pi r^2$$
[2]

12 Make r the subject of the formula.
$$p = 2q - 5r^2$$
[3]

13 Make P the subject of the formula.
$$R = \frac{2}{3}\sqrt{PQ}$$
[3]

14

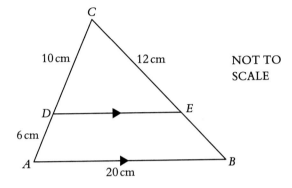

10 cm   12 cm   NOT TO SCALE

6 cm   20 cm

In the diagram, ABC is a triangle and AB is parallel to DE.
$AD = 6$ cm, $DC = 10$ cm, $CE = 12$ cm and $AB = 20$ cm.

(a) Find DE. [2]

(b) Find EB. [3]

15 Change $47\,500\,000\,\text{cm}^3$ to m^3. [1]

16

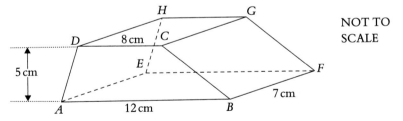

NOT TO SCALE

5 cm   8 cm   7 cm   12 cm

The diagram shows a prism $ABCDEFGH$ of length 7 cm.
Trapezium $ABCD$ is a cross section of the prism.
AB is parallel to DC and the distance between these two sides is 5 cm.
$AB = 12$ cm and $DC = 8$ cm.

(a) Calculate the area of trapezium $ABCD$. [2]

(b) Calculate the volume of the prism. [1]

17

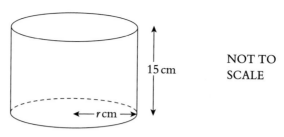

15 cm

NOT TO SCALE

←— r cm —→

The diagram shows a solid circular cylinder.
The height is 15 cm and the radius is r cm.
The volume of the cylinder is 3600 cm³.

(a) Find the value of r. [3]

(b) Calculate the total surface area of the cylinder. [4]

18

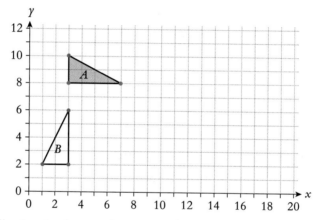

(a) Describe fully the **single** transformation that maps triangle A onto triangle B. [3]

(b) Draw the image of triangle A after translation by the vector $\begin{pmatrix} 2 \\ -5 \end{pmatrix}$. [2]

(c) Draw the image of triangle A after enlargement, scale factor −2, centre (8, 8). [3]

19

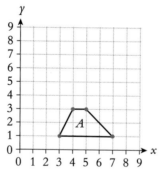

(a) Draw the image of shape A after refection in the line $y = x$.
Label the mage B. [2]

(b) Draw the image of shape A after rotation 180° centre (4.5, 4.5).
Label the image C. [3]

(c) Describe fully the single transformation that maps shape B onto shape C. [2]

20

| P | E | P | P | E | R |

One of the six cards is chosen at random.

Find the probability that

(a) the letter on the card is P,   [1]

(b) the letter on the card is not R,   [1]

(c) the letter on the card is W.   [1]

21

Score	1	2	3	4	5	6
Probability	0.2	x	0.15	0.05	0.3	0.2

The table shows the probabilities of getting scores on a biased 6-sided dice.

(a) Find the value of x.   [2]

(b) What is the most likely score?   [1]

(c) Find the probability of a score greater than 3.   [1]

22 Two fair six-sided dice are rolled.

The numbers are added together to give the score.

(a) Complete the possibility diagram.

First dice

		1	2	3	4	5	6
	1	1		3			
	2				8		
Second dice	3			9			18
	4	4					
	5		10				
	6				24		36

[2]

(b) **(i)** Find the probability of a score of 12.   [2]

(ii) Find the probability of a score less than 8.   [2]

23 The probability that a biased dice lands on the number 4 is 0.18

The dice is rolled 500 times.

Find the number of times the dice is expected to land on the number 4.   [1]

Percentages 2

THIS SECTION WILL SHOW YOU HOW TO
• Express one quantity as a percentage of another quantity
• Calculate percentage increase and decrease
• Calculate percentage profit and loss

 ## Expressing one quantity as a percentage of a second quantity

To write one quantity as a percentage of a second quantity
● Write the first quantity as a fraction of the second quantity
● Multiply by 100 to change the fraction into a percentage

EXAMPLE

Write 52 as a percentage of 65.

$$\text{Percentage} = \frac{\text{first quantity}}{\text{second quantity}} \times 100\% = \frac{52}{65} \times 100\% = 80\%$$

Percentage increase and percentage decrease

$$\% \text{ increase} = \frac{\text{increase}}{\text{original value}} \times 100\% \quad \% \text{ decrease} = \frac{\text{decrease}}{\text{original value}} \times 100\%$$

EXAMPLE

The population of a village increases from 2400 to 2520. Calculate the percentage increase.

Increase = 2520 − 2400 = 120

$$\% \text{ increase} = \frac{\text{increase}}{\text{original value}} \times 100\%$$

$$= \frac{120}{2400} \times 100\% = 5\%$$

Percentage profit and loss

When a question involves money you are often asked to work out the **percentage profit** or the **percentage loss**.

$$\% \text{ profit} = \frac{\text{profit}}{\text{original cost}} \times 100\% \quad \% \text{ loss} = \frac{\text{loss}}{\text{original cost}} \times 100\%$$

EXAMPLE

A car bought for $5500 is sold for $5280. Calculate the percentage loss.

Loss = 5500 − 5280 = 220

$$\% \text{ loss} = \frac{\text{loss}}{\text{original cost}} \times 100\%$$

$$= \frac{220}{5500} \times 100\% = 4\%$$

EXERCISE 4.1

1   Jarred scores 69 out of 120 in a test. Write this as a percentage.

2   Express $44.40 as a percentage of $120.

3   Eugenio buys a washing machine for $845 and then pays an installation charge of $30.
    Express the installation charge as a percentage of the washing machine price.

4   In a sale the price of a bag is reduced from $50 to $45.
    Find the percentage decrease.

5   A factory produces 55 000 torches one year and 88 000 torches the next year.
    Find the percentage increase.

6   A set of kitchen scales records a mass of 2.1 kg when the true mass is 2 kg.
    Calculate the percentage error.

7   The number 3.1 is used as an approximation for π.
    Calculate the percentage error.

8   A computer is bought for $1358 and is then sold for $1400.
    Calculate the percentage profit.

9   A clock valued at $600 is sold for $570.
    Calculate the percentage loss.

10 Cecilia's income increases from $70 000 a year to $85 000 a year.
    Calculate the percentage increase.

11 The number of students in a school decreases from 640 to 620.
    Calculate the percentage decrease.

12 In 2005 the population of Malaysia was 2.56×10^7.
    In 2009 the population of Malaysia was 2.75×10^7.
    Calculate the percentage increase in the population.

13 Fernando is a tax payer. He earns $60 000 a year.
    *   The first $12 000 of his earnings is tax free.
    *   He pays 10% tax on the next $8 000 of his income.
    *   He pays 22% tax on the rest of his earnings.
    Express the total amount of tax that he pays as a percentage
    of the $60 000.

UNIT 4

Expanding double brackets

 The area of a rectangle that has sides of length $x + 3$ and length $x + 8$ can be found by splitting the rectangle into four parts.

Area $= (x + 3)(x + 8)$ Area $= x^2 + 8x + 3x + 24$

So $(x + 3)(x + 8) = x^2 + 8x + 3x + 24$
$$= x^2 + 11x + 24$$

EXAMPLE

Use a diagram to expand $(x + 2)(x + 7)$

	x	7
x	x^2	$7x$
2	$2x$	14

$(x + 2)(x + 7) = x^2 + 7x + 2x + 14$
$$= x^2 + 9x + 14$$

EXERCISE 4.2

1   Copy and complete the following.

	x	10
x	....	$10x$
3	....	....

$(x + 3)(x + 10) = \ldots\ldots + 10x + \ldots\ldots + \ldots\ldots$
$$= $$

Use diagrams to help you expand these brackets.

2 $(x + 3)(x + 4)$ 3 $(x + 7)(x + 3)$

4 $(x + 4)(x + 2)$ 5 $(x + 1)(x + 5)$

6 $(x + 8)(x + 7)$ 7 $(x + 2)(x + 6)$

8 $(x + 6)(x + 7)$ 9 $(x + 4)(x + 4)$

10 $(x + 15)(x + 4)$ 11 $(x + 6)(x + 12)$

12 $(2x + 3)(x + 5)$ 13 $(3x + 2)(x + 5)$

First – Outside – Inside – Last

You can expand double brackets without drawing a diagram.

> To expand double brackets you multiply each term in the first bracket by each term in the second bracket.

The mnemonic **FOIL** will help you remember what to do when expanding double brackets.

F	first
O	outside
I	inside
L	last

$$(x + 2)(x + 7) = x^2 + 7x + 2x + 14 = x^2 + 9x + 14$$

with F, L, I, O arcs shown

EXAMPLE

Expand and simplify   **a** $(x + 8)(x + 7)$ **b** $(x + 4)(x - 5)$ **c** $(x - 3)(x - 10)$

a $(x + 8)(x + 7)$ **F** $x \times x = x^2$ **O** $x \times 7 = 7x$ **I** $8 \times x = 8x$ **L** $8 \times 7 = 56$
   $= x^2 + 7x + 8x + 56$
   $= x^2 + 15x + 56$

b $(x + 4)(x - 5)$ **F** $x \times x = x^2$ **O** $x \times -5 = -5x$ **I** $4 \times x = 4x$ **L** $4 \times -5 = -20$
   $= x^2 - 5x + 4x - 20$
   $= x^2 - x - 20$

c $(x - 3)(x - 10)$ **F** $x \times x = x^2$ **O** $x \times -10 = -10x$ **I** $-3 \times x = -3x$ **L** $-3 \times -10 = 30$
   $= x^2 - 10x - 3x + 30$
   $= x^2 - 13x + 30$

➡ **NOTE:** remember to look out for double negatives: $-3 \times -10 = +30$

You need to be careful when squaring a bracket.
$(x + 6)^2$ means $(x + 6)(x + 6)$
$$= x^2 + 6x + 6x + 36$$
$$= x^2 + 12x + 36$$

EXAMPLE

Expand and simplify   **a** $(x - 7)^2$ **b** $(3x + 4)(2x - 5)$

a $(x - 7)^2$
   $= (x - 7)(x - 7)$ **F** $x \times x = x^2$ **O** $x \times -7 = -7x$ **I** $-7 \times x = -7x$ **L** $-7 \times -7 = 49$
   $= x^2 - 7x - 7x + 49$
   $= x^2 - 14x + 49$

b $(3x + 4)(2x - 5)$ **F** $3x \times 2x = 6x^2$ **O** $3x \times -5 = -15x$ **I** $4 \times 2x = 8x$ **L** $4 \times -5 = -20$
   $= 6x^2 - 15x + 8x - 20$
   $= 6x^2 - 7x - 20$

EXERCISE 4.3

1 Rose has made mistakes in her expanding brackets homework.

Copy out each question and correct her mistakes.

a $(x + 3)(x + 4) = x^2 + 4x + 3x + 7 = x^2 + 7x + 7$

b $(x + 4)(x - 6) = x^2 - 6x + 4x - 2 = x^2 - 10x - 2$

c $(x - 5)(x - 4) = x^2 - 4x - 5x - 20 = x^2 - 9x - 20$

d $(x + 4)^2 = x^2 + 16$

Expand and simplify:

2 a $(x + 1)(x + 2)$ b $(x + 5)(x + 7)$ c $(x + 3)(x + 8)$ d $(x + 4)(x + 2)$

   e $(x + 4)(x + 5)$ f $(x + 3)(x + 1)$ g $(x + 9)(x + 3)$ h $(x + 5)(x + 6)$

   i $(x + 4)(x + 3)$ j $(x + 2)(x + 3)$ k $(x + 8)(x + 2)$ l $(1 + x)(4 + x)$

3 a $(x - 1)(x + 2)$ b $(x - 2)(x + 6)$ c $(x + 6)(x - 3)$ d $(x + 4)(x - 1)$

   e $(x - 9)(x + 7)$ f $(x - 2)(x + 8)$ g $(x - 8)(x + 4)$ h $(x - 7)(x + 2)$

   i $(x + 2)(x - 5)$ j $(x - 3)(x + 8)$ k $(x - 3)(x + 1)$ l $(9 + x)(4 - x)$

4 a $(x + 3)(x - 3)$ b $(x + 8)(x - 8)$ c $(x - 6)(x + 6)$ d $(x + 10)(x - 10)$

   e $(x - 4)(x + 4)$ f $(x - 9)(x + 9)$ g $(x - 1)(x + 1)$ h $(12 - x)(12 + x)$

5 a $(x - 5)(x - 2)$ b $(x - 4)(x - 1)$ c $(x - 3)(x - 8)$ d $(x - 6)(x - 2)$

   e $(x - 7)(x - 7)$ f $(x - 6)(x - 3)$ g $(x - 5)(x - 4)$ h $(x - 4)(x - 7)$

   i $(x - 9)(x - 4)$ j $(x - 1)(x - 1)$ k $(x - 5)(x - 1)$ l $(2 - x)(2 - x)$

6 a $(x + 3)^2$ b $(y + 5)^2$ c $(x - 4)^2$ d $(x + 7)^2$

   e $(x + 8)^2$ f $(a - 10)^2$ g $(6 - x)^2$ h $(2 + x)^2$

7 a $(2y + 1)(y - 3)$ b $(4x - 3)(x + 2)$ c $(5x + 2)(x + 4)$ d $(7y - 2)(y + 5)$

   e $(4y + 3)(2y - 7)$ f $(2x - 11)(5x - 3)$ g $(5x - 6)(3x - 4)$ h $(9y - 2)(3y - 10)$

   i $(8y - 5)(3y - 4)$ j $(3a - 7)(2a + 3)$ k $(1 - 3a)(3 - 4a)$ l $3(5x - 3)(2x + 1)$

8 a $(2x + 1)(2x - 1)$ b $(3x + 2)(3x - 2)$ c $(5x + 7)(5x - 7)$ d $(5x - 2)(5x + 2)$

9 a $(2x - 1)^2$ b $(5x + 2)^2$ c $(3x + 2y)^2$ d $(8 - 3y)^2$

10 a $(x + 1)(x - 9) + (x + 4)(x + 7)$ b $(2x + 3)(x - 1) + (3x - 5)(2x + 7)$

   c $(2x + 1)(2x - 5) - (3x - 1)(x + 2)$ d $(4x - 3)(3x + 2) + (2x - 9)(x - 1)$

   e $(3x + 1)^2 + (2x - 5)^2$ f $(2x - 3)^2 + (2x + 1)^2$

   g $(6x + 5)^2 - (2x - 3)^2$ h $2(3x + 1)^2 - 3(2x + 5)^2$

EXERCISE 4.4

1   Solve these equations.
    a $(x + 3)(x + 4) = (x - 2)(x + 5)$
    b $(3x + 2)(x + 4) = 3x(x + 6)$
    c $(x + 2)^2 = (x - 5)(x + 2)$

2   Find x for each of these right angled triangles.

    a

    b

3   Order

    Which two cards when multiplied together give:
    a $x^2 + 2x - 8$ b $x^2 - 7x + 12$ c $x^2 - 16$ d $x^2 + 6x + 8$
    e $x^2 + x - 12$ f $x^2 - 4$ g $x^2 - 5x + 6$ h $x^2 - 6x + 8$

4   These rectangles have the same area. Find the value of x.

5   Write down and simplify an expression for
    a   the volume of the cuboid
    b   the surface area of the cuboid.

    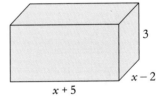

6   Show that $(n - 2)^2 + (n - 1)^2 + n^2 + (n + 1)^2 + (n + 2)^2$ simplifies to $5(n^2 + 2)$.

7   a   Write down an expression for the area of the white square
        in terms of c.
    b   Write down an expression for the area of the large square
        in terms of a and b.
    c   Write down an expression for the area of all four of the
        shaded right-angled triangles in terms of a and b.
    d   Use your answers from parts a, b and c to prove that $a^2 + b^2 = c^2$.

    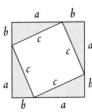

UNIT 4

Quadratic graphs

THIS SECTION WILL SHOW YOU HOW TO
- Recognise quadratic graphs
- Draw quadratic graphs
- Use quadratic graphs in practical situations

 $y = ax^2 + bx + c$ is called a **quadratic function**.
The simplest quadratic function is $y = x^2$.

The graph of $y = x^2$ is a smooth $\cup$-shaped curve.
The graph is symmetrical about the y-axis and it
passes through the point (0, 0).

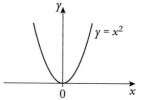

EXAMPLE

a Complete the table of values for $y = x^2 - 5x + 4$
b Draw the graph of $y = x^2 - 5x + 4$
c Name the line of symmetry of the curve.
d Use your graph to find the values of x when $y = 2$

x	0	1	2	3	4	5
y		0		-2		4

a

x	0	1	2	3	4	5	2.5
y	4	0	-2	-2	0	4	-2.25

The extra column in the table is needed to find where the curve turns

When $x = 0$, $y = (0)^2 - (5 \times 0) + 4 = 0 - 0 + 4 = 4$
When $x = 2$, $y = (2)^2 - (5 \times 2) + 4 = 4 - 10 + 4 = -2$
When $x = 4$, $y = (4)^2 - (5 \times 4) + 4 = 16 - 20 + 4 = 0$
When $x = 2.5$, $y = (2.5)^2 - (5 \times 2.5) + 4$
$$= 6.25 - 12.5 + 4 = -2.25$$

b

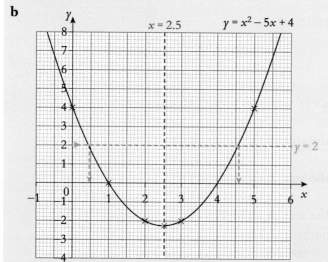

The points should be marked with a cross.

The points must be joined with a smooth curve.
They must not be joined with straight lines.

The axes and the curve should be labelled.

c The line of symmetry is $x = 2.5$
d When $y = 2$, $x \approx 0.4$ or $x \approx 4.6$

The symbol '$\approx$' means 'is approximately equal to'.

EXERCISE 4.5

1 Copy and complete the table for each of these quadratic functions.
Draw the graph of each function.
State the equation of the line of symmetry for each graph.

a $y = x^2 + 1$

x	-3	-2	-1	0	1	2	3
y						5	

b $y = x^2 - 2$

x	-3	-2	-1	0	1	2	3
y	7						

c $y = -x^2$

x	-3	-2	-1	0	1	2	3
y						-4	

d $y = 2x^2 - 5$

x	-3	-2	-1	0	1	2	3
y			-3				

e $y = \frac{1}{2}x^2 - 2$

x	-3	-2	-1	0	1	2	3
y		0					

f $y = x^2 + 2x$

x	-4	-3	-2	-1	0	1	2
y		3					

g $y = x^2 - 3x$

x	-1	0	1	2	3	4
y				-2		

h $y = 3x - x^2$

x	-1	0	1	2	3	4
y				2		

2 a Copy and complete the table of values for $y = x^2 - 4x + 3$

x	-1	0	1	2	3	4	5
y	8						

b Draw the graph of $y = x^2 - 4x + 3$
c Use your graph to find the values of x when $y = 7$

3 a Copy and complete the table of values for $y = x^2 - x - 2$

x	-2	-1	0	1	2	3
y			-2			

b Draw the graph of $y = x^2 - x - 2$
c Use your graph to find the values of x when $y = 2$

4 a Copy and complete the table of values for $y = 2 + x - x^2$

x	-2	-1	0	1	2	3
y	-4					

b Draw the graph of $y = 2 + x - x^2$
c Use your graph to find the values of x when $y = 1$

5 a Copy and complete the table of values for $y = 2x^2 - 5x + 1$

x	-1	0	1	2	3	4
y				-1		

b Draw the graph of $y = 2x^2 - 5x + 1$
c Use your graph to find the values of x when $y = 0$

TOP TIP

$2x^2$ means $2 \times x^2$
You must square the number and then multiply by 2.

Quadratic graphs   169

In the last exercise you should have found that the graphs of quadratic functions are always ∨ - shaped or ∧ - shaped.

| $y = ax^2 + bx + c$ |

if a is positive then the graph is ∨ - shaped
if a is negative then the graph is ∧ - shaped
c is the intercept on the y-axis

Gradient of a curve

The gradient of a curve changes as you move along it.
To estimate the gradient of a curve at a point you draw a
tangent to the curve at the point.
(A tangent is a straight line, which just touches the curve at the point.)
You then work out the gradient of the tangent.

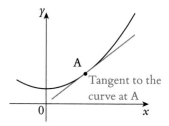

EXAMPLE

By drawing tangents to the graph, estimate the gradient of the curve when
a $x = 5$ **b** $x = 1$

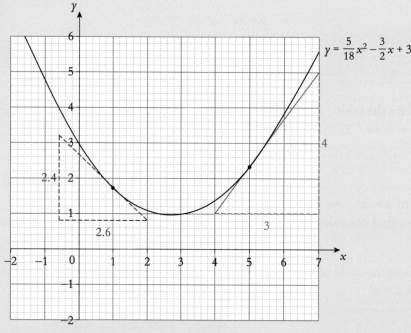

$y = \dfrac{5}{18}x^2 - \dfrac{3}{2}x + 3$

a   When $x = 5$, the gradient of the graph $\approx \dfrac{4}{3} = 1.33$ (to 3 s.f.)

b   When $x = 1$, the gradient of the graph $\approx -\dfrac{2.4}{2.6} = -0.923$ (to 3 s.f.)

EXERCISE 4.6

1 Match the quadratic functions to the correct graph.

a

b

c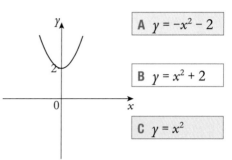

| A | $y = -x^2 - 2$ |

| B | $y = x^2 + 2$ |

| C | $y = x^2$ |

d

e

f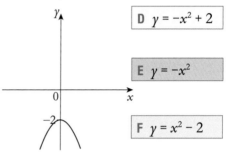

| D | $y = -x^2 + 2$ |

| E | $y = -x^2$ |

| F | $y = x^2 - 2$ |

2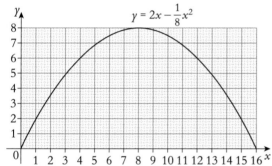

$y = 2x - \frac{1}{8}x^2$

Copy the graph. Draw tangents to estimate the gradient of the graph when
a $x = 2$ b $x = 4$ c $x = 6$ d $x = 8$ e $x = 10$ f $x = 12$ g $x = 14$
Comment on your results.

3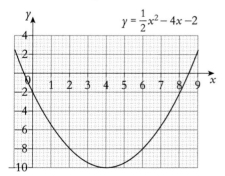

$y = \frac{1}{2}x^2 - 4x - 2$

➡ **NOTE:** the scales are not the same on the x and y-axis. You must consider this when calculating the gradient.

Copy the graph. Draw tangents to estimate the gradient of the graph when
a $x = 0$ b $x = 2$ c $x = 4$ d $x = 6$ e $x = 8$
Comment on your results.

Practical applications of quadratic graphs

EXAMPLE

Anu wants to make a rectangular enclosure for his donkey. He uses 100 m of fencing.

a If the length of the rectangle is x m, explain why the width is $(50 - x)$ m.

b Show that the area, A m^2, of the rectangular enclosure is given by the formula $A = 50x - x^2$.

c Copy and complete the table below.

x	0	10	20	30	40	50
A					400	

d Draw the graph of $A = 50x - x^2$ for $0 \le x \le 50$.

e What is the largest possible area for the rectangular enclosure?

---

a Perimeter of rectangle = 100

$$2x + 2y = 100$$ *subtract 2x from both sides*
$$2y = 100 - 2x$$ *divide both sides by 2*
$$y = 50 - x$$
$$\text{width} = 50 - x$$

b Area of rectangle = length × width
$$= x(50 - x)$$
$$= 50x - x^2$$

c

x	0	10	20	30	40	50	25
A	0	400	600	600	400	0	625

➡ **NOTE:** the extra column in the table is needed to find where the curve turns.

When $x = 25$, $A = 50 \times 25 - 25^2 = 1250 - 625 = 625$

d

e The largest possible area for the rectangular enclosure is 625 m^2.

EXERCISE 4.7

1   The water tank has a rectangular base with sides of length
    $(x + 1)$ m and x m. The height of the tank is 1 m.
    a   Show that the volume, V m³, of the tank is given by the
        formula $V = x^2 + x$
    b   Copy and complete the table below.

x	0	0.2	0.4	0.6	0.8	1
V		0.24				

    c   Draw the graph of $V = x^2 + x$ for $0 \leq x \leq 1$
    d   What value of x gives a volume of 1.3 m³?

2   A stone is projected vertically upwards with a speed of 25 m/s.
    Its height, h m, above the ground after t s is given by the formula $h = 25t - 5t^2$.
    a   Copy and complete the table below.

t	0	1	2	3	4	5
h				30		

    b   Draw the graph of $h = 25t - 5t^2$ for $0 \leq t \leq 5$
    c   What is the maximum height reached by the stone?
    d   What values of t give a height of 26 m?

3   A ball is kicked on horizontal ground.
    The equation for the path of the ball is $y = x - 0.02x^2$
    where y m is the height of the ball above the ground and
    x m is the horizontal distance travelled by the ball.
    a   Copy and complete the table below.

x	0	10	20	30	40	50
y				12		

    b   Draw the graph of $y = x - 0.02x^2$ for $0 \leq x \leq 50$.
    c   What is the maximum height reached by the ball?
    d   Between what distances is the ball at least 10 m
        above the ground?

KEY WORDS

quadratic function

tangent

Bearings

THIS SECTION WILL SHOW YOU HOW TO
- Use bearings to describe directions

 Bearings are used to describe directions.
In this diagram the bearing of B from A is 100°.

Bearings are always measured **clockwise** from the **north** line.

EXAMPLE

Draw diagrams to show these bearings.
- **a** The bearing of P from Q is 068°.
- **b** The bearing of Y from X is 250°.
- **c** The bearing of C from D is 300°.

➡ **NOTE:** bearings are always written as three-figure numbers.
e.g. 068° not 68°

a

b

c

EXAMPLE

The bearing of B from A is 060°.
Draw a diagram to show the positions of A and B.
Use the diagram to work out the bearing of A from B.

To find the bearing of A from B you must draw a north line
at B and find the angle measured clockwise from the north line at B.
$x = 60°$ *alternate angles*
Bearing of A from B = 180° + 60° = 240°

B is 5 km due east of A. C is 5 km from A on a bearing of 060°.
Find the bearing of C from B.

First draw a diagram to show the
positions of A, B and C.

∠CAB = 90° − 60° = 30°

Next draw a north line at B and
indicate the required angle.

Triangle ABC is isosceles.

∠ACB = ∠ABC = 75°

Bearing of C from B = 270° + 75°
$$= 345°$$

EXERCISE 4.8

1 Draw diagrams to show these bearings:
   a The bearing of B from A is 056°
   c The bearing of N from M is 135°

   b The bearing of F from G is 270°
   d The bearing of P from Q is 340°

2 Write down the bearing for each of
   these compass directions.
   a south east
   b due south
   c due west
   d south west
   e north east
   f north west

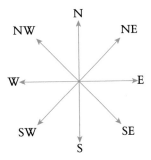

3 Write down the bearing of
   a Dubai from Doha
   b Doha from Kuwait City
   c Shiraz from Doha
   d Kuwait City from Dubai.

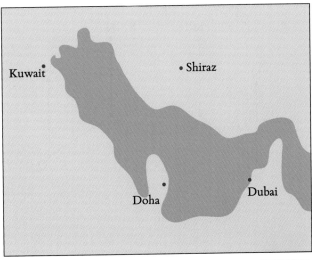

4   Bermuda is 1650 km from Orlando on a bearing of 077°.
    Jamaica is 1990 km from Bermuda on a bearing of 220°.
    Draw a scale diagram to show the positions of Bermuda, Orlando and Jamaica.

5   A boat sets sail from port A and sails 16 km due east to port B.
    The boat then sails 12 km on a bearing of 140° to port C.
    a   Using a scale of 1 cm to represent 2 km draw a scale diagram to show the journey.
    b   Use your scale diagram to find the bearing of port C from port A.
    c   Use your scale diagram to find the distance between port A and port C.

6   Work out the bearing of A from B for these diagrams.

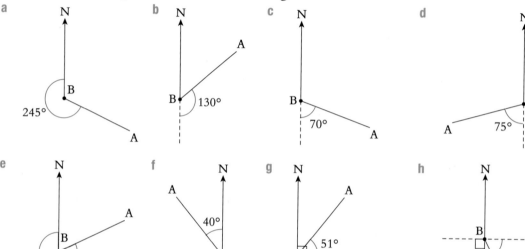

7   B is 8 km due east of A.
    C is 8 km from A on a bearing of 130°.
    Find the bearing of C from B.

8   Work out the bearing of P from Q for these diagrams:

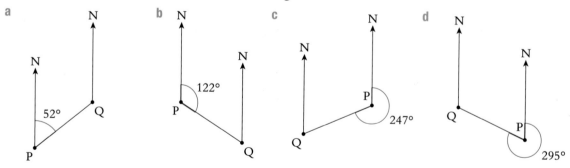

9   The diagram shows the positions of three towns A, B and C.
    Find the bearing of

    a   B from C
    b   C from B
    c   A from B
    d   B from A
    e   A from C
    f   C from A.

10 The bearing of B from A is 070°, the bearing of C from A is 120°
    and the bearing of C from B is 125°.
    a   Find the bearing of A from C.
    b   Find the bearing of B from C.

11 Two runners, Deepika and Khadeeja, set off from the point A.
    Deepika runs 8 km on a bearing of 095° to the point B.
    Khadeeja runs 8 km on a bearing of 155° to the point C.
    a   Find the distance between B and C.
    b   Find the bearing of B from C.
    c   Find the bearing of C from B.

12 B is 5 km from A on a bearing of 038°.
    C is 12 km from B on a bearing of 128°.
    Find the distance between A and C.

13 A ship sails on a bearing of 110° from a port P.
    A lighthouse L is 8 km south east of port P.
    a   Draw a scale diagram to show the positions of P and L and the path of the ship.
    b   Mark clearly on your scale diagram the locus of points where the ship is less than 4 km
        from the lighthouse.

14 The bearing of Q from P is 120°.
    The bearing of R from Q is 240°.
    The bearing of P from R is 020°.
    Find the values of x, y and z.

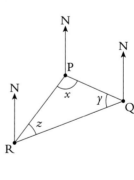

15 The bearing of B from A is 140°.
    The bearing of C from B is 275°.
    The bearing of A from C is 043°.
    Find the values of x, y and z.

UNIT 4

Trigonometry

Trigonometry is used to find lengths and angles in a right-angled triangle without using scale drawings.

The sides of a right-angled triangle are given special names.
The longest side is called the **hypotenuse**.
The side opposite the angle $x°$ is called the **opposite** side.
The side next to the angle $x°$ is called the **adjacent** side.

The different relationships or ratio of the sides to each other in a triangle make up trigonometric formulae. The three trigonometrical ratios that you have to know are tangent, cosine and sine.

The tangent ratio

$$\tan x = \frac{\text{opposite}}{\text{adjacent}}$$

Calculating sides

The following examples show you how to use the tangent ratio to find the length of a side.

EXAMPLE

Find the length of x.

$\tan 63° = \dfrac{\text{opp}}{\text{adj}}$ *replace opp by x and adj by 4*

$\tan 63° = \dfrac{x}{4}$ *multiply both sides by 4*

$x = 4 \tan 63°$

$= 7.85 \text{ cm (to 3 s.f.)}$

EXAMPLE

Find the length of x.

$\tan 48° = \dfrac{\text{opp}}{\text{adj}}$ *replace opp by 6 and adj by x*

$\tan 48° = \dfrac{6}{x}$ *multiply both sides by x*

$x \times \tan 48° = 6$ *divide both sides by tan 48°*

$x = \dfrac{6}{\tan 48°}$

$= 5.40 \text{ cm (to 3 s.f.)}$

EXERCISE 4.9

In this exercise all lengths are in cm.

1 Find the length x for each triangle.

a

b

c

d

e

f

g

h

i

j

k

l

m

n

o

2 Find the lengths of x and y.

a

b

c

d

e

f

UNIT 4

Calculating angles using the tangent ratio

If you know both the opposite and adjacent sides in a right-angled triangle, you can calculate the size of an angle inside the triangle.

To do this you must use the 'inverse tan' button on your calculator. (On most calculators this is labelled tan⁻¹)

EXAMPLE

Find the size of angle x.

(opp) 4 cm

(adj) 5 cm

$\tan x = \dfrac{\text{opp}}{\text{adj}}$ *replace opp by 4 and adj by 5*

$\tan x = \dfrac{4}{5}$ *to find x use the tan⁻¹ button on your calculator*

$x = \tan^{-1}\left(\dfrac{4}{5}\right)$

$x = 38.7°$ (to 1 d.p.)   ➡ **NOTE:** you should give angle answers correct to 1 d.p.

EXAMPLE

ABCD is a rectangle.
Calculate the size of angle x.

D   C

8 cm

A   18 cm   B

The tangent ratio can only be used for right-angled triangles, so split the bottom triangle into two identical right-angled triangles.

D   C

y 4 (adj)

A (opp)   B
9

$\tan y = \dfrac{\text{opp}}{\text{adj}}$ *replace opp by 9 and adj by 4*

$\tan y = \dfrac{9}{4}$ *to find y use the tan⁻¹ button on your calculator*

$y = \tan^{-1}\left(\dfrac{9}{4}\right)$

$y = 66.0375.....$
$x = 2 \times y$
$\quad = 132.1°$ (to 1 d.p.)

EXERCISE 4.10

In this exercise all lengths are in cm.

1   Find the size of angle x for each triangle.

a

b

c

d

e

f

g

h

i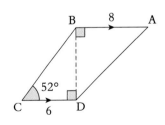

2   A hospital H is 7 km East and 5 km North of a school S.
Calculate the bearing of
a   H from S,   b   S from H.

3   ABCD is a rectangle.
Find the size of angles x and y.

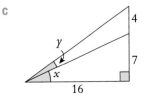

4   Find angle BAD for each of these diagrams.

a

b

c

5   Find the size of angles x and for each of these diagrams.

a

b

c

The sine and cosine ratios:

$$\sin x = \frac{\text{opposite}}{\text{hypotenuse}} \qquad \cos x = \frac{\text{adjacent}}{\text{hypotenuse}}$$

The following examples show you how to use the sine and cosine ratios to find the length of a side.

EXAMPLE

Find the length of x.

(hyp) 6 cm

x (opp)

25°

$\sin 25° = \dfrac{\text{opp}}{\text{hyp}}$ *replace opp by x and hyp by 6*

$\sin 25° = \dfrac{x}{6}$ *multiply both sides by 6*

$x = 6 \times \sin 25°$

$x = 2.54 \text{ cm (to 3 s.f.)}$

TOP TIP

It helps to label the sides opp, adj and hyp when solving problems.

EXAMPLE

Find the length of x.

x (adj)

34°

15 cm (hyp)

$\cos 34° = \dfrac{\text{adj}}{\text{hyp}}$ *replace adj by x and hyp by 15*

$\cos 34° = \dfrac{x}{15}$ *multiply both sides by 15*

$x = 15 \times \cos 34°$

$x = 12.4 \text{ cm (to 3 s.f.)}$

EXAMPLE

Find the length of x.

(adj) 3 cm

65°

x (hyp)

$\cos 65° = \dfrac{\text{adj}}{\text{hyp}}$ *replace adj by 3 and hyp by x*

$\cos 65° = \dfrac{3}{x}$ *multiply both sides by x*

$x \times \cos 65° = 3$ *divide both sides by cos 65°*

$x = \dfrac{3}{\cos 65°}$

$x = 7.10 \text{ cm (to 3 s.f.)}$

EXERCISE 4.11

In this exercise all lengths are in cm.

1   Find the length of x for each triangle.

a

b

c

d

e

f

g

h

i

j

k

l

2   Find the length of x for each of these triangles.

a

b

c

3   Calculate the height and area of each of these triangles.

a

b

c

4   Calculate the value of x and the area of this trapezium.

Calculating angles using the sine and cosine ratios

Find the size of angle x

(hyp) 8 cm   4 cm (opp) x

$\sin x = \dfrac{\text{opp}}{\text{hyp}}$ *replace opp by 4 and hyp by 8*

$\sin x = \dfrac{4}{8}$ *to find x use the sin^{-1} button on your calculator*

$x = \sin^{-1}\left(\dfrac{4}{8}\right)$

$x = 30°$

EXERCISE 4.12

In this exercise all lengths are in cm.
Find the size of angle x for each triangle.

1

x 7   5

2

6   x 12

3

10   x 14

4

5   2 x

5

x 3   9

6

6   x 4

7

5   12 x

8

10   x 3

9

13   x 8

10

7   x 3

11

x 5   9

12

6.3 x 4

13

6   x 15.4

14

6.62 x 3.7

15

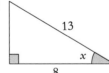

x 9.55   7.5

Summary of rules for right-angled triangles

The three trigonometric ratios are:

$$\text{Sin}\,x = \frac{\text{Opposite}}{\text{Hypotenuse}} \quad \text{Cos}\,x = \frac{\text{Adjacent}}{\text{Hypotenuse}} \quad \text{Tan}\,x = \frac{\text{Opposite}}{\text{Adjacent}}$$

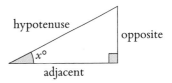

A useful memory aid for remembering these three ratios is

SOHCAHTOA

Pythagoras' theorem also applies to right-angled triangles.

Pythagoras' $a^2 + b^2 = c^2$

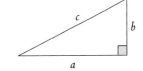

Sometimes problems involve both Pythagoras' theorem and trigonometry.

EXAMPLE

a Calculate the length of AC.
b Calculate the length of DC.
c Calculate the size of angle x.

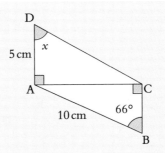

---

a Using triangle ABC:

$$\sin 66° = \frac{AC}{10}$$

$AC = 10 \times \sin 66°$

$AC = 9.135...$

$AC = 9.14\,\text{cm (to 3 s.f.)}$

b Using Pythagoras on triangle ACD:

$DC^2 = AC^2 + AD^2$

$DC^2 = 9.135^2 + 5^2$

$DC^2 = 108.4...$

$DC = 10.4\,\text{cm (to 3 s.f.)}$

c Using triangle ACD:

$$\tan x = \frac{AC}{5} = \frac{9.135...}{5}$$

$$x = \tan^{-1}\left(\frac{9.135...}{5}\right)$$

$x = 61.3°\,\text{(to 1 d.p.)}$

➡ **NOTE:** when using a previous answer in another calculation you should always use the unrounded value.

EXERCISE 4.13

In this exercise all lengths are in cm.

1   Find the value of x for each triangle.

a

b

c

d

e

f

g

h

i

j

k

l

m

n

o

p

q

r

2   Find the values of x and y in each of these triangles.

a

b

c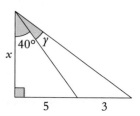

3 Find the values of x, y and z in each of these triangles.

a

b

c
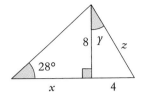

4 Calculate the size of angle x in this trapezium.

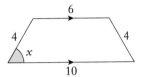

5 Find the values of x and y in these diagrams.

a

b
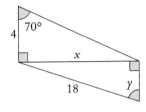

6 Find the values of x, y and z in this diagram.

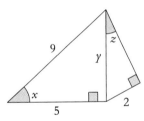

7 Find the area of each of these regular polygons.

a

b

c
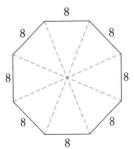

8 The cross-section of this solid prism is a regular pentagon.
   The length of each side of the pentagon is 8 cm.
   The length of the prism is 20 cm.
   Calculate:
   a the surface area of the prism,
   b the volume of the prism.

Practical applications of trigonometry and Pythagoras

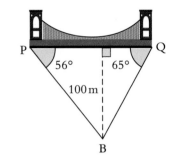

EXERCISE 4.14

1 The diagram shows a bridge over a river.
  A boat B is 100 m vertically below the bridge.
  Angle QPB = 56° and angle PQB = 65°.
  Calculate the length of the bridge PQ.

2 ABCDE is the cross-section of a tent.
  AB = DE = 1.7 m BC = CD = 1.3 m
  Angle EAB = angle AED = 75°
  Angle CBD = angle CDB = 22°
  Calculate
  a the length of BD
  b the length of AE
  c the height (*h*) of the tent.

3 The diagram shows a 25 m high radio mast PQ.
  Two wires PA and PB secure the mast.
  PA = 30 m and PB = 35 m
  Calculate
  a angle PAB
  b angle PBA
  c the distance between A and B.

4 A cable car travels at 50° to the horizontal for 70 m
  and then 35° to the horizontal for 100 m. Calculate
  the vertical height (*h*) gained when travelling
  from A to C.

5 ABCD is a field.
  Calculate
  a the length of AC
  b the length of CD
  c angle BAD
  d angle BCD
  e the area of the field.

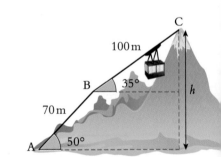

6 The vertices of a regular pentagon lie on the
  circumference of a circle radius 10 cm.
  Calculate
  a the lengths of the sides of the pentagon
  b the difference in area between the circle and the pentagon.

UNIT 4

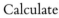

7 The Tower of Pisa leans at an angle of 4° to the vertical.
The top of the tower stands 56.7 m above the ground.
a Calculate the height of the tower.
b The tower used to lean at an angle of 5.5° to the vertical.
How much lower did the top of the tower used to stand
above the ground?

8 A boat sails 50 km on a bearing of 080°.
Calculate:
a How far north it travels,
b How far east it travels.

9 A hot air balloon flies 3000 km on a bearing of 245°.
Calculate:
a How far south it travels
b How far west it travels.

10 An aircraft flies 500 km from an airport A on a bearing of 070°
to arrive at airport B.
The plane then flies 800 km from airport B on a bearing of 035°
to arrive at airport C.
a Calculate how far north C is from A
b Calculate how far east C is from A
c Calculate the direct distance between A and C
d Calculate the bearing of C from A
e What is the bearing of A from C?

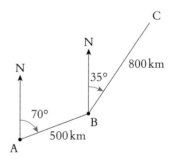

Three-dimensional trigonometry

To find the angle between the line AB and the plane PQRS:
- drop a perpendicular from the point B to meet the plane at X
- draw the right-angled triangle BAX
- the angle between AB and the plane is angle BAX

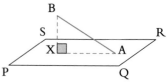

When doing a 3D trigonometry question it is important to draw clearly the triangle (usually right-angled) that you are going to use in your calculations. On your triangle show all the known lengths and angles.

ABCDEFGH is a cuboid.
AB = 7 cm, BC = 4 cm and CG = 6 cm.
Calculate
a   the length of BD
b   the angle between the line BH and the base ABCD.

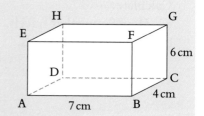

a   Draw the rectangular base of the cuboid and on it show the line BD.
Use Pythagoras on the right-angled triangle DAB.
$$BD^2 = 7^2 + 4^2$$
$$BD^2 = 65$$
$$BD = \sqrt{65}$$
$$BD = 8.062...$$
$$BD = 8.06 \text{ cm (to 3 s.f.)}$$

b   Drop a perpendicular from H to meet the base ABCD.
The perpendicular meets the base at the point D.
The angle between the line BH and the base ABCD is angle HBD.
Draw triangle HBD. (It has a right angle at D.)
$$\tan x = \frac{\text{opp}}{\text{adj}}$$
$$\tan x = \frac{6}{\sqrt{65}}$$
$$x = \tan^{-1}\left(\frac{6}{\sqrt{65}}\right)$$
$$x = 36.7° \text{ (to 1 d.p.)}$$

EXERCISE 4.15

1   ABCDEFGH is a cube.
Calculate:
a   the length of AC
b   the length of AG
c   the angle between AG and the base ABCD.

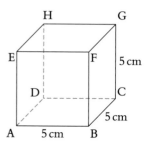

2   ABCDEFGH is a cuboid.
    Calculate:
    a   the length of AC
    b   the length of AG
    c   the angle between AG and the base ABCD.

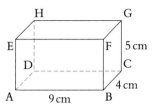

3   ABCDEF is a triangular prism.
    Calculate:
    a   the length of BD
    b   the length of DE
    c   the angle between DE and the base ABCD.

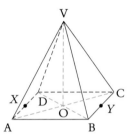

4   ABCDV is a square-based pyramid.
    AB = 4 cm and VC = 5 cm.
    O is the middle of the square base.
    V is vertically above O.
    X is the midpoint of AD.
    Y is the midpoint of BC.
    Calculate:
    a   the lengths of AC, VO and VY
    b   the angle between VC and the base ABCD
    c   angle XVY.

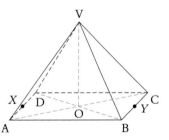

5   ABCDV is a rectangular-based pyramid.
    AB = 12 cm, BC = 9 cm and VO = 6 cm.
    O is the middle of the rectangular base.
    V is vertically above O.
    X is the midpoint of AD.
    Y is the midpoint of BC.
    Calculate:
    a   the lengths of OB, VB and VY
    b   the angle between VB and the base ABCD
    c   angle XVY.

6   ABCDEF is a triangular prism.
    Triangle ABE is equilateral.
    AB = 5 cm and BC = 15 cm.
    Calculate the angle between AF
    and the base ABCD.

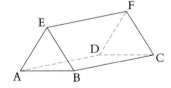

UNIT 4

Angles of elevation and depression

THIS SECTION WILL SHOW YOU HOW TO
• Use angles of elevation and depression

The **angle of elevation** is the angle measured upwards from the horizontal.

The **angle of depression** is the angle measured downwards from the horizontal.

e = angle of elevation

d = angle of depression

EXAMPLE

A radio mast stands on horizontal ground. The angle of elevation of the top of the mast from a point 200 m away from the base of the mast is 17°.
Calculate the height, h, of the radio mast.

$$\tan 17° = \frac{h}{200}$$
$$h = 200 \times \tan 17°$$
$$h = 61.1 \text{ m}$$

EXERCISE 4.16

1 An electricity pylon stands on horizontal ground. The angle of elevation of the top of the pylon from a point 150 m away from the base of the pylon is 44°. Calculate the height of the pylon.

2 A tree stands on horizontal ground. The angle of elevation of the top of the tree from a point 50 m away from the base of the tree is 11.3°. Calculate the height of the tree.

3 The picture shows the CN tower in Canada.
The angle of elevation of the top of the tower from a point 100 m away from the base of the tower is 79.75°. Calculate the height of the CN tower.

4   The picture shows the Burj Khalifa tower in Dubai.
    The angle of elevation of the top of the tower from a
    point 100 m away from the base of the tower is 83.11°.
    Calculate the height of the Burj Khalifa tower.

5   Use your answers to questions 3 and 4 to find the difference in
    heights between the CN tower and the Burj Khalifa tower.

6   An aeroplane is flying at a height of 1000 m.
    The angle of depression of airport A from the plane is 15°.
    Calculate the horizontal distance between
    the aeroplane and the airport.

7   The lighthouse is 36 m high. Two boats A and B are due South
    of the lighthouse.
    From the top of the lighthouse the angles of depression of
    boats A and B are 22° and 15°.
    Calculate the distance AB.

8   A hot air balloon is 70 m above the sea.
    Two buoys A and B are due East of the balloon.
    The angle of depression from the balloon to buoy A is 60°.
    The angle of depression from the balloon to buoy B is 40°.
    Calculate the distance AB.

9   The diagram shows a tower.
    The point A is 30 m from the base of the tower.
    On top of the tower is a flagpole PQ.
    The angle of elevation of P from the point A is 53°.
    The angle of elevation of Q from the point A is 50°.
    Calculate the length of PQ.

10 PQRS is a rectangular horizontal car park.
    PT is a vertical lamp-post.
    PS = 50 m and PQ = 40 m.
    The angle of elevation of T from S is 8°.
    Calculate:
    a   PT and TR
    b   the angle of elevation of T from Q
    c   the angle of depression of R from T.

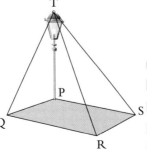

UNIT 4

Scatter diagrams

THIS SECTION WILL SHOW YOU HOW TO

- Draw scatter diagrams and lines of best fit
- Understand positive, negative and zero correlation

 You can use a **scatter diagram** to represent paired **data**.

EXAMPLE

The table shows the heights and masses of ten adult males.

Height (cm)	160	166	170	175	180	185	188	190	195	200
Mass (kg)	66	76	70	90	82	100	94	90	110	104

Draw a scatter diagram to show this information.

➡ **NOTE:** the information is plotted as coordinate points: (160, 66), (166, 76), (170, 70)...

➡ **NOTE:** a jagged line shows that the scale does not start at zero.

Correlation

A scatter diagram shows you if there is **correlation** (a connection) between the two variables.

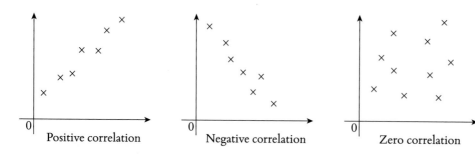

Positive correlation · Negative correlation · Zero correlation

In the example above, the scatter diagram shows that there is positive correlation between the two variables.

EXERCISE 4.17

1   Name the type of correlation shown by each of these scatter diagrams.

2   The table shows the test results for eight students in mathematics and art.

Mathematics	5	8	8	10	13	15	17	18
Art	10	6	18	13	13	19	15	11

a   Show this information on a scatter diagram.
b   Name the type of correlation shown.

3   The table shows information collected by a café owner for eight days.

Midday temperature (°C)	11	30	18	24	25	12	17	22
Number of hot drinks sold	24	4	11	8	11	20	18	15

a   Show this information on a scatter diagram.
b   Name the type of correlation shown.

4   The table shows the test results of ten students in chemistry and physics.

Chemistry	6	8	9	9	11	12	13	15	16	19
Physics	6	7	9	11	15	15	17	14	16	18

a   Show this information on a scatter diagram.
b   Name the type of correlation shown.

5   The table shows the age and value of eight cars.
    a   Show this information on a scatter diagram.
    b   Name the type of correlation shown.

Age (years)	Value ($)
0	18 000
1	15 000
2	12 000
4	8 000
4	10 000
5	7 000
5	8 000
6	5 000

6   Name the type of correlation that you would expect for each of these:
    a   The number of hours of sunshine in a day and the number of cold drinks sold.
    b   The midday temperature and the number of coats sold.
    c   The distance travelled by a car and the amount of money spent on petrol.
    d   The height of an adult and the IQ of the adult.
    e   The age of a child and the mass of the child.

Lines of best fit

When a scatter diagram shows positive or negative (linear) correlation you can draw a **line of best fit**.

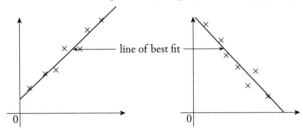

line of best fit

A line of best fit is usually drawn 'by eye' and should

- follow the general trend of the points
- have a similar number of points above and below the line.

The closer the points are to the line of best fit, the stronger the correlation.
The line of best fit can be used to predict data values within the range of data collected.
If you are asked to calculate the mean of the two data sets, then the mean point can also be plotted on the scatter graph and the line of best fit drawn through it.

EXAMPLE

The table shows the daily amount of rainfall (mm) and the number of sun hats sold in a shop over a period of ten days.

Rainfall (mm)	0	1	3	5	2	6	8	4	2	6
Number of sunhats sold	26	23	18	11	21	9	2	15	17	5

a   Calculate the mean rainfall for the ten days.
b   Calculate the mean number of sunhats sold for the ten days.
c   Show the information from the table on a scatter diagram and draw the line of best fit.
d   Name the type of correlation shown by the diagram.
e   Use your line of best fit to predict the number of sunhats sold on a day with 7 mm of rainfall.

a   Mean rainfall = $\dfrac{0+1+3+5+2+6+8+4+2+6}{10} = \dfrac{37}{10} = 3.7$

b   Mean number of hats sold = $\dfrac{26+23+18+11+21+9+2+15+17+5}{10} = \dfrac{147}{10} = 14.7$

c

Plot the mean point.

Draw the line of best fit through the mean point.

d   The scatter graph shows negative correlation
e   From the graph the predicted number of sunhats is approximately 4.

UNIT 4

EXERCISE 4.18

1   The scatter diagram shows information
    about the marks earned by a group of
    students in two examinations.
    a   Use the line of best fit to predict
        the economics mark for a student who
        scored 60% in the mathematics examination.
    b   Use the line of best fit to predict
        the mathematics mark for a student who
        scored 40% in the economics examination.

2   The table shows information about the number of
    hours spent doing homework per week and the
    number of hours spent watching television per week for ten students.

Homework (hours)	3	13	10	6	1	5	8	14	12	11
Television (hours)	9	3	7	8	12	9	8	2	5	5

    a   Calculate the mean number of hours spent doing homework per week.
    b   Calculate the mean number of hours spent watching television per week.
    c   Show the information from the table on a scatter diagram and draw the line of best fit.
    d   Name the type of correlation shown by the diagram.
    e   A student watched six hours of television in one week. Use your line of best fit to predict
        the number of hours this student spent doing homework that week.

3   The table shows information about the hand span and the height of ten adult females.

Hand span (cm)	20.5	18	22.4	22.7	23.5	19	19.7	21.5	22.2	21
Height (m)	170	160	186	183	190	167	171	177	181	177

    a   Calculate the mean hand span.
    b   Calculate the mean height.
    c   Show the information from the table on a scatter diagram
        and draw the line of best fit.
    d   Name the type of correlation shown by the diagram.
    e   An adult female has a hand span of 20.7 cm.
        Use your line of best fit to predict the height of this female.

KEY WORDS

scatter diagram
correlation
line of best fit

1 Work out 45 cents as a percentage of $18. [1]

2 A car is bought for $5600 and it is then sold for $6272.

Calculate the percentage profit. [3]

3 In 2010 the population of a country was 3.24×10^6.
In 2015 the population of the same country was 3.19×10^6.

Calculate the percentage decrease in the population. [3]

4 Expand and simplify.
$$(x + 5)(x - 8)$$
[2]

5 Expand and simplify.
$$(2a - 3b)(3a - 5b)$$
[3]

6 Simplify.
$$100 - 3(4y - 5)^2$$
[3]

7 The table shows some values for $y = x^2 - 5x + 3$.

x	−1	0	1	2	3	4	5	6
y				−3		−1	3	

(a) Complete the table. [3]

(b) On the grid, draw the graph of $y = x^2 - 5x + 3$ for $-1 \le x \le 6$.

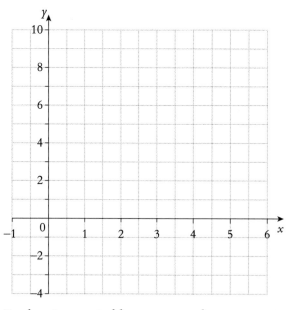

[3]

(c) By drawing a suitable tangent to the curve, estimate the gradient of the curve at the point (5, 3). [3]

8   The bearing of P from Q is $228°$.

Find the bearing of Q from P.   [2]

9

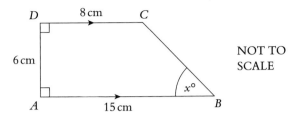

The diagram shows trapezium $ABCD$.

(a)   Find BC.

(b)   Find the value of x.

10

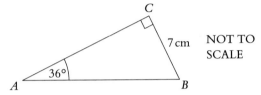

The diagram shows a right-angled triangle ABC.

(a)   Find AC.   [3]

(b)   Find the area of this triangle.   [2]

11

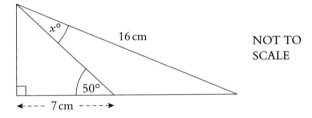

Find the value of x.   [5]

12

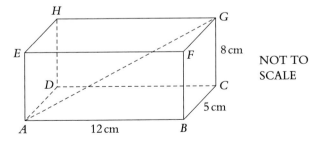

The diagram shows a cuboid $ABCDEFGH$.
$AB = 12$ cm, $BC = 5$ cm and $CG = 8$ cm.

Calculate the angle between the line AG and the base $ABCD$.   [4]

13

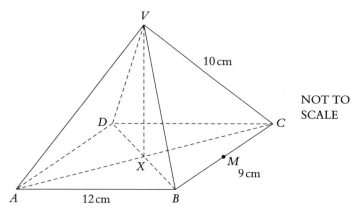

NOT TO SCALE

The diagram shows a pyramid on a rectangular base $ABCD$.
$AB = 12$ cm, $BC = 9$ cm and each of the sloping edges is 10 cm.
AC and BD intersect at X and V is vertically above X.

(a) Calculate angle BVC. [3]
(b) Calculate angle VCX. [4]
(c) M is the midpoint of BC.
   Calculate angle VMX. [4]

14 A flagpole stands on horizontal ground.
P is a point, on the ground, 50 metres away from the base of the flagpole.
The angle of elevation of the top of the flagpole from P is 6°.

Calculate the height of the flagpole. [2]

15 A group of ten students take a mathematics test and a biology test.
The table shows the scores in each test for each student.

Student	A	B	C	D	E	F	G	H	I	J
Mathematics score	3	16	13	17	8	12	19	7	13	2
Biology score	9	16	15	17	13	14	18	11	14	10

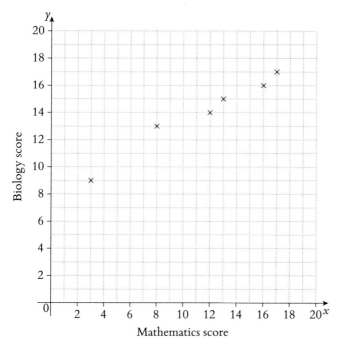

Biology score

Mathematics score

(a) Complete the scatter diagram for the scores of the ten students.
The first six have been plotted for you. [2]

(b) Draw the line of best fit. [1]

(c) Name the type of correlation shown in the scatter diagram. [1]

(d) Another student, Amy, scored 12 in the biology test.
Estimate the score for this student in the mathematics test. [1]

Direct and inverse proportion

THIS SECTION WILL SHOW YOU HOW TO
- Solve problems involving direct and inverse proportion
- Calculate money conversions

Direct proportion

Two quantities are in **direct proportion** if the graph of one quantity against the other quantity is a straight line through the origin. For example, if one quantity doubles then the other quantity doubles.

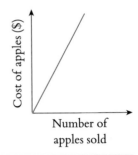

EXAMPLE

The cost of three apples is $2.37
What is the cost of five apples?

3 apples cost $2.37
1 apple costs $2.37 ÷ 3 = $0.79
5 apples cost $0.79 × 5 = $3.95

Inverse proportion

Two quantities are in **inverse proportion** if one quantity increases at the same rate as the other quantity decreases. For example, if one quantity doubles then the other quantity halves.

EXAMPLE

Seven men build a wall in 3 hours.
How long will it take two men to build the same wall?

7 men take 3 hours
1 man will take 7 × 3 = 21 hours
2 men will take 21 ÷ 2 = 10.5 hours

EXAMPLE

A bag of birdseed will feed 30 birds for 12 days.
a   For how many days will the bag of birdseed feed 40 birds?
b   How many birds will the bag of birdseed feed for 15 days?

a   30 birds for 12 days
    1 bird for 30 × 12 = 360 days
    40 birds for 360 ÷ 40 = 9 days

b   30 birds for 12 days
    1 bird for 30 × 12 = 360 days
    360 ÷ 15 = 24 birds

EXERCISE 5.1

1 Twelve metres of material costs $31.56
  Calculate the cost of five metres of the same material.

2 Three kilograms of fish costs $11.25
  Calculate the cost of eight kilograms of fish.

3 Jarred earns $101.50 for working 7 hours in a café.
  Calculate how much he will be paid for working 10 hours.

4 A car uses 20 litres of petrol to travel 120 kilometres.
   a How far will the car travel if it uses 25 litres of petrol?
   b How many litres of petrol are needed for a journey of 315 kilometres?

5 The recipe for pancakes will make 8 pancakes.
  Anna wants to make 60 pancakes.
  Calculate the amount of each ingredient needed.

RECIPE:
200g flour
480ml milk
2g salt
2 eggs

6 A machine fills 600 bottles in 4 minutes.
  How long does the machine take to fill 40 bottles?
  Give your answer in seconds.

7 Three people take 4 hours to paint a fence.
  How long will it take five people?
  Give your answer in hours and minutes.

8 Six people take 5 days to pick a crop of oranges.
  How long would it take 4 people to pick the same crop?

9 A bag of sweets is shared between 8 children so that they each receive 9 sweets.
  How many sweets would each child receive if there were 12 children?

10 It takes 48 hours to fill a swimming pool with water using 3 identical pumps.
   a How long would it take to fill the pool if there were eight of these pumps?
   b How many pumps would be needed to fill the pool in 12 hours?

11 A hotel has 120 rooms.
   It takes 6 cleaners 4 hours to clean all the rooms.
   How many cleaners would be needed to clean all the rooms in 3 hours?

12 One sack of rice will feed 100 people for 10 days.
   a For how many days will the sack of rice feed 250 people?
   b How many people will the sack of rice feed for 40 days?

Converting money from one currency to another currency

You can use a conversion graph to convert one currency to another currency.

The graph below can be used to convert between US dollars ($) and South African Rand (ZAR).

The blue dashed lines show how to convert 500 ZAR into US dollars ($).

> 500 ZAR = $73.50

The red dashed lines show how to convert $40 into South African Rand (ZAR).

> $40 = 272 ZAR

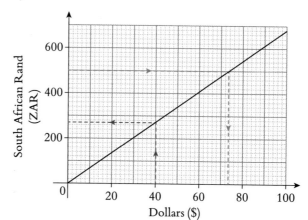

If you know the exchange rate you can use proportion to convert money from one currency to another.

EXAMPLE

Rafael changed $500 into Japanese Yen when the exchange rate was $1 = 83.7 Yen.
How many Japanese Yen did he receive?

$1 = 83.7 Yen
$500 = 500 × 83.7 Yen
$500 = 41850 Yen

EXAMPLE

Jani changed $350 into pounds (£) when the exchange rate was £1 = $1.315
How many pounds did he receive?
Give your answer correct to 2 decimal places.

$1.315 = £1

$1 = £$\frac{1}{1.315}$

$350 = 350 × £$\frac{1}{1.315}$ = £266.159 … = £266.16

EXERCISE 5.2

1

The graph can be used to convert between US dollars ($) and Maldives Rufiyaa (Rf).
a   Use the graph to convert the amounts in dollars into Maldives Rufiyaa (Rf).
   i $25   ii $54   iii $81   iv $200
b   Use the graph to convert the amounts in Maldives Rufiyaa (Rf) into dollars.
   i   600 Rf   ii   1100 Rf   iii   240 Rf   iv   2000 Rf

2 If the exchange rate between US dollars and Argentine Peso (ARS) is $1 = 3.98 ARS,
   a   Change the following amounts of money into Argentine Peso (ARS).
      i $50   ii $300   iii $72   iv $2000
   b   Change the following amounts of money into US dollars ($).
      i   40 ARS   ii   82 ARS   iii   500 ARS   iv   36.4 ARS

3 If the exchange rate between Malaysian Ringgit (MYR) and US dollars ($) is
   1 MYR = $0.319,
   a   Change the following amounts of money into Malaysian Ringgit (MYR).
      i $80   ii $20   iii $74   iv $500
   b   Change the following amounts of money into US dollars ($).
      i   60 MYR   ii   18 MYR   iii   300 MYR   iv   470 MYR

4 Zara changed 800 US dollars ($) into Thai Baht (THB) when the
   exchange rate was 1 THB = $0.032
   One month later she changed all the Thai Baht back into
   US dollars when the exchange rate was 1 THB = $0.035
   Calculate how much profit she made.
   Give your answer in dollars.

> **KEY WORDS**
> direct proportion
> inverse proportion

Increase and decrease in a given ratio

THIS SECTION WILL SHOW YOU HOW TO
- Increase or decrease a quantity in a given ratio

 If you want to increase \$60 in the ratio 5 : 4 there are two possible methods.

Method 1
4 parts = \$60
1 part = \$60 ÷ 4 = \$15
5 parts = 5 × \$15 = \$75
So the answer is \$75.

Method 2
$\$60 \times \dfrac{5}{4} = \$75$

EXAMPLE

Decrease 540 kg in the ratio 17 : 20

Method 1
20 parts = 540 kg
1 part = 540 kg ÷ 20 = 27 kg
17 parts = 17 × 27 kg = 459 kg
So the answer is 459 kg.

Method 2
$540 \text{ kg} \times \dfrac{17}{20} = 459 \text{ kg}$

EXAMPLE

A photograph measures 15 cm by 10 cm.
The photograph is enlarged in the ratio 3 : 2
a Calculate the measurements of the enlarged photograph.
b Calculate i the area of the original photograph
           ii the area of the enlarged photograph.
c Write down and simplify the following ratio
     area of enlarged photograph : area of original photograph

---

a $15 \text{ cm} \times \dfrac{3}{2} = 22.5 \text{ cm}$ and $10 \text{ cm} \times \dfrac{3}{2} = 15 \text{ cm}$

   Enlarged photograph is 22.5 cm by 15 cm.

b i Area of original photograph = 15 × 10 = 150 cm^2

   ii Area of enlarged photograph = 22.5 × 15 = 337.5 cm^2

c area of enlarged photograph : area of original photograph

   = 337.5 : 150   *divide both sides by 37.5*

   = 9 : 4

➡ **NOTE:** it is important to notice that 9 : 4 = 3^2 : 2^2

EXERCISE 5.3

1 Increase $60 in the following ratios
     a   5 : 3   b   7 : 4   c   13 : 12   d   11 : 8

2 Decrease 45 kg in the following ratios
     a   4 : 9   b   11 : 15   c   2 : 3   d   4 : 5

3 One year a farmer grows 5000 kg of potatoes.
   The next year he uses a fertiliser to increase the total mass of potatoes that he grows.
   The mass of potatoes that he grows increases in the ratio 5 : 4
   Calculate the new mass of potatoes that he grows.

4 Robert runs in an 800-metres race and he takes 2 minutes 15 seconds.
   He trains hard for his next competition to try to improve the time that he takes.
   He decreases the time he takes in the ratio 13 : 15
   Calculate the new time that he takes to complete the race.

5 A car manufacturer produces 480 cars a week.
   The demand for new cars increases so the car manufacturer increases the number of
   cars that are produced each week in the ratio 7 : 6
   Calculate the new number of cars produced each week.

6 Daisy has a mass of 120 kg.
   She is told that she must diet.
   She diets and decrease her mass in the ratio 7 : 8
   Calculate her new mass.

7 A shop has a sale and reduces the cost of a computer in the ratio 23 : 25
   The original cost of the computer was $1800.
   Calculate the sale price of the computer.

8 A rectangle measures 6 cm by 8 cm.
   The lengths of the sides of the rectangle are increased in the ratio 5 : 4
     a   What are the lengths of the new rectangle?
     b   What is the area of   i   the new rectangle   ii   the original rectangle?
     c   Write down and simplify the following ratio
          the area of the new rectangle : the area of the original rectangle.

9 A cuboid measures 6 cm by 15 cm by 21 cm.
   The lengths of the sides of the cuboid are increased in the ratio 4 : 3
     a   What are the measurements of the new cuboid?
     b   What is the volume of   i   the new cuboid   ii   the original cuboid?
     c   Write down and simplify the following ratio
          the volume of the new cuboid : the volume of the original cuboid.

Functions

 Function notation

A **mapping** transforms one set of numbers into a different set of numbers.
A **function** is a special mapping that maps each number of a set to only one number in another set.

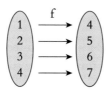

The function f for the diagram above is 'add 3'.
This can be written using function notion in two ways:

$f : x \rightarrow x + 3$ which is read as   f is such that x is mapped to $x + 3$
or $f(x) = x + 3$ which is read as   f of $x = x + 3$

$f(1) = 4$ means that the function f maps the number 1 to the number 4.
$f(2) = 5$ means that the function f maps the number 2 to the number 5.

EXAMPLE

If $f(x) = x^2 + 5x$ Find   **a** $f(6)$ **b** $f(-4)$

a   f is the function that squares the number and then adds
5 lots of the number, so
$f(6) = 6^2 + 5 \times 6$
$= 36 + 30$
$= 66$

b $f(-4) = (-4)^2 + (5 \times -4)$
$= 16 + -20$
$= -4$

Sometimes you have to work in reverse.

EXAMPLE

If $f(x) = 3x + 4$.   Find the value of x for which $f(x) = 25$.

Replace $f(x)$ in the function $f(x) = 3x + 4$ by the number 25.
$3x + 4 = 25$
$3x = 21$
$x = 7$

➡ **CHECK:**
$3 \times 7 + 4 = 25$ ✓

EXERCISE 5.4

1 $f(x) = 2x + 3$. Find the value of
  a $f(4)$ b $f(-6)$ c $f\left(\dfrac{1}{2}\right)$ d $f(0)$

2 $f(x) = 5 - 3x$. Find the value of
  a $f(8)$ b $f(-4)$ c $f\left(\dfrac{1}{2}\right)$ d $f\left(-\dfrac{1}{2}\right)$

3 $f(x) = x^2 + 3x$. Find the value of
  a $f(2)$ b $f(-3)$ c $f(0)$ d $f\left(\dfrac{1}{2}\right)$

4 $f(x) = 2x^2 + x - 5$. Find the value of
  a $f(3)$ b $f(-1)$ c $f\left(\dfrac{1}{2}\right)$ d $f(0)$

5 $f(x) = x^3 + 2$. Find the value of
  a $f(4)$ b $f(-2)$ c $f\left(\dfrac{1}{2}\right)$ d $f(0)$

6 $f(x) = \dfrac{3x^2 + 1}{4}$. Find the value of

  a $f(4)$ b $f(-6)$ c $f\left(\dfrac{1}{2}\right)$ d $f(0)$

7 $g(x) = 5x - 2$. Find the value of x when $g(x) = 13$

8 $f(x) = x^2 + 2$. Find the values of x when $f(x) = 38$

9 $f(x) = \dfrac{1}{2x + 4}$. Find the value of x when $f(x) = 2$

10 $f(x) = \dfrac{5}{2x + 3}$. Find the value of x when $f(x) = -2$

11 $f(x) = 3x - 2$ and $g(x) = 4x + 1$.
Find the value of x such that $f(x) = g(x)$.

TOP TIP

Put the two functions equal to
each other and solve to find x.

12 $f(x) = x^2 + 7x$ and $g(x) = x^2 - x + 4$.
Find the value of x such that $f(x) = g(x)$.

13 $f(x) = x^2 + 3x - 8$ and $g(x) = 3x + 1$. Find the values of x such that $f(x) = g(x)$.

14 $f(x) = \dfrac{1}{x + 2}$ and $g(x) = \dfrac{3}{2x - 1}$. Find the value of x such that $f(x) = g(x)$.

Composite functions

When one function is followed by another function, the resulting function is called a **composite function**.

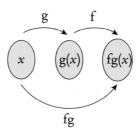

fg (x) means the function g acts on x first, then f acts on the result.

EXAMPLE

$f(x) = x^2 \quad g(x) = x + 5$
Find   **a**   fg (3)   **b**   fg (−7)   **c**   fg (x)

a   fg (3)
     $= f(8)$ *g acts on 3 first and g(3) = 3 + 5 = 8*
     $= 8^2$ *f is the function 'square'*
     $= 64$

b   fg (−7)
     $= f(-2)$ *g acts on −7 first and g (−7) = −7 + 5 = −2*
     $= (-2)^2 = 4$ *f is the function 'square'*

c   fg (x)
     $= f(x + 5)$ *g acts on x first and g (x) = x + 5*
     $= (x + 5)^2$ *f is the function 'square'*

EXAMPLE

$f(x) = 2x + 1 \quad g(x) = x^2 + 3$
Find   **a**   fg (x)   **b**   gf (x)   **c**   ff (x)

a   fg (x)
     $= f(x^2 + 3)$ *g acts on x first and g(x) = x² + 3*
     $= 2(x^2 + 3) + 1$ *f is the function 'double and add 1'*
     $= 2x^2 + 7$

b   gf (x)
     $= g(2x + 1)$ *f acts on x first and f(x) = 2x + 1*
     $= (2x + 1)^2 + 3$ *g is the function 'square and add 3'*
     $= 4x^2 + 4x + 1 + 3$ *(2x + 1)² = (2x + 1)(2x + 1) = 4x² + 2x + 2x + 1*
     $= 4x^2 + 4x + 4$

c   ff (x)
     $= f(2x + 1)$ *f acts on x first and f(x) = 2x + 1*
     $= 2(2x + 1) + 1$ *f is the function 'double and add 1'*
     $= 4x + 3$

EXERCISE 5.5

1 $f(x) = 2x$ and $g(x) = x - 8$ Find   a $fg(5)$ b $gf(5)$

2 $f(x) = 3x + 1$ and $g(x) = 2 - 3x$ Find   a $fg(4)$ b $gf(4)$

3 $f(x) = x - 3$ and $g(x) = x^2$ Find   a $fg(-2)$ b $gf(-2)$

4 $f(x) = 5 + \dfrac{6}{x}$ and $g(x) = x - 4$ Find   a $fg(1)$ b $gf(1)$

5 $f(x) = \dfrac{4}{x+1}$ and $g(x) = \dfrac{1}{x-3}$ Find   a $fg(3)$ b $gf(3)$

6 $f(x) = (x+1)^2$, $g(x) = 3 - x$ and $h(x) = \dfrac{1}{x-4}$
   Find   a $f(-4)$ b $gf(2)$ c $fh(6)$ d $fgh(5)$ e $ff(-2)$

7 $p : x \to x - 5$, $q : x \to \dfrac{x}{2}$ and $r : x \to x^2 + 3$
   Find   a $q(-12)$ b $qr(5)$ c $pq(-4)$ d $pqr(6)$ e $qq(3)$

8 If $f(x) = 2x + 3$ and $g(x) = 2x - 3$, match these cards

   a $fg(x)$ b $gf(x)$ c $gg(x)$ d $ff(x)$

   A $4x + 3$ B $4x - 9$ C $4x + 9$ D $4x - 3$

9 $f(x) = x - 3$ and $g(x) = x + 8$
   Find   a $fg(x)$ b $gf(x)$ c $ff(x)$

10 $p(x) = 2x + 1$ and $q(x) = x - 5$
    Find   a $qp(x)$ b $pq(x)$ c $pp(x)$

11 $f(x) = x^2 + 3$ and $g(x) = 5x$
    Find   a $gf(x)$ b $fg(x)$ c $gg(x)$

12 $p(x) = \dfrac{3}{x-2}$ and $q(x) = x + 1$
    Find   a $pq(x)$ b $qp(x)$

13 $f(x) = x + 6$ and $g(x) = 3x$
    Find x if $fg(x) = 27$

14 $f(x) = 2x - 3$ and $g(x) = \dfrac{x}{5}$
    Find x if $gf(x) = 6$

15 $f(x) = x^2 + 2$ and $g(x) = \dfrac{1}{x-2}$
    Find x if $gf(x) = 4$

Inverse functions

The inverse of a function $f(x)$ is the function that undoes what $f(x)$ has done.
The inverse of the function $f(x)$ is written as $f^{-1}(x)$.

If $f(x) = x + 4$ then $f^{-1}(x) = x - 4$
If $f(x) = x - 5$ then $f^{-1}(x) = x + 5$
If $f(x) = 2x$ then $f^{-1}(x) = \dfrac{x}{2}$

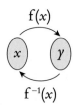

For many straightforward functions the inverse can be found using a flow chart.
The flow chart for finding the inverse of the function $f(x) = \dfrac{3x+1}{4}$ is

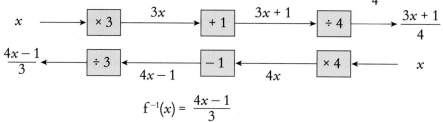

$$f^{-1}(x) = \frac{4x-1}{3}$$

You can also find the inverse of the function $f(x) = \dfrac{3x+1}{4}$ using an algebraic method:

Step 1: Write the function as $y =$ $\longrightarrow$ $y = \dfrac{3x+1}{4}$

Step 2: Interchange the x and y variables. $\longrightarrow$ $x = \dfrac{3y+1}{4}$

Step 3: Rearrange to make y the subject. $\longrightarrow$ $x = \dfrac{3y+1}{4}$

$$4x = 3y + 1$$
$$4x - 1 = 3y$$
$$y = \frac{4x-1}{3}$$

➡ CHECK:

$f(5) = \dfrac{3 \times 5 + 1}{4} = \dfrac{15+1}{4} = 4$

$f^{-1}(4) = \dfrac{4 \times 4 - 1}{3} = \dfrac{16-1}{3} = 5$

$$f^{-1}(x) = \frac{4x-1}{3}$$

EXAMPLE

Find the inverse of the function $f(x) = \dfrac{5}{x-2}$, $x \neq 2$.

Step 1: $y = \dfrac{5}{x-2}$ $\longrightarrow$ Step 2: $x = \dfrac{5}{y-2}$ $\longrightarrow$ Step 3: $x(y-2) = 5$
$$xy - 2x = 5$$
$$xy = 2x + 5$$
$$y = \frac{2x+5}{x}$$

➡ CHECK:

$f(7) = \dfrac{5}{7-2} = \dfrac{5}{5} = 1$

$f^{-1}(1) = \dfrac{2 \times 1 + 5}{1} = \dfrac{7}{1} = 7$

$$f^{-1}(x) = \frac{2x+5}{x}$$

EXERCISE 5.6

1 Write down the inverse of these functions.

a $f(x) = x + 2$
b $f(x) = x - 7$
c $f(x) = 22 + x$
d $f(x) = x - 0.5$

e $f(x) = 3x$
f $f(x) = 8x$
g $f(x) = \dfrac{x}{4}$
h $f(x) = \dfrac{x}{6}$

2 Find the inverse of these functions.

a $f(x) = 2x - 5$
b $f(x) = 3x + 8$
c $f(x) = 5x - 2$
d $f(x) = 3 + 4x$

e $f(x) = 3(x + 2)$
f $f(x) = 4(x - 7)$
g $f(x) = 2(x - 10)$
h $f(x) = 2(5 + x)$

i $f(x) = 2(5x + 4)$
j $f(x) = 3(5 - 2x)$
k $f(x) = 4(7 - 3x)$
l $f(x) = 3(2x - 9)$

m $f(x) = \dfrac{x - 2}{4}$
n $f(x) = \dfrac{x + 6}{5}$
o $f(x) = \dfrac{2x - 3}{4}$
p $f(x) = \dfrac{5 - 3x}{6}$

3 Find the inverse of these functions.

a $f(x) = \dfrac{5}{x} - 3$
b $f(x) = \dfrac{3}{x} + 2$
c $f(x) = \dfrac{6}{x} - 7$
d $f(x) = 4 - \dfrac{5}{x}$

e $f(x) = \dfrac{2}{3 + x}$
f $f(x) = \dfrac{4}{2x + 1}$
g $f(x) = \dfrac{3}{2x - 5}$
h $f(x) = \dfrac{6}{3 - 2x}$

i $f(x) = \dfrac{2x + 1}{x - 3}$
j $f(x) = \dfrac{x - 7}{2x + 5}$
k $f(x) = \dfrac{x + 6}{x - 8}$
l $f(x) = \dfrac{1 - 2x}{3 - 4x}$

4 Find the inverse of these functions.

a $f(x) = (x + 3)^3$
b $f(x) = (x - 5)^3$

c $f(x) = (2x + 7)^3$
d $f(x) = (5 - 3x)^3$

5 If $f(x) = 2x + 3$, find

a $f^{-1}(0)$
b $f^{-1}(7)$
c $f^{-1}(2)$

6 If $f(x) = 6 - 5x$, find

a $f^{-1}(4)$
b $f^{-1}(-2)$
c $f^{-1}(6)$

7 If $f(x) = 2x - 1$, solve the equation $f(x) = f^{-1}(x)$

8 If $f(x) = 3x + 2$, solve the equation $f(x) = f^{-1}(x)$

9 An important result to remember is: $f^{-1}f(x) = ff^{-1}(x) = x$. This is because f^{-1} undoes what f has done. So if you have the function $f(x) = 3x - 1$ and you are asked to write down the value of $f^{-1}f(5)$ the answer is 5. Similarly $ff^{-1}(2) = 2$

a If $f(x) = 2x - 9$, write down the value of $f^{-1}f(3)$

b If $f(x) = 2(5x - 11)$, write down the value of $f^{-1}f(2.5)$

c If $f(x) = \dfrac{2x - 9}{3x + 4}$, write down the value of $ff^{-1}(-29)$

UNIT 5

Factorising 2

 A **quadratic** expression is an expression of the form $ax^2 + bx + c$ where a, b and c are numbers and $a \neq 0$.

Examples of quadratic expressions are $3x^2 - 5x + 4$ $2x^2 - 6x$ $x^2 - 9$

Factorising quadratic expressions of the form $ax^2 + bx$

Reminder: $x^2 + 3x = x(x + 3)$

$5x - x^2 = x(5 - x)$

$6x^2 - 4x = 2x(3x - 2)$

Factorising quadratic expressions of the form $x^2 + bx + c$

Factorising is the reverse of expanding.

To factorise you need to find two numbers that multiply to give the **constant** and also add to give the **coefficient** of x.

Expand

$(x + 2)(x + 5) = x^2 + 7x + 10$

Factorise $2 + 5$ 2×5

EXAMPLE

Factorise   **a** $x^2 + 10x + 16$ **b** $x^2 - 2x - 15$ **c** $x^2 - 5x + 6$

a $x^2 + 10x + 16$

*List the pairs of numbers that **multiply** to give 16 and then check to see which pair **add** to give 10.*

1 and 16   〔2 and 8〕   4 and 4

so

$x^2 + 10x + 16 = (x + 2)(x + 8)$

➡ **CHECK:**

$(x + 2)(x + 8) = x^2 + 8x + 2x + 16 = x^2 + 10x + 16 \checkmark$

b $x^2 - 2x - 15$

*List the pairs of numbers that **multiply** to give −15 and then check to see which pair **add** to give −2.*

1 and −15   〔3 and −5〕 −1 and 15   −3 and 5

so

$x^2 - 2x - 15 = (x + 3)(x - 5)$

➡ **CHECK:**

$(x + 3)(x - 5) = x^2 - 5x + 3x - 15 = x^2 - 2x - 15 \checkmark$

c $x^2 - 5x + 6$

*List the pairs of numbers that **multiply** to give 6 and then check to see which pair **add** to give −5.*

1 and 6   2 and 3   −1 and −6   〔−2 and −3〕

so

$x^2 - 5x + 6 = (x - 2)(x - 3)$

➡ **CHECK:**

$(x - 2)(x - 3) = x^2 - 3x - 2x + 6 = x^2 - 5x + 6 \checkmark$

EXERCISE 5.7

1 Factorise these expressions.

a $x^2 + 5x$ b $x^2 - 7x$ c $3x^2 - 15x$ d $12x - 18x^2$

2 Factorise these expressions.

a $x^2 + 4x + 3$ b $x^2 + 7x + 10$ c $x^2 + 2x + 1$ d $x^2 + 9x + 18$

e $x^2 + 6x + 8$ f $x^2 + 6x + 5$ g $x^2 + 5x + 6$ h $x^2 + 20x + 36$

i $x^2 + 10x + 25$ j $x^2 + 13x + 36$ k $x^2 + 9x + 20$ l $x^2 + 9x + 14$

m $x^2 + 10x + 21$ n $x^2 + 11x + 28$ o $x^2 + 22x + 21$ p $x^2 + 8x + 15$

3 Factorise these expressions.

a $x^2 + x - 6$ b $x^2 - 5x - 6$ c $x^2 + 4x - 21$ d $x^2 - 6x - 16$

e $x^2 + 6x - 16$ f $x^2 - 15x - 16$ g $x^2 + 6x - 7$ h $x^2 - 3x - 40$

i $x^2 + 17x - 38$ j $x^2 - 8x - 33$ k $x^2 + 7x - 30$ l $x^2 - 2x - 15$

m $x^2 + x - 20$ n $x^2 - 19x - 20$ o $x^2 + 20x - 21$ p $x^2 - 6x - 7$

4 Factorise these expressions.

a $x^2 - 7x + 10$ b $x^2 - 16x + 15$ c $x^2 - 10x + 21$ d $x^2 - 8x + 12$

e $x^2 - 11x + 10$ f $x^2 - 7x + 12$ g $x^2 - 8x + 7$ h $x^2 - 6x + 9$

i $x^2 - 11x + 30$ j $x^2 - 11x + 28$ k $x^2 - 22x + 21$ l $x^2 - 8x + 15$

m $x^2 - 9x + 14$ n $x^2 - 10x + 24$ o $x^2 - 14x + 13$ p $x^2 - 15x + 26$

5

> You may need to take out a common factor before using double brackets.
>
> $2x^2 - 10x - 72 \longrightarrow 2(x^2 - 5x - 36) \longrightarrow 2(x - 9)(x + 4)$
>
>   Common factor   Double brackets

Factorise these expressions.

a $2x^2 + 12x + 16$ b $3x^2 - 3x - 16$ c $2x^2 - 8x - 10$ d $3x^2 - 36x + 33$

e $4x^2 + 16x + 12$ f $2x^2 + 20x + 18$ g $2x^2 - 12x + 18$ h $3x^2 - 15x - 108$

i $5x^2 - 20x - 25$ j $4x^2 + 32x + 60$ k $7x^2 + 21x + 14$ l $2x^2 + 4x - 70$

6

> To simplify algebraic fractions you must first factorise and then cancel any common factors.
>
> $$\frac{x^2 + 9x + 14}{x + 7} = \frac{\cancel{(x+7)}(x+2)}{\cancel{x+7}} = x + 2$$

Simplify these algebraic fractions.

a $\dfrac{x^2 + 4x + 3}{x + 1}$ b $\dfrac{x^2 + 8x + 15}{x + 5}$ c $\dfrac{x^2 + 11x + 18}{x + 2}$ d $\dfrac{x^2 + 13x + 22}{x + 2}$

e $\dfrac{x^2 + 2x - 3}{x + 3}$ f $\dfrac{x^2 - 5x - 36}{x - 9}$ g $\dfrac{x - 1}{x^2 + 23x - 24}$ h $\dfrac{x^2 + 5x + 6}{x^2 - 2x - 8}$

i $\dfrac{x^2 - 3x - 40}{x^2 + 2x - 15}$ j $\dfrac{x^2 + 3x - 28}{x^2 - 9x + 20}$ k $\dfrac{x^2 - 5x}{x^2 + x - 30}$ l $\dfrac{x^2 + x - 2}{x^2 + 2x}$

The difference of two squares

Expand

$$(x + 5)(x - 5) \;=\; x^2 - 25$$

Factorise

In general $x^2 - a^2 = (x + a)(x - a)$
This result is called the **difference of two squares**.

EXAMPLE

Factorise these expressions   **a** $x^2 - 81$ **b** $25x^2 - 36$

a $x^2 - 81 = (x + 9)(x - 9)$

➡ **CHECK:**
$(x + 9)(x - 9) = x^2 - 9x + 9x - 81 = x^2 - 81\checkmark$

b $25x^2 - 36 = (5x + 6)(5x - 6)$

➡ **CHECK:**
$(5x + 6)(5x - 6) = 25x^2 - 30x + 30x - 36$
$= 25x^2 - 36\checkmark$

Factorising expressions of the form $ax^2 + bx + c$

Factorising quadratic expressions with more than one x^2 is difficult.
To factorise $2x^2 + 7x + 3$:

- first look at the x^2 term, $2x^2$ must come from $2x \times x$, so use $(2x + ?)(x + ?)$
- next look at the constant term, 3 must come from 3×1 or 1×3
- expand both options, $(2x + 3)(x + 1)$ and $(2x + 1)(x + 3)$, to find which is correct.
$(2x + 3)(x + 1) = 2x^2 + 2x + 3x + 3 = 2x^2 + 5x + 3$ ✗
$(2x + 1)(x + 3) = 2x^2 + 6x + x + 3 = 2x^2 + 7x + 3$ ✓
So $2x^2 + 7x + 3 = (2x + 1)(x + 3)$

EXAMPLE

Factorise $3x^2 - 10x + 8$

$3x^2$ comes from $3x \times x$, so use $(3x + ?)(x + ?)$
-8 comes from 1×-8 or -1×8 or 2×-4 or -2×4
$(3x + 1)(x - 8) = 3x^2 - 24x + x - 8 = 3x^2 - 23x - 8$ ✗
$(3x - 1)(x + 8) = 3x^2 + 24x - x - 8 = 3x^2 + 23x - 8$ ✗
$(3x + 2)(x - 4) = 3x^2 - 12x + 2x - 8 = 3x^2 - 10x - 8$ ✓
$(3x - 2)(x + 4) = 3x^2 + 12x - 2x - 8 = 3x^2 + 10x - 8$ ✗
So $3x^2 - 10x - 8 = (3x + 2)(x - 4)$

EXERCISE 5.8

1 Factorise these expressions.

 a $x^2 - 81$ b $y^2 - 1$ c $x^2 - 64$ d $a^2 - 36$

 e $y^2 - 100$ f $16 - a^2$ g $x^2 - y^2$ h $144 - x^2$

 i $4x^2 - 9$ j $16y^2 - 1$ k $25x^2 - 36$ l $9 - 16x^2$

 m $100x^2 - 81y^2$ n $25a^2 - 49b^2$ o $81x^2 - 49y^2$ p $121x^2 - 100$

2 Factorise these expressions.

 a $2x^2 - 50$ b $2y^2 - 8$ c $3x^2 - 3$

 d $5y^2 - 80$ e $3y^2 - 192$ f $4x^2 - 4y^2$

 g $2x^2 - 242$ h $6n^2 - 600$ i $75y^2 - 108$

TOP TIP

Take out a common factor first.

3 Factorise $x^4 - y^4$

TOP TIP

You will need to factorise twice.

4 Factorise these expressions.

 a $2x^2 + 11x + 5$ b $2x^2 + 5x + 3$ c $2x^2 + 15x + 7$ d $2x^2 + 13x + 11$

 e $3x^2 + 5x + 2$ f $3x^2 + 16x + 5$ g $3x^2 + 10x + 3$ h $3x^2 + 10x + 7$

 i $2x^2 + 5x - 3$ j $3x^2 + 2x - 5$ k $3x^2 - 22x + 7$ l $5x^2 - 2x - 3$

 m $7x^2 - 9x + 2$ n $5x^2 + 3x - 2$ o $11x^2 - 21x - 2$ p $2x^2 - 15x + 13$

5 Factorise these expressions.

 a $2x^2 + 11x + 12$ b $2x^2 + 9x + 10$ c $3x^2 + 14x + 8$ d $7x^2 + 38x + 15$

 e $6x^2 + 7x + 2$ f $6x^2 + 11x + 5$ g $8x^2 + 14x + 3$ h $10x^2 + 71x + 7$

 i $3x^2 + 7x - 6$ j $5x^2 + 22x + 8$ k $2x^2 - 11x + 12$ l $7x^2 + 26x - 8$

 m $5x^2 + 21x - 20$ n $3x^2 + x - 10$ o $2x^2 - 9x + 10$ p $3x^2 + 14x + 16$

6 Factorise these expressions.

 a $4x^2 + 2x - 42$ b $6x^2 + 21x + 9$ c $6x^2 + 16x + 8$

 d $12x^2 + 28x + 8$ e $16x^2y - 20xy - 6y$ f $6x^3 - 10x^2 - 4x$

TOP TIP

Take out a common factor first.

7 Simplify these algebraic fractions.

 a $\dfrac{2x^2 + 7x + 3}{x^2 + 3x}$ b $\dfrac{3x^2 + 5x - 2}{x^2 - 4}$ c $\dfrac{2x^2 + 3x - 20}{x^2 + 6x + 8}$

 d $\dfrac{4x^2 - 9}{2x^2 - x - 3}$ e $\dfrac{x^2 - 5x}{2x^2 - 7x - 15}$ f $\dfrac{2x^2 - 50}{3x^2 + 7x - 40}$

TOP TIP

Factorise the numerator and the denominator before cancelling factors.

8 Factorise $(3x + 2)^4 - 4(3x + 2)^2$

```
KEY WORDS
    quadratic
coefficient, constant
difference of two squares
```

Cubic graphs

THIS SECTION WILL SHOW YOU HOW TO
- Recognise cubic graphs
- Draw cubic graphs
- Use cubic graphs in practical situations

$y = ax^3 + bx^2 + cx + d$ is called a **cubic function** where a, b, c and d are constants and $a \neq 0$.
The simplest cubic function is $y = x^3$.
The curve has rotational symmetry of order 2 about the origin.

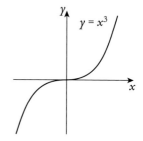

EXAMPLE

Draw the graph of $y = x^3 - 5x + 3$ for $-3 \leq x \leq 3$.
Use your graph to find the values of x when $y = 5$.

First work out a table of values for the graph.

When $x = -3$, $\quad y = (-3)^3 - (5 \times -3) + 3$
$\quad\quad\quad\quad\quad\quad y = -27 - -15 + 3$
$\quad\quad\quad\quad\quad\quad y = -27 + 15 + 3$
$\quad\quad\quad\quad\quad\quad y = -9$ etc

x	-3	-2	-1	0	1	2	3
y	-9	5	7	3	-1	1	15

Use your table of values to draw the graph of the function.

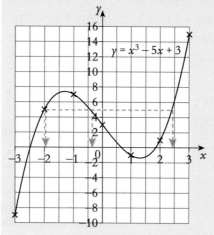

To find the values of x when $y = 5$ you need to draw the line $y = 5$ and then find the x coordinates of the three points where the line intersects the curve.

The graphs intersect in three places.
$x = -2$ $\quad$ $x = -0.4$ $\quad$ $x = 2.4$

The general shape of a cubic graph depends on the value of a

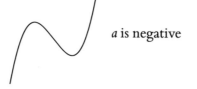

a is positive $\quad\quad\quad\quad\quad\quad$ a is negative

EXERCISE 5.9

1 Copy and complete the table for each of these cubic functions.
Draw the graph of each function.

a $y = x^3 + 1$

x	-3	-2	-1	0	1	2	3
y					9		

b $y = 2 - x^3$

x	-3	-2	-1	0	1	2	3
y			3				

c $y = -x^3$

x	-3	-2	-1	0	1	2	3
y						-8	

d $y = x^3 + 2x$

x	-3	-2	-1	0	1	2	3
y					3		

e $y = 3x^2 - x^3$

x	-2	-1	0	1	2	3	4
y				4			

f $y = x^3 - 2x^2 - 4x$

x	-2	-1	0	1	2	3	4
y		1					

g $y = x^3 - 4x^2 + 2$

x	-1	0	1	2	3	4
y				-6		

h $y = \frac{1}{2}x^3 - 3x^2 - 2$

x	-6	-5	-4	-3	-2	-1	0	1	2
y					10				

2 a Copy and complete the table of values for $y = x^3 + 2$

x	-3	-2	-1	0	1	2	3
y			1				

b Draw the graph of $y = x^3 + 2$
c Use your graph to find the value of x when $y = 7$
d By drawing a tangent to the graph estimate the gradient of the curve when $x = 1$.

3 a Copy and complete the table of values for
$y = \frac{1}{2}x^3 - 2x^2 + 6$

x	-2	-1	0	1	2	3	4
y					2		

b Draw the graph of $y = \frac{1}{2}x^3 - 2x^2 + 6$
c Use your graph to find the values of x when $y = 4$
d By drawing a tangent to the graph estimate the gradient of the curve when $x = 2$.

4 The function $f(x) = \frac{1}{2}x^3$, draw the graph of $y = f(x)$ for $-3 \le x \le 3$
On the same axes draw the graph of $y = 2x$
Write down the coordinates of the points of intersection of the curve and the line.

5 Draw the graph of $y = x^3 - 4x^2 + 3$ for $-1 \le x \le 4$
On the same axes draw the graph of $x + y = 1$
Write down the coordinates of the points of intersection of the curve and the line.

6 The function $f(x) = x^3 - 3x^2$, draw the graph of $y = f(x)$ for $-2 \le x \le 4$
Write down the values of x where the graph has negative gradient.

Practical applications of cubic graphs

A square piece of card has sides of length 20 cm.
A square of length x cm is removed from each of the four corners of the card.
The remaining piece of card is then folded to make an open box as shown below.

a Show that the volume, V cm³, of the box is given by the formula
$$V = 400x - 80x^2 + 4x^3$$
b Draw the graph of $V = 400x - 80x^2 + 4x^3$ for $0 \leq x \leq 10$.
c Use your graph to estimate the maximum possible volume of the box
and the value of x that gives the maximum volume.

a $y = 20 - 2x$ Volume $= y \times y \times x$
$$= (20 - 2x)(20 - 2x)x \qquad \textit{expand brackets}$$
$$= (400 - 40x - 40x + 4x^2)x$$
$$= 400x - 80x^2 + 4x^3$$

b

x	0	1	2	3	4	5	6	7	8	9	10
V	0	324	512	588	576	500	384	252	128	36	0

c Maximum volume ≈ 590 cm³ when $x \approx 3.3$

EXERCISE 5.10

1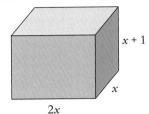

The rectangular tank has sides of length $2x$, x and $(x + 1)$ m.

a Show that the volume, V cm^3, of the tank is given by the formula
   $$V = 2x^3 + 2x^2$$

b Copy and complete the table of values.

x	0	0.2	0.4	0.6	0.8	1
V	0					

c Draw the graph of $V = 2x^3 + 2x^2$ for $0 \leq x \leq 1$

d Use your graph to estimate the value of x that gives a volume of 2 m^3.

2 A rectangular piece of card has sides of length 20 cm and 16 cm.
A square of length x cm is removed from each of the four corners of the card.
The remaining piece of card is then folded to make an open box as shown below.

a Show that the volume, V cm^3, of the box is given by the formula
   $$V = 320x - 72x^2 + 4x^3$$

b Copy and complete the table of values.

x	0	1	2	3	4	5	6	7	8
V	0								

c Draw the graph of $V = 320x - 72x^2 + 4x^3$ for $0 \leq x \leq 8$

d Use your graph to estimate the maximum possible volume of
  the box and the value of x that gives the maximum volume.

KEY WORDS

cubic function

UNIT 5

Surface area and volume 2

 Pyramids

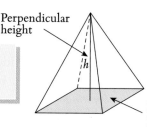

Volume of a pyramid = $\frac{1}{3}$ × base area × perpendicular height

Surface area = sum of areas of all the faces of the pyramid

EXAMPLE

ABCDE is a square-based pyramid.

AB = BC = 6 cm.

The perpendicular height of the pyramid is 4 cm.

P is the mid-point of BC and O is the middle of the base.

  a Calculate the volume of the pyramid.

  b Calculate the length of EP.

  c Calculate the area of △ BCE.

  d Calculate the surface area of the pyramid.

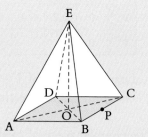

---

a Volume of pyramid = $\frac{1}{3}$ × base area × perpendicular height

$$= \frac{1}{3} \times (6 \times 6) \times 4$$

$$= 48 \text{ cm}^3$$

b Using Pythagoras on △ EOP: $EP^2 = 4^2 + 3^2$

$$EP^2 = 25$$

$$EP = 5 \text{ cm}$$

c Area of △ BCE = $\frac{1}{2}$ × base × height

$$= \frac{1}{2} \times 6 \times 5 = 15 \text{ cm}^2$$

d Surface area = sum of all the faces of the pyramid

$$= \text{area of base} + \text{area of four triangular faces}$$

$$= 36 + (4 \times 15)$$

$$= 96 \text{ cm}^2$$

Net of pyramid

EXERCISE 5.11

1 Find the volume of each of these pyramids.
The base area (A cm^2) and the perpendicular height (h cm) are given for each pyramid.

a

A = 15, h = 8

b

A = 11, h = 9

c

A = 28, h = 6

d

A = 12, h = 5

2 A pyramid has a square base of side 8 cm.
The perpendicular height is 6 cm.
Calculate the volume of the pyramid.

3 A pyramid has a rectangular base of side 6 cm and 10 cm.
The perpendicular height is 7 cm.
Calculate the volume of the pyramid.

4 A pyramid has an equilateral triangular base of side 5 cm.
The perpendicular height is 4 cm.
Calculate the volume of the pyramid.

5 A pyramid has a square base of side x cm.
The perpendicular height is x cm.
The volume of the pyramid is 72 cm^3. Find the value of x.

6 The Great Pyramid of Khutu in Egypt is a square-based pyramid.
The square base has sides of length 241 m.
The perpendicular height of the pyramid is 153 m.
Calculate the volume of the pyramid.
Give your answer in standard form correct to 3 s.f.

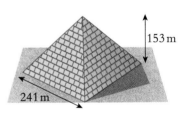

153 m

241 m

7 The Louvre Pyramid in France is a large glass and
metal square-based pyramid.
The square base has sides of length 35.42 m.
The perpendicular height of the pyramid is 21.64 m.
Calculate the volume of the pyramid.
Give your answer in standard form correct to 3 s.f.

21.64 m

35.42 m

8 A crystal is in the form of a **regular octahedron**.
The edges of the octahedron are all 4 mm long.
Calculate the volume of the crystal.

4 mm

UNIT 5

9 A square-based pyramid has a base of side 8 cm and a height of 12 cm.
A square-based pyramid of height 6 cm is removed by cutting parallel to the base, leaving the solid shown.
Calculate the volume of the **truncated pyramid**.

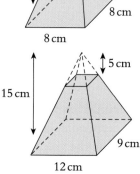

10 A rectangular-based pyramid has a base of sides 12 cm and 9 cm and a height of 15 cm.
A rectangular-based pyramid of height 5 cm is removed by cutting parallel to the base, leaving the solid shown.
Calculate the volume of the truncated pyramid.

11 Find the surface area of each of these pyramids.

a
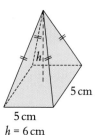
5 cm
5 cm
h = 6 cm

b
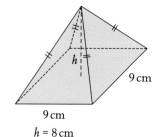
9 cm
9 cm
h = 8 cm

c
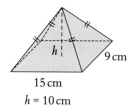
2 cm
2 cm
h = 1.5 cm

d
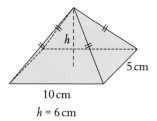
5 cm
10 cm
h = 6 cm

e
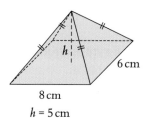
6 cm
8 cm
h = 5 cm

f
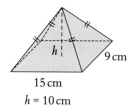
9 cm
15 cm
h = 10 cm

12 Find the surface area of these **regular tetrahedrons**.

a

10 cm

b

4.8 cm

TOP TIP

Tetrahedron is the name for a triangular-based pyramid (tetra- for 4 faces).
Regular means that all the sides are the same length so each face is an equilateral triangle.

13 Find the volume of each regular tetrahedron in question 12.

Cones

A **cone** is a pyramid with a circular base.

Volume of a pyramid $= \frac{1}{3} \times$ base area $\times$ perpendicular height

So, Volume of a cone $= \frac{1}{3} \times \pi r^2 \times h$

The surface of a cone is made from a flat circular base and a curved surface.
The curved surface is made from a sector of a circle.

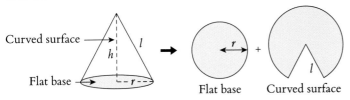

Curved surface

Flat base

Flat base   Curved surface

Volume of a cone $= \frac{1}{3}\pi r^2 h$

Curved surface area of a cone $= \pi r l$, where l is the slant height

Total surface area of cone $= \pi r^2 + \pi r l$

When you make a cut parallel to the base of a cone and remove the top part, the part that is left is called a **frustum**.

Frustum

Volume of frustum = volume of whole cone – volume of smaller cone

EXAMPLE

The cone has base radius 3 cm and
perpendicular height 4 cm.
  a Calculate the volume of the cone.
  b Calculate the curved surface area of the cone.
  c Calculate the total surface area of the cone

4 cm

3 cm

a Volume $= \frac{1}{3} \times \pi r^2 h = \frac{1}{3} \times \pi \times 3^2 \times 4 = 37.7 \text{ cm}^3$

b Curved surface area $= \pi r l$
   (so you must first calculate the slant height, l)
   Using Pythagoras: $l^2 = 3^2 + 4^2$
   $\qquad\qquad\qquad\;\; l^2 = 25$
   $\qquad\qquad\qquad\;\; l = 5$

4 cm

3 cm

   Curved surface area $= \pi r l = \pi \times 3 \times 5 = 47.1 \text{ cm}^2$

c Total surface area $= \pi r^2 + \pi r l = \pi \times 3^2 + 47.1 = 75.4 \text{ cm}^2$

EXERCISE 5.12

1 Calculate the volume of these cones.

a
4 cm
7 cm

b
3 cm
6 cm

c
5 cm
9 cm

2 A solid cone has a base radius of 4 cm.
The volume of the cone is 100 cm³.
Calculate the height of the cone.

3 A solid cone has a height of 12 cm.
The volume of the cone is 250 cm³.
Calculate the radius of the base of the cone.

4 The diagram shows a toy rocket made from
a cylinder and a cone.
Calculate the volume of the toy rocket.

8 cm
10 cm
4 cm

5 A drinking glass is a truncated cone.
Calculate the volume of the drinking glass.

10 cm
15 cm
15 cm

6 Calculate the volume of each of these frustums.

a
3 cm
10 cm
6 cm

b
6 cm
5 cm
8 cm

c
3 cm
6 cm
12 cm

7 The diagram shows a frustum of a cone.
Find an expression in terms of r and h for
the volume of the frustum.

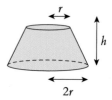
r
h
2r

8 Calculate the **curved** surface area of each of these cones.

a
6 cm
3 cm

b
8 cm
5 cm

c
9 cm
4 cm

9 Calculate the **total** surface area of each of these cones.

a
10 cm
6 cm

b
8 cm
4 cm

c
15 cm
9 cm

10 Each of these sectors forms the curved surface of a cone.
Calculate the curved surface area of each cone.

a
160°
2 cm

b
250°
5 cm

c
143°
8 cm

11 The straight edges of each of these sectors are joined together to make a cone.
Calculate: **i** the curved surface area of each cone,
 ii the radius of the base of each cone,
 iii the height of each cone.

a
138°
6 cm

b
165°
14 cm

c
242°
25 cm

12 Calculate the **total** surface area of each of these solid frustums.

a
5 cm
4 cm
10 cm

b
4 cm
12 cm
12 cm

c
6 cm
10 cm
9 cm

Spheres

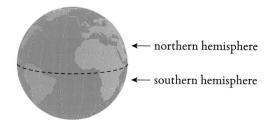

← northern hemisphere

← southern hemisphere

Volume of a **sphere** = $\frac{4}{3}\pi r^3$
Surface area of a sphere = $4\pi r^2$

A **hemisphere** is half a sphere.
The earth is divided into two hemispheres.

EXAMPLE

A football has a radius of 11.1 cm.
Calculate:
a the volume
b the surface area of the football.

a   Volume of football = $\frac{4}{3}\pi r^3 = \frac{4}{3} \times \pi \times 11.1^3 = 5730\,\text{cm}^3$ (to 3 s.f.)

b   Surface area of football = $4\pi r^2 = 4 \times \pi \times 11.1^2 = 1550\,\text{cm}^2$ (to 3 s.f.)

EXAMPLE

A solid hemisphere has radius 6 cm.
Calculate:
a the volume
b the total surface area of the hemisphere.

6 cm

a   Volume = $\frac{1}{2} \times \frac{4}{3}\pi r^3 = \frac{1}{2} \times \frac{4}{3} \times \pi \times 6^3 = 452\,\text{cm}^3$

b   Area of base = $\pi r^2 = \pi \times 6^2 = 36\pi$
    Curved surface area = $\frac{1}{2} \times 4\pi r^2 = \frac{1}{2} \times 4\pi \times 36 = 72\pi$
    Total surface area = area of base + curved surface area
    $\qquad\qquad = 36\pi + 72\pi = 108\pi = 339\,\text{cm}^2$

EXAMPLE

The diagram shows a toy that is made from a cone
on top of a hemisphere.
Calculate the volume of the toy.

3 cm

10 cm

Volume of hemisphere = $\frac{1}{2} \times \frac{4}{3}\pi r^3 = \frac{1}{2} \times \frac{4}{3}\pi \times 5^3 = 261.8\,\text{cm}^3$

Volume of cone = $\frac{1}{3}\pi r^2 h = \frac{1}{3} \times \pi \times 5^2 \times 3 = 78.54\,\text{cm}^3$

Volume of toy = 261.8 + 78.54 = $340\,\text{cm}^3$ (to 3 s.f.)

EXERCISE 5.13

1 Find the volume of each of these spheres.

a
3 cm

b
8 cm

c
5.7 cm

2 Find the surface area of each sphere in question 1.

3 Find the volume of each of these solid hemispheres.

a
4 cm

b
16 cm

c
10 cm

4 Find the total surface area of each of the solid hemispheres in question 3.

5 The volume of a sphere is 432 cm³. Calculate the radius of the sphere.

6 The surface area of a sphere is 500 cm². Calculate the radius of the sphere.

7 A cylindrical tube contains two tennis balls.
The radius of each tennis ball is 3.75 cm.
The tennis balls touch the sides, top and bottom of the tube.
Calculate the volume of empty space inside the tube.

8 A cricket ball is dropped into a cylindrical tank of water.
The ball sinks to the bottom of the tank.
The diameter of the cricket ball is 7.2 cm
The diameter of the cylindrical tank is 15 cm.
Calculate the increase in height of the water in the tank.

9 A solid metal cube of side 8 cm is melted and then recast to make a solid sphere.
Calculate the radius of the sphere.

10 Calculate the volume of these solid shapes.

a
Hemisphere
Cylinder
height 8 cm, radius 6 cm

b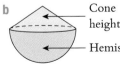
Cone
height 10 cm, radius 14 cm
Hemisphere

11 Calculate the total surface area of the solid shapes in question 10.

Areas of similar shapes

1 cm

2 cm

Area = 2 cm²

enlarge with a length
scale factor of 2

2 cm

4 cm

Area = 8 cm²

The diagram shows that if the **length scale factor** is 2, then the **area scale factor** is 4.

1 cm

2 cm

Area = 2 cm²

enlarge with a length
scale factor of 3

3 cm

6 cm

Area = 18 cm²

The diagram shows that if the length scale factor is 3, then the area scale factor is 9.

General rule: If the length scale factor is k, then the area scale factor is k^2.

EXAMPLE

The two quadrilaterals are similar.
The area of the smaller quadrilateral
is 5 cm².
Find the area of the larger quadrilateral.

2 cm

6 cm

The length scale factor $k = \dfrac{6}{2} = 3$.

The area scale factor $k^2 = 3^2$.

So the area of the larger quadrilateral = $3^2 \times 5 = 45$ cm².

EXAMPLE

The two triangles are similar.
The area of the larger triangle is 10.8 cm².
Find the area of the smaller triangle.

3 cm

2 cm

The length scale factor $k = \dfrac{2}{3}$

The area scale factor $k^2 = \left(\dfrac{2}{3}\right)^2$

So the area of the smaller triangle = $\left(\dfrac{2}{3}\right)^2 \times 10.8 = 4.8$ cm²

EXAMPLE

The two shapes are similar.
The area of the larger shape is 32 cm².
The area of the smaller shape is 8 cm².
Find the value of x.

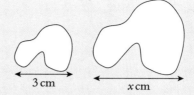

3 cm x cm

The area scale factor $k^2 = \dfrac{32}{8} = 4$.

The length scale factor $k = \sqrt{4} = 2$.
So $x = 2 \times 3 = 6$ cm.

EXERCISE 5.14

In each question the pair of shapes are similar.
The area of each shape is written inside the shape.
Find the value of x for each question.

1

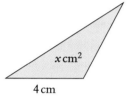

x cm²

4 cm   5 cm²   2 cm

2

15 cm   5 cm

x cm²   10 cm²

3

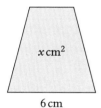

x cm²   12 cm²

6 cm   4 cm

4

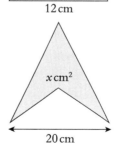

120 cm² x cm²

12 cm   6 cm

5

x cm²

3 cm   99 cm²

9 cm

6

x cm²   12 cm²

20 cm   8 cm

7

108 cm² x cm²

9 cm   4.5 cm

8

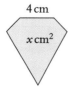

4 cm   8 cm

x cm²   80 cm²

UNIT 5

9

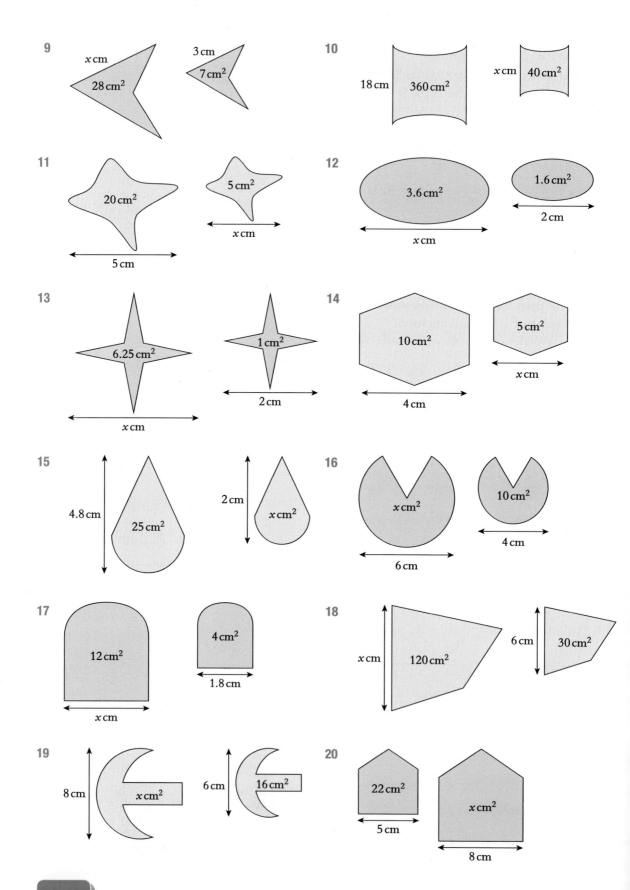

x cm
28 cm²

3 cm
7 cm²

10

18 cm
360 cm²

x cm
40 cm²

11

20 cm²

5 cm

5 cm²

x cm

12

3.6 cm²

x cm

1.6 cm²

2 cm

13

6.25 cm²

x cm

1 cm²

2 cm

14

10 cm²

4 cm

5 cm²

x cm

15

4.8 cm

25 cm²

2 cm

x cm²

16

x cm²

6 cm

10 cm²

4 cm

17

12 cm²

x cm

4 cm²

1.8 cm

18

x cm

120 cm²

6 cm

30 cm²

19

8 cm

x cm²

6 cm

16 cm²

20

22 cm²

5 cm

x cm²

8 cm

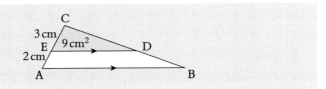

EXAMPLE

Area of △CDE = 9 cm².
a Calculate the area of △ABC
b Calculate the area of ABDE

---

a △ABC and △CDE are similar.
  The length scale factor $k = \dfrac{5}{3}$

  The area scale factor $k^2 = \left(\dfrac{5}{3}\right)^2$

  Area of △ABC = $\left(\dfrac{5}{3}\right)^2 \times 9 = 25$ cm²

b Area of ABDE = area of △ABC − area of △CDE = 25 − 9 = 16 cm²

EXERCISE 5.15

1 Calculate the area of △ABC and the area of ABDE for each of these diagrams.

a

b
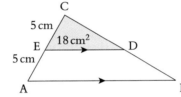

2 Find the value of x in each of these diagrams.

a

b

c

d
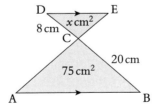

┌ ─ ─ ─ ─ ─ ─ ─ ─ ┐
│   **KEY WORDS**   │
│ length scale factor │
│   area scale factor   │
└ ─ ─ ─ ─ ─ ─ ─ ─ ┘

UNIT 5

Volumes of similar objects

THIS SECTION WILL SHOW YOU HOW TO:
- Find lengths and volumes of similar objects using scale factors

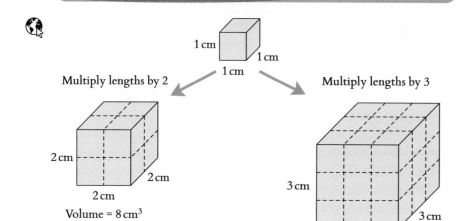

Multiply lengths by 2

2 cm, 2 cm, 2 cm

Volume = 8 cm³

Multiply lengths by 3

3 cm, 3 cm, 3 cm

Volume = 27 cm³

The diagram shows that:
- If the length scale factor is 2, then the **volume scale factor** is 8.
- If the length scale factor is 3, then the volume scale factor is 27.

General rule: If the length scale factor is k, then the volume scale factor is k^3.

EXAMPLE

The two solid hexagonal prisms are similar.
The volume of the smaller prism is 24 cm³
Calculate the volume of the larger prism.

6 cm

12 cm

The length scale factor $k = \dfrac{12}{6} = 2$

The volume scale factor $k^3 = 2^3$

So the volume of the larger prism = $2^3 \times 24 = 192$ cm³.

EXAMPLE

The two cones are similar.
The volume of the larger cone is 54 cm³.
The volume of the smaller cone is 16 cm³.
Find the height of the smaller cone.

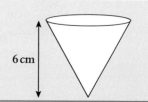

x cm

6 cm

The volume scale factor $k^3 = \dfrac{16}{54} = \dfrac{8}{27}$ and the length scale factor $k = \sqrt[3]{\dfrac{8}{27}} = \dfrac{2}{3}$

So the height of the smaller cone = $\dfrac{2}{3} \times 6 = 4$ cm.

EXERCISE 5.16

In questions 1 to 10 each pair of objects are similar.
The volume of each object is written inside the object.
Find the value of x for each question.

1

$9\,\text{cm}^3$

$3\,\text{cm}$

$x\,\text{cm}^3$

$6\,\text{cm}$

2

$x\,\text{cm}^3$ $5\,\text{cm}$

$600\,\text{cm}^3$ $10\,\text{cm}$

3

$6\,\text{cm}$

$x\,\text{cm}^3$

$8\,\text{cm}^3$ $2\,\text{cm}$

4

$40\,\text{cm}^3$

$5\,\text{cm}$

$x\,\text{cm}^3$

$7.5\,\text{cm}$

5

$6\,\text{cm}$

$189\,\text{cm}^3$

$4\,\text{cm}$

$x\,\text{cm}^3$

6

$100\,\text{cm}^3$

$6\,\text{cm}$

$x\,\text{cm}^3$

$10\,\text{cm}$

7

$1200\,\text{cm}^3$

$12\,\text{cm}$

$150\,\text{cm}^3$

$x\,\text{cm}$

8

$54\,\text{cm}^3$

$x\,\text{cm}$

$16\,\text{cm}^3$

$6\,\text{cm}$

9

$810\,\text{cm}^3$

$12\,\text{cm}$

$x\,\text{cm}^3$

$8\,\text{cm}$

10

$162\,\text{cm}^3$

$30\,\text{cm}$

$48\,\text{cm}^3$

$x\,\text{cm}$

11 The two bottles are similar in shape.
The larger bottle holds 100 mℓ of perfume.
Calculate how many millilitres of perfume the smaller bottle holds.

 10 cm

 5 cm

12 The two bars of chocolate are similar in shape.
The smaller bar has a mass of 150 grams.
Calculate the mass of the larger chocolate bar.

 18 cm

 6 cm

13 The two vases are similar in shape.
The largest vase holds 1.5 litres of water when full.
How much water does the smaller vase hold when full?

 15 cm

 20 cm

14 The two buckets are similar in shape.
The larger bucket holds 10 litres of water when full.
How much water does the smaller bucket hold when full?

 25 cm

 15 cm

15 The two eggs are similar in shape.
Calculate the length of the smaller egg.

mass = 50 g

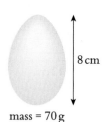 8 cm

mass = 70 g

16 The two shampoo bottles are similar in shape.
Calculate the height of the larger bottle.

500 mℓ

500 mℓ

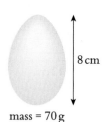 20 cm

300 mℓ

300 mℓ

17 A cylindrical cup has a height of 6 cm and a base radius of 4 cm.
A large cylindrical jug is a similar shape to the cup.
The jug is full of mango juice.
The cup can be filled with mango juice from the jug exactly 125 times.
Calculate the height and radius of the jug.

18 Two vases are similar in shape.
The ratio of their heights is 3:2
   a The volume of the larger vase is 810 cm³.
      Calculate the volume of the smaller vase.
   b The surface area of the smaller vase is 240 cm².
      Calculate the surface area of the larger vase.

19 Two similar objects have a surface area of 4 cm² and 9 cm².
The mass of the smaller object is 200 grams.
Find the mass of the larger object.

20 Two similar cones have surface areas in the ratio 9:16
   a Find the ratio of their lengths.
   b Find the ratio of their volumes.

21 The two Russian dolls are similar.
   a The surface area of the larger doll is 150 cm².
      Calculate the surface area of the smaller doll.
   b The volume of the larger doll is 120 cm³.
      Calculate the volume of the smaller doll.

10 cm   8 cm

22 A model plane is made on a scale of 1 : 50
Copy and complete the table.

	Real plane	Model plane
Wingspan	11.23 m	22.46 cm
Length of plane	9.12 m	……. cm
Wing area	22.48 m²	……. cm²

23 A model car is made on a scale of 1 : 40
Copy and complete the table.

	Real car	Model car
Length of car	3.723 m	……..cm
Area of windscreen	0.4835 m²	……. cm²
Storage space in boot	160 litres	……. m*l*

KEY WORDS
volume scale factor

Grouped frequency tables

THIS SECTION WILL SHOW YOU HOW TO
- Find the modal group from a grouped frequency table
- Estimate the mean from a grouped frequency table

 Large sets of data are often shown in a **grouped frequency table**.
The **modal class** is the group with the highest frequency.
In a grouped frequency table you do not know the individual data values so you can only estimate the value of the mean.
The **mid-value** of the groups is used to estimate the sum of the figures in each group.
For example, if you have 5 people whose heights, h cm, are in the group $164 < h \le 168$ you can estimate the sum of their heights by calculating $5 \times 166 = 830$ cm.

EXAMPLE

The table shows the time, t minutes, taken by 100 people to complete a Sudoku puzzle.
a   Write down the modal class.
b   Calculate an estimate of the mean time taken.

Time (t minutes)	Frequency
$0 < t \le 10$	20
$10 < t \le 20$	32
$20 < t \le 30$	41
$30 < t \le 40$	5
$40 < t \le 50$	2

a   The highest frequency is 41, so the modal class is $20 < t \le 30$.

b   The mid-value of the group $0 < t \le 10$ is 5, the mid-value of the group $10 < t \le 20$ is 15 etc.
Two extra columns need to be added to the table for the calculations.

➡ **NOTE:** to find the mid-value of the group $10 < t \le 20$ you calculate $\dfrac{10 + 20}{2} = \dfrac{30}{2} = 15$

Time (t minutes)	Frequency (f)	mid-value (x)	($f \times x$)
$0 < t \le 10$	20	5	$20 \times 5 = 100$
$10 < t \le 20$	32	15	$32 \times 15 = 480$
$20 < t \le 30$	41	25	$41 \times 25 = 1025$
$30 < t \le 40$	5	35	$5 \times 35 = 175$
$40 < t \le 50$	2	45	$2 \times 45 = 90$
	Total = 100		**Total = 1870**

The estimated mean time $= \dfrac{\text{total time}}{\text{total number of people}}$

$= \dfrac{1870}{100} = 18.7$ minutes

The table shows the number of points scored by a rugby team in a series of 50 games.

Estimate the mean number of points scored per game.

Points	Frequency
5–15	6
16–20	13
21–25	26
26–36	5

The mid-value of the group 5–15 is $\dfrac{5+15}{2} = 10$

The mid-value of the group 16–20 is $\dfrac{16+20}{2} = 18$ etc.

Two extra columns need to be added to the table for the calculations.

Points	Frequency (f)	Mid-value(x)	($f \times x$)
5–15	6	10	6 × 10 = 60
16–20	13	18	13 × 18 = 234
21–25	26	23	26 × 23 = 598
26–36	5	31	5 × 31 = 155
	Total = 50		**Total = 1047**

The estimated mean number of points $= \dfrac{\text{total number of points}}{\text{total number of games}}$

$$= \dfrac{1047}{50} = 20.94 \text{ points.}$$

EXERCISE 5.17

1 Write down the mid-value for each of the following groups.

   a $40 < v \le 50$ b $4 < t \le 4.5$ c $9 < h \le 15$ d $2.3 < x \le 2.8$

   e   5 to 7   f   3 to 8   g   3.9 to 4.2   h   15 to 28

2 The table shows the speeds of 200 cars on a road.

Speed (v km/h)	$30 < v \le 40$	$40 < v \le 50$	$50 < v \le 60$	$60 < v \le 70$
Number of cars	37	85	76	2

   a   Write down the modal class.

   b   Copy and complete the table below and use it to calculate an estimate of the mean speed.

Speed (v km/h)	Number of cars (f)	Mid-value (x)	($f \times x$)
$30 < v \le 40$	37	35	37 × 35 =
$40 < v \le 50$	85		
$50 < v \le 60$	76		
$60 < v \le 70$	2		
	Total =		**Total =**

3   The table shows the heights of 150 students in a school.
    a   Write down the modal class.
    b   Calculate an estimate of the mean height.

Height (h cm)	Frequency
120 < h ≤ 130	3
130 < h ≤ 140	19
140 < h ≤ 150	36
150 < h ≤ 160	57
160 < h ≤ 170	22
170 < h ≤ 180	11
180 < h ≤ 190	2

4   The temperature of a fridge is checked regularly.
    The results are shown in the table.
    a   Write down the modal class.
    b   Calculate an estimate of the mean temperature.

Temperature (t °C)	Frequency
2.5 < t ≤ 3	4
3 < t ≤ 3.5	25
3.5 < t ≤ 4	13
4 < t ≤ 4.5	5
4.5 < t ≤ 5	3

5   The depth of water in a lake is
    recorded each day for 100 days.
    a   Write down the modal
        class.
    b   Calculate an estimate of
        the mean depth.

Depth (d metres)	Frequency
10 < d ≤ 10.5	8
10.5 < d ≤ 11	49
11 < d ≤ 11.5	38
11.5 < d ≤ 12	4
12 < d ≤ 12.5	1

6   Fifty new-born babies are weighed.
    The results are shown in the table.
    a   Write down the modal class.
    b   Calculate an estimate of the mean mass.
    c   Calculate the percentage of new-born babies that
        had a mass greater than 4 kg.

Mass (m kg)	Frequency
1 < m ≤ 2	3
2 < m ≤ 3	18
3 < m ≤ 4	25
4 < m ≤ 5	3
5 < m ≤ 6	1

7   One hundred people are asked to record how many
    times they visit a doctor in one year.
    a   Write down the modal class.
    b   Calculate an estimate of the mean number of visits.

Number of visits	Frequency
0 to 2	58
3 to 5	24
6 to 8	15
9 to 14	3

8   Two hundred students record the number of hours of
    homework they do in a week.
    a   Calculate an estimate of the mean number of hours
        of homework.
    b   A student is chosen at random.
        Calculate the probability that they do more than
        5 hours of homework in a week.

Hours (h hours)	Frequency
$0 < h \le 2$	6
$2 < h \le 5$	76
$5 < h \le 9$	108
$9 < h \le 15$	10

9   The table shows the lengths of 150 journeys made by a
    taxi driver in one week.
    a   Calculate an estimate of
        the mean length of a
        journey.
    b   Calculate the percentage
        of journeys that are over
        4 miles in length.

Length (x miles)	Frequency
$0 < x \le 1$	35
$1 < x \le 2$	62
$2 < x \le 3$	38
$3 < x \le 4$	12
$4 < x \le 5$	3

10 The table shows the times taken by 100 students to
    complete a test.
    a   Write down the modal class.
    b   Calculate an estimate of the mean time.
    c   The data is regrouped to give the following table.

Time (t minutes)	Frequency
$0 < t \le 30$	2
$30 < t \le 60$	6
$60 < t \le 90$	40
$90 < t \le 120$	32
$120 < t \le 150$	20

Time (t minutes)	Frequency
$0 < t \le 60$	p
$60 < t \le 120$	q
$120 < t \le 150$	20

Write down the values of p and q.
    d   Use the table in part c to calculate a new estimate
        of the mean time.

UNIT 5

Unit 5 Examination-style questions

1   A sack of rice will feed 35 people for 28 days.

How many people will this sack of rice feed for 10 days? [2]

2   Harry changed $30 into pounds (£) when the exchange rate was $1 = £0.703

How many pounds did he receive? [2]

3   Rebecca changed 100 Euros (€) into dollars ($) when the exchange rate was $1 = €0.872

How many dollars did she receive? [2]

4   f: $x \mapsto 3x - 4$

(a)   Find f(−5). [1]
(b)   Find $f^{-1}(x)$. [2]
(c)   Find $f^{-1}f(8)$. [1]

5 $f(x) = \dfrac{2x+5}{x-2}$, $x \neq 2$

(a)   Calculate f(0.5). [1]
(b)   Solve f(x) = 3. [2]

6 $f(x) = 3x^2 - 5x + 2$ $g(x) = 3 - 2x$

(a)   Find gf(−2). [2]
(b)   Find fg(x) in its simplest form. [3]
(c)   Find $g^{-1}(x)$. [2]

7 $f(x) = 3^x$ $g(x) = x^2 + 3$

(a)   Find ff(2). [2]
(b)   Find g(2x − 5). [2]
(c)   Find gf(x). [2]

8   Factorise.

(a) $4x^2 - 25$ [1]
(b) $4x^2 - 25x + 6$ [2]

9   Factorise.

(a) $y^2 - 16$ [1]
(b) $y^2 + 6y - 16$ [2]

10 Factorise.

$10(a - b)^2 - 6(a - b)$ [2]

11 Simplify.

$$\dfrac{x^2 - 4}{x^2 - 10x + 16}$$ [4]

12 Simplify.

$$\dfrac{x^2 + 5x - 24}{2x^2 - 7x + 3}$$ [5]

13 The table shows some values for $y = \dfrac{1}{2}x^3 - 2x + 1$.

x	-2.5	-2	-1.5	-1	-0.5	0	0.5	1	1.5	2	2.5
y	-1.8		2.3		1.9			0.06	-0.5	1	3.8

(a) Complete the table.   [3]

(b) On the grid, draw the graph of $y = \dfrac{1}{2}x^3 - 2x + 13$ for $-2.5 \le x \le 2.5$.

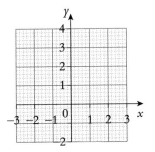

[4]

(c) By drawing a suitable tangent to the curve, estimate the gradient of the curve at the point (2, 1).   [3]

14

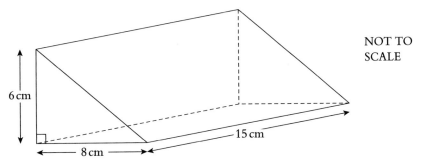

NOT TO SCALE

The diagram shows a solid triangular prism.
The cross-section of the prism is a right-angled triangle.

Calculate the surface area of this prism.   [4]

15

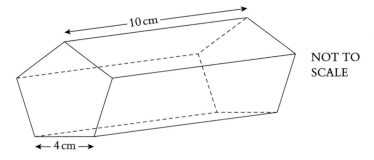

The diagram shows a solid prism of length 10 cm.
The cross-section of the prism is a regular pentagon of side length 4 cm.

Calculate the surface area of this prism. [4]

16

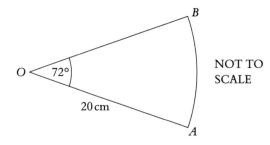

The diagram shows a sector of a circle with radius 20 cm and centre O.
Angle $AOB = 72°$.

(a) Calculate the length of arc AB. [2]

(b) The points A and B are joined together to make a hollow cone as shown in the diagram below.

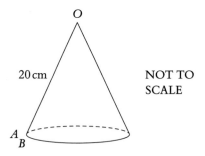

(i) Calculate the radius of the base of the cone. [2]

(ii) Calculate the height of the cone. [3]

(iii) Calculate the volume of the cone.
[The volume, V, of a cone with radius r and height h is $V = \frac{1}{3}\pi r^3 h$.] [2]

17 A solid hemisphere has radius 3.5 cm.

Calculate the volume of this hemisphere.
[The volume, V, of a sphere with radius r is $V = \dfrac{4}{3}\pi r^3$.] [2]

18 **(a)** A cricket ball has radius 7.2 cm.

Calculate the volume of this cricket ball.
[The volume, V, of a sphere with radius r is $V = \dfrac{4}{3}\pi r^3$.] [2]

(b)

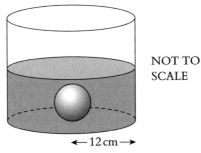

NOT TO SCALE

←12 cm→

A cylindrical tank of radius 12 cm contains water to a depth of 10 cm.
The cricket ball from **part (a)** is dropped into this tank.
The ball sinks to the bottom of the tank.

Calculate the increase in height of the water in the tank. [4]

19

NOT TO SCALE

←12 cm→

←20 cm→

The diagram shows two mathematically similar quadrilaterals.
The area of the smaller quadrilateral is 136 cm².

Calculate the area of the larger quadrilateral. [3]

UNIT 5

20

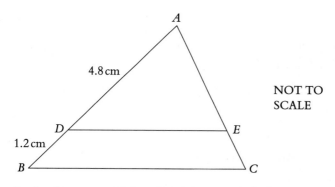

In the diagram, ADB and AEC are straight lines.
$AD = 4.8$ cm, $DB = 1.2$ cm and DE is parallel to BC.
The area of triangle ABC is 9.5 cm².

Calculate the area of trapezium $BCED$.

21

The diagram shows two barrels that are mathematically similar.
The larger barrel has a volume of 502 200 cm³ and a height of 96 cm.
The smaller barrel has a height of 64 cm.

Calculate the volume of the smaller barrel.   [3]

22   Fifty students were timed when solving a problem.
The results are shown in the table.

Time (t minutes)	$5 < t \le 5.5$	$5.5 < t \le 6$	$6 < t \le 6.5$	$6.5 < t \le 7$	$7 < t \le 7.5$
Frequency	2	9	13	18	8

(a)   Write down the modal time interval.   [1]
(b)   Calculate an estimate of the mean time.   [4]

23 One hundred students were asked to record the number of hours homework they do in one week.
The results are shown in the table.

Time (t hours)	$0 < t \le 3$	$3 < t \le 6$	$6 < t \le 9$	$9 < t \le 12$	$12 < t \le 15$	$15 < t \le 18$
Frequency	4	12	17	24	32	11

(a) Write down the modal time interval. [1]

(b) Calculate an estimate of the mean time. [4]

(c) The data is regrouped to give the following table.

Time (t hours)	$0 < t \le 6$	$6 < t \le 12$	$12 < t \le 18$
Frequency	a	41	b

Find the value of a and the value of b. [1]

(d) Use the table in **part (c)** to calculate a new estimate of the mean time. [3]

Percentages 3

 Reverse percentages

Sometimes you are told the final value after a percentage change and you have to calculate the original value.

This process is referred to as carrying out a **reverse percentage** calculation.

> Reminder:
> If a value is increased by 18% the multiplying factor is 1.18   (1 + 0.18)
> If a value is decreased by 13% the multiplying factor is 0.87   (1 − 0.13)

EXAMPLE

During 2015 the population of a small village increased by 4%.
At the end of the year the population was 468.
Calculate the population of the village at the beginning of the year.

original population × 1.04 = final population   *multiplying factor is 1.04   (= 1 + 0.04)*

$$x \times 1.04 = 468$$

$$x = \frac{468}{1.04}$$

$$x = 450$$

The population at the beginning of the year was 450.

➡ **CHECK:**
450 × 1.04 = 468 ✓

EXAMPLE

Benito pays $159.29 for a surfboard in a sale.
The original price had been reduced by 15%.
Calculate the original price of the surfboard.

original price × 0.85 = final price   *multiplying factor is 0.85   (= 1 − 0.15)*

$$x \times 0.85 = 159.29$$

$$x = \frac{159.29}{0.85}$$

$$x = 187.40$$

The original price of the surfboard was $187.40

➡ **CHECK:**
187.40 × 0.85 = 159.29 ✓

EXERCISE 6.1

1 In 2006 the population of Singapore was 4.5×10^6.
   This was 50% greater than it was in 1990.
   Calculate the population of Singapore in 1990.

2 Carla makes a profit of 15% when she sells a mobile phone for $92.
   Calculate how much Carla paid for the mobile phone.

3 In 2015 a train ticket cost $22.
   This is 10% more than the cost of the ticket in 2010.
   Calculate the price of the ticket in 2010.

4 Sunita pays $240 for a bike in a sale.
   The original price had been reduced by 20%.
   Calculate the original price of the bike.

5 Gregor travels to work by train.
   One day, the train is slow and the journey takes 42 minutes.
   This is 10% more than the normal time taken.
   Calculate how long the journey normally takes.

6 The rent for a house is increased by 20% to $19 800.
   Calculate the original rent.

7 The price of bananas is reduced by 25% to $1.74 per kilogram.
   Calculate the original price.

8 The cost of a holiday is reduced by 15% to $3009.
   Calculate the original cost of the holiday.

9 The cost of a cinema ticket is increased by 12% to $9.52.
   Calculate the original cost of the cinema ticket.

10 The cost of renting a car is reduced by 4% to $124.80.
   Calculate the original cost of renting the car.

11 The price of gold increased by 2.5% to $45.92 per gram.
   Calculate the original price.

12 The temperature decreased by 25% to 16.2 °C.
   Calculate the original temperature.

13 Zoe paid $5628 tax in 2015.
   This was 5% more than the amount of tax that she paid in 2014.
   Calculate the amount of tax that Zoe paid in 2014.

Simple interest

With **simple interest**, the interest earned is not reinvested.
This means that the amount of interest earned each year is unchanged.

EXAMPLE

Richard invests $400 at a rate of 5% per year simple interest.
Calculate the amount Richard has after 3 years.

Interest earned in first year = 5% of $400 = 0.05 × 400 = $20
Interest earned in 3 years = 3 × 20 = $60
Value of investment after 3 years = $400 + $60 = $460

Compound interest

With **compound interest**, the interest earned each year is reinvested.
This means that the amount of interest earned each year increases.
The following example shows three methods for finding the final value of an investment.

EXAMPLE

Richard invests $400 at a rate of 5% per year compound interest.
Calculate the amount Richard has after 3 years.

Method 1
    Interest in first year = 0.05 × 400 = $20
    Value of investment after 1 year = 400 + 20 = $420

    Interest in second year = 0.05 × 420 = $21
    Value of investment after 2 years = 420 + 21 = $441

    Interest in third year = 0.05 × 441 = $22.05
    Value of investment after 3 years = 441 + 22.05 = $463.05

Method 2 (Quicker method)
    Value of investment after 1 year   = 400 × 1.05 = $420   *multiplying factor is 1.05 (= 1 + 0.05)*
    Value of investment after 2 years = 420 × 1.05 = $441
    Value of investment after 3 years = 441 × 1.05 = $463.05

Method 3 (Quickest method!)
    Value of investment after 3 years = 400 × 1.05^3 = $463.05

EXAMPLE

Simone invests $200 at a rate of 4% per year compound interest.
Calculate the amount Simone has after 5 years.

Value of investment after 5 years
= 200 × 1.04^5
= $243.33 (to the nearest cent)

UNIT 6

EXERCISE 6.2

1 Amelia invests $80 at a rate of 15% per year, simple interest.
Calculate the amount of interest Amelia earns in 5 years.

2 Karl invests $700 at a rate of 2% per year, simple interest.
Calculate the total amount Karl has after 4 years.

3 Barbara invests $250 at a rate of 6% per year, simple interest.
Calculate the total amount Barbara has after 3 years.

4 Sebastian invests $450 at a rate of 3.5% per year, simple interest.
Calculate the total amount Sebastian has after 2 years.

5 Jack invests $500 at a rate of 3% per year, compound interest.
Calculate the total amount Jack has after 2 years.

6 Omar invests $2000 at a rate of 2.5% per year, compound interest.
Calculate the amount Omar has after 3 years.

7 Eduard invests $700 at a rate of 2% per year, compound interest.
Calculate the amount Eduard has after 4 years.

8 Anelie invests $400 at a rate of 5% per year, compound interest.
Calculate the amount of interest Anelie earns in 3 years.

9 Ferdinand invests $50 at a rate of r % per year, simple interest.
After 4 years he has a total amount of $56.
Calculate the value of r.

10 Hanna invests $400 at a rate of r % per year, simple interest.
After 5 years she has a total amount of $700.
Calculate the value of r.

11 Ferdinand invests $720 at a rate of 5% per year, compound interest.
How many years will it be before his investment is worth more than $1000?

12 Robert bought his car 4 years ago.
Each year the value of the car has depreciated by 15%.
The car is now worth $6264.
Calculate how much the car was worth when Robert bought it.

13 In 2009 the manatee population in Florida was estimated at 3800.
The population is declining at a rate of approximately 1.1% per year.
Estimate what the manatee population will be in the year in 2020.

> **KEY WORDS**
> reverse percentage
> simple interest
> compound interest

Speed, distance and time

THIS SECTION WILL SHOW YOU HOW TO
- Calculate speed, distance and time

 Time

You need to be able to convert a time in minutes to a fraction (or decimal) of an hour.
To do this you must divide by 60.
You also need to be able to change a fraction (or decimal) of an hour into minutes.
To do this you must multiply by 60.

EXAMPLE

a Write 21 minutes as a fraction of an hour.
b Write 36 minutes as a decimal of an hour.

a 21 minutes = $\dfrac{21}{60}$ hour

   = $\dfrac{7}{20}$ hour

b 36 minutes = $\dfrac{36}{60}$ hour

   = 0.6 hours

EXAMPLE

a Change $\dfrac{5}{12}$ hour into minutes.   **b** Change 0.9 hours into minutes.

a $\dfrac{5}{12}$ hour = $\dfrac{5}{12}$ × 60 minutes

   = 25 minutes

b 0.9 hours = 0.9 × 60 minutes

   = 54 minutes

Speed

Speed is a measure of how fast an object is travelling.
When the speed is constant, the formula connecting speed, distance and time is

$$\text{speed} = \frac{\text{distance}}{\text{time}}$$

If the distance is measured in metres and the time is measured in seconds then the speed is measured in metres per second (m/s or ms^{-1}).
If the distance is measured in kilometres and the time is measured in hours then the speed is measured in kilometres per hour (km/h or kmh^{-1}).

EXAMPLE

A train takes 2 hours 55 minutes to travels 350 km at a constant speed.
Find the speed of the train in km/h.

$\text{speed} = \dfrac{\text{distance}}{\text{time}} = \dfrac{350}{2\frac{11}{12}}$

   = 120 km/h

➡ **NOTE:** you must change the 55 minutes into hours.

55 minutes = $\dfrac{55}{60}$ hour = $\dfrac{11}{12}$ hour

So, 2 hours 55 minutes = $2\dfrac{11}{12}$ hour

Change 36 km/h into m/s.

36 kilometres/hour = 36 000 metres/hour

$$= \frac{36\,000}{60} \text{ metres/minute}$$

$$= \frac{36\,000}{60 \times 60} \text{ metres/second}$$

$$= 10\,\text{m/s}$$

EXERCISE 6.3

1   Write these time intervals as fractions of an hour.
    a   20 minutes   **b**   30 minutes   **c**   10 minutes   **d**   15 minutes
    e   25 minutes   **f**   32 minutes   **g**   45 minutes   **h**   4 minutes
    i   54 minutes   **j**   24 minutes   **k**   40 minutes   **l**   48 minutes

2   Change these time intervals into minutes.
    a   0.5 hours   **b**   0.05 hours   **c**   0.25 hours   **d**   0.35 hours
    e   0.8 hours   **f**   0.7 hours   **g**   0.1 hours   **h**   0.45 hours
    i $\frac{2}{5}$ hour   **j** $\frac{3}{4}$ hour   **k** $\frac{5}{12}$ hour   **l** $\frac{3}{10}$ hour

3   Calculate the speed, in km/h, of an object that moves:
    a   500 km in 8 hours   **b**   152 km in 4 hours   **c**   65 km in 5 hours
    d   24 km in $\frac{1}{2}$ hours   **e**   6 km in 20 minutes   **f**   25 km in $2\frac{1}{2}$ hours
    g   504 km in 10 h 30 min   **h**   76 km in 3 h 10 min   **i**   348 km in 2 h 54 min

4   Calculate the speed, in m/s, of an object that moves:
    a   80 m in 4 s   **b**   125 m in 5 s   **c**   600 m in 12 s
    d   72000 m in 1 h   **e**   5400 m in 3 min   **f**   49.68 km in 2 h 18 min

5   **a**   Change 72 km/h into m/s   **b**   Change 12 km/h into m/s
    c   Change 360 km/h into m/s   **d**   Change 20 m/s into km/h
    e   Change 35 m/s into km/h   **f**   Change 41 m/s into km/h

6   A train of length 200 m passes through a tunnel of length 740 m.
    It takes 47 seconds to pass completely through the tunnel.
    Calculate the speed of the train in m/s.

7   Light travels a distance of 6×10^9 metres in 20 seconds.
    Calculate the speed of light in m/s.

8   Sound travels a distance of 2.06×10^4 metres in 1 minute
    Calculate the speed of sound in m/s.

The formula speed $= \dfrac{\text{distance}}{\text{time}}$ can be rearranged to give

distance = speed × time   or   time $= \dfrac{\text{distance}}{\text{speed}}$

This triangle is a useful memory aid for remembering the three formulae.
To obtain the formula for finding S put your finger over the letter S.

This gives you $S = \dfrac{D}{T}$

Similarly, the formula for finding D is D = S × T and the formula
for finding T is $T = \dfrac{D}{S}$.

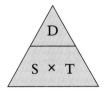

EXAMPLE

A car travels 200 km at a constant speed of 60 km/h.
Calculate the time taken in hours and minutes.

$$\text{time} = \frac{\text{distance}}{\text{speed}} = \frac{200}{60} = 3\frac{1}{3} \text{ hours}$$

Time taken = 3 hours 20 minutes.

➡ **NOTE:** $\dfrac{1}{3}$ hour $= \dfrac{1}{3} \times 60$ minutes
= 20 minutes

Average speed

You can calculate the average speed for a journey using

average speed $= \dfrac{\text{total distance travelled}}{\text{total time taken}}$

EXAMPLE

A train travels 100 km at 80 km/h and then a further 150 km at 100 km/h.
a Calculate the total time taken in hours and minutes.
b Calculate the average speed for the whole journey.

a time $= \dfrac{\text{distance}}{\text{speed}}$ time $= \dfrac{\text{distance}}{\text{speed}}$

$\quad = \dfrac{100}{80}$ $= \dfrac{150}{100}$

$\quad = 1.25$ hours $= 1.5$ hours

Total time = 1.25 + 1.5 = 2.75 hours
$\qquad\qquad = 2$ hours 45 minutes

➡ **NOTE:** 0.75 hour = 0.75 × 60 minutes
= 45 minutes

b Average speed $= \dfrac{\text{total distance travelled}}{\text{total time taken}}$

$\qquad\qquad = \dfrac{100 + 150}{1.25 + 1.5}$

$\qquad\qquad = \dfrac{250}{2.75}$

$\qquad\qquad = 90.9$ km/h (to 3 s.f)

EXERCISE 6.4

1 Find the time taken, in hours and minutes, for the following journeys.
   a 70 km at 35 km/h   **b** 150 km at 60 km/h   **c** 16 km at 32 km/h

   d 18 km at 8 km/h   **e** 34 km at 12 km/h   **f** 53 km at 20 km/h

2 Find the distance travelled, in km, for the following journeys.
   a 28 km/h for 2 hours   **b** 36 km/h for 6 hours   **c** 90 km/h for $3\frac{1}{2}$ hours

   d 50 km/h for 30 minutes   **e** 60 km/h for 10 minutes   **f** 75 km/h for 4 minutes

3 A train travels 24 000 m in 40 minutes.
   Find the speed of the train in km/h.

4 A bird flies for 30 minutes at a speed of 7 m/s.
   Find the distance, in metres, travelled by the bird.

5 A car is travelling at a speed of 32 m/s.
   Calculate the time taken, in seconds, for the car to travel
   one kilometre.

6 A cyclist travels a distance of 91 km in 2 hours 12 minutes.
   Calculate the speed of the cyclist in km/h.

7 An aircraft travels at 1200 km/h for 2 hours and then 1500 km/h for 4 hours.
   a Calculate the total distance travelled.
   b Calculate the average speed for the whole journey.

8 A long distance runner runs at 5 m/s for 30 minutes and then
   at 4 m/s for 1 hour.
   a Calculate the total distance travelled in km.
   b Calculate the average speed of the runner in m/s.

9 A car travels at 80 km/h for 4 hours and then a speed
   of 100 km/h for a further 2 hours.
   a Calculate the total distance travelled.
   b Calculate the average speed for the whole journey.

10 A train of length 200 metres passes completely through a tunnel
    of length 250 metres in 15 seconds.
    Calculate the speed of the train.

11 Zavia drives at a speed of x km/h for 1 hour.
    She then drives at a speed of $(x + 20)$ km/h for the
    next 2 hours.
    The total distance travelled is 280 km.
    Calculate the value of x.

UNIT 6

> **KEY WORDS**
> speed

Sets and Venn diagrams

THIS SECTION WILL SHOW YOU HOW TO
- Use set language and notation
- Use Venn diagrams

The language of sets

A **set** is a collection of items.
Let A = The set of days in the week that begin with the letter T.
Then in set notation A = {Tuesday, Thursday}.

The items in the set are called **elements** or **members** of the set.
The list of elements is enclosed by {   } and commas are used to separate the elements.

The **number of elements** in the set A is denoted by n(A).
In the above example: n(A) = 2.

The symbol ∈ means 'is a member of'.
The symbol ∉ means 'is not a member of'.
In the above example Tuesday ∈ A and Wednesday ∉ A.

The symbol ∅, or { }, is used to represent the **empty set**.
For example, if B = {days in the week that begin with the letter P} then B = ∅.

The **universal set** is denoted by the symbol ℰ.
The universal set contains all the elements being considered in a particular problem.
The sets
ℰ = {days of the week} and
A = {Tuesday, Thursday} can be shown on a Venn diagram.

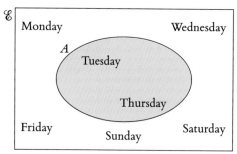

The set A has been shaded on the diagram.

EXERCISE 6.5

1 List these sets.
   a {square numbers less than 50}
   b {prime numbers less than 25}
   c {months of the year}
   d {factors of 12}
   e {prime factors of 25}
   f {even numbers less than 15}
   g {odd numbers between 20 and 30}
   h {prime numbers between 150 and 200}

2 List these sets.
   a {factors of 49}
   b {cube numbers between 100 and 200}
   c {prime factors of 100}
   d {factors of 20}
   e {prime factors of 36}
   f {months of the year beginning with J}

3 Describe these sets by a rule.
   a {1, 4, 9, 16}
   b {1, 3, 5, 7, ...}
   c {March, May}
   d {4, 8, 12, 16, 20, 24, ...}
   e {1, 8, 27, 64, ...}
   f {red, blue, green, yellow, ...}

4 Describe these sets by a rule.
   a {2, 3, 5, 7, 11, ...}
   b {1, 2, 4, 5, 10, 20}
   c {2, 4, 8, 16, 32}
   d {(3, 4, 5), (6, 8, 10), (5, 12, 13), ...}

5 Which of these statements are true?
   a $y = 2x + 1 \notin$ {linear graphs}
   b $y = x^3 + 1 \in$ {non-linear graphs}
   c $1 \in$ {prime numbers}
   d parallelogram $\in$ {triangles}
   e kite $\notin$ {quadrilaterals}
   f trapezium $\notin$ polygons

6 Which of these statements are true?
   a $5 \in$ {factors of 56}
   b $3 \in$ {factors of 4350}
   c $2 \notin$ {factors of $2x^2 - 4x$}
   d $x \in$ {factors $x^2 - 3x$}

7 Which of these statements are true?
   a $x - 2 \in$ {factors of $x^2 - 2x$}
   b $x + 2 \in$ {factors of $x^2 + 2x - 8$}
   c $x + 5 \notin$ {factors of $x^2 - 25$}
   d $3x + 2 \in$ {factors of $6x^2 + x - 2$}

8 Which of these statements are true?
   a {odd numbers divisible by 2} $= \varnothing$
   b {even numbers divisible by 3} $= \varnothing$
   c {prime numbers between 48 and 52} $= \varnothing$
   d {months of the year beginning with the letter B} $= \varnothing$
   e {common factors of 23 and 29} $= \varnothing$
   f {answers to the equation $x^2 = -4$} $= \varnothing$

Venn diagrams

The **complement** of set A is the set of all elements not in A.
The complement of set A is denoted by A'.

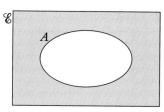

Shaded region shows A'

The **intersection** of A and B is the set of elements that are in both A and B.
The intersection of A and B is denoted by $A \cap B$.

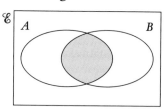

Shaded region shows $A \cap B$

The **union** of A and B is the set of elements that are in A or B or both.
The union of A and B is denoted by $A \cup B$.

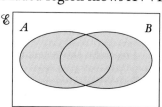

Shaded region shows $A \cup B$

Representing sets on a Venn diagram

When the expressions are more complicated you many need to use some diagrams for your working before deciding on your answer.

EXAMPLE

On a Venn diagram shade the regions   **a** $A \cap B'$ **b** $A \cup B'$

Working

shade set A in one direction

shade set B' in the opposite direction

a $A \cap B'$ is the region that is in both A and B' so you need the region with double shading.

shaded region shows $A \cap B'$

b $A \cup B'$ is the region that is in A or B' or both so you need all of the shaded regions.

shaded region shows $A \cup B'$

UNIT 6

EXERCISE 6.6

1 On copies of this diagram shade the following regions.

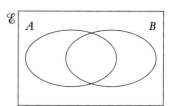

- **a** B'
- **b** $A \cup B$
- **c** $A \cap B$
- **d** $A' \cap B$
- **e** $A' \cap B'$
- **f** $(A' \cup B)'$
- **g** $(A \cap B') \cup (A' \cap B)$
- **h** $(A \cap B) \cup (A \cup B)'$

If $\mathscr{E} = \{1, 2, 3, 4, 5\}$, $A = \{1, 3, 5\}$ and $B = \{3, 5\}$ then B is called a **proper subset** of A.
This is written as $B \subset A$.
On a Venn diagram the set B is drawn inside the set A.

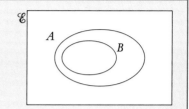

---

2 On copies of this diagram shade the following regions.

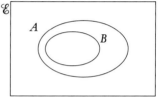

- **a** A'
- **b** $A \cup B$
- **c** $A \cap B$
- **d** $A' \cap B$
- **e** $A' \cap B'$
- **f** $(A \cup B)'$
- **g** $A \cup B'$
- **h** $(A' \cup B)'$
- **i** $(A \cap B) \cup (A \cup B)'$

If $\mathscr{E} = \{1, 2, 3, 4, 5\}$, $A = \{1, 2\}$ and $B = \{3, 5\}$ then A and B do not intersect. $A \cap B = \emptyset$.
On a Venn diagram the sets A and B are drawn so that they do not overlap.

---

3 On copies of this diagram shade the following regions.

- **a** B'
- **b** $A \cup B$
- **c** $(A \cap B)'$
- **d** $A \cap B'$
- **e** $A' \cap B'$
- **f** $(A \cup B)'$

---

4 On copies of this diagram shade the following regions.

- **a** $A \cap B \cap C$
- **b** $(A \cap B \cap C)'$
- **c** $A \cup B \cup C$
- **d** $(A \cup B \cup C)'$
- **e** $A \cup (B \cap C)$
- **f** $A \cap (B \cup C)$
- **g** $A' \cap B' \cap C'$
- **h** $(A \cap B)' \cap C$
- **i** $(A \cup C)' \cap (A \cup B)'$

You might be given a Venn diagram and then be asked to use set
notation to describe the shaded region.

$A \cap B'$

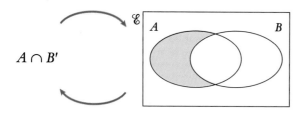

Describe the shaded regions using set notation.

a   b   c

a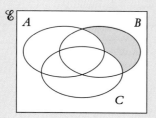

The shaded region is in A, B and C.
The region is $A \cap B \cap C$.

b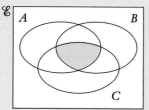

The shaded region is in B and outside $A \cup C$.
The region is $B \cap (A \cup C)'$.

c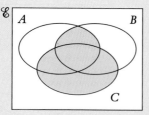

The shaded region contains C and $A \cap B$.
The region is $C \cup (A \cap B)$.

1 Describe the shaded regions using set notation.

a   b   c

d   e   f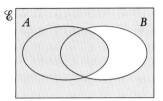

2 Describe the shaded regions using set notation.

a   b   c

d   e   f

g   h   i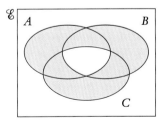

3 Describe the shaded regions using set notation.

a   b   c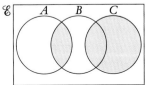

UNIT 6

Further set language

If $A = \{1, 3, 5\}$ and $B = \{1, 3, 5\}$ then A is called a **subset** of B.
'A is a subset of B' means that all the elements of set A are contained in set B.
This is written as $A \subseteq B$
[$C \nsubseteq D$ means C is **not a subset** of D]

If $A = \{3, 5\}$ and $B = \{1, 3, 5\}$ then A is called a **proper subset** of B.
'A is a proper subset of B' means that all the elements of set A
are contained in set B but there is at least one element of set B that is not in set A.
This is written as $A \subset B$
[$C \not\subset D$ means C is **not a proper subset** of D]

$A = \{x : x \text{ is a multiple of } 4\}$ means
'A is the set of numbers x such that x is a multiple of 4' so $A = \{4, 8, 12, 16, \ldots\}$
$B = \{(x, y): y = x + 1\}$ means 'B is the set of points (x, y) that lie on the line $y = x + 1$'.

Listing sets and illustrating on a Venn diagram.

EXAMPLE

$\mathcal{E} = \{1, 2, 3, 4, 5, 6, 7, 8, 9, 10\}$
$A = \{2, 4, 6, 8\}$　　$B = \{1, 4, 9\}$　　$C = \{1, 2, 5, 7\}$
a　List A'　　**b**　List $B \cap C$　　**c**　List $A \cap B \cap C$　　**d**　List $A' \cup B$
e　Draw a Venn diagram to illustrate the sets $\mathcal{E}$, A, B and C.

a　A' means every element in $\mathcal{E}$ that is not in A.
　　$A' = \{1, 3, 5, 7, 9, 10\}$

b　$B \cap C$ means the elements that are common to both B and C.
　　$B \cap C = \{1\}$

c　$A \cap B \cap C$ means the elements that are common to all three sets.
　　$A \cap B \cap C = \varnothing$ or $A \cap B \cap C = \{ \}$

d　$A' \cup B$ means the elements that are in A' or B or both.
　　$A' = \{1, 3, 5, 7, 9, 10\}$ and $B = \{1, 4, 9\}$
　　$A' \cup B = \{1, 3, 4, 5, 7, 9, 10\}$

e

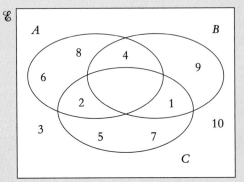

UNIT 6

EXERCISE 6.8

1 List the following sets.

  a $A = \{x : x \text{ is a multiple of } 3\}$ b $B = \{x : x \text{ is a factor of } 20\}$

  c $C = \{x : x \text{ is an odd number}\}$ d $D = \{x : x \text{ is a prime number less than } 20\}$

  e $E = \{x : x \text{ is a prime factor of } 36\}$ f $F = \{x : 2x + 1 = 5\}$

  g $G = \{x : x^2 = 25\}$ h $H = \{x : x^3 = 27\}$

  i $I = \{x : 2x + 3 = 2x - 5\}$

2 List the following sets.

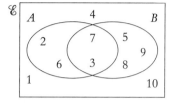

  a A b B

  c A' d B'

  e $A \cup B$ f $A \cap B$

  g $(A \cup B)'$ h $A \cap B'$

3 List the following sets.

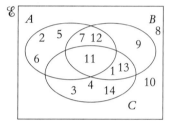

  a A' b B'

  c $A \cap B \cap C$ d $B \cup C$

  e $(A \cap B \cap C)'$ f $A' \cap B$

  g $(A \cup C)'$ h $B \cap C'$

4 $\mathscr{E} = \{x : x \text{ is an integer and } 1 \le x \le 10\}$

  $A = \{\text{factors of } 10\}$ $B = \{\text{multiples of } 4\}$ $C = \{\text{prime numbers}\}$

  List the following sets.

  a A b B c C d $A \cap B \cap C$

  e $A \cap B$ f $A \cap C$ g $B \cap C$ h $(A \cup B \cup C)'$

  i   Draw a Venn diagram to illustrate the sets $\mathscr{E}$, A, B and C.

5 $\mathscr{E} = \{a, b, c, d, e, f, g\}$

  $A = \{a, c, g\}$ $B = \{b, c, d\}$

  List the following sets.

  a A' b B' c $A \cap B$ d $A \cup B$

  e $A' \cap B$ f $A \cap B'$ g $(A \cap B)'$ h $A' \cap B'$

  i   Draw a Venn diagram to illustrate the sets $\mathscr{E}$, A and B.

6 $\mathscr{E} = \{\text{triangles}\}$ $E = \{\text{equilateral triangles}\}$ $I = \{\text{isosceles triangles}\}$

  Draw a Venn diagram to illustrate these sets.

7 $\mathscr{E} = \{\text{quadrilaterals}\}$ $P = \{\text{parallelograms}\}$ $R = \{\text{rectangles}\}$

  Draw a Venn diagram to illustrate these sets.

Using sets to solve problems

You can also use Venn diagrams to show the number of elements in each set.
This is particularly useful when solving problems.

EXAMPLE

$n(P) = 35$, $n(Q) = 31$, $n(R) = 32$,
$n(P \cap Q) = 13$, $n(P \cap R) = 16$, $n(Q \cap R) = 7$,
$n(P \cap Q \cap R) = 4$ and $n(P \cup Q \cup R)' = 6$.
Draw a Venn diagram to find $n(\mathscr{E})$.

The first pieces of information to go on the Venn
diagram are
$n(P \cap Q \cap R) = 4$ and $n(P \cup Q \cup R)' = 6$.

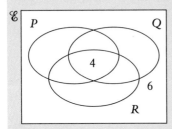

$n(P \cap Q) = 13$	$13 - 4 = 9$
$n(P \cap R) = 16$	$16 - 4 = 12$
$n(Q \cap R) = 7$	$7 - 4 = 3$

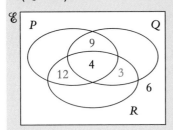

$n(P) = 35$	$35 - (9 + 12 + 4) = 10$
$n(Q) = 31$	$31 - (9 + 3 + 4) = 15$
$n(R) = 32$	$32 - (12 + 3 + 4) = 13$

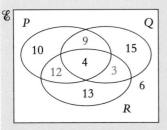

Now add all the numbers on the Venn diagram
together to find $n(\mathscr{E})$.
$n(\mathscr{E}) = 10 + 9 + 15 + 12 + 4 + 3 + 13 + 6 = 72$

UNIT 6

EXERCISE 6.9

1 The Venn diagram shows information about the number of elements in the sets.

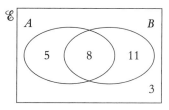

For example n(A) = 5 + 8 = 13.
Find

a   n(A')
b   n(B)
c   n(B')
d   n($A \cap B$)
e   n($A \cup B$)
f   n($A \cup B$)$'$
g   n($A' \cap B$)
h   n($A \cap B'$).

2   n(A) = 18, n(B) = 13 and n($A \cap B$) = 3. Draw a Venn diagram to find n($A \cup B$).

3   n(A) = 12, n(B) = 11 and n($A \cap B$) = 4. Draw a Venn diagram to find n($A \cup B$).

4   n(A) = 35, n(B) = 33 and n($A \cap B$) = 13. Draw a Venn diagram to find n($A \cup B$).

5   n(A) = 9, n(B) = 11 and n($A \cup B$) = 13. Draw a Venn diagram to find n($A \cap B$).

6   n(A) = 65, n(B) = 57 and n($A \cup B$) = 114. Draw a Venn diagram to find n($A \cap B$).

7   n($\mathscr{E}$) = 27, n(A) = 12, n(B) = 9 and n($A \cap B$) = 4.
    Draw a Venn diagram to find   a   n($A \cup B$)   b   n($A \cup B$)$'$ c   n($A \cap B'$).

8   n($\mathscr{E}$) = 40, n(A) = 25, n(B) = 22 and n($A \cup B$)$'$ = 3.
    Draw a Venn diagram to find   a   n($A \cap B$)   b   n($A \cap B'$).

9   n($\mathscr{E}$) = 50, n(A) = 26, n(B) = 22 and n($A \cap B$) = 12.
    Draw a Venn diagram to find   a   n($A \cup B$)   b   n($A \cup B$)$'$ c   n($A' \cap B$).

10 n(A) = 15, n($A \cap B$) = 10 and n($A' \cap B$) = 7.
    Draw a Venn diagram to find   a   n(B)   b   n($A \cup B$).

11 n(A) = 11, n(B) = 15, n(C) = 10, n($A \cap B$) = 5, n($A \cap C$) = 4,
    n($B \cap C$) = 7 and n($A \cap B \cap C$) = 3.
    Draw a Venn diagram to find n($A \cup B \cup C$).

12 n(A) = 16, n(B) = 12, n(C) = 9, n($B \cap C$) = 3, n($A \cap C$) = 5,
    n($A \cup B$) = 22 and n($A \cap B \cap C$) = 2.
    Draw a Venn diagram to find n($A \cup B \cup C$).

13 n(A) = 17, n(B) = 13, n(C) = 16, n($A \cap B$) = 10, n($A \cap C$) = 6, n($B \cap C$) = 7,
    n($A \cap B \cap C$) = 4 and n($A \cup B \cup C$)$'$ = 8.
    Draw a Venn diagram to find n($\mathscr{E}$).

There are 29 students in a class.
22 study biology (*B*), 19 study chemistry (*C*) and 3 study neither biology or chemistry.
How many students study both biology and chemistry?

Method 1
3 students study neither biology or chemistry so the number
3 goes outside the sets *B* and *C*.

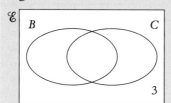

29 − 3 = 26 so there are now 26 students left to put on the Venn diagram.
22 + 19 = 41 and 41 − 26 = 15
The number that goes in the intersection is 15 and the remaining numbers
can now be filled in

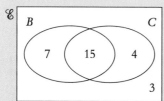

The number of students who study both biology and chemistry is 15.

Method 2 (Using algebra)
The number 3 goes outside the sets *B* and *C* on the Venn diagram.
Let x = the number of students that study both biology and chemistry.

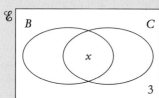

The number of students who study biology and not chemistry is $22 - x$.
The number of students who study chemistry and not biology is $19 - x$.
So the Venn diagram becomes

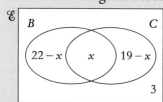

There are a total of 29 students.
So $(22 - x) + x + (19 - x) + 3 = 29$ $\qquad 44 - x = 29$ $\qquad x = 15$
The number of students who study both biology and chemistry is 15.

EXERCISE 6.10

1   There are 30 students in a class.
    17 study geography (*G*), 16 study history (*H*) and 6 study
    neither geography or history.
    Copy and complete the Venn diagram to show
    this information.
    How many students study both geography and history?

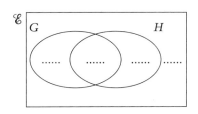

2   There are 34 students in a class.
    20 like apple juice, 28 like orange juice and 2 students don't like either drink.
    How many students like both apple and orange juice?

3   50 people were asked if they had ever been to Mauritius or the Seychelles on holiday.
    11 had been to Mauritius, 7 had been to the Seychelles and 35 had been to neither.
    How many had been to both?

4   26 students go on an activity holiday.
    15 have sailed before, 8 have rock climbed before and 7 have done neither.
    How many have done both before?

5   There are 27 students in a class.
    22 have scientific calculators, 7 have graphical calculators and 2 students have neither.
    How many students have both a scientific calculator and a graphical calculator?

6   100 students do a mathematics test.
    89 had a pair of compasses, 87 had a protractor and 86 had a ruler.
    78 students had a ruler and protractor.
    81 had a pair of compasses and a protractor.
    79 had a pair of compasses and a ruler.
    74 students had all three pieces of equipment.
    How many students had
    a   none of the three pieces of equipment,
    b   only a protractor.

7   A group of students are given three problems to solve.
    (Problem *A*, *B* and *C*.)
    13 students solve problem *A*, 17 solve problem *B*
    and 7 solve problem *C*.
    9 solve problems *A* and *B*.
    6 solve problems *B* and *C*.
    5 solve problems *A* and *C*.
    4 solve all three problems.
    2 solve none of the three problems.
    How many students are there altogether.

> **KEY WORDS**
> set, element
> member, empty set
> universal set
> Venn diagram
> complement
> intersection
> union
> subset

Indices 2

THIS SECTION WILL SHOW YOU HOW TO
- Use fraction indices

Reminder: $a^m \times a^n = a^{m+n}$ $a^m \div a^n = a^{m-n}$ $\left(a^m\right)^n = a^{mn}$

$$a^0 = 1 \qquad a^{-n} = \frac{1}{a^n}$$

Fractional indices

Consider $\sqrt{16} \times \sqrt{16}$ and $16^{\frac{1}{2}} \times 16^{\frac{1}{2}}$

 $= 4 \times 4$ $= 16^{\frac{1}{2}+\frac{1}{2}}$ $\;= 16^1$

 $= 16$ $= 16$

$$\text{so} \quad 16^{\frac{1}{2}} = \sqrt{16}$$

The index $\dfrac{1}{2}$ means 'square root' $a^{\frac{1}{2}} = \sqrt{a}$

The index $\dfrac{1}{3}$ means 'cube root' $a^{\frac{1}{3}} = \sqrt[3]{a}$

This can be written more generally as:

The index $\dfrac{1}{n}$ means '*n*th root' $a^{\frac{1}{n}} = \sqrt[n]{a}$

EXAMPLE

Find the value of   **a** $16^{\frac{1}{2}}$ $\qquad$ **b** $27^{\frac{1}{3}}$ $\qquad\qquad$ **c** $32^{-\frac{1}{5}}$

a $16^{\frac{1}{2}} = \sqrt{16} = 4$ $\qquad$ **b** $27^{\frac{1}{3}} = \sqrt[3]{27} = 3$ $\qquad$ **c** $32^{-\frac{1}{5}} = \dfrac{1}{32^{\frac{1}{5}}} = \dfrac{1}{\sqrt[5]{32}} = \dfrac{1}{2}$

$8^{\frac{2}{3}}$ can be written as $\left(8^{\frac{1}{3}}\right)^2 = \left(\sqrt[3]{8}\right)^2 = 2^2 = 4$ $\qquad$ similarly $8^{-\frac{2}{3}} = \dfrac{1}{8^{\frac{2}{3}}} = \dfrac{1}{\left(\sqrt[3]{8}\right)^2} = \dfrac{1}{2^2} = \dfrac{1}{4}$

In general: $a^{\frac{m}{n}} = \left(\sqrt[n]{a}\right)^m$

EXAMPLE

Find the value of   **a** $125^{\frac{4}{3}}$ $\qquad\qquad$ **b** $16^{-\frac{3}{4}}$

a $125^{\frac{4}{3}} = \left(125^{\frac{1}{3}}\right)^4 = \left(\sqrt[3]{125}\right)^4 = 5^4 = 625$ $\qquad$ **b** $16^{-\frac{3}{4}} = \dfrac{1}{16^{\frac{3}{4}}} = \dfrac{1}{\left(\sqrt[4]{16}\right)^3} = \dfrac{1}{2^3} = \dfrac{1}{8}$

EXERCISE 6.11

1 Find the value of

a $9^{\frac{1}{2}}$ b $64^{\frac{1}{2}}$ c $27^{\frac{1}{3}}$ d $81^{\frac{1}{2}}$ e $64^{\frac{1}{3}}$ f $8^{\frac{1}{3}}$

g $100^{\frac{1}{2}}$ h $81^{\frac{1}{4}}$ i $144^{\frac{1}{2}}$ j $169^{\frac{1}{2}}$ k $400^{\frac{1}{2}}$ l $8000^{\frac{1}{3}}$

2 Find the value of

a $9^{-\frac{1}{2}}$ b $4^{-\frac{1}{2}}$ c $27^{-\frac{1}{3}}$ d $25^{-\frac{1}{2}}$ e $81^{-\frac{1}{4}}$ f $125^{-\frac{1}{3}}$

g $8^{-\frac{1}{3}}$ h $64^{-\frac{1}{3}}$ i $100^{-\frac{1}{2}}$ j $36^{-\frac{1}{2}}$ k $121^{-\frac{1}{2}}$ l $16^{-\frac{1}{4}}$

3 Find the value of

a $25^{\frac{3}{2}}$ b $8^{\frac{4}{3}}$ c $4^{\frac{3}{2}}$ d $9^{\frac{3}{2}}$ e $100^{\frac{5}{2}}$ f $1^{\frac{2}{3}}$

g $8^{\frac{2}{3}}$ h $9^{\frac{5}{2}}$ i $1000^{\frac{2}{3}}$ j $169^{\frac{3}{2}}$ k $81^{\frac{3}{4}}$ l $8^{\frac{4}{3}}$

4 Find the value of

a $25^{-\frac{3}{2}}$ b $8^{-\frac{4}{3}}$ c $16^{-\frac{3}{2}}$ d $4^{-\frac{3}{2}}$ e $100^{-\frac{3}{2}}$ f $8^{-\frac{2}{3}}$

g $9^{-\frac{5}{2}}$ h $64^{-\frac{5}{6}}$ i $1000^{-\frac{5}{3}}$ j $64^{-\frac{2}{3}}$ k $81^{-\frac{3}{4}}$ l $1^{-\frac{4}{3}}$

5 Simplify the following. Write your answers in the form x^n.

a $\left(x^3\right)^{\frac{2}{3}}$ b $x^{\frac{1}{2}} \times x^{1\frac{1}{2}}$ c $x^{\frac{1}{4}} \times x^{\frac{1}{4}}$ d $\left(x^{-4}\right)^{\frac{1}{2}}$

e $\left(x^{\frac{1}{3}}\right)^3$ f $x^{2\frac{1}{2}} \times x^{-\frac{1}{2}}$ g $x^{-\frac{1}{2}} \times x^{-\frac{1}{2}}$ h $x^{3\frac{1}{2}} \times x^{\frac{1}{2}}$

i $\left(x^{\frac{3}{4}}\right)^4$ j $x^{\frac{2}{3}} \div x^{-\frac{1}{3}}$ k $\left(x^4\right)^{\frac{1}{2}}$ l $\left(x^{-\frac{1}{4}}\right)^{-8}$

m $x^{1\frac{2}{5}} \div x^{-\frac{3}{5}}$ n $x^{\frac{1}{4}} \times x^{-\frac{1}{4}}$ o $x^{\frac{1}{3}} \times x^{\frac{1}{2}}$ p $x^{\frac{1}{3}} \div x^{\frac{1}{2}}$

6 Simplify

a $3x^{0.5} \times 5x^{0.5}$ b $8x^{0.5} \times 2x^{-0.5}$ c $12x^{1.5} \div 2x^{-2.5}$ d $15x^{\frac{2}{3}} \div 5x^{\frac{1}{3}}$

e $\dfrac{8x^{0.5} \times 3x^{1.5}}{4x^{0.5}}$ f $\dfrac{5x^{0.25} \times 6x^{1.25}}{2x^{-0.5} \times 5x^3}$ g $\dfrac{8x^{-3}}{2x \times 2\,x^{0.5}}$ h $\dfrac{5x^{0.5} + 3x^{0.5}}{2x^{-5}}$

7 Simplify

a $\dfrac{15x^6 y^{0.5}}{3x^9 y^{2.5}}$ b $\left(2x^3 y^{\frac{3}{2}}\right)^6$ c $\sqrt{25x^6 y^{\frac{1}{2}}}$ d $\sqrt{4x^8 y^6} \times \sqrt[3]{8x^3 y^{-6}}$

Find the value of n in these equations.   **a** $2^n = 64$ **b** $3^n = \dfrac{1}{81}$

a $2^n = 64$ *first write 64 as a power of 2* $64 = 2 \times 2 \times 2 \times 2 \times 2 \times 2 = 2^6$
     $2^n = 2^6$
      $n = 6$

b $3^n = \dfrac{1}{81}$ *first write $\dfrac{1}{81}$ as a power of 3* $\dfrac{1}{81} = \dfrac{1}{3 \times 3 \times 3 \times 3} = \dfrac{1}{3^4} = 3^{-4}$
     $3^n = 3^{-4}$
     $n = -4$

Find the value of n in these equations.   **a** $5^{n+1} = 125$ **b** $2^{2n-1} = 32$.

a $5^{n+1} = 125$ *first write 125 as a power of 5* $125 = 5 \times 5 \times 5 = 5^3$
     $5^{n+1} = 5^3$
     $n + 1 = 3$
       $n = 2$

b $2^{2n-1} = 32$ *first write 32 as a power of 2* $32 = 2 \times 2 \times 2 \times 2 \times 2 = 2^5$
     $2^{2n-1} = 2^5$
    $2n - 1 = 5$
      $2n = 6$
       $n = 3$

Find the value of n in these equations.   **a** $9^{n+1} = 3^5$ **b** $8^{n-1} = 2^6$.

a $9^{n+1} = 3^5$ *the base numbers are different so replace 9 with 3^2*
    $\left(3^2\right)^{n+1} = 3^5$ *use the rule $\left(a^m\right)^n = a^{mn}$*
    $3^{2n+2} = 3^5$
   $2n + 2 = 5$
     $2n = 3$
      $n = 1.5$

b $8^{n-1} = 2^6$ *the base numbers are different so replace 8 with 2^3*
    $\left(2^3\right)^{n-1} = 2^6$ *use the rule $\left(a^m\right)^n = a^{mn}$*
    $2^{3n-3} = 2^6$
   $3n - 3 = 6$
     $3n = 9$
      $n = 3$

EXERCISE 6.12

1 Find the value of n in these equations.
   a $2^n = 32$ b $3^n = 9$ c $4^n = 4$ d $2^n = 1$
   e $10^n = 100$ f $5^n = 125$ g $2^n = 256$ h $3^n = 27$
   i $2^n = 2$ j $4^n = 64$ k $3^n = 81$ l $2^n = 16$

2 Find the value of n in these equations.
   a $2^n = \dfrac{1}{16}$ b $3^n = \dfrac{1}{9}$ c $2^n = \dfrac{1}{128}$ d $4^n = \dfrac{1}{16}$

   e $6^n = \dfrac{1}{36}$ f $4^n = \dfrac{1}{64}$ g $2^n = \dfrac{1}{8}$ h $3^n = \dfrac{1}{81}$

   i $3^n = \dfrac{1}{3}$ j $10^n = \dfrac{1}{1000}$ k $5^n = \dfrac{1}{625}$ l $2^n = \dfrac{1}{2}$

3 Find the value of n in these equations.
   a $2^{2n} = 64$ b $2^{n+1} = 16$ c $2^{n-1} = 8$ d $3^{n+2} = 81$

   e $4^{2n} = 64$ f $10^{3n} = 1\,000\,000$ g $2^{n-2} = 128$ h $2^{2n+1} = 8$

   i $2^{2n-1} = 32$ j $3^{2n+1} = 27$ k $5^{n-1} = 125$ l $7^{2n+1} = 49$

4 Find the value of n in these equations.
   a $2^{n+1} = \dfrac{1}{2}$ b $2^{n-1} = \dfrac{1}{4}$ c $3^{2n} = \dfrac{1}{27}$ d $4^{2n} = \dfrac{1}{16}$

   e $10^{n+1} = \dfrac{1}{1000}$ f $5^{2n+1} = \dfrac{1}{625}$ g $2^{3n+2} = \dfrac{1}{128}$ h $10^{2n} = \dfrac{1}{1\,000\,000}$

5 Find the value of x in these equations.
   a $32^x = 2$ b $8^x = 2$ c $9^x = 3$ d $16^x = 4$
   e $10\,000^x = 10$ f $27^x = 3$ g $125^x = 5$ h $169^x = 13$
   i $\left(\dfrac{1}{2}\right)^x = 128$ j $\left(\dfrac{1}{3}\right)^x = 27$ k $\left(\dfrac{1}{5}\right)^{2x} = 25$ l $\left(\dfrac{1}{2}\right)^{2x} = 2$

6 Find the value of n in these equations.
   a $8^{2n+1} = 2^4$ b $9^{n+1} = 3^6$ c $4^{2n+3} = 2^6$ d $25^{2n-1} = 5^4$
   e $3^{n+1} = 9^{n+1}$ f $8^{2n-3} = 2^{n+6}$ g $25^{n+2} = 5^{n+1}$ h $1000^{2n} = 10^{n+10}$

> **KEY WORDS**
> fractional indices

Solving quadratic equations by factorisation

THIS SECTION WILL SHOW YOU HOW TO
- Use factorisation to solve quadratic equations

 A **quadratic equation** is an equation that can be written in the form $ax^2 + bx + c = 0$ where a, b and c are numbers and $a \neq 0$.

Examples of quadratic equations are: $3x^2 - 5x + 4 = 0$ $2x^2 - 6x = 3$ $x^2 - 9 = 0$

A very important concept that is used when solving quadratic equations by factorisation is:

If $a \times b = 0$ then $a = 0$ or $b = 0$

EXAMPLE

Solve these equations   **a** $x^2 - 3x = 0$ **b** $x^2 = 10x$

a $x^2 - 3x = 0$ *factorise*
 $x(x - 3) = 0$ *the product of x and $(x - 3)$ is 0 so one of them must be 0*
 $x = 0$ or $x - 3 = 0$
 $x = 0$ or $x = 3$ ➡ CHECK: $0^2 - 3 \times 0 = 0$ ✓ $3^2 - 3 \times 3 = 0$ ✓

b $x^2 = 10x$ *rearrange so that all the terms are on one side*
 $x^2 - 10x = 0$ *factorise*
 $x(x - 10) = 0$
 $x = 0$ or $x - 10 = 0$
 $x = 0$ or $x = 10$ ➡ CHECK: $0^2 = 10 \times 0$ ✓ $10^2 = 10 \times 10$ ✓

EXAMPLE

Solve these equations   **a** $x^2 = 25$ **b** $x^2 - 5x + 6 = 0$ **c** $2x^2 + x = 21$

a $x^2 = 25$ *rearrange so that all the terms are on one side*
 $x^2 - 25 = 0$ *factorise*
 $(x + 5)(x - 5) = 0$
 $x + 5 = 0$ or $x - 5 = 0$
 $x = -5$ or $x = 5$ ➡ CHECK: $(-5)^2 = 25$ ✓ $5^2 = 25$ ✓

➡ **NOTE:** part a could also be done by simply
saying that if $x^2 = 25$ then $x = \pm 5$.

b $x^2 - 5x + 6 = 0$
 $(x - 2)(x - 3) = 0$ *factorise*
 $x - 2 = 0$ or $x - 3 = 0$
 $x = 2$ or $x = 3$ ➡ CHECK: $2^2 - (5 \times 2) + 6 = 0$ ✓ $3^2 - (5 \times 3) + 6 = 0$ ✓

c $2x^2 + x = 21$ *rearrange so that all the terms are on one side*
 $2x^2 + x - 21 = 0$ *factorise*
 $(2x + 7)(x - 3) = 0$
 $2x + 7 = 0$ or $x - 3 = 0$
 $2x = -7$ or $x = 3$
 $x = -3\frac{1}{2}$ or $x = 3$ ➡ CHECK: $2 \times \left(-3\frac{1}{2}\right)^2 + \left(-3\frac{1}{2}\right) = 21$ ✓
 $\phantom{x = -3\frac{1}{2}}$ $2 \times 3^2 + 3 = 21$ ✓

EXERCISE 6.13

1 Solve these equations.

a $x^2 = 16$ b $x^2 = 36$ c $x^2 = 100$ d $x^2 = \frac{1}{4}$

e $2x^2 = 50$ f $3x^2 = 27$ g $5x^2 = 180$ h $3x^2 = 363$

i $9x^2 = 4$ j $16x^2 = 9$ k $25x^2 = 16$ l $9x^2 = 1$

m $x^2 - 81 = 0$ n $y^2 - 1 = 0$ o $x^2 - 400 = 0$ p $4x^2 - 9 = 0$

2 Is it possible to solve the equation $x^2 + 16 = 0$? Explain your answer.

3 Solve these equations.

a $x^2 + 6x = 0$ b $x^2 - 8x = 0$ c $y^2 - 10y = 0$ d $a^2 + 2a = 0$

e $x^2 - 5x = 0$ f $y^2 - 12y = 0$ g $4x^2 + 9x = 0$ h $3y^2 - y = 0$

i $2x^2 + 13x = 0$ j $x^2 - 25x = 0$ k $x^2 + 40x = 0$ l $x^2 + 3x = 0$

m $x^2 = 4x$ n $y^2 = 15y$ o $a^2 = 11a$ p $b^2 = b$

4 Solve these equations.

a $x^2 + 5x + 6 = 0$ b $x^2 - 5x - 6 = 0$ c $x^2 + x - 6 = 0$ d $a^2 - 9a + 20 = 0$

e $x^2 - 5x - 14 = 0$ f $y^2 + 12y + 27 = 0$ g $x^2 - x - 20 = 0$ h $y^2 - 10y + 16 = 0$

i $x^2 + 7x - 30 = 0$ j $x^2 - 16x + 64 = 0$ k $x^2 - 10x + 25 = 0$ l $x^2 + 4x + 3 = 0$

m $x^2 + 4x - 21 = 0$ n $x^2 - 6x + 9 = 0$ o $x^2 - 9x + 8 = 0$ p $x^2 + 4x - 45 = 0$

5 Solve these equations.

a $2x^2 - 5x - 3 = 0$ b $3x^2 - 5x + 2 = 0$ c $5y^2 + 2y - 3 = 0$

d $2x^2 + 13x - 7 = 0$ e $4x^2 - 12x + 5 = 0$ f $6x^2 + 13x - 5 = 0$

g $10x^2 - 13x + 4 = 0$ h $6x^2 + 29x - 5 = 0$ i $6x^2 + 11x - 10 = 0$

j $4x^2 - 16x + 15 = 0$ k $7x^2 + 33x - 10 = 0$ l $12x^2 - 7x - 10 = 0$

6 Farah was asked to solve the equation $x^2 - 12x + 32 = 12$.

$x^2 - 12x + 32 = 12$
$(x - 8)(x - 4) = 12$
$x - 8 = 12 \text{ or } x - 4 = 12$
$x = 20 \text{ or } x = 16$

She has got it wrong.
Copy out the question and correct her working.

7 Solve these equations.

a $x^2 = 5x - 6$ b $x^2 = 8x - 12$ c $x^2 = 18 - 3x$

d $(x + 3)^2 - 1 = 0$ e $8x - x^2 = 16$ f $7 + 6x = x^2$

g $x^2 - 12x + 37 = 2$ h $2x = x^2 - 15$ i $x(x + 3) = 18$

TOP TIP

Rearrange so that the equations are in the form $ax^2 + bx + c = 0$

8 Solve these equations.

a $x = \dfrac{6}{x - 5}$ b $x = \dfrac{20}{x + 1}$ c $\dfrac{x + 2}{8} = \dfrac{10}{x + 4}$ d $x - 1 = \dfrac{12}{x}$

Problems involving quadratic equations

EXAMPLE

The sum of the squares of three consecutive integers is 110. Find the three numbers.

Let the numbers be x, $x + 1$ and $x + 2$

$x^2 + (x + 1)^2 + (x + 2)^2 = 110$ *expand:* $(x + 1)^2 = x^2 + 2x + 1$ and

$x^2 + x^2 + 2x + 1 + x^2 + 4x + 4 = 110$ $(x + 2)^2 = x^2 + 4x + 4$

$3x^2 + 6x + 5 = 110$ *rearrange to the form* $ax^2 + bx + c = 0$

$3x^2 + 6x - 105 = 0$ *take out a common factor of 3*

$3(x^2 + 2x - 35) = 0$ *factorise*

$3(x - 5)(x + 7) = 0$

$x - 5 = 0$ or $x + 7 = 0$

$x = 5$ or $x = -7$

The three numbers are 5, 6 and 7 or -7, -6 and -5.

EXAMPLE

Find the points of intersection of the graphs of $y = x^2 + 4x - 3$ and $y = x + 1$.

You need to find the points where the curve and the line meet.
This will happen when the y coordinates are equal.

$x^2 + 4x - 3 = x + 1$ *rearrange to the form* $ax^2 + bx + c = 0$

$x^2 + 3x - 4 = 0$ *factorise*

$(x + 4)(x - 1) = 0$

$x + 4 = 0$ or $x - 1 = 0$

$x = -4$ or $x = 1$ *substitute to find* y

when $x = -4$, $y = -4 + 1 = -3$

when $x = 1$, $y = 1 + 1 = 2$ *write the two coordinates*

The points of intersection are $(-4, -3)$ and $(1, 2)$.

EXAMPLE

The sides of the right-angled triangle shown are in cm.
Find   **a**   the value of x
        b   the lengths of the sides of the triangle.

a   Using Pythagoras' theorem:

$(3x + 8)^2 + (2x + 1)^2 = (4x + 1)^2$ *expand the brackets*

$9x^2 + 48x + 64 + 4x^2 + 4x + 1 = 16x^2 + 8x + 1$ *collect like terms*

$13x^2 + 52x + 65 = 16x^2 + 8x + 1$ *rearrange to the form* $ax^2 + bx + c = 0$

$3x^2 - 44x - 64 = 0$ *factorise*

$(3x + 4)(x - 16) = 0$

$3x + 4 = 0$ or $x - 16 = 0$

$3x = -4$ or $x = 16$ *x cannot be negative as this would give*

$x = -1\frac{1}{3}$ or $x = 16$ *negative lengths*

So $x = 16$.

b   The lengths of the sides of the triangle are 33 cm, 56 cm and 65 cm.

EXERCISE 6.14

1   a   If x is subtracted from x^2 the answer is 42. Find the two possible values for x.
       b   If x is added to x^2 the answer is 306. Find the two possible values for x.

2   a   I think of a number. I then square the number and add twice the original number.
         My answer is 99. Find the two possible values for the original number.
       b   I think of a number. I then square the number and subtract twice the original number.
         My answer is 120. Find the two possible values for the original number.

3   The product of two numbers is 270. The two numbers are x and $x + 3$.
     Find the two possible values for x.

4   For this right-angled triangle
     a   Show that $2x^2 + x^2 - 210 = 0$
     b   Hence find the sides of the triangle.

5   The two rectangles have the same area. Find the value of x.

6   Rectangle A is $12\,\text{cm}^2$ bigger than rectangle B. Find the value of x.

7   The lengths of the sides of two squares differ by 3 cm and the sum of their areas is
     $317\,\text{cm}^2$. Find the length of the sides of the two squares.

8   The area of the trapezium is $60\,\text{cm}^2$.
     Find the value of x.

9   A stone is catapulted upwards.
     The height, h metres, of the stone above the ground after t seconds
     is given by the formula $h = 10t - 2t^2$.
     Find the values of t when the stone is 12 meters above the ground.

```
KEY WORDS
quadratic equation
```

10   Find the points of intersection of the graphs of $y = x^2 - x - 12$
      and $y = x + 3$.

Reciprocal graphs

THIS SECTION WILL SHOW YOU HOW TO
- Draw reciprocal graphs

The **reciprocal** of x is $\frac{1}{x}$. The graph of $y = \frac{1}{x}$ is called a reciprocal graph.

Other examples of reciprocal graphs are: $y = \frac{2}{x} + 1$, $y = 2x - \frac{5}{x}$ and $y = \frac{6}{x+2}$

To draw the graph of $y = \frac{6}{x}$ for $-6 \leq x \leq 6$ you must first make a table of values.

x	-6	-5	-4	-3	-2	-1	0	1	2	3	4	5	6
y	-1	-1.2	-1.5	-2	-3	-6		6	3	2	1.5	1.2	1

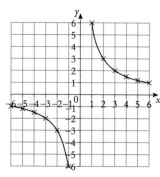

There is no value for y when $x = 0$ because $\frac{6}{0}$ is undefined.

The graph consists of two separate curves, you must not join them together.
The curve approaches but never touches the axes.
The lines that the curve approaches are called **asymptotes**.

➡ NOTE: you do not need to know the word asymptote in the examination.

EXAMPLE

Complete the table and draw the graph of $y = \frac{4}{x-2} + 1$

x	-6	-4	-2	0	1	1.5	2	2.5	3	4	6	8	10
y		0.33			-3			9				1.67	

Write down the equations of the two asymptotes.

x	-6	-4	-2	0	1	1.5	2	2.5	3	4	6	8	10
y	0.5	0.33	0	-1	-3	-7		9	5	3	2	1.67	1.5

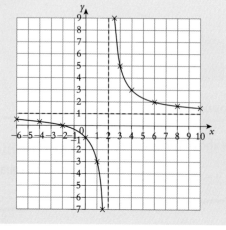

Note there is no y value when $x = 2$.
The asymptotes are represented by dashed lines.
The equations of the asymptotes are $x = 2$ and $y = 1$.

EXERCISE 6.15

For each of these functions make a table of values and draw the graph of the function between the stated x values.

1 $y = \dfrac{5}{x}$ $-5 \le x \le 5$ 2 $y = -\dfrac{5}{x}$ $-5 \le x \le 5$

3 $y = \dfrac{4}{x} + 2$ $-5 \le x \le 5$ 4 $y = \dfrac{5}{x-3}$ $-2 \le x \le 8$

5 $y = \dfrac{6}{x} + x + 1$ $-6 \le x \le 6$ 6 $y = x^2 + \dfrac{6}{x}$ $-4 \le x \le 4$

7 $y = \dfrac{12}{x^2}$ $-6 \le x \le 6$ 8 $y = \dfrac{4}{x^2} + x - 2$ $-6 \le x \le 6$

9 Amir wants to make a rectangular enclosure next to a farm building.
He wants the enclosure to have an area of 500 m².
He will need fencing for three of the sides of the enclosure.

FARM BUILDING

x ENCLOSURE x

y

a By considering the area of the enclosure explain why $y = \dfrac{500}{x}$

b Write down an expression in terms of x and y for the total length, T, of fencing that is needed.

c Show that $T = 2x + \dfrac{500}{x}$

d Copy and complete this table of values for x and T.

x	5	10	15	20	30	40	50
T	110						110

e Draw the graph of $T = 2x + \dfrac{500}{x}$

f Use your graph to estimate the minimum length of fencing that is needed and the value of x that gives the minimum length of fencing.

┌ ─ ─ ─ ─ ─ ─ ┐
│ **KEY WORDS** │
│ reciprocal │
│ asymptote │
└ ─ ─ ─ ─ ─ ─ ┘

The gradients of perpendicular lines

THIS SECTION WILL SHOW YOU HOW TO
- Recognise perpendicular lines
- Solve problems involving perpendicular lines

The lines AB and BC are perpendicular.

The gradient of the line AB = $\dfrac{3}{5}$

The gradient of the line BC = $-\dfrac{5}{3}$

Notice that: $\dfrac{3}{5} \times -\dfrac{5}{3} = -1$

The general rule for perpendicular lines is:

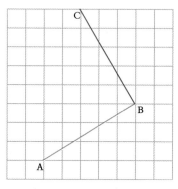

> If a line has gradient m, a line perpendicular to it has gradient $-\dfrac{1}{m}$.

This rule can also be written as:

> If the gradients of two perpendicular lines are m_1 and m_2, then $m_1 \times m_2 = -1$.

EXAMPLE

Find the gradient of a line which is perpendicular to the line joining A(7, −2) and B(5, 4).

Gradient of AB = $\dfrac{4-(-2)}{5-7} = \dfrac{6}{-2} = -3$ *using* $\dfrac{y_2 - y_1}{x_2 - x_1}$

Let m be the gradient of the perpendicular line.
The product of the gradients of perpendicular lines is always −1.

$-3 \times m = -1$ *divide both sides by −3*

$m = \dfrac{-1}{-3}$ *simplify*

$m = \dfrac{1}{3}$

EXAMPLE

Find the equation of the perpendicular bisector of the line joining P(3, 2) and Q(7, 10).

Gradient of PQ = $\dfrac{10-2}{7-3} = \dfrac{8}{4} = 2$ *using* $\dfrac{y_2 - y_1}{x_2 - x_1}$

Gradient of the perpendicular is $-\dfrac{1}{2}$ *using* $m_1 \times m_2 = -1$

Midpoint of PQ = $\left(\dfrac{3+7}{2}, \dfrac{2+10}{2}\right) = (5, 6)$ *using* $\left(\dfrac{x_1 + x_2}{2}, \dfrac{y_1 + y_2}{2}\right)$

So the perpendicular bisector is the line passing through the point (5, 6) with gradient $-\dfrac{1}{2}$.

Substitute $x = 5$, $y = 6$ and $m = -\dfrac{1}{2}$ into the equation of a straight line, $y = mx + c$.

$$6 = -\frac{1}{2} \times 5 + c$$
$$6 = -2.5 + c$$
$$c = 8.5$$

Substitute for m and c in $y = mx + c$ gives

$$y = -\frac{1}{2}x + 8.5$$
$$x + 2y = 17$$

multiply both sides by 2 and rearrange

EXERCISE 6.16

1   Copy each diagram and mark a point C so that angle ABC = 90° and AB = BC.

a   b   c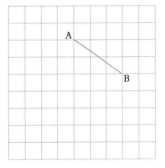

2   Copy each diagram and mark the midpoint of the line segment AB. Use the squares on the grid to help you draw the perpendicular bisector of the line segment AB.

a   b   c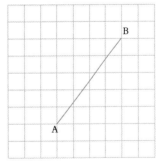

3   Find the gradient of a line perpendicular to a line with gradient:

a   5

b $\dfrac{1}{3}$

c $\dfrac{2}{5}$

d $-\dfrac{2}{3}$

e -4

f $\dfrac{5}{7}$

UNIT 6

4 Work out if these pairs of lines are parallel, perpendicular or neither:

a $y = x + 2$

$y = 2x - 5$

b $y = 3x - 6$

$y + 3x = 1$

c $y = 4x - 1$

$y = \dfrac{1}{4}x + 1$

d $y = \dfrac{1}{2}x + 3$

$y = 5 - 2x$

e $y = 4x - 2$

$4y + x = 5$

f $y = -\dfrac{1}{2}x - 1$

$y = 2x + 4$

g $y = 5x + 1$

$5y + x = 3$

h $x + 2y = 3$

$x - 2y = 4$

i $2x + 3y = 7$

$3y = 8 - 2x$

5 | A $3x + y = 2$ | | B $2y = 3x + 4$ | | C $y = 3x - 1$ | | D $y = 4 - 3x$ | | E $3y + x = 5$ |

a Find two lines from those shown here that are:
   i parallel
   ii perpendicular
b For the one remaining line, write down the equation of a line that is perpendicular to it.

6 Find the equation of the line that passes through the point (5, 0) and is perpendicular to the line $y = 3x - 4$.

7 Find the equation of the line:
   a perpendicular to the line $y = 2x + 4$, passing through the point (6, 2).
   b perpendicular to the line $y = 5x - 1$, passing through the point (0, 7).
   c perpendicular to the line $2x + 3y = 12$, passing through the point (6, 1).
   d perpendicular to the line $4x - y = 6$, passing through the point (4, −1).

8 Two vertices of a rectangle ABCD are: A(−4, 1) and B(−2, 2).
   a Find the gradient of CD.
   b Find the gradient of BC.

9 P(−3, −3), Q(3, −1) and R(2, 2) are the three vertices of a triangle.
   Show that triangle PQR is a right-angled triangle.

10 Line l_1 passes through the points (−2, 3) and (6, −1).
   Line l_2 passes through the points (0, −2) and (3, 4).
   Show that lines l_1 and l_2 are perpendicular.

11 P is the point (1, 1) and Q is the point (6, 0).
   A line l is drawn through P and perpendicular to PQ, to meet the y-axis at the point R.
   a Find the equation of line l.
   b Find the coordinates of point R.

12 Find the equation for the perpendicular bisector of the line joining Q(1, 3) and R(−3, 1).

13 The perpendicular bisector of the line joining A(−1, 4) and B(2, 2) intersects the x-axis at P and the y-axis at Q. Find the coordinates of P and Q.

14 Line l_1 has equation $3x + 2y = 12$.
Line l_2 has equation $y = 2x − 1$.
Lines l_1 and l_2 intersect at point A.
  a Find the coordinates of A.
  b Find the equation of the line through A which is perpendicular to line l_1.

15 A(−1, −2), B(5,1) and C(1, 4)
ABCD is a trapezium.
AB is parallel to DC and angle BAD is 90°.
Find the coordinates of D.

16 E is the point (−6, 0) and F is the point (−2, 6).
Find the point G on the x-axis such that angle EFG is 90°.

17 Angle ABC is 90° and M is the midpoint of the line AB.
The point C lies on the y-axis.
Find the coordinates of B and C.

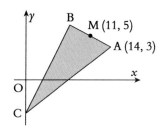

18 The coordinates of three points are A(−2, 6), B(4, 4) and C(k, −7).
M is the midpoint of AB and MC is perpendicular to AB.
  a Find the coordinates of M.
  b Find the value of k.

19 The coordinates of triangle ABC are A(−2, 2), B(5, 6) and C(12, −5).
P is the foot of the perpendicular from B to AC.
  a Find the equation of BP.
  b Find the coordinates of P.

20 The vertices of triangle ABC are A(−3, 2), B(6, −5) and C(k, k + 1).
Find the possible values of k if angle ACB is 90°.

21 The vertices of triangle PQR are P(−4, −k), Q(−1, k) and R(3k, −2).
Find the possible values of k if angle PQR is 90°.

22 The coordinates of triangle EFG are E(−2, 1), F(6, 5) and G(7, −2).
  a Find the equation of the perpendicular bisectors of
     i EF   **ii** FG.
  b Find the coordinates of the point which is equidistant from E, F and G.

TOP TIP

The point is where the perpendicular bisectors of the sides intersect.

UNIT 6

Circle theorems

Tangents

A straight line can intersect a circle in three possible ways. It can be:

A DIAMETER   A CHORD   A TANGENT

    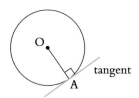

2 points of intersection   2 point of intersection   1 point of intersection

PROPERTY 1

A **tangent** to a circle 'touches' the circle at one point.
The angle between a tangent and a radius is a right angle.
$\widehat{OAP} = 90°$.

PROPERTY 2

The two tangents drawn from a point P outside
a circle are equal in length.

AP = BP.

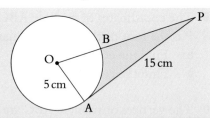

> **EXAMPLE**
>
> In the diagram, O is the centre of the circle radius 5 cm.
> AP is a tangent to the circle at A and AP = 15 cm.
> **a** Calculate the length of OP and the size of angle AOP.
> **b** Calculate the shaded area.

a $\widehat{OAP} = 90°$ *tangent and radius at right angles*

$15^2 + 5^2 = OP^2$ $\qquad$ $\tan \widehat{AOP} = \dfrac{15}{5}$

$\qquad OP^2 = 250$ $\qquad$ $\widehat{AOP} = \tan^{-1}\left(\dfrac{15}{5}\right)$

$\qquad OP = 15.8\,\text{cm}$ $\qquad$ $\widehat{AOP} = 71.6°$

b Area of triangle AOP $= \dfrac{1}{2} \times$ base $\times$ height $= \dfrac{1}{2} \times 15 \times 5 = 37.5\,\text{cm}^2$

Area of sector OAB $= \dfrac{71.6}{360} \times \pi \times 5^2 = 15.6\,\text{cm}^2$

Shaded area = area of triangle AOP − area of sector OAB = 37.5 − 15.6 = 21.9 cm^2

EXERCISE 6.17

1   O is the centre of the circle and AP is a tangent to the circle.
    Calculate the value of x for each diagram.

a

b

c

d
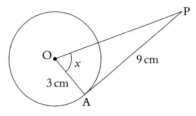

2   O is the centre of the circle.
    AP is a tangent to the circle at A.
    OP = 12 cm and AP = 10 cm.
    Calculate:
    a   the radius of the circle,
    b   angle AOP,
    c   the area of triangle OAP,
    d   the shaded area.

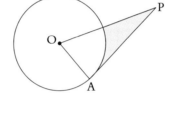

3   O is the centre of the circle, radius 6 cm.
    AP and BP are tangents to the circle.
    AP = 8 cm.
    Calculate:
    a   angle AOP,
    b   angle AOB,
    c   the area of quadrilateral OAPB,
    d   the area of sector OAB,
    e   the shaded area.

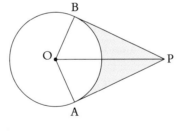

4   ABC is an equilateral triangle.
    AB, BC and AC are tangents to the circle
    at the points P, Q and R.
    O is the centre of the circle, radius 8 cm.
    Calculate:
    a   the length PO,
    b   the length PC,
    c   the length PA,
    d   the area of triangle ABC,
    e   the shaded area.

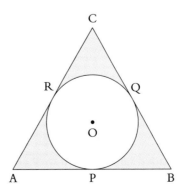

Chords and segments

A straight line joining two points on the circumference of a circle is called a **chord**.

A chord divides a circle into two **segments**.

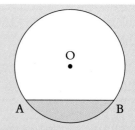

major segment

minor segment

Symmetry properties of chords

PROPERTY 1

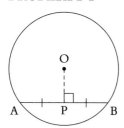

The perpendicular line from the centre of a circle to a **chord** bisects the chord.

AP = PB.

→ **NOTE:** triangle OAB is isosceles.

PROPERTY 2

If two chords AB and CD are the same length then they will be the same perpendicular distance from the centre of the circle.

If AB = CD then OP = OQ.

EXAMPLE

A chord AB lies on a circle of radius 12 cm.
The chord is 18 cm long. M is the midpoint of AB.
a Calculate the length of OM and angle AOB.
b Calculate the shaded area.

a

Using Pythagoras

$x^2 + 9^2 = 12^2$
$x^2 + 81 = 144$
$x^2 = 63$
$x = 7.937...$
OM is 7.94 cm (to 3 s.f.)

Let $A\hat{O}M = \gamma$
$\sin \gamma = \dfrac{9}{12}$

$\gamma = \sin^{-1}\left(\dfrac{9}{12}\right)$

$\gamma = 48.59...$

$A\hat{O}B = 2 \times 48.59...$
$A\hat{O}B = 97.2°$ (to 1 d.p.)

b Area of triangle AOB = $\dfrac{1}{2}$ × base × height = $\dfrac{1}{2}$ × 18 × 7.937 = 71.44 cm²

Area of sector AOB = $\dfrac{97.2}{360}$ × π × 12² = 122.12 cm²

Area of shaded segment = area of sector − area of triangle
Area of shaded segment = 122.12 − 71.44 = 50.7 cm²

1 A chord AB lies on a circle of radius 5 cm.
The chord is 2 cm from the centre of the circle.
Calculate the length of the chord.

2 A chord AB lies on a circle of radius 8 cm.
The chord is 12 cm long.
Calculate the distance of the chord from the centre of the circle.

3 A chord AB is 24 cm long.
The distance of the chord from the centre of the circle is 5 cm.
Calculate the radius of the circle.

4 O is the centre of the circle, radius 15 cm.
The chord AB is 24 cm long.
  a Calculate the distance of the chord from O.
  b Calculate the area of triangle OAB.

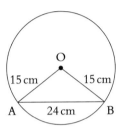

5 O is the centre of the circle, radius 5 cm.
$\widehat{AOB} = 140°$. M is the midpoint of AB.
Calculate:
  a the length of OM,
  b the length of AM,
  c the length of the chord AB,
  d the area of triangle OAB,
  e the area of sector OAB,
  f the area of the shaded segment.

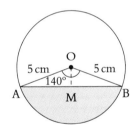

6 O is the centre of the circle, radius 12 cm.
The chords AB and CD are parallel.
AB = 20 cm and CD = 15 cm.
Calculate the distance between the two chords.

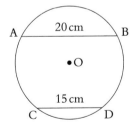

7 O is the centre of the circle, radius 10 cm.
AB = 16 cm and AC = BC.
M is the midpoint of AB.
Calculate:
  a the length of OM,
  b the length of CM,
  c the area of triangle ABC.

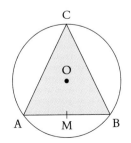

UNIT 6

Find the values of x and y.
Give reasons for your answers.

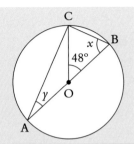

$$x = \frac{180-48}{2} = 66°$$ △BOC *is isosceles*

$$A\hat{O}C = 180 - 48 = 132°$$ *angles on a straight line*

$$y = \frac{180-132}{2} = 24°$$ △AOC *is isosceles*

EXERCISE 6.19

Find the size of each lettered angle.

1

2

3

4

5

6

7

8

9

10

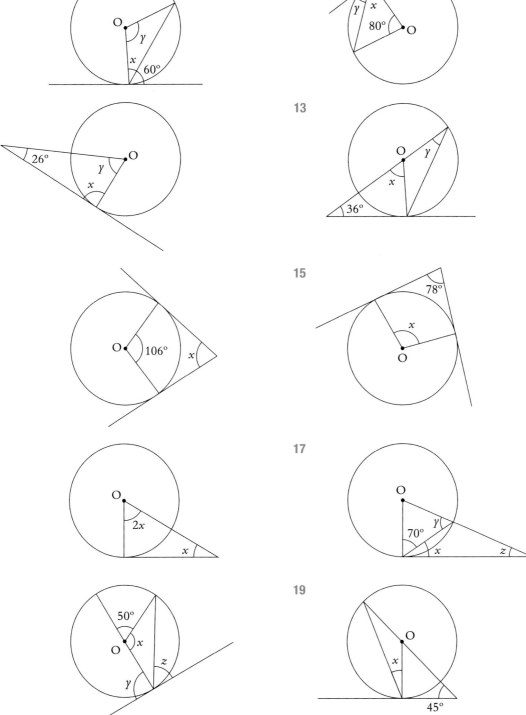

γ
O
x
$60°$

11

γ x
$80°$ O

12

$26°$
O
γ
x

13

O
γ
x
$36°$

14

O $106°$ x

15

$78°$
x
O

16

O
$2x$
x

17

O
γ
$70°$
x z

18

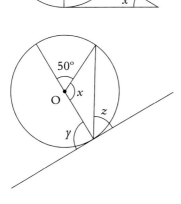

$50°$
O x
z
γ

19

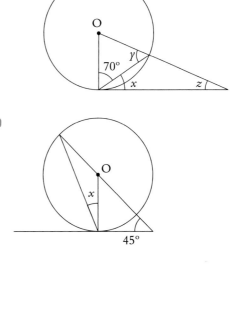

O
x
$45°$

THEOREM 1

The angle at the centre is twice the angle at the circumference.

THEOREM 2

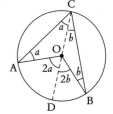

An angle in a semi-circle is always a right angle.

Proof of theorem 1

Let $\hat{OCA} = a$ and $\hat{OCB} = b$
$\qquad \hat{CAO} = a$ and $\hat{CBO} = b$ *isosceles triangles*
$\qquad \hat{AOD} = 2a$ and $\hat{BOD} = 2b$ *exterior angles of triangles*
$\qquad \hat{ACB} = a + b$ and $\hat{AOB} = 2a + 2b$
So $\hat{AOB} = 2 \times \hat{ACB}$

Proof of theorem 2

Angle at centre = 180°
Angle at centre = 2 × angle at circumference
$\qquad\qquad 180° = 2 \times a$
$\qquad\qquad\quad a = 90°$

EXAMPLE

Find the value of x for each of these diagrams.

a   **b**   **c**   **d**

a $x = 2 \times 55°$
     $x = 110°$

b $x = 180° - (90° + 57°)$
     $x = 33°$

c $60° = 2 \times x$
     $x = 30°$

d   (reflex) $\hat{AOB} = 2 \times 125 = 250°$
     $x = 360 - 250 = 110°$

EXAMPLE

Find the values of x and y.
Give reasons for your answers.

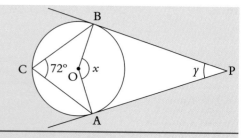

$x = 2 \times 72 = 144°$ *angle at centre = 2 × angle at circumference*
$\hat{OBP} = \hat{OAP} = 90°$ *tangent and radius at right angles*
$y = 360 - (90 + 90 + 144) = 36°$ *angles in a quadrilateral add up to 360°*

EXERCISE 6.20

Find the value of the letters in each of the following diagrams.

1

2

3

4

5

6

7

8

9

10

11

12

13

14

15

16

17

18

THEOREM 3

Opposite angles of a **cyclic quadrilateral** add up to 180°.

THEOREM 4

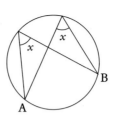

Angles from the same arc in the same segment are equal.

➡ **NOTE:** all four vertices of a cyclic quadrilateral lie on the circumference of a circle.

Proof of theorem 3

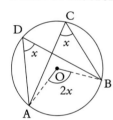

Let	$A\hat{D}C = x$ and $A\hat{B}C = y$	
(reflex)	$A\hat{O}C = 2x$	*angle at centre = 2 × angle at circumference*
(obtuse)	$A\hat{O}C = 2y$	*angle at centre = 2 × angle at circumference*
	$2x + 2y = 360°$	*angles at a point*
So	$x + y = 180°$	

Proof of theorem 4

Let	$A\hat{D}B = x$	
Then	$A\hat{O}B = 2x$	*angle at centre = 2 × angle at circumference*
So	$A\hat{C}B = x$	*angle at centre = 2 × angle at circumference*

EXAMPLE

Find the value of x and y for each of these diagrams.

a

118°
y
76°
x

b

49°
x
y

---

a $x + 118° = 180°$ and $y + 76° = 180°$ *opposite angles in a cyclic quadrilateral*
       $x = 62°$ $y = 104°$

b $x = 49°$ *angles from the same arc in the same segment*
   $y + 49° = 180°$ *opposite angles in a cyclic quadrilateral*
        $y = 131°$

UNIT 6

Find the value of the letters in each of the following diagrams.

1

130°

x

2

124°

80°

y

x

3

100° y

75°

x

4

124° x

57°

y

5

110°

100°

y

x

6

y

x

95°

7

x

58°

8

80°

25°

x

9

24°

x

y

10

50°

x

11

66°

x

12

x

54°

y

13

x

150°

y

14

45°

55°

y

x

15

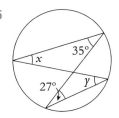

35°

x

27°

y

UNIT 6

Summary of circle theorems:

  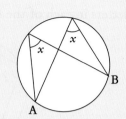

You need to learn all these rules together with the properties of tangents and chords.

EXAMPLE

Find the values of x and y.
Give reasons for your answers.

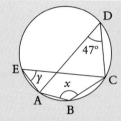

$x = 133°$ *opposite angles of a cyclic quadrilateral*
$y = 47°$ *angles from the same arc in the same segment*

EXAMPLE

Find the values of x, y and z.
Give reasons for your answers.

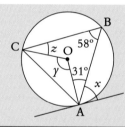

$x = 59°$ *tangent and radius at right angles*
$y = 116°$ *angle at centre = 2 × angle at circumference*

To find z you need to use quadrilateral OABC.
First find the angle at O.

reflex $\widehat{AOC} = 244°$ *angles at a point add up to 360°*
$z = 360 - (58 + 31 + 244)$ *angles in a quadrilateral add up to 360°*
$z = 27°$

EXERCISE 6.22

Find the value of the letters in each of the following diagrams.

1

2

3

4

5

6

7

8

9

10

11

12

13

14

15

16

17

18

19

20

21

22

23

24

25

26

27

28

29

30

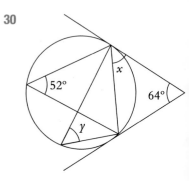

UNIT 6

For questions **31–36** explain how you calculate each variable using the various circle theorems, etc.

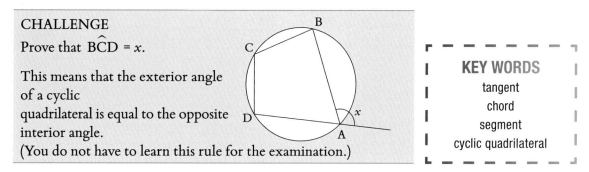

31

B 28° C
γ
A O x
D

32

O
x B
52°
A y
z
C

33

A
D z γ B
40° O
x 70°
C
E

34

A O D
x 34°
C
B

35

B
x
O
y
42°
A C

36

B C
x γ
A
50°
D

37 Use your answers to question **36** to make a general statement about cyclic kites.

CHALLENGE

Prove that $\stackrel{\frown}{BCD} = x$.

This means that the exterior angle of a cyclic quadrilateral is equal to the opposite interior angle.
(You do not have to learn this rule for the examination.)

B
C
D x
A

KEY WORDS
tangent
chord
segment
cyclic quadrilateral

Probability 2

Combined independent events

Two events A and B are **independent** if one event happening has no effect on whether or not the other event happens. If A and B are independent events, then

P(A happening and B happening) = P(A happening) × P(B happening)

P(A and B) = P(A) × P(B)

EXAMPLE

A fair coin is tossed and a fair three-sided spinner is spun.

Find the probability of getting a head on the coin and a 2 on the spinner.

P(head and 2) = P(H and 2) = P(H) × P(2) = $\frac{1}{2} \times \frac{1}{3} = \frac{1}{6}$

Tree diagrams for independent events

A **tree diagram** is a clear way of showing all the possible outcomes of combined events. They can also be used to calculate probabilities of combined events.

You must draw your tree diagram clearly and write the probabilities on each branch.

EXAMPLE

A bag contains 3 red balls and 2 yellow balls.
A ball is chosen at random from the bag, its colour noted and it is then replaced in the bag.
A second ball is then chosen at random from the bag.

a Draw a tree diagram to show all the possible outcomes.
b Find the probability that   **i**   both balls are red   **ii**   both balls are yellow
                               iii different coloured balls are chosen.

a

➡ **NOTE:** multiply along the branches.

➡ **CHECK:** the probabilities of all the routes through the diagram should add to 1.

➡ **NOTE:** if you need more than one of the outcomes add the probabilities together.

b

i P(RR) = $\frac{9}{25}$ **ii** P(YY) = $\frac{4}{25}$ **iii** P(different colours) = P(RY) + P(YR) = $\frac{6}{25} + \frac{6}{25} = \frac{12}{25}$

EXERCISE 6.23

1 The probability that an archer hits a target when he shoots an
   arrow is 0.7. The archer shoots two arrows at a target.
   a Copy and complete the tree diagram.
      (H means he hits the target and M means he misses the target.)

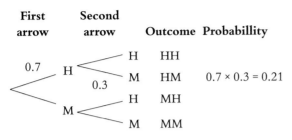

First arrow   Second arrow   Outcome   Probability

H — H   HH
0.7 H
           M   HM   0.7 × 0.3 = 0.21
           0.3
       H   MH
   M
       M   MM

   b Find the probability that
      i   both arrows hit the target,
      ii   neither arrow hits the target,
      iii only one arrow hits the target,
      iv   at least one arrow hits the target.

2 The circular board is divided into five coloured sections.
   When the spinner is spun it is equally likely to stop in any
   of the five sections. The spinner is spun twice.
   Draw a tree diagram to show all the possible outcomes.
   Find the probability that
   a both colours are blue,   b both colours are yellow,
   c the first colour is blue and the second is yellow.

3 Bag A contains 2 green marbles and 1 yellow marble.
   Bag B contains 3 green marbles and 2 yellow marbles.
   One marble from each bag is selected at random.
   Draw a tree diagram to show all the possible outcomes.
   Find the probability of selecting
   a two greens,   b two yellows,   c one of each colour.

Bag A   Bag B

4 The probability that an egg on a production line is cracked is 0.01
   Two eggs are selected at random from the production line.
   Find the probability that,
   a both eggs are cracked,
   b neither egg is cracked,
   c exactly one of the eggs is cracked,
   d at least one egg is cracked.

5 An unbiased six-sided dice is rolled twice.

   a Copy and complete the tree diagram. ($\bar{6}$ means 'not getting a 6' when the dice is rolled.)

   First roll   Second roll   Outcome   Probabillity

   $\frac{1}{6}$ 6 $\frac{1}{6}$ 6 66 $\frac{1}{6} \times \frac{1}{6} =$

   $\bar{6}$ $6\bar{6}$

   $\frac{5}{6}$ $\bar{6}$ 6 $\bar{6}6$

   $\bar{6}$ $\bar{6}\bar{6}$

   b Use the tree diagram to find the probability of obtaining
      i two sixes,   ii no sixes,   iii exactly one six.

6 A bag contains 5 green counters and 2 yellow counters.
   Ali chooses a counter at random from the bag, he notes the colour
   and then he replaces it in the bag.
   He then chooses a second counter at random.
   Draw a tree diagram to show all the possible outcomes.
   Find the probability that he chooses
   a two greens,   b two yellows,
   c two of the same colour, d at least one green.

7 Three unbiased coins are thrown.
   a Copy and complete the tree diagram to show all the possible outcomes.
      (H = head and T = tail)

      First   Second   Third
      throw   throw   throw   Outcome   Probabillity

      $\frac{1}{2}$ $\frac{1}{2}$ H $\frac{1}{2}$ H HHH $\frac{1}{2} \times \frac{1}{2} \times \frac{1}{2} = \frac{1}{8}$

      H T HHT

      $\frac{1}{2}$ H T H
                     T

      $\frac{1}{2}$ T H H
                        T

      T H
         T

   b Use the tree diagram to find the probability of getting
      i three tails,   ii no tails,   iii exactly one head,   iv at least two tails.

8 The probability that a biased coin lands on a head is $\frac{2}{3}$.
   The coin is thrown three times.
   Draw a tree diagram to show all the possible outcomes.
   Use the tree diagram to find the probability of getting
   a three heads,   b three tails,   c exactly one tail,   d at least one head.

9 Three unbiased six-sided dice are rolled.

Find the probability of obtaining

a   three sixes,   b   no sixes,
c   exactly one six,   d   exactly two sixes.

10 Kurt posts three letters on the same day.
The probability that a letter sent by post will arrive the next day is 0.8
Find the probability that
a   all three letters arrive the next day,
b   no letters arrive the next day,
c   only one letter arrives the next day.

11 A bag contains 5 green counters, 3 red counters and 2 yellow counters.
Ali chooses a counter at random from the bag, he notes the colour and
then he replaces it in the bag.
He then chooses a second counter at random.
a   Copy and complete the tree diagram to show all the possible outcomes.

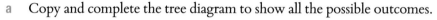

b   Find the probability that he chooses
  i   two greens,   ii   two reds,   iii   two yellows,
  iv   two of the same colour, v   two different colours.

12

Colour	Red	Blue	Yellow
Probability	$\frac{1}{4}$	$\frac{1}{3}$	$\frac{5}{12}$

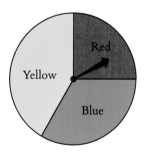

The circular board is divided into three unequal sections.
The table shows the probabilities of the spinner landing on each
of the three colours. The spinner is spun three times.
Draw a tree diagram to show all the possible outcomes.
Find the probability of getting
a   three reds,   b   three blues,   c   three yellows,   d   one of each colour.

Tree diagrams for dependent events

Two events A and B are **dependent** if one event happening has an effect on whether or not the other event happens.

A bag contains 3 red balls and 2 yellow balls.
A ball is chosen at random from the bag.
The ball is **not** replaced in the bag.
A second ball is then chosen at random from the bag.

a Draw a tree diagram to show all the possible outcomes.

b Find the probability that
  i both balls are red,
  ii both balls are yellow,
  iii different coloured balls are chosen.

---

a If the first ball chosen is a red then the probabilities for the second ball are:

$P(R) = \dfrac{2}{4}$ *because there are now* **two** *red balls and only* **four** *balls to chose from*

$P(Y) = \dfrac{2}{4}$ *because there are* **two** *yellow balls and only* **four** *balls to chose from*

If the first ball chosen is a yellow then the probabilities for the second ball are:

$P(R) = \dfrac{3}{4}$ *because there are* **three** *red balls and only* **four** *balls to chose from*

$P(Y) = \dfrac{1}{4}$ *because there is now* **one** *yellow ball and only* **four** *balls to chose from*

You can now put the probabilities on a tree diagram.

First choice	Second choice	Outcome	Probabillity
	$\frac{2}{4}$ R	RR	$\frac{3}{5} \times \frac{2}{4} = \frac{6}{20}$
$\frac{3}{5}$ R	$\frac{2}{4}$ Y	RY	$\frac{3}{5} \times \frac{2}{4} = \frac{6}{20}$
$\frac{2}{5}$ Y	$\frac{3}{4}$ R	YR	$\frac{2}{5} \times \frac{3}{4} = \frac{6}{20}$
	$\frac{1}{4}$ Y	YY	$\frac{2}{5} \times \frac{1}{4} = \frac{2}{20}$

b i $P(RR) = \dfrac{6}{20} = \dfrac{3}{10}$ **ii** $P(YY) = \dfrac{2}{20} = \dfrac{1}{10}$

iii $P(\text{different colours}) = P(RY) + P(YR) = \dfrac{6}{20} + \dfrac{6}{20} = \dfrac{12}{20} = \dfrac{3}{5}$

EXERCISE 6.24

1   A bag contains 5 orange balls and 2 blue balls.
    Raju chooses a ball at random from the bag.
    It is **not** replaced in the bag.
    He then chooses a second ball at random from the bag.
    Find the probability that he chooses

    a   two orange balls,   b   two blue balls,
    c   two balls the same colour, d   two different coloured balls.

2   Shona has 3 one-dollar coins and 1 half-dollar coin in her purse.
    She chooses a coin at random from the purse.
    It is **not** replaced in the purse.
    She then chooses a second coin at random from the purse.
    Find the probability that she chooses

    a   2 one-dollar coins,
    b   2 half-dollar coins,
    c   at least 1 one-dollar coin.

3   A box contains 4 blue crayons and 2 yellow crayons.
    Kurt chooses a crayon at random from the box.
    It is **not** replaced in the box.
    He then chooses a second crayon at random from the box.
    Find the probability that he chooses

    a   two blue crayons,   b   two yellow crayons,
    c   two different colour crayons, d   at least one yellow crayon.

4   A bag contains 6 orange sweets and 3 yellow sweets.
    Priya chooses a sweet at random and eats it.
    She then chooses a second sweet at random.
    Find the probability that she chooses

    a   two orange sweets,
    b   two yellow sweets,
    c   two different coloured sweets,
    d   at least one orange sweet.

5   A bag contains 4 blue marbles, 3 red marbles and 2
    yellow marbles.
    Ali chooses a marble at random from the bag.
    It is **not** replaced in the bag.
    He then chooses a second marble at random from the bag.
    Find the probability that he chooses

    a   two blues,   b   two reds,
    c   two yellows,   d   two of the same colour,
    e   two different colours.

6 A ball is chosen at random from bag A, the colour is noted and then the ball is placed in bag B. A ball is then chosen at random from bag B. Find the probability of choosing

Bag A   Bag B

  a two blacks   **b** two whites

  c two different colours   **d** at least one black.

7 Omar either walks or cycles to school.
The probability that he cycles to school is 0.2.
If Omar cycles, the probability that he is late is 0.1.
If Omar walks, the probability he is late is 0.3.

  a Copy and complete the tree diagram.
     (C = cycle   W = walk   L = late   and $\overline{L}$ = not late)

	Outcome	Probabillity

$$0.2 \quad C \quad \begin{array}{c} 0.1 \; L \quad CL \qquad 0.2 \times 0.1 = 0.02 \\ \overline{L} \quad C\overline{L} \end{array}$$

$$W \quad \begin{array}{c} 0.3 \; L \quad WL \\ \overline{L} \quad W\overline{L} \end{array}$$

  b Calculate the probability that Omar will be
    i late to school,   **ii** not late to school.

8 **a** Jacob is asked to select one shape at random from either bag A or bag B.
The probability that he chooses from bag A is $\frac{2}{5}$.

Bag A   Bag B

    i Copy and complete the tree diagram.

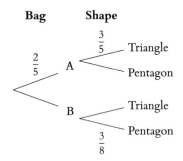

Bag	Shape

$$\frac{2}{5} \quad A \quad \begin{array}{c} \frac{3}{5} \; \text{Triangle} \\ \text{Pentagon} \end{array}$$

$$B \quad \begin{array}{c} \text{Triangle} \\ \frac{3}{8} \; \text{Pentagon} \end{array}$$

    ii Calculate the probability that Jacob chooses a triangle.
    iii Calculate the probability that Jacob chooses a pentagon.

  b Eduardo is asked to select 2 shapes at random from bag A or two shapes at random from bag B. (He does not replace the first shape before selecting the second shape.)

    The probability that he chooses from bag A is $\frac{1}{3}$.

    i Calculate the probability that Eduardo chooses two triangles.
    ii Calculate the probability that Eduardo chooses two different shapes.

Further probability

The probability that Anna hits the bullseye on a dartboard is 0.1.
Find the probability that she hits the bullseye for the first
time on her fourth attempt.

She must miss on her first three attempts and hit on her fourth attempt.
   Let M = miss and H = hit.
   P(M) = 0.9 and P(H) = 0.1.
   P(M M M H) = P(M) × P(M) × P(M) × P(H)
            = 0.9   × 0.9   × 0.9   × 0.1 = 0.0729

EXERCISE 6.25

1   The circular board is divided into eight numbered sections.
    When the arrow is spun it is equally likely to stop in any of the
    eight sections.
    The spinner is spun several times until it lands on the number 2.
    Find the probability that this happens on the fourth spin.

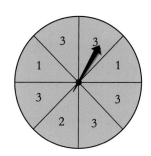

2   A fair coin is tossed repeatedly until it lands on a head.
    Find the probability that this happens on the sixth toss.

3   A six-sided dice is unbiased.
    It is numbered 1, 2, 3, 4, 5 and 6 on its faces.
    The dice is rolled several times until it lands on the number 5.
    Find the probability that this happens on the fifth roll.

4   The probability that Robert will pass his driving test on his
    first attempt is $\frac{2}{3}$.
    If he fails, the probability that he passes on any future attempt is $\frac{3}{4}$.
    Find the probability that he passes on his fifth attempt.

5   The bag contains 5 black marbles and 4 white marbles.
    Marbles are selected at random from the bag
    until a white marble is selected.
    (The marbles are **not** replaced.)
    Find the probability that this happens on the
    third selection.

┌ ─ ─ ─ ─ ─ ─ ─ ─ ┐
│   **KEY WORDS**   │
│   tree diagram   │
│ independent events │
│   dependent events   │
└ ─ ─ ─ ─ ─ ─ ─ ─ ┘

1   Tom pays $528.90 for a computer in a sale.
    The original price had been reduced by 18%.

    Calculate the original price of the computer.   [3]

2   The cost of a holiday increases by 6% to $882.

    Calculate the original cost of the holiday.   [3]

3   Colin invests $600 at a rate of 1.5% per year compound interest.

    Calculate the amount he has after 8 years.   [2]

4   Carol invests $5000 at a rate of 2% per year compound interest.
    Phillip invests $5000 at a rate of 2.5% per year simple interest.

    Calculate the difference between these two investments
    after 10 years.
    Give your answer in dollars correct to the nearest cent.   [4]

5   Raju invests $8500.
    At the end of 7 years, he has an amount of $10 454.

    Find the yearly compound interest rate.   [3]

6   Amanda and Paul both invest $20 000.
    Amanda invests her $20 000 at a rate of 2% per year
    compound interest.
    Paul invests his $20 000 in a bank that x% pays per year
    simple interest.
    After 5 years their investments are worth the same amount.

    Calculate the value of x correct to 3 significant figures.   [5]

7   Change 54 kilometres per hour to metres per second.   [2]

8   A cyclist travels a distance of 200 kilometres in 5 hours 15 minutes.

Calculate the average speed of the cyclist in km/h.   [3]

9   A train of length 250 metres passes completely through a tunnel of length 290 metres in 18 seconds.

Calculate the speed of the train in metres per second.   [3]

10   The Venn diagram shows numbers of students.

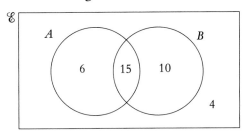

$\mathcal{E}$ = {students in a class}
A = {students who study art}
B = {students who study biology}

(a) **(i)**   Find the number of students who study art or biology.   [1]
          (ii) Find the number of students who do not study art.   [1]
(b)   Find $n(A \cup B)$.   [1]
(c)   On the Venn diagram below, shade the region $C \cup D$.   [1]

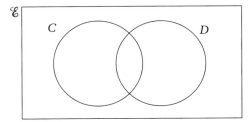

11 Describe the shaded regions using set notation.

(a)

[1]

(b)

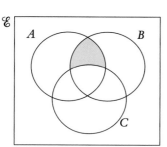

[1]

12 $n(\mathscr{E}) = 30 \qquad n(A) = 15 \qquad n(B) = 18 \qquad n(A \cap B) = 7$

Find $n(A \cup B)$. [2]

13 A group of tourists visit a museum.

$\mathscr{E}$ = {tourists visiting the museum}
E = {tourists who speak English}
G = {tourists who speak German}
$n(E) = 20 \qquad n(G) = 17 \qquad n(E \cap G) = x \qquad n(E' \cap G') = 47$

(a) Represent this information on the Venn diagram.

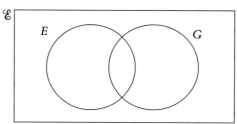

[3]

(b) There are 80 tourists in the group.
Write down an equation in x. [2]

(c) Find the number of tourists visiting the museum who speak both English and German. [2]

14 $8x^3 = 125$

   Find the value of x.   [1]

15 $2^9 \times 2^x = 0.125$

   Find the value of x.   [1]

16   Simplify.

   (a) y^0 [1]
   (b) $p^{10} \div p^2$ [1]
   (c) $(2q^4)^3$ [1]

   (d) $\left(\dfrac{6}{a}\right)^{-3}$ [1]

17   Simplify.

   (a) $\dfrac{x^5 \times x^4}{x^2}$ [1]

   (b) $4x^2\,y^3 \times 5xy^8$ [2]

   (c) $\left(27x^6\right)^{\frac{2}{3}}$ [2]

18 $100^{3x-1} = 10^{5-3x}$

   Find the value of x.   [3]

19   **(a)**   Factorise $x^2 + 3x - 40$.   [2]
       (b)   Solve $x^2 + 3x - 40 = 0$.   [1]

20   **(a)**   Factorise $3x^2 - 2x - 8$.   [2]
       (b)   Solve $3x^2 - 2x - 8 = 0$.   [1]

21   Solve.

$$2x - \frac{5}{x} = 3$$ [4]

UNIT 6

22   In this diagram all lengths are in centimetres.

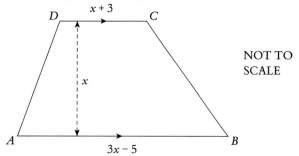

NOT TO SCALE

Trapezium $ABCD$ has a perpendicular height of x cm and an area of 171 cm^2.
$AB = (3x - 5)$ cm and $DC = (x + 3)$ cm.

(a)   Show that $4x^2 - 2x - 342 = 0$.   [3]
(b)   Factorise $4x^2 - 2x - 342$.   [2]
(c)   Find the length of AB.   [2]

23

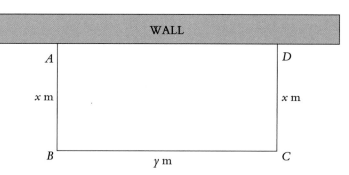

The diagram shows a rectangular enclosure, $ABCD$, with area 48 m^2.
One of the sides of the rectangle is a wall.
The other three sides have fencing.
$AB = x$ m and $BC = y$ m.

(a)   Find y in terms of x.   [1]
(b)   The total length of the fencing is L metres.

Show that $L = 2x + \dfrac{48}{x}$.   [2]

(c)   The table below shows some values for L and x.

x	1	2	4	6	10	15	20
L	50		20		26.8	33.2	

Complete the table.   [3]

(d) On the grid, draw the graph of $L = 2x + \dfrac{48}{x}$.

[3]

(e) What is the smallest length of fencing needed to make this rectangular enclosure? [1]

24 A is the point $(-3, 5)$ and B is the point $(5, 7)$.

(a) Find the equation of the straight line through A and B. [3]
(b) Find the equation of the perpendicular bisector of the line AB. [3]

25 Find the equation of the straight line that
- passes through the point $(0, -2)$ and
- is perpendicular to the line $4x + 3y = 12$.

Write your answer in the form $y = mx + c$. [3]

26 The coordinates of triangle ABC are $A(-5, 1)$, $B(3, -3)$ and $C(4, 4)$.
P is the foot of the perpendicular from C to the line AB.

(a) Find the equation of the line AB. [3]
(b) Find the equation of the line CP. [3]
(c) Find the coordinates of P. [2]

27

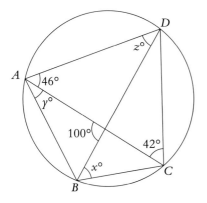

NOT TO SCALE

A, B, C and D lie on the circle.

Find the values of x, y and z. [4]

28

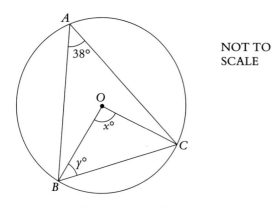

NOT TO SCALE

A, *B* and *C* lie on the circle, centre *O*.

Find the value of *x* and the value of *y*. [2]

29

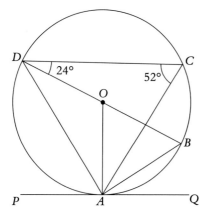

NOT TO SCALE

A, *B*, *C* and *D* lie on the circle, centre *O*.
BD is a diameter and *PQ* is a tangent at the point *A*.

(a) Find angle *ABO*. [1]
(b) Find angle *BAQ*. [1]
(c) Find angle *AOB*. [1]
(d) Find angle *ODA*. [1]
(e) Find angle *OAC*. [1]

30 The probability that Robert is late to school is 0.7

Calculate the probability that Robert is late to school for each of the
next two days. [2]

31 Janet spins a 6-sided spinner numbered 1 to 6.
The probability of it landing on each number is shown in the table.

Number	1	2	3	4	5	6
Probability	0.21	0.07	*x*	0.15	0.22	0.21

(a) Find the value of x. [1]

(b) Janet spins the spinner twice.

    (i) Find the probability that it lands on the number 4 both times. [2]

    (ii) Find the probability that the sum of the two numbers is 10. [3]

32 The probability that a biased dice lands on the number six is $\dfrac{1}{4}$.

(a) The dice is rolled two times.

    (i) Complete the tree diagram.

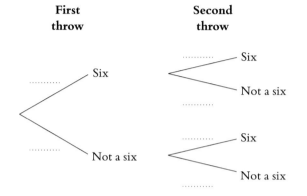

First throw   **Second throw**

Six

.... Six

.... Not a six

....

Not a six

.... Six

.... Not a six

.... [3]

    (ii) Find the probability of throwing at least one six. [3]

(b) The dice is rolled three times.

Find the probability of throwing exactly two sixes. [4]

33 A bag contains 5 red sweets and 4 yellow sweets.
Ali chooses a sweet at random from the bag and eats it.
He then chooses a second sweet at random.

Find the probability that he chooses two different coloured sweets. [3]

34

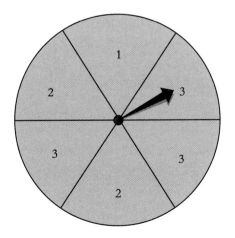

The circular board is divided into six numbered sections.

When the arrow is spun it is equally likely to stop in any of the six sections.
The spinner is spun several times until it lands on the number 2.

Find the probability that this happens on the fifth spin. [3]

35 A bag contains 5 red balls and 3 green balls.
Jane selects balls at random from the bag, without replacement, until a green ball is selected.

Find the probability that this happens on the fourth selection. [3]

36 In this question all lengths are in centimetres.

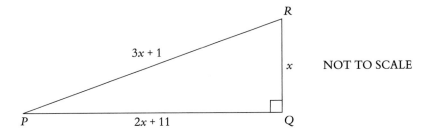

NOT TO SCALE

(a) Show that $2x^2 - 19x - 60 = 0$. [6]
(b) Solve the equation $2x^2 - 19x - 60 = 0$. [3]
(c) Write down the length of PQ. [1]

37 In this question all lengths are in centimetres.

 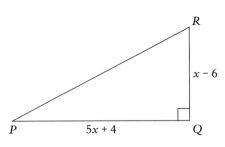

NOT TO SCALE

The area of the rectangle is equal to the area of the triangle.
(a) Show that $3x^2 - 34x - 24 = 0$. [3]
(b) Solve the equation $3x^2 - 34x - 24 = 0$. [3]
(c) Write down the length of AB. [1]

38

Box A contains 4 black balls and 1 white ball.

Box B contains 4 black balls and 3 white balls.

(a) A ball is chosen at random from box A.

Find the probability that this ball is white. [1]

(b) Anna chooses a box at random and then chooses a ball at random
from this box.

The probability that she chooses box A is $\frac{3}{5}$.

(i) Copy and complete the tree diagram.

Box   **Colour**

.... black

$\frac{3}{5}$ A

.... white

.... black

.... B

.... white

[2]

(ii) Find the probability that Anna chooses box B
and a white ball. [2]

(iii) Find the probability that Anna chooses a black ball. [3]

(c) Robert is asked to choose 2 balls at random from bag A or 2 balls
at random from box B.

He does not replace the first ball before choosing the second ball.

The probability that he chooses from bag A is $\frac{5}{8}$.

(i) Find the probability that Robert chooses two black balls. [2]

(ii) Find the probability that Robert chooses two
different coloured balls. [3]

Distance–time graphs

THIS SECTION WILL SHOW YOU HOW TO
- Read information from a distance–time graph
- Find the speed from a distance–time graph

 You can use travel graphs of distance against time to find out how the distance is changing. Speed is calculate using the formula:

$$\text{speed} = \frac{\text{distance travelled}}{\text{time taken}}$$

So the steepness of a **distance–time graph** represents the speed.

A straight line shows that the speed is constant (steady)

A horizontal line shows that the speed is zero

The steeper a line is, the greater the speed

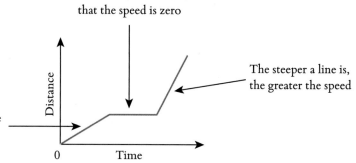

EXAMPLE

Roxy leaves home at 8:00 am to go on a bike ride.
She stops once for a rest. The travel graph shows information about her journey.

a   How long does she stop for a rest?

b   At what time does she arrive back home?

c   How far does she travel in total?

d   Calculate her average speed, in km/h, for the whole journey.

e   Calculate her fastest speed, in km/h, for the whole journey.

---

a   Four large squares on the horizontal axis represents one hour.
    So, each large square represents 15 minutes. She stops for a rest for 15 minutes.

b   She arrives back home at 10:30 am.

c   Total distance travelled = 20 + 20 = 40 km.

d   Average speed = $\dfrac{\text{total distance travelled}}{\text{total time taken}} = \dfrac{40}{2.5} = 16\,\text{km/h}$

e   Her fastest speed is when the graph is steepest. (This occurs between 8:00 and 8:30 am.)

    Speed = $\dfrac{\text{distance travelled}}{\text{time taken}} = \dfrac{12}{0.5} = 24\,\text{km/h}$

EXERCISE 7.1

1

Time (minutes)

The distance–time graph shows information about Paulo's car journey to work.

a Calculate the speed of the car during the first stage of the journey.
Give your answer in   **i**   kilometres/minute,   **ii**   kilometres/hour.

b Calculate the speed of the car during the second stage of the journey.
Give your answer in   **i**   kilometres/minute,   **ii**   kilometres/hour.

c Calculate the speed of the car during the third stage of the journey.
Give your answer in   **i**   kilometres/minute,   **ii**   kilometres/hour.

d Calculate the average speed for the whole journey.
Give your answer in kilometres/hour.

2

Time (am)

The travel graph shows information about Cara's walk to school each day.
She stops at a friend's house on the way.

a How long does she stop at her friend's house?

b Calculate her speed, in km/h, between 08:05 am and 08:15 am.
Give your answer in   **i**   kilometres/minute,   **ii**   kilometres/hour.

c Calculate her speed, in km/h, between 08:20 am and 08:35 am.
Give your answer in   **i**   kilometres/minute,   **ii**   kilometres/hour.

d Calculate her average speed, in km/h, for the whole journey.

3

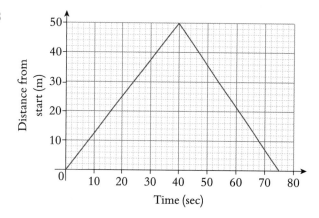

Henri swims in a 100-metre race. The swimming pool is 50 metres long.
He swims the first length in 40 seconds and the second length in 35 seconds.
a   Calculate his speed, in m/s, for the first length.
b   Calculate his speed, in m/s, for the second length.
c   Calculate his average speed, in m/s, for the total 100 metres.

4

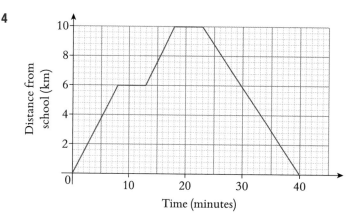

A school bus takes students home from school.
The bus stops at two villages. The bus then returns to school.
The distance–time graph shows information about the journey.
a   How far are the two villages from the school?
b   How long does the bus stop at each of the two villages?
c   Calculate the greatest speed of the bus.
     Give your answer in   i   kilometres/minute,   ii   kilometres/hour.
d   Calculate the average speed for the whole bus journey.
     Give your answer in   i   kilometres/minute,   ii   kilometres/hour.

5

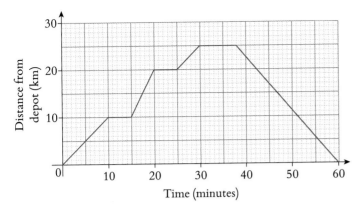

The distance–time graph shows information about the journey of a delivery van.

It starts at the depot and returns to the depot after 60 minutes.

a   How many times does the delivery van stop?

b   How many minutes did the delivery van stop altogether?

c   For which part of the journey did the delivery van travel fastest?

d   What is the total distance travelled by the delivery van?

e   Calculate the delivery van's average speed for the whole journey.

6   A train (P) leaves station A at 8 am and travels at a constant speed of 240 km/h towards station B.

The distance between the two stations is 180 km.

a   Show that the train arrives at station B at 8:45 am.

At 8:15 am a second train (Q) leaves station B and travels towards station A at a constant speed of 200 km/h.

b   Calculate the time that the train arrives at station A.

c   Copy and complete this travel graph to show the journey of the second train.

d   Use your graph to estimate the time at which the two trains pass each other.

UNIT 7

Speed–time graphs

THIS SECTION WILL SHOW YOU HOW TO

- Find the acceleration and distance travelled from a speed–time graph

You can use travel graphs of speed against time to find out how the speed is changing. The rate of change of speed is called the **acceleration**.

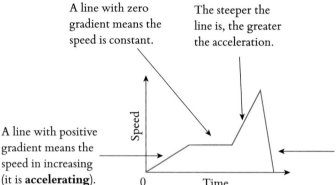

A line with zero gradient means the speed is constant.

The steeper the line is, the greater the acceleration.

A line with positive gradient means the speed in increasing (it is **accelerating**).

A line with negative gradient means the speed in decreasing (it is **decelerating**).

You must learn the following two rules:

In a speed–time graph,

acceleration = gradient of line = $\dfrac{\text{change in speed}}{\text{time}}$

distance travelled = area under the graph

The units for acceleration are metres per second or m/s² (or ms⁻²).

EXAMPLE

The speed–time graph shows the speed of a car over 100 seconds.

a Calculate the acceleration of the car over the first 20 seconds.

b Calculate the acceleration of the car over the last 40 seconds.

c Calculate the distance travelled by the car in the 100 seconds.

a Acceleration = gradient of line = $\dfrac{30}{20}$ = 1.5 m/s²

b Acceleration = gradient of line = $-\dfrac{30}{40}$ = −0.75 m/s²

➡ **NOTE:** this can also be called a deceleration of 0.75 m/s².

c Distance travelled = area under the graph

$= \left(\dfrac{1}{2} \times 20 \times 30\right) + (40 \times 30) + \left(\dfrac{1}{2} \times 40 \times 30\right)$

= 2100 m

➡ **NOTE:** the quickest method for finding the area under this graph is to use

Area of trapezium = $\dfrac{1}{2}(a + b)h$

$= \dfrac{1}{2}(100 + 40) \times 30 = 2100$

EXERCISE 7.2

1   The speed–time graph shows the speed of a car over the
    first 10 seconds of a journey.
    a   Calculate the acceleration between 0 and 3 seconds.
    b   Calculate the acceleration between 3 and 10 seconds.
    c   Calculate the total distance travelled by the car
        in the first 10 seconds of its journey.

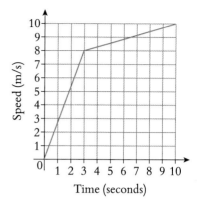

2   The speed–time graph shows the speed of a train over
    60 seconds.
    a   Calculate the acceleration between 0 and 20 seconds.
    b   Calculate the deceleration between 30 and 60 seconds.
    c   Calculate the total distance travelled by the train.

3   The speed–time graph shows the speed of a cyclist
    over 60 seconds.
    a   Calculate the acceleration between 0 and 20 seconds.
    b   Calculate the deceleration between 20 and 60 seconds.
    c   Calculate the total distance travelled by the cyclist.
    d   Calculate the average speed of the cyclist over the 60 seconds.

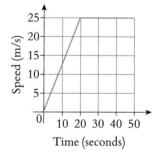

4   The speed–time graph shows the speed of a car over the first 50
    seconds of a journey.
    a   Calculate the acceleration between 0 and 20 seconds.
    b   Calculate the distance travelled in the first 20 seconds.
    c   Calculate the total distance travelled by the car in the first 50
        seconds of its journey.
    d   Calculate the average speed in the first 50 seconds of the journey.

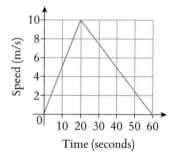

UNIT 7

5 The speed–time graph shows the speed of a cyclist over the first 100 seconds of a journey.

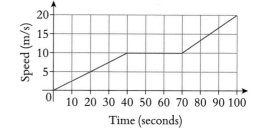

a Calculate the acceleration between 0 and 40 seconds.

b Calculate the acceleration between 70 and 100 seconds.

c Calculate the distance travelled in the first 40 seconds.

d Calculate the total distance travelled by the cyclist in the first 100 seconds of the journey.

6 The speed–time graph shows the first 60 seconds of a journey.

a Calculate the acceleration between 0 and 20 seconds.

b Calculate the acceleration between 20 and 40 seconds.

c Calculate the distance travelled in the first 60 seconds of the journey.

d Calculate the average speed in the first 60 seconds of the journey.

7 The speed–time graph shows the speed of a truck over a 3 minute journey.
The truck travels a total distance of 2.5 km.

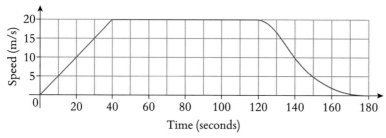

a Calculate the acceleration between 0 and 40 seconds.

b Calculate the distance travelled in the first 2 minutes of the journey.

c Estimate the distance travelled by the truck while it was decelerating.

8 The speed–time graph shows the speed of a car and the speed of a cyclist over a period of 140 seconds.

a Calculate the acceleration of the car during the first 40 seconds.

b Calculate the deceleration of the car between 60 and 140 seconds.

c Calculate the distance travelled by the cyclist in the 140 seconds.

d Calculate the distance travelled by the car in the 140 seconds.

e Calculate the distance travelled by the car while it was travelling faster than the cyclist.

9 The speed–time graph shows the speed for the first 7 minutes of a journey.

Calculate the distance travelled, in kilometres, during the 7 minutes.

10 The speed–time graph shows the speed of a car over 80 seconds. The total distance travelled is 1.28 km.

a Calculate the greatest speed of the car during the journey.

b Calculate the average speed of the car for the journey.

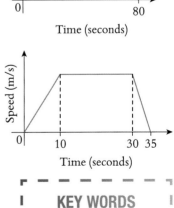

11 The speed–time graph shows the speed of a motorbike for a journey lasting 35 seconds.

The total distance travelled is 540 metres.

a Calculate the greatest speed of the motorbike during the journey.

b Calculate the acceleration between 0 and 10 seconds.

UNIT 7

Rearranging formulae 2

THIS SECTION WILL SHOW YOU HOW TO

- Change the subject of a formula where the variable appears more than once

EXAMPLE

a Make x the subject of $ax + bx = c$

$ax + bx = c$ *factorise*

$x(a + b) = c$ *divide both sides by $(a + b)$*

$$x = \frac{c}{a+b}$$

b Make x the subject of $a(x - b) = c(x + d)$

$a(x - b) = c(x + d)$ *expand the brackets*

$ax - ab = cx + cd$ *collect the x's on one side*

$ax - cx = ab + cd$ *factorise*

$x(a - c) = ab + cd$ *divide both sides by $(a - c)$*

$$x = \frac{ab+cd}{a-c}$$

EXAMPLE

Make x the subject of $a = \dfrac{bx+c}{dx+e}$

$a = \dfrac{bx+c}{dx+e}$ *multiply both sides by $(dx + e)$*

$a(dx + e) = bx + c$ *expand the brackets*

$adx + ae = bx + c$ *collect the x's on one side*

$adx - bx = c - ae$ *factorise*

$x(ad - b) = c - ae$ *divide both sides by $(ad - b)$*

$$x = \frac{c-ae}{ad-b}$$

EXAMPLE

Make x the subject of $a = \sqrt{\dfrac{b-x}{x}}$

$a = \sqrt{\dfrac{b-x}{x}}$ *square both sides*

$a^2 = \dfrac{b-x}{x}$ *multiply both sides by x*

$a^2x = b - x$ *collect the x's on one side*

$a^2x + x = b$ *factorise*

$x(a^2 + 1) = b$ *divide both sides by $(a^2 + 1)$*

$$x = \frac{b}{a^2 +1}$$

EXERCISE 7.3

Make x the subject of these formulae.

1   $px - qx = r$ 2 $ax = b + cx$ 3 $ax = bx + c$

4   $x = a + bx$ 5 $x + a = bx + c$ 6 $ax - b = cx + 5$

7   $3 - 2x = ax + b$ 8 $a^2 + ax + bx = 0$ 9 $a(x - 3) = b(x + 4)$

10   $7(ax + b) = 3(cx - d)$ 11 $a = \dfrac{x - 2}{x + 3}$ 12 $x = \dfrac{ax + b}{c}$

13   $e = \dfrac{dx + 1}{2 - 3x}$ 14 $\dfrac{ax + b}{2} = \dfrac{cx + d}{4}$ 15 $\dfrac{x - 4}{a} = \dfrac{x + 3}{b}$

16   $a = \dfrac{\sqrt{x + bx}}{c}$ 17 $a = \sqrt{\dfrac{2 + x}{x}}$ 18 $2\sqrt{\dfrac{x - p}{x}} = q$

19   $x^2 = a + bx^2$ 20 $ax^2 + b = c - dx^2$ 21 $f = \dfrac{xy}{x + y}$

22   $2a = \dfrac{a^2 x}{x + a}$

23

To make x the subject of the formula $a = \dfrac{b}{x} - c$ there are two possible methods:

Method 1		Method 2	
$a = \dfrac{b}{x} - c$	*multiply by x*	$a = \dfrac{b}{x} - c$	*add c to both sides*
$ax = b - cx$	*collect x's*	$a + c = \dfrac{b}{x}$	*multiply by x*
$ax + cx = b$	*factorise*	$x(a + c) = b$	*divide by (a + c)*
$x(a + c) = b$	*divide by (a + c)*	$x = \dfrac{b}{a + c}$	
$x = \dfrac{b}{a + c}$			

a $\dfrac{5}{x} + a = b$ b $a - \dfrac{b}{x} = c$ c $\dfrac{p}{x} + 5q = 2r$

d $\dfrac{6f}{x} + g = 7h$ e $\dfrac{a}{x} + 2 = \dfrac{b}{x} + 3c$ f $\dfrac{a}{x} - b = c - \dfrac{d}{x}$

Sequences

Linear sequences

A **sequence** is a list of numbers or diagrams that are connected by a rule.

4, 7, 10, 13, ...   and   ... are sequences.

The numbers in a sequence are called the **terms** of the sequence.

The **nth term** is used to describe a general term in a sequence.

If the *n*th term = 5*n* + 3   1st term = 5 × 1 + 6 = 11
                            2nd term = 5 × 2 + 6 = 16
                            3rd term = 5 × 3 + 6 = 21
                            4th term = 5 × 4 + 6 = 26
                The sequence is 11, 16, 21, 26, ...

It is called a linear sequence because the differences between terms are all the same.
The rule to find the next term (the **term-to-term rule**) is +5 or add 5.

EXAMPLE

Find the *n*th term of these sequences
a   1, 5, 9, 13, ...   **b**   45, 38, 31, 24, ...

---

a   1   5   9   13   The difference between the terms is 4.
       +4   +4   +4   The *n*th term formula will contain the expression 4*n*.

Term position   1   2   3   4

                              The rule is: multiply the term position by 4
                              and then subtract 3.

Term   1   5   9   13

*n*th term = 4*n* − 3

b   45   38   31   24   The difference between the terms is −7.
       −7   −7   −7   The *n*th term formula will contain the expression −7*n*

Term position   1   2   3   4

                              The rule is: multiply the term position by −7
                              and then add 52.

Term   45   38   31   24

*n*th term = −7*n* + 52   or   *n*th term = 52 − 7*n*

EXERCISE 7.4

1 Write down the next two terms for each of the following sequences.

  a 7, 11, 15, 19, ...
        b 10, 15, 20, 25, ...
        c 1, 2, 4, 8, 16, ...

  d 8, 9.5, 11, 12.5, ...
      e 20, 17, 14, 11, ...
       f 2, 5, 12.5, 31.25, ...

  g 108, 36, 12, 4, ...
     h 100, 48, 22, 9, ...
       i 1, 1, 2, 3, 5, 8, ...

  j 1, 3, 7, 15, 31, ...
     k −1, 4, 3, 7, 10, ...
     l 0.01, 0.1, 1, 10, ...

2 Write down the first 5 terms of the sequence whose nth term is

  a $n + 6$
       b $5n - 3$
      c $4n + 2$
      d $2n - 1$

  e $3n + 5$
      f $2n - 4$
      g $50 - 2n$
    h $16 - n$

  i $25 - 3n$
     j $0.5n + 2$
    k $30 - 0.5n$
   l $-4n + 7$

3

  Diagram 1   Diagram 2   Diagram 3   Diagram 4

  Omar says the nth diagram has $n + 2$ squares.
  Is he correct? Explain your answer.

4

  Diagram 1   Diagram 2   Diagram 3   Diagram 4
  1 cube   4 cubes   7 cubes   10 cubes
  How many cubes are in   **a** diagram 5,   **b** diagram 20,   **c** diagram n?

5 Find the nth term for these linear sequences.

  a 7, 11, 15, 19, ...
        b 0, 3, 6, 9, ...
        c 8, 13, 18, 23, ...

  d −4, −1, 2, 5, ...
      e 2, 4.5, 7, 9.5, ...
     f −8, −1, 6, 13, ...

  g 1, 4, 7, 10, ...
       h −1, 3, 7, 11, ...
      i −2, 4, 10, 16, ...

  j −5.5, −4, −2.5, −1, ...
   k 8, 10.5, 13, 15.5, ...
  l 6.02, 6.04, 6.06, 6.08, ...

6 Find the nth term for these linear sequences.

  a 21, 19, 17, 15, ...
     b 100, 96, 92, 88, ...
    c 15, 8, 1, −6, ...

  d 17, 14, 11, 8, ...
      e 5, 3, 1, −1, ...
       f 1.7, 1.3, 0.9, 0.5, ...

  g −2, −5, −8, −11, ...
   h 13, 11, 9, 7, ...
      i 2, 1.5, 1, 0.5, ...

7 nth term $= 8n - 5$. Which term in the sequence has a value of 155?

8 nth term $= 3n - 6$. Which term in the sequence has a value of 108?

9 nth term $= 54 - 4n$. Which term in the sequence has a value of −46?

10 nth term $= \dfrac{7n - 3}{2}$. Which term in the sequence has a value of 219?

Non-linear sequences

The sequence 5,   7,   10,   14, … is called a non-linear sequence

       + 2   + 3   + 4

because the differences between the terms are not the same.
You should be able to recognise and use the following non-linear sequences:

Square numbers   1, 4, 9, 16, … nth term = n^2

Cube numbers   1, 8, 27, 64, … nth term = n^3

Powers   For example 2, 4, 8, 16, … nth term = 2^n

EXAMPLE

Find the nth term of these sequences
a   1, 2, 4, 8, …   **b**   5, 8, 13, 20, …   **c**   2, 9, 28, 65, …

a   Term position   1   2   3   4

      Term   1   2   4   8
                 (2^0) (2^1) (2^2) (2^3)

      nth term = 2^{n-1}

The rule is: subtract 1 from the term position then do $2^{\text{(term position − 1)}}$

b   Term position   1   2   3   4

      Term   5   8   13   20
              $(1^2 + 4)$ $(2^2 + 4)$ $(3^2 + 4)$ $(4^2 + 4)$

      nth term = $n^2 + 4$

The rule is: square the term position then add 4.

c   Term position   1   2   3   4

      Term   2   9   28   65
              $(1^3 + 1)$ $(2^3 + 1)$ $(3^3 + 1)$ $(4^3 + 1)$

      nth term = $n^3 + 1$

The rule is: cube the term position and then add 1.

UNIT 7

EXERCISE 7.5

1 Write down the first 5 terms of the non-linear sequence whose nth term is

  a $n^2 + 2$ b $n^2 - 3$ c $3n^2$ d $n(n-2)$

  e $n^3 + 1$ f $n^3 - 4$ g $\dfrac{n+2}{n}$ h $\dfrac{n(n+1)(n+2)}{6}$

2 Find the nth term for these non-linear sequences.

  a   1, 4, 9, 16, …   b   0, 3, 8, 15, …

  c   2, 8, 18, 32, …   d   3, 6, 11, 18, …

  e   11, 14, 19, 26, …   f   3, 12, 27, 48, …

TOP TIP

These sequences are connected with square numbers.

3 Find the nth term for these non-linear sequences.

  a   1, 8, 27, 64, 125, …   b   0, 7, 26, 63, 124, …

  c   −1, 6, 25, 62, 123, …   d   2, 16, 54, 128, 250, …

  e   3, 10, 29, 66, 127, …

TOP TIP

These sequences are connected with cube numbers.

4 Find the nth term for these non linear sequences.

  a   10, 100, 1000, 10 000, …   b   2, 4, 8, 16, …

  c   3, 9, 27, 81, …   d   4, 8, 16, 32, …

  e   1, 3, 9, 27, …   f   0.1, 1, 10, 100, …

5 Find the nth term for the following sequences.

  a $1 \times 3, 2 \times 4, 3 \times 5, 4 \times 6, \dots$ b $1 \times 2 \times 3, 2 \times 3 \times 4, 3 \times 4 \times 5, 4 \times 5 \times 6, \dots$

  c $\dfrac{1}{6}, \dfrac{2}{7}, \dfrac{3}{8}, \dfrac{4}{9}, \dots$ d $\dfrac{2}{5}, \dfrac{3}{10}, \dfrac{4}{17}, \dfrac{5}{26}, \dots$

6 Write down the **next** term in each of the following sequences:

  a $128x^2, 64x^3, 32x^4, 16x^5, \dots$ b $6x^3, 9x^5, 12x^7, 15x^9, \dots$

  c $3x^2, 4x^3, 5x^4, 6x^5, \dots$ d $x^6y^2, x^5y^3, x^4y^4, x^3y^5, \dots$

7 The table shows the first four terms in three sequences A, B and C.

	Term 1	Term 2	Term 3	Term 4
Sequence A	1	8	27	64
Sequence B	4	7	10	13
Sequence C	−3	1	17	51

  a   Find the nth term of sequence A.

  b   Find the nth term of sequence B.

  c   Use your answers to parts **a** and **b** to write down the nth term of sequence C.

8 The diagram below shows how the fourth square pyramid number is made.

1 + 4 + 9 + 16 = 30

=

The fourth square pyramid number is 30.

Calculate the fifth and sixth square pyramid numbers.

9

Diagram 1   Diagram 2   Diagram 3   Diagram 4

  a How many circles are in diagram 4?
  b Draw the next diagram in the sequence.
  c Copy and complete the following table.

Diagram	1	2	3	4	5
Number of circles	$1 = \dfrac{1 \times 2}{2}$	$3 = \dfrac{2 \times 3}{2}$	$6 = \dfrac{3 \times 4}{2}$		

  d How many circles are in diagram n?
  e How many circles are in diagram 15?

10 The diagram shows four polygons. The diagonals for each polygon are shown.

  a Draw a polygon with seven sides. Show all the diagonals.
  b Copy and complete the table.

Number of sides	3	4	5	6	7	8
Number of diagonals	0	2				

  c How many diagonals are there in a 9-sided polygon?
  d How many diagonals are there in a 20-sided polygon?
  e Write down an expression for the number of diagonals in a polygon with n sides.

11 nth term $= 3n^2 + 7$. Which term in the sequence has a value of 3682?

12 nth term $= n^2 + 2n - 99$. Which term in the sequence has a value of 2501?

UNIT 7

13 a Write down the next row for the number pattern.

b The sum of the numbers in row 6 is $1 + 5 + 10 + 10 + 5 + 1 = 32 = 2^5$.
   Copy and complete the table.

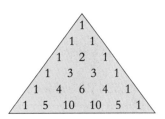

Row 1
Row 2
Row 3
Row 4
Row 5
Row 6

Row	1	2	3	4	5	6	7
Sum of numbers in row	$1 = 2^0$	$2 = 2^1$				$32 = 2^5$	

c Write down an expression for the sum of the numbers in row n.
d Which row has a sum of 32 768?

14

Year 1   Year 2   Year 3

The diagram shows the growth of a plant over three years.
Each year a flower is replaced by two stems and two flowers.
a Draw a diagram to show the plant in year 4.
b Copy and complete the table.

Year	1	2	3	4	5
Number of flowers	1	2	4		
Number of stems	1	3	7		

c How many flowers are there in year 6?
d How many flowers are there in year n?
e How many stems are there in year 6?
f How many stems are there in year n?

15 97, 75, 47, 40, …

The rule to find the next term in the sequence is: multiply together the digits of the last number and then add 12.
(To find the second term you work out $9 \times 7 + 12 = 63 + 12 = 75$.)
What is the 100th number in the sequence?

Further non-linear sequences

EXAMPLE

The nth term of the sequence 6, 11, 18, 27, ... is given by the formula
$$n\text{th term} = n^2 + bn + c$$
Find the values of b and c.

The 1st term is 6, so substitute $n = 1$ into the formula.
$$1^2 + b \times 1 + c = 6$$
$$b + c = 5$$
The 2nd term is 11, so substitute $n = 2$ into the formula.
$$2^2 + b \times 2 + c = 11$$
$$2b + c = 7$$
You now have a pair of simultaneous equations to solve.
$$2b + c = 7$$
$$b + c = 5$$
Subtracting gives $\quad b = 2 \quad$ so $\quad 2 + c = 5 \quad$ so $\quad c = 3$
$b = 2$ and $c = 3$

If you are asked to find the values of a, b and c when the nth term $= an^2 + bn + c$ for a given sequence then the problem is more complicated.
One method is to look at the differences in the terms.

For example

	6		13		24		39		58
First difference $\quad\quad\quad\quad$ 7 $\quad\quad$ 11 $\quad\quad$ 15 $\quad\quad$ 19

Second difference $\quad\quad\quad\quad\quad$ 4 $\quad\quad$ 4 $\quad\quad$ 4

The second differences are all the same.
This means that it is a quadratic sequence.

A second difference of 2	$\Rightarrow$	the nth term will contain n^2
A second difference of 4	$\Rightarrow$	the nth term will contain $2n^2$
A second difference of 6	$\Rightarrow$	the nth term will contain $3n^2$

The sequence 6, 13, 24, 39, 58, ... has a second difference of 4 so the nth term will contain the term $2n^2$

So $\quad\quad\quad\quad\quad\quad\quad\quad\quad n\text{th term} = 2n^2 + bn + c$

The 1st term is 6 $\quad\quad\quad\quad\quad 2 \times 1^2 + b \times 1 + c = 6$
$$b + c = 4$$
The 2nd term is 13 $\quad\quad\quad\quad 2 \times 2^2 + b \times 2 + c = 13$
$$2b + c = 5$$
Simultaneous equations are $\quad 2b + c = 5$
$\quad\quad\quad\quad\quad\quad\quad$ and $\quad\quad b + c = 4$
Subtracting gives $\quad\quad\quad\quad b = 1 \quad$ so $\quad 1 + c = 4 \quad$ so $\quad c = 3$
$$a = 2, b = 1 \quad \text{and} \quad c = 3$$

EXERCISE 7.6

1 8, 14, 22, 32, …

The nth term of the sequence is given by the formula nth term $= n^2 + bn + c$.
Find the values of b and c.

2 8, 16, 26, 38, 52, …

The nth term of the sequence is given by the formula nth term $= n^2 + bn + c$.
Find the values of b and c.

3 3, 4, 7, 12, 19, …

The nth term of the sequence is given by the formula nth term $= n^2 + bn + c$.
Find the values of b and c.

4 6, 15, 28, 45, 66, …

The nth term of the sequence is given by the formula nth term $= 2n^2 + bn + c$.
Find the values of b and c.

5 6, 16, 32, 54, 82, …

The nth term of the sequence is given by the formula nth term $= 3n^2 + bn + c$.
Find the values of b and c.

6 9, 20, 35, 54, 77, …

The nth term of the sequence is given by the formula nth term $= an^2 + bn + c$.
Find the values of a, b and c.

7 4, 7, 14, 25, 40, …

The nth term of the sequence is given by the formula nth term $= an^2 + bn + c$.
Find the values of a, b and c.

8 1, 11, 27, 49, 77, …

The nth term of the sequence is given by the formula nth term $= an^2 + bn + c$.
Find the values of a, b and c.

9 4.5, 12, 20.5, 30, 40.5, …

The nth term of the sequence is given by the formula nth term $= an^2 + bn + c$.
Find the values of a, b and c.

10 A sequence is made from sticks.

Diagram 1	Diagram 2	Diagram 3
4 sticks	12 sticks	24 sticks

How many sticks are needed to make:

  a diagram 4   **b** diagram 5   **c** diagram n?

11 A sequence is made from small squares.

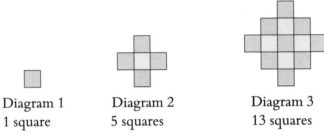

Diagram 1	Diagram 2	Diagram 3
1 square	5 squares	13 squares

How many small squares are needed to make:

  a diagram 4   **b** diagram 5   **c** diagram n?

12 The nth term of the sequence 2, 8, 20, 40, 70, … is $\dfrac{n(n+1)(n+2)}{3}$.

Write down the nth term of the sequence 4, 16, 40, 80, 140, …

13 a Find the value of $1^2 + 2^2 + 3^2 + 4^2$.

  b The sum of the first n square numbers can be found using the formula

$$1^2 + 2^2 + 3^2 + 4^2 + 5^2 + 6^2 + \ldots + n^2 = \frac{n(n+1)(2n+1)}{k}$$

    Use your answer to part **a** to find the value of k.

14 2, 21, 70, 161, 306, …

The nth term of the sequence is given by the formula nth term $= an^3 + 3n^2 + bn + 1$.
Find the values of a and b.

Further sequence notation

There are different ways of writing the terms of sequences, such as u_1, u_2, u_3, u_4, ...

EXAMPLE

A sequence is defined by $u_n = 3n + 5$.
Write down the first four terms of the sequence.

$u_1 = (3 \times 1) + 5 = 8$
$u_2 = (3 \times 2) + 5 = 11$
$u_3 = (3 \times 3) + 5 = 14$
$u_4 = (3 \times 4) + 5 = 17$
The first four terms of the sequence are 8, 11, 14 and 17.

EXAMPLE

$T_1 = 2$ $T_2 = 5$ $T_3 = 10$ $T_4 = 17$
Write down an expression for T_n

$T_1 = 1^2 + 1$
$T_2 = 2^2 + 1$
$T_3 = 3^2 + 1$
$T_4 = 4^2 + 1$
So $T_n = n^2 + 1$.

➡ **NOTE:** You should be able to recognise that the numbers 2, 5, 10 and 17 are connected to the square numbers 1, 4, 9 and 16.

EXERCISE 7.7

1   Write down the first four terms of these sequences.

   a $u_n = 2n - 3$ b $u_n = 5n + 1$ c $u_n = 3n + 2$
   d $u_n = n^2$ e $u_n = n^2 + 2$ f $u_n = (n - 1)^2$
   g $u_n = n^3$ h $u_n = n^3 - n^2$ i $u_n = (n + 1)^3$
   j $u_n = 2^n$ k $u_n = 3^{n-2}$ l $u_n = 10^{n+3}$
   m $u_n = \dfrac{n}{n+2}$ n $u_n = \dfrac{n+4}{n+5}$ o $u_n = \dfrac{n^2}{2n+3}$

2   Find the formula for the nth term (u_n) for each of these sequences.

   a $u_1 = 4$ $u_2 = 9$ $u_3 = 14$ $u_4 = 19$
   b $u_1 = 8$ $u_2 = 11$ $u_3 = 14$ $u_4 = 17$
   c $u_1 = 20$ $u_2 = 17$ $u_3 = 14$ $u_4 = 11$
   d $u_1 = 0$ $u_2 = 3$ $u_3 = 8$ $u_4 = 15$
   e $u_1 = 1$ $u_2 = 3$ $u_3 = 9$ $u_4 = 27$
   f $u_1 = \dfrac{4}{7}$ $u_2 = \dfrac{5}{9}$ $u_3 = \dfrac{6}{11}$ $u_4 = \dfrac{7}{13}$

┌─────────────────────────┐
│   **KEY WORDS**   │
│   sequence   │
│   term   │
│   term-to-term rule   │
│ nth term   │
└─────────────────────────┘

Exponential graphs

THIS SECTION WILL SHOW YOU HOW TO

- Recognise exponential graphs
- Draw exponential graphs
- Use exponential graphs in practical situations

Exponential functions are functions of the form $y = a^x$ where a is a positive constant.
Examples of exponential functions include $y = 2^x$, $y = 3^x$, etc.
The graph of an exponential function has a characteristic shape.

EXAMPLE

a Draw the graph of $y = 2^x$ for $-3 \leq x \leq 3$.
b Use your graph to estimate the value of x when $2^x = 6$.
c By drawing a tangent to your graph estimate the gradient of the graph when $x = 1$.

a First make a table of values for x and y

when $x = -3$, $y = 2^{-3} = \dfrac{1}{2^3} = \dfrac{1}{8} = 0.125$ when $x = -2$, $y = 2^{-2} = \dfrac{1}{2^2} = \dfrac{1}{4} = 0.25$

when $x = -1$, $y = 2^{-1} = \dfrac{1}{2^1} = \dfrac{1}{2} = 0.5$ when $x = 0$, $y = 2^0 = 1$

when $x = 1$, $y = 2^1 = 2$ when $x = 2$, $y = 2^2 = 4$

when $x = 3$, $y = 2^3 = 8$

x	−3	−2	−1	0	1	2	3
y	0.125	0.25	0.5	1	2	4	8

b When $2^x = 6$, $x \approx 2.6$

c When $x = 1$, gradient $\approx \dfrac{2.8}{2} = 1.4$

EXERCISE 7.8

For each of these functions make a table of values and draw the graph of the function between the stated x values.

1 $y = 3^x$ $\qquad -3 \le x \le 3$

2 $y = 3^{-x}$ $\qquad -3 \le x \le 3$

3 $y = 3^x + 1$ $\qquad -3 \le x \le 3$

4 $y = 3^x - 5$ $\qquad -3 \le x \le 3$

5 $y = 3^{x-2}$ $\qquad -1 \le x \le 5$

6 $y = 2^{-x}$ $\qquad -3 \le x \le 3$

7 $y = 2^x + 1$ $\qquad -3 \le x \le 3$

8 $y = 2^{x+1}$ $\qquad -4 \le x \le 2$

9 $y = 1 - 2^x$ $\qquad -3 \le x \le 3$

10 $y = \left(\dfrac{1}{2}\right)^x$ $\qquad -3 \le x \le 3$

11

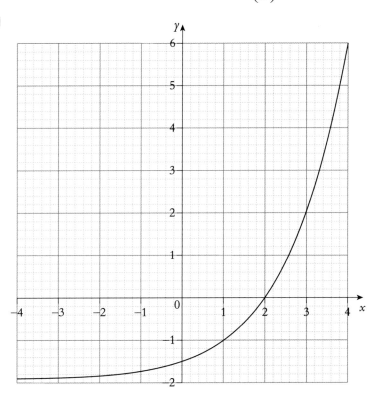

The diagram shows the accurate graph of $y = f(x)$

a Use the graph to find
  i $f(3)$
  ii $f(0)$.

b Use the graph to solve
  i $f(x) = 0$
  ii $f(x) = 4$.

c Copy the graph and draw a tangent to your graph to estimate the gradient of the graph when $x = 3$.

Practical applications of exponential graphs

Exponential curves are often used to model real-life situations.

A patch of mould is increasing in size.
The area (A cm^2) of the mould at time t days is given by the formula
$A = 0.9 \times (1.5)^t$.

a Use this formula to complete the table of values for t and A.

t	0	2	4	6	8	10
A	0.9					

b Draw the graph of $A = 0.9 \times (1.5)^t$

c Use your graph to estimate the number of days it will take for the area of the patch of mould to exceed 20 cm^2.

---

a when $t = 0$, $A = 0.9 \times 1.5^0 = 0.9$ when $t = 2$, $A = 0.9 \times 1.5^2 = 2.03$
when $t = 4$, $A = 0.9 \times 1.5^4 = 4.56$ when $t = 6$, $A = 0.9 \times 1.5^6 = 10.3$
when $t = 8$, $A = 0.9 \times 1.5^8 = 23.1$ when $t = 10$, $A = 0.9 \times 1.5^{10} = 51.9$

t	0	2	4	6	8	10
A	0.9	2.03	4.56	10.3	23.1	51.9

b

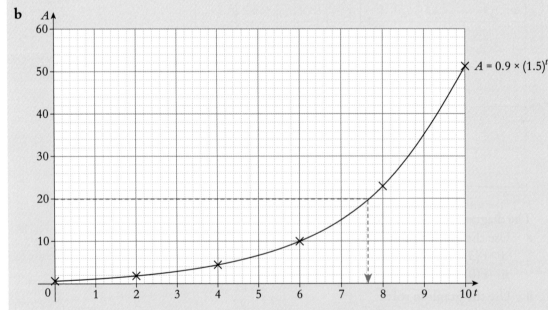

c When $A = 20$, $t \approx 7.65$ days.

EXERCISE 7.9

1   Kris invests $100 in a savings account.
    The number of dollars (y) in the savings account after x years is give by the formula
    $$y = 100 \times 1.1^x$$
    a   Use this formula to copy and complete the table of values for x and y.

x	0	4	8	12	16	20
y	100	146				

    b   Draw the graph of $y = 100 \times 1.1^x$
    c   Use your graph to estimate how many years, to the nearest year,
        it takes for Kris to have $500.

2   A car is bought for $40 000. The value, y, of the car after x years is given by the formula
    $$y = 40\,000 \times 0.9^x$$
    a   Use this formula to copy and complete the table of values for x and y.

x	0	2	4	6	8	10
y	40 000	32 400				

    b   Draw the graph of $y = 40\,000 \times 0.9^x$
    c   Use your graph to estimate the number of years that it takes for the car to halve in value.

3   The population of lizards on an island is increasing.
    The population, P, over time t years, is given by the formula
    $$P = 250 \times (1.2)^t$$
    a   Use this formula to copy and complete the table of values for t and P.

t	0	1	2	3	4	5	6
P	250						

    b   Draw the graph of $P = 250 \times (1.2)^t$
    c   Use your graph to estimate the number of years that it takes for the population to double.

4   The population of an endangered species of bird on an island is decreasing.
    The population, P, over time t years, is given by the formula
    $$P = 100 \times (0.75)^t$$
    a   Use this formula to copy and complete the table of values for t and P.

t	0	1	2	3	4	5	6	7	8
P	100								

    b   Draw the graph of $P = 100 \times (0.75)^t$
    c   Use your graph to estimate the number of years that
        it takes for the population to fall below 20.

> **KEY WORDS**
> exponential

Exponential graphs

UNIT 7

Sine and cosine ratios up to 180°

THIS SECTION WILL SHOW YOU HOW TO
- Draw the sine and cosine graphs from 0° to 180°
- Solve trigonometric equations using the symmetry properties of the sine and cosine curves

The sine curve

You can use your calculator to find the y values, in the table below, for the graph of $y = \sin x$.

x	0	30	60	90	120	150	180
y	0	0.5	0.87	1	0.87	0.5	0

The graph of $y = \sin x$ can then be drawn using the values in the table.

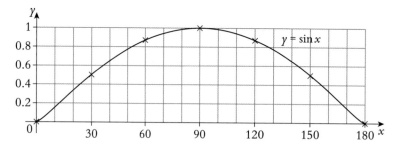

This graph starts at 0, increases to a maximum of 1 at 90° and then decreases to 0 at 180°.

The cosine curve

You can use your calculator to find the y values, in the table below, for the graph of $y = \cos x$.

x	0	30	60	90	120	150	180
y	1	0.87	0.5	0	-0.5	-0.87	-1

The graph of $y = \cos x$ can then be drawn using the values in the table.

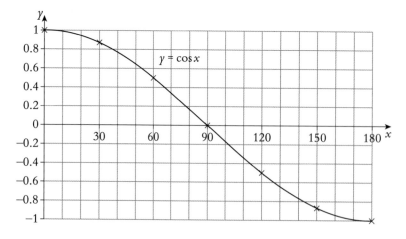

This graph starts at 1, decreases to 0 at 90° and then decreases further to −1 at 180°.
It is important to remember the shape of the sine and cosine curves.

Solving trigonometric equations

You are expected to be able to solve **trigonometric equations**, giving your answers in the range $0° \leq x \leq 180°$.

EXAMPLE

Solve the equation $\sin x = 0.4$ for $0° \leq x \leq 180°$.

You can find one answer to the equation $\sin x = 0.4$ using your calculator as follows
$$x = \sin^{-1}(0.4)$$
$$x = 23.6°$$
You must now check the sine curve
to see if there are any more answers.
The graph shows that there is another answer.
Using the symmetry of the curve,
the second answer is $x = 180° - 23.6° = 156.4°$
So the solution is $x = 23.6°$ or $x = 156.4°$

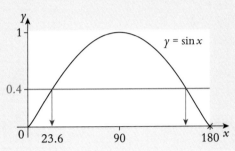

EXAMPLE

Solve the equation $\cos x = 0.624$ for $0° \leq x \leq 180°$.

Using a calculator
$$x = \cos^{-1}(0.624)$$
$$x = 51.4°$$
Now check the cosine curve
to see if there are any more answers.
There are no more answers.
So the only solution is $x = 51.4°$

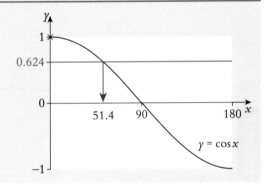

EXERCISE 7.10

Solve these equations for angles in the range $0° \leq x \leq 180°$.

1   $\cos x = 0.2$
2   $\cos x = 0.7$
3   $\sin x = 0.88$

4   $\cos x = -0.35$
5   $\sin x = 0.2$
6   $\sin x = 1$

7   $\cos x = -1$
8   $\sin x = 0$
9   $\cos x = -2$

10 $\sin x = -0.75$
11 $\cos x = -0.76$
12 $\sin x = 0.81$

13 $\cos x = \dfrac{2}{7}$
14 $\sin x = \dfrac{3}{5}$
15 $\cos x = -\dfrac{3}{4}$

16 $5\sin x = 4$
17 $3\sin x = -1$
18 $8\cos x = -9$

19 $2 + \cos x = 2.5$
20 $1 - \sin x = 0.66$
21 $3 + 2\sin x = 4$

22 $(\cos x)^2 = \dfrac{1}{4}$
23 $(\sin x)^2 = \dfrac{4}{9}$
24 $2 + (\cos x)^2 = 2.9$

> **KEY WORDS**
> sine curve
> cosine curve
> trigonometric equation

Area of a triangle

 You can use trigonometry to work out the area of a triangle.

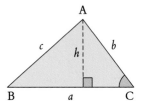

➡ **NOTE:**
angle A is opposite side a
angle B is opposite side b
angle C is opposite side c

Using the right-hand triangle $\sin C = \dfrac{h}{b}$ so $h = b \sin C$

Area of triangle $= \dfrac{1}{2} \times$ base $\times$ perpendicular height $= \dfrac{1}{2} \times a \times h$

replacing h by $b \sin C$ gives area $= \dfrac{1}{2} ab \sin C$

> Area of triangle $= \dfrac{1}{2} ab \sin C$

You can use this formula when you know two sides and the angle between them.

EXAMPLE

Find the area of these triangles.

a

b

a Area $= \dfrac{1}{2} \times 8.7 \times 5.6 \times \sin 35°$

$= 14.0 \text{ cm}^2$ (to 3 s.f.)

b Equilateral triangle so each angle is 60°

Area $= \dfrac{1}{2} \times 5 \times 5 \times \sin 60°$

$= 10.8 \text{ cm}^2$ (to 3 s.f.)

EXAMPLE

Find the area of the parallelogram.

Divide the parallelogram into two congruent triangles.

Area of triangle $= \dfrac{1}{2} \times 8 \times 4 \times \sin 120° = 13.856...$

Area of parallelogram $= 2 \times 13.856 = 27.7 \text{ cm}^2$ (to 3 s.f.)

EXERCISE 7.11

1 Find the area of each triangle.

a

5 cm

8 cm 130°

b

10 cm 54° 11 cm

c

5 cm

140°

6 cm

d

4.5 cm

82°

3 cm

e

6 cm

35°

9 cm

f

9.4 cm

58°

8.2 cm

2 Find the area of each equilateral triangle.

a

7 cm

b

10 cm

c

8.2 cm

3 Find the area of each parallelogram.

a

15 cm

72°

12 cm

b

7.4 cm

105°

3.6 cm

c

10 cm

7 cm

58°

4 Find the area of each rhombus.

a

6 cm

44°

b

8.2 cm

25°

c

4.6 cm

100°

5 Find the area of a regular hexagon with sides of length 12 cm.

UNIT 7

6 The area of the equilateral triangle is 40 cm².
Calculate the value of x.

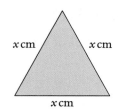

7 The area of the rhombus is 65 cm².
Calculate the value of x.

8 The area of the regular hexagon is 100 cm².
Calculate the value of x.

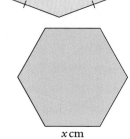

9 The area of the triangle is 20 cm².
Calculate the value of x.

10 The area of the isosceles triangle is 82 cm².
Calculate the value of x.

11 The regular tetrahedron has edges of length 10 cm.
Calculate the total surface area of the tetrahedron.

12 The regular octahedron has edges of length 6 cm.
Calculate the total surface area of the octahedron.

13 The triangle has an area of 18 cm².
Calculate the two possible values of x.

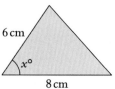

Area of a segment

segment

You can calculate the area of a segment of a circle using

> Area of segment = area of sector − area of triangle

Find the area of the shaded segment.

Area of segment = area of sector − area of triangle

$$= \frac{100}{360} \times \pi \times 5^2 - \frac{1}{2} \times 5 \times 5 \times \sin 100°$$

$$= 9.51 \text{ cm}^2 \text{ (to 3 s.f.)}$$

EXERCISE 7.12

1   Calculate the area of the shaded segment in each circle.

a

b

c

d

e

f

2   The area of the shaded segment is 100 cm².
    Calculate the value of r.

UNIT 7

Cumulative frequency

THIS SECTION WILL SHOW YOU HOW TO

- Construct and use cumulative frequency diagrams
- Estimate and interpret the median, percentiles, quartiles and inter-quartile range

Cumulative frequency tables and diagrams

You can construct a **cumulative frequency** table from a grouped frequency table.

The grouped frequency table below shows information about the times taken, t seconds, for 25 students to solve a puzzle.

The cumulative frequency (cf) of the data is found by calculating the running total of the frequencies (f).

For example, to find the number of people taking twenty seconds or less ($t \leq 20$) you add 3 and 6. To find the number of people taking thirty seconds or less ($t \leq 30$) you add 3, 6 and 10.

Grouped frequency table

Time (t)	f
$0 < t \leq 10$	3
$10 < t \leq 20$	6
$20 < t \leq 30$	10
$30 < t \leq 40$	4
$40 < t \leq 50$	2

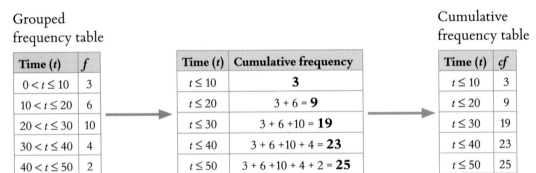

Time (t)	Cumulative frequency
$t \leq 10$	**3**
$t \leq 20$	3 + 6 = **9**
$t \leq 30$	3 + 6 +10 = **19**
$t \leq 40$	3 + 6 +10 + 4 = **23**
$t \leq 50$	3 + 6 +10 + 4 + 2 = **25**

Cumulative frequency table

Time (t)	cf
$t \leq 10$	3
$t \leq 20$	9
$t \leq 30$	19
$t \leq 40$	23
$t \leq 50$	25

To draw a cumulative frequency diagram (or c.f. graph), you must use the values from the cumulative frequency table.

So for the above example, you must plot (10, 3), (20, 9), (30, 19), (40, 23) and (50, 25). It is important to note that the points are plotted at the upper end of the class.

Cumulative frequency diagram

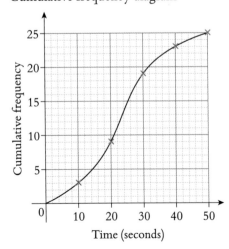

There are no students who took 0 seconds or less so the point (0, 0) can also be plotted. Draw a smooth curve through the points.

➡ **NOTE:** it is important to remember that the cumulative frequency diagram shows the number of students taking less than or equal to a particular time.

A cumulative frequency diagram can be used to find estimates.

The green line shows how the curve can be used to estimate the number of students that took 26 seconds or less to solve the puzzle.

The number of students taking 26 seconds or less = 15

The red line shows how the curve can be used to estimate the number of students that took more than 35 seconds to solve the puzzle.

The number of students taking 35 seconds or less = 21
So, the number of people taking more than 35 seconds
= 25 − 21 = 4

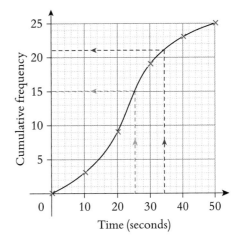

EXERCISE 7.13

1   The grouped frequency table shows information about the lengths of 50 telephone calls.

Time (t mins)	Frequency
$0 < t \leq 2$	15
$2 < t \leq 4$	12
$4 < t \leq 6$	10
$6 < t \leq 8$	8
$8 < t \leq 10$	5

Time (t mins)	Cumulative frequency
$t \leq 2$	15
$t \leq 4$	27
$t \leq 6$	
$t \leq 8$	
$t \leq 10$	

a   Copy and complete the cumulative frequency table.
b   Draw a cumulative frequency diagram to show the information.
c   Estimate the number of phone calls that took 7 minutes or less.
d   Estimate the number of phone calls that took more than 3 minutes.

2   The grouped frequency table shows information about the heights of 100 boys.

Height (h cm)	Frequency
$155 < h \leq 160$	7
$160 < h \leq 165$	24
$165 < h \leq 170$	35
$170 < h \leq 175$	22
$175 < h \leq 180$	12

Height (h cm)	Cumulative frequency
$h \leq 160$	7
$h \leq 165$	31
$h \leq 170$	
$h \leq 175$	
$h \leq 180$	

a   Copy and complete the cumulative frequency table.
b   Draw a cumulative frequency diagram to show the information.
c   Estimate the number of boys that are 162 cm or less in height.
d   Estimate the number of boys that are more than 173 cm in height.

3 The table shows information about the marks, m %, achieved in an examination by a group of students.

Mark (m %)	Frequency
$0 < m \leq 20$	5
$20 < m \leq 40$	10
$40 < m \leq 60$	14
$60 < m \leq 80$	17
$80 < m \leq 100$	4

    a Construct a cumulative frequency table for this data.
    b Draw a cumulative frequency diagram to show the data.
    c Estimate the number of students that scored 68% or less.
    d The pass mark was 48%.
       Estimate the number of students that passed the exam.

4 60 newborn babies are weighed.
The table shows the results.

Mass (m kg)	Frequency
$2 < m \leq 2.5$	6
$2.5 < m \leq 3$	10
$3 < m \leq 3.5$	17
$3.5 < m \leq 4$	13
$4 < m \leq 4.5$	8
$4.5 < m \leq 5$	6

    a Construct a cumulative frequency table for this data.
    b Draw a cumulative frequency diagram to show the data.
    c Estimate the number of newborn babies with a mass of 3.2 kg or less.
    d Estimate the number of newborn babies with a mass greater than 3.7 kg.

5 The table shows information about the midday temperatures, t °C, recorded over fifty consecutive days.

Temperature (t ° C)	Frequency
$6 < t \leq 10$	2
$10 < t \leq 14$	4
$14 < t \leq 18$	20
$18 < t \leq 22$	15
$22 < t \leq 26$	9

    a Draw a cumulative frequency diagram to show the data.
    b Estimate the number of days with a temperature of 17 °C or less.
    c Estimate the percentage of days when the temperature was over 21 °C.

6 The cumulative frequency table shows information about the speeds, v km/h, of sixty cars passing a checkpoint.

Speed (v km/h)	Cumulative frequency
$v \leq 30$	6
$v \leq 40$	24
$v \leq 50$	50
$v \leq 60$	60

Speed (v km/h)	Frequency
$0 < v \leq 30$	6
$30 < v \leq 40$	18
$40 < v \leq 50$	
$50 < v \leq 60$	

Copy and complete the grouped frequency table for this data.

7 The cumulative frequency table shows information about the marks, $m\%$, obtained in an examination by a group of eighty students.

Mark ($m\ \%$)	Cumulative frequency
$m \leq 20$	3
$m \leq 40$	21
$m \leq 60$	58
$m \leq 80$	79
$m \leq 100$	80

Mark ($m\ \%$)	Frequency
$0 < m \leq 20$	3
$20 < m \leq 40$	18
$40 < m \leq 60$	
$60 < m \leq 80$	
$80 < m \leq 100$	

Copy and complete the grouped frequency table for this data.

8 The cumulative frequency diagram shows information about the waiting times of forty patients at a doctor's surgery.

Time (minutes)

a Estimate the number of patients that waited 24 minutes or less.

b Estimate the number of patients that waited more than 36 minutes.

c Use the information in the diagram to copy and complete the following two tables.

Time (t mins)	Cumulative frequency
$t \leq 10$	
$t \leq 20$	
$t \leq 30$	
$t \leq 40$	
$t \leq 50$	

Time (t mins)	Frequency
$0 < t \leq 10$	
$10 < t \leq 20$	
$20 < t \leq 30$	
$30 < t \leq 40$	
$40 < t \leq 50$	

d Calculate an estimate of the mean waiting time.

9 Forty light bulbs were tested to see how long they would last. The cumulative frequency diagram shows information about how long they lasted.

Time (hours)

a Estimate the number of light bulbs that lasted 740 hours or less.

b Estimate the percentage of light bulbs that lasted more than 960 hours.

c Use the information in the diagram to complete the following two tables.

Time (t hours)	Cumulative frequency
$t \leq 700$	
$t \leq 800$	
$t \leq 900$	
$t \leq 1000$	
$t \leq 1100$	

Time (t hours)	Frequency
$600 < t \leq 700$	
$700 < t \leq 800$	
$800 < t \leq 900$	
$900 < t \leq 1000$	
$1000 < t \leq 1100$	

d Calculate an estimate of the mean time.

The median, quartiles and inter-quartile range

The median, **lower quartile** (LQ), **upper quartile** (UQ) and **inter-quartile range** (IQR) for a set of data can be estimated using a cumulative frequency diagram.

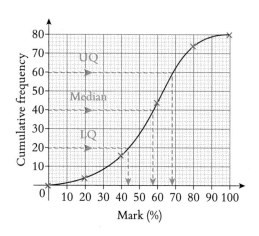

To find the median:
Draw a horizontal line from 40 $\left(\frac{1}{2} \text{ of } 80\right)$ on the cf axis to meet the curve.
The median value is where the vertical line from this point meets the horizontal axis.

To find the lower quartile:
Draw a horizontal line from 20 $\left(\frac{1}{4} \text{ of } 80\right)$ on the cf axis to meet the curve.
The LQ value is where the vertical line from this point meets the horizontal axis.

To find the upper quartile:
Draw a horizontal line from 60 $\left(\frac{3}{4} \text{ of } 80\right)$ on the cf axis to meet the curve.
The UQ value is where the vertical line from this point meets the horizontal axis.

The values are taken from the horizontal axis.

Median = 58%   Lower quartile = 44%   Upper quartile = 68%

The inter-quartile range is a measure of spread of the middle 50% of the data and is calculated using:

> Inter-quartile range = upper quartile – lower quartile

So for this cumulative frequency diagram:
Inter-quartile range = 68% – 44% = 24%

Percentiles
Percentiles divide the cumulative frequency into hundredths.
The lower quartile is the 25th percentile.
The median is the 50th percentile.
The upper quartile is the 75th percentile.

To find the 60th percentile for this diagram:
Draw a horizontal line from 48 (60% of 80) on the cumulative frequency axis to meet the curve.
The 60th percentile value is where the vertical line from this point meets the horizontal axis.
60th percentile = 62%

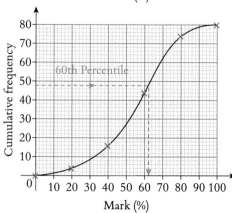

Comparing data sets

You can compare data sets using information obtained from a cumulative frequency diagram.
To do this you compare:

- The medians (this is a measure of average),
- The inter-quartile ranges (this is a measure of spread).

The table shows information about the examination results of a group of boys and girls.
Compare the boys' results with the girls' results.

	Median mark	IQR
Boys	56	24
Girls	52	35

The boys' median is greater than the girls' median, so on average the boys achieved higher marks.
The IQR for the girls is greater than the IQR for the boys, so the marks for the girls are more varied.

EXERCISE 7.14

1 For each of the cumulative frequency diagrams find estimates for
  i   the median,   ii   the LQ,   iii   the UQ,
  iv   the IQR,   v   the 40th percentile.

a

b

c

d

2   200 apples are weighed.
The table shows the results.
a   Draw a cumulative frequency diagram to
show the data.
b   Use your cumulative frequency diagram to find
i   the median,
ii   the lower quartile,
iii the upper quartile,
iv   the inter-quartile range,
v   the 68th percentile.

Mass (m kg)	Frequency
$100 < m \leq 110$	2
$110 < m \leq 120$	2
$120 < m \leq 130$	9
$130 < m \leq 140$	19
$140 < m \leq 150$	40
$150 < m \leq 160$	48
$160 < m \leq 170$	40
$170 < m \leq 180$	24
$180 < m \leq 190$	12
$190 < m \leq 200$	4

3   150 passengers on an aircraft had their baggage weighed.
The table shows the results.
a   Draw a cumulative frequency diagram to show the data.
b   Use your cumulative frequency diagram to find
i   the median,
ii   the lower quartile,
iii the upper quartile,
iv   the inter-quartile range,
v   the 84th percentile.

Mass (m kg)	Frequency
$0 < m \leq 5$	10
$5 < m \leq 10$	20
$10 < m \leq 15$	38
$15 < m \leq 20$	35
$20 < m \leq 25$	25
$25 < m \leq 30$	12
$30 < m \leq 35$	10

4   60 potatoes are weighed.
The table shows the results.
a   Draw a cumulative frequency diagram to show the data.
b   Use your cumulative frequency diagram to find
i   the median,
ii   the lower quartile,
iii the upper quartile,
iv   the inter-quartile range,
v   the 36th percentile.

Mass (m g)	Frequency
$200 < m \leq 250$	4
$250 < m \leq 300$	7
$300 < m \leq 350$	3
$350 < m \leq 400$	16
$400 < m \leq 450$	21
$450 < m \leq 500$	9

5

	Median time	IQR
10 to 20 year olds	150	20
60 to 70 year olds	300	28

The table shows information about the reaction times (milliseconds) of a group of 10 to 20
year olds and the reaction times of a group of 60 to 70 year olds.
Compare the two sets of data.

6

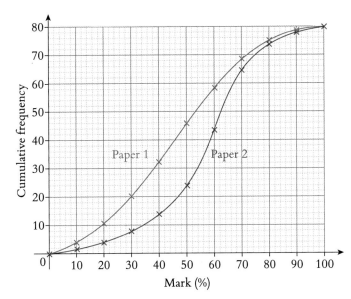

Mark (%)

The cumulative frequency diagram shows information about the marks scored by a group of eighty students on Paper 1 and Paper 2 of a mathematics examination.

a   Use the cumulative frequency diagram to copy and complete the following table.

	Median	LQ	UQ	IQR
Paper 1				
Paper 2				

b   Compare the marks for Paper 1 and Paper 2.

7   In a survey, 100 shoppers leaving two different supermarkets were asked how much they had just spent. The results are shown in the two tables.

Supermarket A

Amount ($ x)	Frequency
$0 < x \leq 30$	2
$30 < x \leq 60$	25
$60 < x \leq 90$	47
$90 < x \leq 120$	16
$120 < x \leq 150$	10

Supermarket B

Amount ($ x)	Frequency
$0 < x \leq 30$	14
$30 < x \leq 60$	24
$60 < x \leq 90$	34
$90 < x \leq 120$	26
$120 < x \leq 150$	2

a   Draw a cumulative frequency diagram to show the information about the amounts spent in supermarket A and in supermarket B.

b   Use the cumulative frequency diagram to copy and complete the following table.

	Median	LQ	UQ	IQR
Supermarket A				
Supermarket B				

c   Compare the amounts of money spent in supermarkets A and B.

UNIT 7

1 The diagram shows a speed-time graph for the journey of a car.

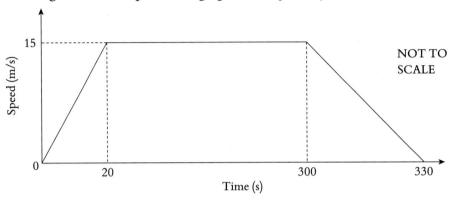

(a) Calculate the acceleration during the first 20 seconds. [1]

(b) Calculate the total distance travelled. [3]

2 The diagram shows information about the first 200 seconds of a train journey.

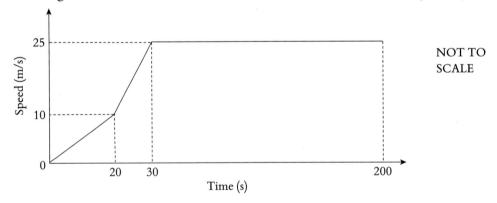

(a) Calculate the acceleration during the first 20 seconds. [1]

(b) Calculate the distance travelled by the car in the first 200 seconds. [3]

(c) Calculate the average speed of the car for the first 200 seconds. [2]

3 Rearrange the formula to make c the subject.

$$a = \frac{2bc}{b+c}$$

[4]

4 Rearrange the formula to make p the subject.

$$\frac{3}{p} - 4q = 5r$$ [4]

5 Rearrange the formula to make x the subject.

$$ax^2 - c = bx^2 - d$$ [4]

6 The nth term of a sequence is $7 - 4n$.

Write down the first two terms of this sequence. [1]

7 The nth term of a sequence is $3n - 11$.

Which term in this sequence has a value of 124? [2]

8 Find the nth term of these sequences.

(a) 4,   11,   18,   25,   ... [2]
(b) 4,   8,   16,   32,   ... [2]

9 Find the nth term of these sequences.

(a) 7,   4,   1,   −2,   ... [2]
(b) −1,   8,   16,   32,   ... [2]
(c) x^2, $3x^3$, $6x^4$, $10x^5$, $15x^6$,   ... [2]

10 The nth term of a sequence is $n^2 - 13n - 15$.

Which term in this sequence has a value of 53? [3]

11 10,   21,   36,   41,   55,   ...

The nth term of this sequence is given by the formula nth term $= 2n^2 + an + b$.

Find the value of a and the value of b. [4]

12 −2,   0,   8,   22,   42,   ...

The nth term of this sequence is given by the formula nth term $= pn^2 + qn + r$.

Find the values of p, q and r. [6]

13 The table shows the first four terms in sequences A, B, C, D and E.

Term	1	2	3	4	5		nth term
Sequence A	3	5	7	9			
Sequence B	$\dfrac{2}{9}$	$\dfrac{3}{16}$	$\dfrac{4}{25}$	$\dfrac{5}{36}$			
Sequence C	1	2	8	16			
Sequence D	−2	1	6	13			
Sequence E	3	1	2	3			

Complete the table to show 5th term and the nth term of each sequence. [14]

14 The table shows some values for $y = 3 - 1.8^x$.

x	−2	−1.5	−1	−0.5	0	0.5	1	1.5	2	2.5	3
y	2.69		2.44		2	1.66	1.2	0.59	−0.24		−2.83

(a) Complete the table. [3]
(b) On the grid, draw the graph of $y = 3 - 1.8^x$ for $-2 \le x \le 3$.

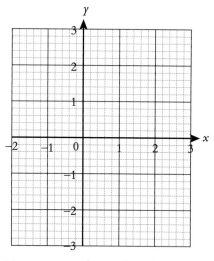

[4]
(c) Use your graph to solve the equation $3 - 1.8^x = 1$. [2]
(d) By drawing a suitable tangent to the curve, estimate the gradient of the curve at the point (1, 1.2). [3]

15 One hundred students were timed when solving a problem.
The results are shown in the table.

Time (t minutes)	$5 < t \le 5.5$	$5.5 < t \le 6$	$6 < t \le 6.5$	$6.5 < t \le 7$	$7 < t \le 7.5$	$7.5 < t \le 8$
Frequency	11	24	33	16	12	4

(a) Complete the cumulative frequency table.

Time (t minutes)	$t \le 5.5$	$t \le 6$	$t \le 6.5$	$t \le 7$	$t \le 7.5$	$t \le 8$
Frequency	11	35				100

[1]

(b) On the grid, draw a cumulative frequency diagram to show this information.

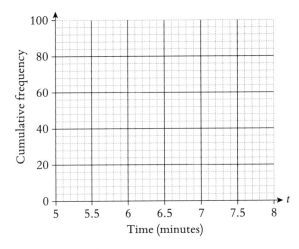

[3]

(c) Use your graph to estimate
  (i) the median, [1]
  (ii) the inter-quartile range, [2]
  (iii) the number of people that took more than 7.3 minutes. [2]

UNIT 7

16 Solve the equation $\sin x = 0.5$ for $0° \leq x \leq 360°$. [2]

17

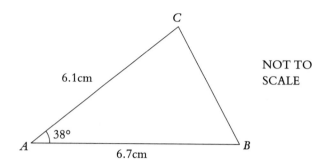

Calculate the area of triangle ABC. [2]

18

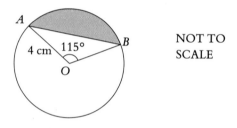

The diagram shows a circle, centre O, with radius 4 cm.
AB is a chord of the circle and angle AOB is $115°$.
Calculate the shaded area. [3]

19

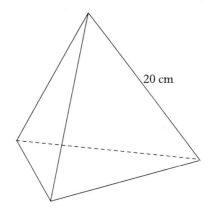

NOT TO
SCALE

20 cm

The diagram shows a solid triangular-based pyramid.
The length of each edge of the pyramid is 20 cm.
Calculate the total surface area of this pyramid.

[3]

UNIT 7

Rational and irrational numbers

THIS SECTION WILL SHOW YOU HOW TO
- Change a recurring decimal to a fraction
- Identify rational and irrational numbers

Recurring decimals

Recurring decimals contain digits that are repeated over and over again.

Dots are used to show how the decimals recur.

$$\frac{2}{3} = 0.666... = 0.\dot{6}$$

$$\frac{4}{11} = 0.363636... = 0.\dot{3}\dot{6}$$

$$\frac{5}{12} = 0.41666... = 0.41\dot{6}$$

$$\frac{2}{7} = 0.2857142857142... = 0.\dot{2}8571\dot{4}$$

➡ **NOTE:** to change a fraction to a decimal divide the numerator by the denominator.

eg $\frac{2}{3} = 2 \div 3$

To change $0.\dot{2}\dot{3}$ to a fraction use the following method:

let $x = 0.232323...$	*multiply both sides by 100*
$100x = 23.232323...$	*write $x = 0.232323...$ underneath*
$x = 0.232323...$	*subtract the two equations*

$$99x = 23$$

$$x = \frac{23}{99}$$

➡ **NOTE:** if 1 digit recurs multiply by 10.
If 2 digits recur multiply by 100.
If 3 digits recur multiply by 1000.

➡ **CHECK:**
   $23 \div 99 = 0.232323...$ ✓

Rational numbers

A **rational number** is a number that can be written in the form $\frac{a}{b}$ where a and b are integers.

Rational numbers include:

- All fractions, for example $\frac{4}{5}$
- All integers, for example $5 = \frac{5}{1}$
- All mixed numbers, for example $2\frac{1}{3} = \frac{7}{3}$
- All terminating decimals, for example $5.19 = \frac{519}{100}$
- All recurring decimals, for example $0.\dot{6} = \frac{2}{3}$
- All square roots that can be calculated exactly, for example $\sqrt{25} = 5 = \frac{5}{1}$

Irrational numbers

An **irrational number** is a number that *cannot* be written in the form $\frac{a}{b}$ where a and b are integers. Examples of irrational numbers are π, $\sqrt{7}$ and $\sqrt[3]{2}$.

EXERCISE 8.1

1   Write these fractions as recurring decimals.

a $\dfrac{1}{3}$ b $\dfrac{5}{9}$ c $\dfrac{2}{11}$ d $\dfrac{7}{22}$ e $\dfrac{11}{18}$

f $\dfrac{59}{90}$ g $\dfrac{5}{33}$ h $\dfrac{19}{111}$ i $\dfrac{2}{7}$ j $\dfrac{5}{13}$

2   Write these recurring decimals as fractions.

a $0.\dot{3}$ b $0.\dot{7}$ c $0.\dot{3}\dot{6}$ d $0.\dot{6}\dot{8}$ e $0.1\dot{4}$

f $0.1\dot{4}\dot{5}$ g $0.2\dot{3}\dot{8}$ h $0.5\dot{2}$ i $0.6\dot{1}$ j $0.1\dot{3}\dot{6}$

3   $\sqrt{49}$ $\sqrt{36}$ $\sqrt{40}$ $\sqrt{\dfrac{4}{9}}$ $\sqrt{64}$

From the list above, write down
a   a factor of 12   b   an irrational number
c   a cube number   d   a prime number
e   a number smaller than 1.

4   Which of these numbers are **not** rational numbers?

$\dfrac{4}{7}$ π $7\dfrac{1}{11}$ $\sqrt{\dfrac{5}{8}}$ 0.003 $\sqrt{0.04}$ $\sqrt[3]{8}$

5   Which of these numbers are irrational?

$\sqrt{1}$ $\sqrt{2}$ $\sqrt{3}$ $\sqrt{4}$ $\sqrt{5}$ $\sqrt{6}$

6   Is x rational or irrational for each of these right-angled triangles.

a

b

7   The circle has radius 5 cm.
The circle touches the sides of the square.
Calculate
a   the area of the circle,
b   the area of the square,
c   the shaded area.
State whether each of your answers is rational or irrational.

UNIT 8

Solving quadratic equations using the formula

THIS SECTION WILL SHOW YOU HOW TO
- Solve quadratic equations using the quadratic formula

 Some quadratic equations do not factorise.
For example: $x^2 - 5x + 3 = 0$ does not factorise because you cannot find two integers that multiply to give 3 and add to give -5.

> Quadratic equations of the form $ax^2 + bx + c = 0$ can be solved using the formula
> $$x = \frac{-b \pm \sqrt{b^2 - 4ac}}{2a}$$

In the formula:

a is the coefficient of the x^2 term

b is the coefficient of the x term

c is the constant.

The $\pm$ symbol means 'plus or minus'.

➡ **NOTE:** the quadratic formula is not given to you in the examination. You must learn the formula carefully.

Factorising gives exact answers. If a question asks you to give your answer to 2 d.p., it is a clue that you need to use the formula.

EXAMPLE

Solve $2x^2 - 9x + 8 = 0$, giving your answers to two decimal places.

$2x^2 - 9x + 8 = 0$ *first write down the values of a, b and c.*

$a = 2$ $b = -9$ $c = 8$

$x = \dfrac{-b \pm \sqrt{b^2 - 4ac}}{2a}$ *substitute the values into the formula*

$x = \dfrac{-(-9) \pm \sqrt{(-9)^2 - 4 \times 2 \times 8}}{2 \times 2}$ $-(-9) = 9$ and $(-9)^2 = 81$

$x = \dfrac{9 \pm \sqrt{81 - 64}}{4}$

$x = \dfrac{9 \pm \sqrt{17}}{4}$

$x = \dfrac{9 + \sqrt{17}}{4}$ or $x = \dfrac{9 - \sqrt{17}}{4}$

$x = 3.28$ or $x = 1.22$ (2 d.p.)

EXERCISE 8.2

1 Rafiu is asked to solve the equation $x^2 + 11x - 5 = 0$ correct to 3 s.f.
  He writes

$$x = \frac{-11 \pm \sqrt{121 + 20}}{2}$$

$$= \frac{-11 \pm 11.9}{2}$$

$$= 0.450 \text{ or } -11.5$$

The correct solution is $x = 0.437$ or $x = -11.4$
Explain why his answers are not accurate.

2 Solve these equations using the quadratic formula.
  Where appropriate give your answers correct to 2 decimal places.
  a $x^2 + 2x - 24 = 0$ b $x^2 + 3x - 2 = 0$ c $x^2 - x - 7 = 0$
  d $a^2 - 2a - 2 = 0$ e $x^2 - 6x + 2 = 0$ f $y^2 + 3y - 14 = 0$
  g $x^2 + 4x - 7 = 0$ h $3y^2 - 8y + 2 = 0$ i $2x^2 - 5x - 6 = 0$
  j $3x^2 - 5x - 1 = 0$ k $x^2 + 10x - 400 = 0$ l $4x^2 + 7x - 5 = 0$
  m $2x^2 - 3x - 4 = 0$ n $x^2 + 2x - 5 = 0$ o $2x^2 + 6x - 5 = 0$
  p $x^2 + 10x + 11 = 0$

3 Use the quadratic formula to solve the equation $x^2 + 5x + 9 = 0$
  Explain what happens.

4 Use the quadratic formula to solve the equation $4x^2 - 20x + 25 = 0$
  Explain what happens.

5 Solve these equations.
  Give your answers correct to 2 decimal places.
  a $x(x + 2) = 12$ b $x(x + 2) = 9 - 2x$
  c $(x - 2)^2 = 6$ d $x(x + 8) = x - 3$
  e $2x^2 = x(x - 7) - 3$ f $(3x - 2)(x - 2) = 7$
  g $(3x)^2 = x + 4$ h $(x - 3)^2 + x = 28$

TOP TIP

You need to expand the brackets
and rearrange to the form
$ax^2 + bx + c = 0$ before using
the formula.

6 Solve these equations.
  Give your answers correct to 2 decimal places.

  a $x + 4 = \dfrac{9}{x}$

  b $x - \dfrac{11}{x} = 2$

TOP TIP

You need to multiply both
sides of the equation by x
and then rearrange to the form
$ax^2 + bx + c = 0$ before using
the formula.

7 Solve these equations.
  Give your answers correct to 2 decimal places.

  a $1 + \dfrac{2}{x} = \dfrac{14}{x^2}$ b $x - 3 = \dfrac{5}{3x}$ c $x - 2 = \dfrac{1}{x + 5}$

The number of roots of a quadratic equation

The answers to an equation are called the **roots** of the equation.
Consider solving the following three equations using the formula $x = \dfrac{-b \pm \sqrt{b^2 - 4ac}}{2a}$

$x^2 + 2x - 15 = 0$

$x = \dfrac{-2 \pm \sqrt{2^2 - 4 \times 1 \times -15}}{2 \times 1}$

$x = \dfrac{-2 \pm \sqrt{64}}{2}$

$x = 3$ or $x = -5$

two roots

$x^2 + 2x + 1 = 0$

$x = \dfrac{-2 \pm \sqrt{2^2 - 4 \times 1 \times 1}}{2 \times 1}$

$x = \dfrac{-2 \pm \sqrt{0}}{2}$

$x = -1$ (repeated)

one root

$x^2 + x + 9 = 0$

$x = \dfrac{-1 \pm \sqrt{1^2 - 4 \times 1 \times 9}}{2 \times 1}$

$x = \dfrac{-1 \pm \sqrt{-35}}{2}$

no roots

A quadratic equation can have two, one or no roots.

The part of the quadratic formula underneath the square root sign is called the **discriminant**.

→ **NOTE:** you will not be tested on the use of a discriminant in the examination.

discriminant $= b^2 - 4ac$

The discriminant tells you how many roots there are for the equation.

$b^2 - 4ac$

> 0 means there will be **two** roots

$= 0$ means there will be **one** root

< 0 means there will be **no** roots

EXAMPLE

Calculate the discriminant for the equation $x^2 - 3x + 4 = 0$.
How many roots does the equation have?

$x^2 - 3x + 4 = 0$ $\qquad a = 1 \quad b = -3 \quad c = 4$
discriminant $= b^2 - 4ac = (-3)^2 - 4 \times 1 \times 4$
$= 9 - 16$
$= -7$

The discriminant is negative so there are no roots.

EXERCISE 8.3

1   State whether these equations will have two, one or no roots.

   a $x^2 + 9x - 12 = 0$ **b** $x^2 - 6x + 9 = 0$ **c** $x^2 + 8x + 20 = 0$

   d $x^2 - 3x - 11 = 0$ **e** $x^2 + 12x + 36 = 0$ **f** $x^2 + 2x - 17 = 0$

   g $2x^2 + x + 2 = 0$ **h** $x^2 + 16 = 8x$ **i** $6x^2 - 19x + 15 = 0$

   j $7x^2 = 6x + 7$

2   Find the values of k for which $x^2 + kx + 25 = 0$ has one root.

3   Find the values of k for which $kx^2 + 8x + 8 = 0$ has two roots.

EXERCISE 8.4

1   The area of the rectangle is 15 cm².
    Find the value of x.

2   The area of the right-angled triangle is 6 cm².
    Find the value of x.

3   The area of the right-angled triangle is 38 cm².
    Find the value of x.

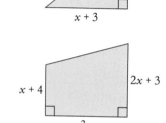

4   The area of the trapezium is 62 cm².
    Find the value of x.

5   A ball is thrown upwards. The height, h metres, of the ball above
    the ground after t seconds is given by the formula $h = 2 + 15t - 5t^2$.
    Find the values of t when the ball is 4 metres above the ground.

6   The length of a rectangular field is 20 metres greater than its width, w metres.
    a   Write down an expression for the area, A m², of the field.
    b   The area of the field is 7000 m². Find the width and perimeter of the field.

7   The solid circular cylinder has a base radius of r cm and a height of 8 cm.
    The total surface area of the cylinder is 130π cm².
    a   Show that $r^2 + 8r - 65 = 0$.
    b   Solve the equation to find the value of r.

8   The two rectangles have the same area.
    Find the value of x.

9   Find the points of intersection of the graphs of
    $y = x^2 + 3x - 2$ and $y = x - 1$.

10 Raju runs at a speed of $(x - 2)$ m/s for $(x + 2)$ seconds and the
    distance he travels is $(9x + 6)$ metres.
    a   Show that $x^2 - 9x - 10 = 0$.
    b   Solve the equation to find x.
    c   Write down the time taken and the distance travelled.

┌ ─ ─ ─ ─ ─ ─ ─ ┐
    KEY WORDS
        roots
      discriminant
└ ─ ─ ─ ─ ─ ─ ─ ┘

Further algebraic fractions

THIS SECTION WILL SHOW YOU HOW TO

- Add and subtract more complicated algebraic fractions
- Solve more complicated equations that involve algebraic fractions

EXAMPLE

Write $\dfrac{2}{x}+\dfrac{1}{x+2}$ as a single fraction.

$\dfrac{2}{x}+\dfrac{1}{x+2}$

$=\dfrac{2(x+2)}{x(x+2)}+\dfrac{x}{x(x+2)}$

$=\dfrac{2(x+2)+x}{x(x+2)}$

$=\dfrac{2x+4+x}{x(x+2)}=\dfrac{3x+4}{x(x+2)}$

the common denominator is $x(x+2)$

$\dfrac{2}{x}=\dfrac{2(x+2)}{x(x+2)}$ *and* $\dfrac{1}{x+2}=\dfrac{x}{x(x+2)}$

EXAMPLE

Write $\dfrac{3}{x-2}-\dfrac{4}{x+5}$ as a single fraction.

$\dfrac{3}{x-2}-\dfrac{4}{x+5}$

$=\dfrac{3(x+5)}{(x-2)(x+5)}-\dfrac{4(x-2)}{(x-2)(x+5)}$

$=\dfrac{3(x+5)-4(x-2)}{(x-2)(x+5)}$

$=\dfrac{3x+15-4x+8}{(x-2)(x+5)}=\dfrac{23-x}{(x-2)(x+5)}$

the common denominator is $(x-2)(x+5)$

$\dfrac{3}{x-2}=\dfrac{3(x+5)}{(x-2)(x+5)}$ *and* $\dfrac{4}{x+5}=\dfrac{4(x-2)}{(x-2)(x+5)}$

EXAMPLE

Solve $\dfrac{2x+4}{x-1}=\dfrac{x+4}{x-2}$

$\dfrac{2x+4}{x-1}=\dfrac{x+4}{x-2}$

$(2x+4)(x-2)=(x+4)(x-1)$
$2x^2-8=x^2+3x-4$

$x^2-3x-4=0$

$(x-4)(x+1)=0$

$\qquad x-4=0 \quad$ or $\quad x+1=0$

$\qquad\qquad x=4 \quad$ or $\quad x=-1$

there is a single fraction on each side
so you can cross multiply

expand the brackets
rearrange to the form $ax^2+bx+c=0$

factorise

Solve $\dfrac{x}{x+3} - \dfrac{2}{x-4} = 1$

Method 1

$$\dfrac{x}{x+3} - \dfrac{2}{x-4} = 1$$

$$\dfrac{x(x-4)}{(x+3)(x-4)} - \dfrac{2(x+3)}{(x+3)(x-4)} = 1$$

$$\dfrac{x(x-4) - 2(x+3)}{(x+3)(x-4)} = 1$$

$$\dfrac{x^2 - 4x - 2x - 6}{(x+3)(x-4)} = 1$$

$$x^2 - 6x - 6 = (x+3)(x-4)$$

$$x^2 - 6x - 6 = x^2 - x - 12$$

$$6 = 5x$$

$$x = 1\tfrac{1}{5}$$

Method 2

$$\dfrac{x}{x+3} - \dfrac{2}{x-4} = 1$$

multiply all 3 terms by $(x+3)(x-4)$

$$(x+3)(x-4) \times \dfrac{x}{x+3} - (x+3)(x-4) \times \dfrac{2}{x-4}$$
$$= (x+3)(x-4) \times 1$$

$$x(x-4) - 2(x+3) = (x+3)(x-4)$$

$$x^2 - 4x - 2x - 6 = x^2 - x - 12$$

$$x^2 - 6x - 6 = x^2 - x - 12$$

$$6 = 5x$$

$$x = 1\tfrac{1}{5}$$

EXERCISE 8.5

1 Write as a single fraction.

a $\dfrac{3}{x} + \dfrac{2}{x-5}$

b $\dfrac{6}{x+3} + \dfrac{5}{x+2}$

c $\dfrac{8}{x-2} - \dfrac{3}{x+7}$

d $\dfrac{8}{2x} - \dfrac{1}{3x+1}$

e $\dfrac{7}{2x+5} - \dfrac{2}{3x-2}$

f $\dfrac{6}{1-2x} + \dfrac{5}{x-4}$

g $\dfrac{x+3}{x+2} - \dfrac{x+2}{x+3}$

h $\dfrac{x+5}{x+1} - \dfrac{x-2}{x+3}$

i $\dfrac{2}{x(x+1)} + \dfrac{3}{x+1}$

j $\dfrac{1}{x^2+6x+8} + \dfrac{1}{x+4}$

k $\dfrac{2}{x^2-2x-3} - \dfrac{3}{x-3}$

l $\dfrac{x(x-y)}{x+y} + y$

2 Solve these equations.

a $\dfrac{x+3}{x-3} = \dfrac{x+2}{x+4}$

b $\dfrac{x-6}{x+7} = \dfrac{x+3}{x-2}$

c $\dfrac{x+2}{5x+2} = \dfrac{2x-1}{4x+1}$

3 Solve these equations.

a $\dfrac{6}{x-1} + \dfrac{5}{x+2} = 4$

b $\dfrac{7}{2x-3} - \dfrac{5}{2x+1} = 6$

c $\dfrac{8}{x+1} + \dfrac{20}{x+4} = 2$

d $\dfrac{3x}{x-2} - \dfrac{2}{x-3} = 4$

e $\dfrac{6}{x+3} - \dfrac{5}{2x+1} = 8$

f $\dfrac{4}{x-3} + \dfrac{9}{2x-5} = 7$

g $\dfrac{2x}{4-x} + \dfrac{8}{x} = 6$

h $\dfrac{2x}{6+2x} - \dfrac{8}{2x+1} = 3$

i $\dfrac{x}{x-4} - \dfrac{x}{x-3} = 1$

Variation

Direct variation (linear relationships)

 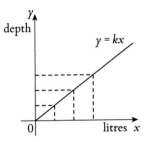

When a cylinder is filled with water, each litre of water increases
the depth of water in the cylinder by the same amount.
The graph of the depth of the water against the number of litres
in the cylinder is a straight line passing through the origin.
This type of relationship is known as **direct (linear) proportion**
or **direct variation**.
(This means that if x is doubled then y also doubles.)

There are other ways of describing the relationship.
You need to be familiar with all of them.

- y is directly proportional to x
- y is proportional to x
- y varies directly as x
- y varies as x

The symbol for proportionality is $\propto$

y is proportional to x
$$y \propto x$$
$$y = kx$$

k is called the **constant of proportionality**.

(It has the same value as the gradient of the graph.)

EXAMPLE

y is directly proportional to x and $y = 48$ when $x = 8$.
a   Find the formula for y in terms of x.
b   Find the value of y when $x = 2.5$
c   Find the value of x when $y = 120$

---

a $y \propto x$ so $y = kx$
     substituting $y = 48$ and $x = 8$ into $y = kx$ gives $48 = k \times 8$ $k = 6$
     The formula is $y = 6x$
b   substituting $x = 2.5$ into $y = 6x$ gives $y = 6 \times 2.5$ $\Rightarrow$ $y = 15$
c   substituting $y = 120$ into $y = 6x$ gives $120 = 6 \times x$ $\Rightarrow$ $x = 20$

EXERCISE 8.6

1 y is proportional to x and $y = 30$ when $x = 6$
   a Find the formula for y in terms of x.   b Find the value of y when $x = 8$
   c Find the value of x when $y = 7$

2 y is proportional to x and $y = 56$ when $x = 7$
   a Find the formula for y in terms of x.   b Find the value of y when $x = 3$
   c Find the value of x when $y = 6$

3 y is proportional to x and $y = 4.5$ when $x = 9$
   a Find the formula for y in terms of x.   b Find the value of y when $x = 2.4$
   c Find the value of x when $y = 5$

4 y is proportional to x and $y = 6$ when $x = 18$
   a Find the formula for y in terms of x.   b Find the value of y when $x = 4$
   c Find the value of x when y $= 3.4$

5 y is proportional to x and $y = 0.6$ when $x = 6$
   a Find the formula for y in terms of x.   b Find the value of y when $x = 8$
   c Find the value of x when $y = 7$

6 If y is directly proportional to x, copy and complete this table.

x	2	5	
y		15	39

7 A stone is dropped from the top of a cliff. The speed of the
stone, v m/s, varies directly with the time, t seconds, after it
was dropped. After 2 seconds its speed is 19.6 m/s.

   a Find the formula for v in terms of t.
   b Find the speed when $t = 3$
   c Find the time when $v = 24.5$

8 The extension of a spring, e cm, is proportional to the mass,
m kg, that hangs from it.
When a mass of 0.5 kg hangs from the spring its extension is 2.2 cm.
   a Find the formula for e in terms of m.
   b Find the extension when $m = 0.8$
   c Find the mass when $e = 1.76$

9 The depth of oil, d m, in a tank varies directly with the volume,
V m³, of oil that is in the tank. When $d = 0.9$, $V = 0.6$

   a Find the formula for d in terms of V.
   b Find the depth when $V = 1.2$
   c Find the volume when $d = 0.57$

Direct variation (nonlinear relationships)

depth

litres

When the frustum of the cone is filled with water, each litre of water increases the depth of the water by different amounts.
A graph of the depth of the water against the number of litres in the frustum is a curve passing through the origin.

This relationship is known as a direct non-linear relationship.

EXAMPLE

y is proportional to the square of x and $y = 12$ when $x = 2$
a Find the formula for y in terms of x.
b Find the value of y when $x = 4$ **c** Find the value of x when $y = 3$

---

a $y \propto x^2$ so $y = kx^2$
substituting $y = 12$ and $x = 2$ into $y = kx^2$ gives $12 = k \times 2^2$
$12 = 4 \times k$
$k = 3$

The formula is $y = 3x^2$

b substituting $x = 4$ into $y = 3x^2$ gives $y = 3 \times 4^2$
$y = 3 \times 16$ $y = 48$

c substituting $y = 3$ into $y = 3x^2$ gives $3 = 3x^2$
$x^2 = 1$ ➡ **NOTE:** there are two
$x = \pm 1$ numbers that square to give
the number 1.

EXAMPLE

The time for a pendulum to swing, t seconds, is proportional to the square root of the length, l m, of the pendulum.
$l = 0.81$ when $t = 1.8$. Find the value of t when $l = 0.49$

You must first find the formula connecting t and l.

$t \propto \sqrt{l}$ so $t = k\sqrt{l}$
substituting $t = 1.8$ and $l = 0.81$ into $t = k\sqrt{l}$ gives $1.8 = k \times \sqrt{0.81}$
$1.8 = k \times 0.9$
$k = 2$

The formula is $t = 2\sqrt{l}$

substituting $l = 0.49$ into $t = 2\sqrt{l}$ gives $t = 2 \times \sqrt{0.49}$
$t = 2 \times 0.7$
$t = 1.4$

EXERCISE 8.7

1 y is proportional to the square of x and $y = 32$ when $x = 4$
   a Find the formula for y in terms of x.
   b Find the value of y when $x = 5$
   c Find the values of x when $y = 128$

2 y varies directly as the square of x and $y = 4.5$ when $x = 3$
   a Find the formula for y in terms of x.
   b Find the value of y when $x = 9$
   c Find the value of x when $y = 32$

3 y is proportional to the cube of x and $y = 108$ when $x = 3$
   a Find the formula for y in terms of x.
   b Find the value of y when $x = 2$
   c Find the value of x when $y = 256$

4 y is directly proportional to $(x + 3)^2$ and $y = 32$ when $x = 1$
   a Find the formula for y in terms of x.
   b Find the value of y when $x = 4$
   c Find the values of x when $y = 50$

5 y varies directly as $(x - 2)^2$ and $y = 20$ when $x = 4$
   a Find the formula for y in terms of x.
   b Find the value of y when $x = 8$

6 y is proportional to the square root of x and $y = 12$ when $x = 4$
   a Find the formula for y in terms of x.
   b Find the value of y when $x = 6.25$
   c Find the value of x when $y = 48$

7 If y varies directly as the cube of x, copy and complete this table.

x	1	2	
y		16	250

8 The breaking distance, d m, of a car is proportional to the square of the speed, v mph.
   $d = 6$ when $v = 20$
   a Find the formula for d in terms of v.
   b Find the value of d when $v = 40$

9 The energy (E) stored in a spring is proportional to the square
   of the extension (e).
   $E = 300$ when $e = 5$
   a Find the formula for E in terms of e.
   b Find the value of E when $e = 2.5$

10 The air resistance (R) to a car varies directly with the square of the speed (v).
   $v = 40$ when $R = 3200$
   a Find the formula for R in terms of v.
   b Find the value of R when $v = 35$

Inverse variation

When two variables are in **inverse proportion** (or **inverse variation**), one of the variables increases as the other decreases.

The number of tractors ploughing a field and the time taken are in inverse proportion. If 1 tractor takes 6 hours then 2 tractors will take 3 hours and the following table can be obtained.

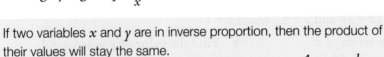

Number of tractors (x)	1	2	3	4	5	6
Time taken (y hours)	6	3	2	1.5	1.2	1

Notice that the product of corresponding x and y values in the table above always give the number 6. So $xy = 6$.

Dividing by x gives $y = \dfrac{6}{x}$.

> If two variables x and y are in inverse proportion, then the product of their values will stay the same.
> 'y is inversely proportional to x' can be written as $y \propto \dfrac{1}{x}$ or $y = \dfrac{k}{x}$ where k is the constant of proportionality.

EXAMPLE

y is inversely proportional to x and $y = 8$ when $x = 2$

a Find the formula for y in terms of x

b Find the value of y when $x = 4$

c Find the value of x when $y = 0.5$

---

a $y \propto \dfrac{1}{x}$

  $y = \dfrac{k}{x}$

  $8 = \dfrac{k}{2}$

  $k = 16$

  The formula is $y = \dfrac{16}{x}$

b $y = \dfrac{16}{x}$

  $y = \dfrac{16}{4}$

  $y = 4$

c $y = \dfrac{16}{x}$

  $0.5 = \dfrac{16}{x}$

  $x = \dfrac{16}{0.5}$

  $x = 32$

EXAMPLE

y is inversely proportional to x.

a Find the formula for y in terms of x.

b Find the values of a and b.

x	a	5	20
y	15	6	b

a $5 \times 6 = 30$ so $xy = 30$ so formula is $y = \dfrac{30}{x}$

b $a \times 15 = 30$ so $a = 2$
  $20 \times b = 30$ so $b = 1.5$

EXERCISE 8.8

1   y is inversely proportional to x and $y = 3$ when $x = 2$
    a   Find the formula for y in terms of x.   b   Find the value of y when $x = 6$
    c   Find the value of x when $y = 1.5$

2   y varies inversely as x and $y = 10$ when $x = 2.4$
    a   Find the formula for y in terms of x.   b   Find the value of y when $x = 4$
    c   Find the value of x when $y = 8$

3   y is inversely proportional to x and $y = 5$ when $x = 2$
    a   Find the formula for y in terms of x.   b   Find the value of y when $x = 0.5$
    c   Find the value of x when $y = 2.5$

4   y varies inversely as x and $y = 5$ when $x = 0.1$
    a   Find the formula for y in terms of x.   b   Find the value of y when $x = 2$
    c   Find the value of x when $y = 1$

5   If y varies inversely as x, copy and complete this table.

x	2	4	
y	18		6

6   If y is inversely proportional to x, copy and complete this table.

x	2.5	4	
y		25	20

7   The wave length, w, of a radio signal varies inversely as its frequency, f.
    $w = 1000$ when $f = 300$
    a   Find the formula for w in terms of f.
    b   Find the value of w when $f = 150$
    c   Find the value of f when $w = 200$

8   The pressure, P, of a gas varies inversely as the volume,
    V, of the gas.
    $P = 1.5$ when $V = 200$
    a   Find the formula for P in terms of V.
    b   Find the value of P when $V = 150$
    c   Find the value of V when $P = 2.5$

9   The time taken, t hours, to build a brick wall is inversely
    proportional to the number of men, n, that build the wall.
    $t = 12$ when $n = 2$
    a   Find the formula for t in terms of n.
    b   Find the value of t when $n = 3$
    c   Find the value of n when $t = 4$

Further inverse variation

EXAMPLE

y varies inversely as $(x - 2)^2$ and $y = 1$ when $x = 5$
a   Find the formula for y in terms of x b   Find the value of y when $x = 4$
c   Find the values of x when $y = 9$

a $y \propto \dfrac{1}{(x-2)^2}$ so $y = \dfrac{k}{(x-2)^2}$

substituting $y = 1$ and $x = 5$ into $y = \dfrac{k}{(x-2)^2}$ gives $1 = \dfrac{k}{(5-2)^2}$

$$1 = \frac{k}{9}$$

$$k = 9$$

The formula is $y = \dfrac{9}{(x-2)^2}$

b   substituting $x = 4$ into $y = \dfrac{9}{(x-2)^2}$ gives $y = \dfrac{9}{(4-2)^2}$

$$y = \frac{9}{4}$$

$$y = 2.25$$

c   substituting $y = 9$ into $y = \dfrac{9}{(x-2)^2}$ gives $9 = \dfrac{9}{(x-2)^2}$

$9(x - 2)^2 = 9$ *multiply both sides by $(x - 2)^2$*
$(x - 2)^2 = 1$ *divide both sides by 9*
$x^2 - 4x + 4 = 1$ *expand brackets*
$x^2 - 4x + 3 = 0$ *collect on one side*
$(x - 3)(x - 1) = 0$ *factorise*
$x - 3 = 0$ or $x - 1 = 0$
$x = 3$ or $x = 1$ ➡ CHECK: $\dfrac{9}{(3-2)^2} = \dfrac{9}{1^2} = 9$ and $\dfrac{9}{(1-2)^2} = \dfrac{9}{(-1)^2} = \dfrac{9}{1} = 9$ ✓

EXERCISE 8.9

1   Match these cards.

a y varies inversely as the square of x

b y is proportional to the cube of x

c y varies inversely as the cube of x

d y varies inversely as the square root of x

e y varies directly as the square of x

A $y \propto \dfrac{1}{\sqrt{x}}$ B $y \propto \dfrac{1}{x^2}$

C $y \propto x^3$ D $y \propto x^2$

E $y \propto \dfrac{1}{x^3}$

2   y is inversely proportional to the square of x and $y = 4$ when $x = 3$
    a   Find the formula for y in terms of x.   b   Find the value of y when $x = 2$
    c   Find the value of x when $y = 1$

3 y varies inversely as the square root of x and $y = 10$ when $x = 4$
  a Find the formula for y in terms of x.   b Find the value of y when $x = 16$
  c Find the value of x when $y = 4$

4 y is inversely proportional to $(x + 2)$ and $y = 3$ when $x = 3$
  a Find the formula for y in terms of x.   b Find the value of y when $x = 8$
  c Find the value of x when $y = 3.75$

5 y varies inversely as $(x + 1)^2$ and $y = 4$ when $x = 1$
  a Find the formula for y in terms of x.   b Find the value of y when $x = 3$
  c Find the values of x when $y = 16$

6 If y is inversely proportional to x^2, copy and complete this table.

x		2	5
y	50		2

7 The force of attraction, F newtons, between two magnets, is inversely proportional to the square of the distance, d cm, between them. $F = 5$ when $d = 2$
  a Find the formula for F in terms of d.   b Find the value of F when $d = 0.5$
  c Find the value of d when $F = 0.2$

8 The intensity of sound (I decibels) varies inversely as the square of the distance (d m) from the source. For a jet engine the sound intensity is 140 decibels at a distance of 30 metres from the engine.
  a Find the formula for I in terms of d.   b Find the value of I when $d = 100$
  c Find the value of d when $I = 2$

9 Match the four variation equations with the correct sketch graph.

a   b   c   d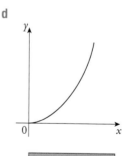

A $y = \dfrac{k}{x}$ B $y = kx$ C $y = kx^2$ D $y = k\sqrt{x}$

KEY WORDS
direct proportion
direct variation
constant of proportionality
inverse proportion
inverse variation

The sine and cosine rules

THIS SECTION WILL SHOW YOU HOW TO
- Find lengths and angles in triangles that are not right-angled

The sine rule

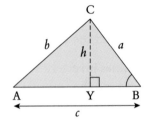

Using triangle AYC: Using triangle BYC:

$$\sin A = \frac{h}{b}$$ $$\sin B = \frac{h}{a}$$

so $h = b \sin A$ so $h = a \sin B$

so $b \sin A = a \sin B$

Rearranging gives $\dfrac{\sin A}{a} = \dfrac{\sin B}{b}$ or $\dfrac{a}{\sin A} = \dfrac{b}{\sin B}$

➡ **NOTE:**
angle A is opposite side a
angle B is opposite side b,
angle C is opposite side c.

This rule is called the **sine rule** and it can be extended to include the third side and angle.

The sine rule: $\dfrac{a}{\sin A} = \dfrac{b}{\sin B} = \dfrac{c}{\sin C}$

or $\dfrac{\sin A}{a} = \dfrac{\sin B}{b} = \dfrac{\sin C}{c}$

The sine rule is used when you are working with two sides and two angles.

EXAMPLE

Find the value of x in each of these triangles.

a

b

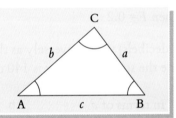

➡ **NOTE:**
to find a side, use $\dfrac{a}{\sin A} = \dfrac{b}{\sin B}$

to find an angle, use $\dfrac{\sin A}{a} = \dfrac{\sin B}{b}$

a $\dfrac{x}{\sin 42°} = \dfrac{18}{\sin 105°}$

$x = \sin 42° \times \dfrac{18}{\sin 105°}$

$x = 12.5\,\text{cm}$ (to 3 s.f.)

b $\dfrac{\sin x}{4.8} = \dfrac{\sin 25°}{6.2}$

$\sin x = 4.8 \times \dfrac{\sin 25°}{6.2}$

$x = \sin^{-1}\left(4.8 \times \dfrac{\sin 25°}{6.2}\right)$

$x = 19.1°$ or $\boxed{160.9°}$ ⟵ This value is impossible because

$x = 19.1°$ (to 1 d.p.)

angles in a triangle add up to 180°
$(160.9° + 25° = 185.9°)$

EXERCISE 8.10

1 Find the value of *x* for each of these triangles.

a

b

c

d

e

f

g

h

i

2 Find the value of *x* for each of these triangles.

a

b

c

d

e

f

g

13 cm · 15 cm · 82° · $x°$

h

20 cm · 15 cm · 100° · $x°$

i

8 cm · 65° · 11 cm · $x°$

3   Triangle ABC is isosceles.
    Use the sine rule to calculate the value of x.

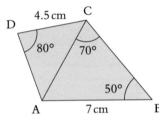

C · 8 cm · 8 cm · 64° · A · x cm · B

4   ABCD is a quadrilateral.
    a   Calculate the length of AC.
    b   Calculate the size of angle CAD.

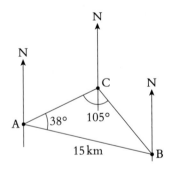

D · 4.5 cm · C · 80° · 70° · A · 50° · 7 cm · B

5   Calculate the size of angle ACB.

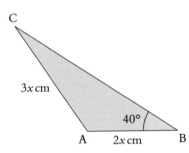

C · $3x$ cm · 40° · A · $2x$ cm · B

6   The diagram shows three straight roads
    connecting points A, B and C.
    The length of AB is 15 km.
    a   Calculate the length of the road BC.
    b   The bearing of A from B is 290°.
        i   Find the bearing of B from A.
        ii Find the bearing of B from C.

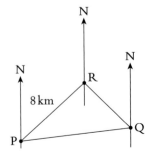

N · N · C · N · A · 38° · 105° · 15 km · B

7   The diagram shows three straight roads
    connecting points P, Q and R.
    The length of PR is 8 km.
    The bearing of R from P is 055°.
    The bearing of Q from P is 080°.
    The bearing of Q from R is 110°.
    Calculate the length of PQ.

N · N · R · N · 8 km · P · Q

Sine rule – the ambiguous case

If you construct this triangle accurately, you will find there are two possible triangles that can be drawn.

ACCURATE CONSTRUCTIONS:

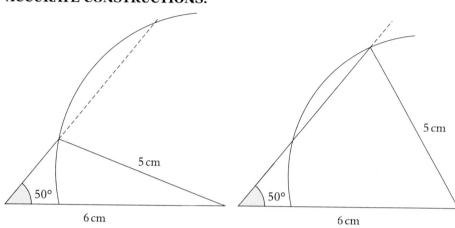

SOLVING USING SINE RULE

$$\frac{\sin x}{6} = \frac{\sin 50°}{5}$$

$$\sin x = 6 \times \frac{\sin 50°}{5}$$

$\sin x = 0.919...$

$x = 66.8°$ or $x = 180° - 66.8°$

$x = 66.8°$ or $x = 113.2°$

So the two possible triangles are

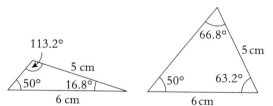

EXERCISE 8.11

Calculate the two possible values of x for each of these triangles.
Check your calculations by constructing the triangles accurately.

1

2

The cosine rule

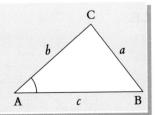

Using Pythagoras on triangle BYC:
$$h^2 = a^2 - (b - x)^2$$

Using Pythagoras on triangle AYB:
$$h^2 = c^2 - x^2$$

$$a^2 - (b - x)^2 = c^2 - x^2 \qquad \textit{rearrange}$$
$$a^2 = c^2 - x^2 + (b - x)^2 \qquad \textit{expand brackets}$$
$$a^2 = c^2 - x^2 + b^2 - 2bx + x^2 \qquad \textit{collect like terms}$$
$$a^2 = b^2 + c^2 - 2bx$$

but, using $\triangle$AYB $\cos A = \dfrac{x}{c}$ so $x = c \cos A$

so $a^2 = b^2 + c^2 - 2bc \cos A$

The cosine rule: $a^2 = b^2 + c^2 - 2bc \cos A$

or $\cos A = \dfrac{b^2 + c^2 - a^2}{2bc}$

The cosine rule is used when you are working with three sides of a triangle and one angle.

Use $a^2 = b^2 + c^2 - 2bc \cos A$ to find the length of a side.

Use $\cos A = \dfrac{b^2 + c^2 - a^2}{2bc}$ to find the size of an angle.

EXAMPLE

Find the value of x in each of these triangles.

a

b

4 cm · 6 cm · x · 8 cm

---

a Using the cosine rule:
$$x^2 = 5^2 + 7^2 - 2 \times 5 \times 7 \times \cos 72°$$
$$x^2 = 52.368...$$
$$x = 7.24 \, \text{cm} \quad \text{(to 3 s.f.)}$$

b Using the cosine rule:
$$\cos x = \left(\frac{4^2 + 6^2 - 8^2}{2 \times 4 \times 6} \right)$$
$$x = \cos^{-1} \left(\frac{4^2 + 6^2 - 8^2}{2 \times 4 \times 6} \right)$$
$$x = 104.5° \quad \text{(to 1 d.p.)}$$

EXERCISE 8.12

1 Find the length of x for each of these triangles.

a
9 cm
25°
8 cm
x cm

b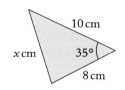
10 cm
x cm
35°
8 cm

c
6 cm 20°
4 cm
x cm

d
x cm 11 cm
30°
12 cm

e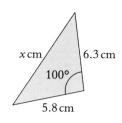
6 cm
x cm
80°
2 cm

f
x cm
7.6 cm
8 cm 40°

g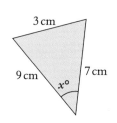
x cm
5 cm
45°
7.5 cm

h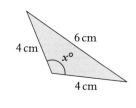
x cm 6.3 cm
100°
5.8 cm

i
7 cm 30° 10.2 cm
x cm

2 Find the value of x for each of these triangles.

a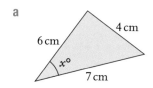
4 cm
6 cm
x°
7 cm

b
3 cm
9 cm 7 cm
x°

c
1.8 cm 2 cm
x°
2.5 cm

d
10 cm x°
8.3 cm
5.6 cm

e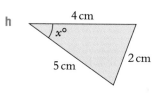
6 cm
4 cm
x°
4 cm

f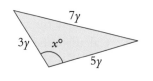
2 cm x° 3 cm
1.8 cm

g
12 cm 7.4 cm
x°
7 cm

h
4 cm
x°
2 cm
5 cm

i
7y
3y x°
5y

The sine and cosine rules

UNIT 8

Solving problems using the sine and cosine rules

The sine and cosine rules are used to solve problems in triangles that are not right-angled.

Sometimes both of the rules have to be used.

Sometimes you have to choose carefully which rule is needed.

If no diagram is given, you must always start by sketching a clear diagram.

EXERCISE 8.13

1 Find the length of x for each of these triangles.

a

b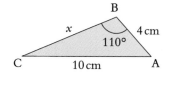

•••••••••••••••••

TOP TIP

You must first calculate angle ACB.

•••••••••••••••••

2 ABCD is a quadrilateral.
  a Find the length of BD.
  b Calculate the size of angle BCD.

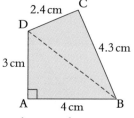

3 A, B and C are three points on horizontal ground.
  Point B is 5 km from A on a bearing of 120°, and C is 7 km from A on a bearing of 200°.
  a Find the size of angle BAC.
  b Calculate the length of BC.

4 In △ABC, AB = 6 cm, AC = 8 cm and BC = 4 cm.
  Calculate the size of the smallest angle.

••••••••••••••••••

TOP TIP

The smallest angle is always opposite the shortest side.

••••••••••••••••••

5 The lengths of the sides of a triangle are in the ratio 2 : 3 : 4
  Calculate the size of the largest angle.

6 Calculate the value of x.

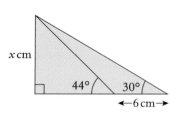

7 a Find the size of angle DBE.
  b Calculate the area of triangle DBE.
  c Calculate the value of x.
  d Calculate the value of y.
  e Calculate the angle of depression of E from D.

8 Two sides of a triangle are 9.4 cm and 11.6 cm.
The angle between the two sides is 65°.
Calculate the perimeter of the triangle.

9 The parallelogram has sides of length 10 cm and 7 cm.
The longest diagonal is 16 cm.
  a   Calculate the length of the shortest diagonal.
  b   Calculate the area of the parallelogram.

10 ABCD is a trapezium.
  a   Calculate the length of BD.
  b   Calculate the length of AD.
  c   Calculate the area of the trapezium.

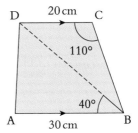

11 Calculate the area of the quadrilateral.

12 Triangle ABC has vertices A(1, 2), B(4, 6) and C(12, 0).
  a   Calculate the length of
      i   AB   ii   BC   iii   AC
  b   Calculate the area of triangle ABC.

13 a Show that $x^2 + 3x - 27 = 0$.
  b   Solve the equation to find the value of x.
  c   Calculate the area of the triangle.

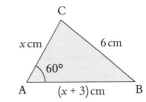

14 a Show that $3x^2 + 6x - 96 = 0$.
  b   Solve the equation to find the value of x.
  c   Calculate the area of the triangle.

KEY WORDS
sine rule
cosine rule

UNIT 8

Histograms

THIS SECTION WILL SHOW YOU HOW TO
- Draw and use a histogram

 Grouped continuous data can be represented on a **histogram**.

In a histogram, the area of each bar is proportional to the frequency.

The bars can have different widths. (The width of a bar is called the **class width**.)
The vertical axis represents the **frequency density**.

Frequency density = $\dfrac{\text{frequency}}{\text{class width}}$ or   frequency = frequency density × class width

EXAMPLE

The heights, h cm, of 200 plants are recorded.
The results are shown in the frequency table.
Draw a histogram to represent this information.

Height (h cm)	Frequency
$10 < h \leq 20$	20
$20 < h \leq 30$	40
$30 < h \leq 35$	40
$35 < h \leq 40$	45
$40 < h \leq 50$	25
$50 < h \leq 80$	30

Height (h cm)	Frequency	Class width	Frequency density
$10 < h \leq 20$	20	10	$20 \div 10 = 2$
$20 < h \leq 30$	40	10	$40 \div 10 = 4$
$30 < h \leq 35$	40	5	$40 \div 5 = 8$
$35 < h \leq 40$	45	5	$45 \div 5 = 9$
$40 < h \leq 50$	25	10	$25 \div 10 = 2.5$
$50 < h \leq 80$	30	30	$30 \div 30 = 1$

Add columns to the table to show the class widths and to calculate the frequency density.

➡ **NOTE:** the vertical axis must be labelled frequency density.

EXERCISE 8.14

1 The masses of 100 sweets are recorded.
  The results are shown in the frequency table.
  a Calculate the frequency density for each group.
  b Draw a histogram to represent this information.

Mass (m grams)	Frequency
$5 < m \leq 10$	5
$10 < m \leq 20$	35
$20 < m \leq 30$	45
$30 < m \leq 35$	15

2 The table shows the time, t hours, spent on
  homework each week by 100 students.
  a Calculate the frequency density for each group.
  b Draw a histogram to represent this information.

Time (t hours)	Frequency
$0 < t \leq 1$	7
$1 < t \leq 4$	39
$4 < t \leq 7$	42
$7 < t \leq 13$	12

3 The lengths of 85 phone calls are recorded.
  The results are shown in the table.
  a Calculate the frequency density for each group.
  b Draw a histogram to represent this information.

Time (t minutes)	Frequency
$0 < t \leq 1$	5
$1 < t \leq 3$	16
$3 < t \leq 7$	28
$7 < t \leq 9$	12
$9 < t \leq 15$	24

4 The heights of 200 students are measured.
  The results are shown in the table.
  a Calculate the frequency density for each group.
  b Draw a histogram to represent this information.

Height (h cm)	Frequency
$150 < h \leq 160$	24
$160 < h \leq 170$	58
$170 < h \leq 175$	63
$175 < h \leq 180$	45
$180 < h \leq 200$	10

5 The speeds of 130 cars passing a 70 km/h speed
  limit sign are recorded.
  The results are shown in the table.
  Use this information to draw a histogram.

Speed (v km/h)	Frequency
$50 < v \leq 60$	15
$60 < v \leq 65$	30
$65 < v \leq 70$	40
$70 < v \leq 75$	35
$75 < v \leq 90$	10

6 200 students are given a puzzle to solve.
  The results are shown in the table.
  Use this information to draw a histogram.

Time (t minutes)	Frequency
$0 < t \leq 1$	4
$1 < t \leq 3$	45
$3 < t \leq 6$	90
$6 < t \leq 7$	26
$7 < t \leq 12$	35

7   The table shows information about the time spent on the internet one evening by a group of 160 students. Draw a histogram to represent this information.

Time (t minutes)	Frequency
$0 < t \le 40$	36
$40 < t \le 70$	90
$70 < t \le 150$	34

8   The histogram shows information about the lengths of 35 phone calls.

TOP TIP
frequency = frequency density × class width

  a   Use the information in the histogram to copy and complete the following table.

Time (t mins)	$0 < t \le 3$	$3 < t \le 5$	$5 < t \le 6$	$6 < t \le 9$	$9 < t \le 14$
Frequency					5

  b   Use the information in the table to calculate an estimate of the mean length of a phone call.

9   The histogram shows information about the masses of 25 newborn babies.

  a   Use the information in the histogram to copy and complete the following table.

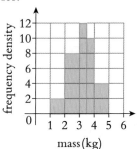

Mass (m kg)	$1 < m \le 2$	$2 < m \le 3$	$3 < m \le 3.5$	$3.5 < m \le 4$	$4 < m \le 5$
Frequency			6		

  b   Use the information in the table to calculate an estimate of the mean mass.

10   75 students do a sponsored swim to raise money for charity.
The table shows information about the amounts of money ($\$x$) raised.

Amount ($\$x$)	$0 < x \le 10$	$10 < x \le 20$	$20 < x \le 35$	$35 < x \le 50$
Frequency	15	40	15	5

When a histogram was drawn to show this information, the height of the column for the interval $20 < x \le 35$ was 6 cm. Calculate the height of each of the other columns.

UNIT 8

11 45 batteries are tested to see how long they last.
The table shows the results

Number of hours (t)	$10 < t \leq 15$	$15 < t \leq 17$	$17 < t \leq 20$	$20 < t \leq 30$
Frequency	10	8	15	12

When a histogram was drawn to show this information, the
height of the column for the interval $10 < t \leq 15$ was 4 cm.
Calculate the height of each of the other columns.

12 A group of students are asked how long they spent watching television one evening.
The information is shown in the histogram.

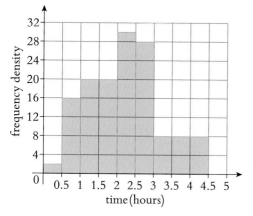

Time (t hours)	Frequency
$0 < t \leq 0.5$	1
$0.5 < t \leq 1$	
$1 < t \leq 2$	
$2 < t \leq 2.5$	
$2.5 < t \leq 3$	
$3 < t \leq 4.5$	

a Use the information in the histogram to copy and complete the table.
b Estimate how many students spent less than 1.5 hours watching television.
c Use the information in the table to calculate an estimate of the mean number of hours.
d A student is chosen at random.
Find the probability that the student spent more than 2 hours watching television.

13 The frequency table and histogram are incomplete.
They show information about the distances travelled to work by a group of workers.
No worker travelled more than 28 km.

Distance (d km)	Frequency
$0 < d \leq 4$	8
$4 < d \leq 10$	
$10 < d \leq 12$	
$12 < d \leq 14$	20
$14 < d \leq 22$	40
$22 < d \leq 28$	18

a Use the information given in the histogram to find the
missing frequencies in the table.
b Use the information given in the table to draw the missing
bars on the histogram.
c Calculate an estimate of the mean distance travelled.

1   Write the recurring decimal $0.\dot{5}$ as a fraction.
     You must show all your working.   [2]

2   Write the recurring decimal $0.3\dot{5}$ as a fraction in its lowest terms.
     You must show all your working.   [3]

3   Write the recurring decimal $0.8\dot{0}\dot{4}$ as a fraction in its lowest terms.
     You must show all your working.   [3]

4    $2\dfrac{1}{4}$ π $\sqrt{\dfrac{4}{9}}$ $0.0\dot{4}$ -8 $\sqrt{7}$

     From this list of numbers, write down two numbers that are irrational.   [2]

5   Solve $2x^2 + 5x - 8 = 0$.
     You must show all your working and give your answers correct to 2 decimal places.   [4]

6   Solve $3x - \dfrac{2}{x+1} = 7$.
     You must show all your working and give your answers correct to 2 decimal places.   [6]

7   A solid circular cylinder has a base radius of r cm and a height of 5 cm.
     The total surface area of this cylinder is 150π cm^2.
     (a) Show that $r^2 + 5r - 75 = 0$.   [2]
     (b) Solve the equation in **part (a)** to find the value of r.
              Give your answer correct to 2 decimal places.   [4]

8   Write as a single fraction in its simplest form.
     $$\dfrac{7}{x-3} - \dfrac{5}{x+2}$$ [3]

9   Write as a single fraction in its simplest form.
     $$\dfrac{3x+7}{4} + \dfrac{2}{x-3}$$ [3]

10   Solve.
     $$\dfrac{5}{x-1} - \dfrac{2}{x+3} = 1$$ [7]

11   y is directly proportional to $\sqrt{x+2}$.
     When $x = 7$, $y = 12$.

     Find y when $x = 0.25$.   [3]

12 y is inversely proportional to x^2.
When $x = 5$, $y = 10$.

Find y in terms of x. [2]

13

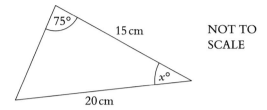

Find the value of x. [3]

14

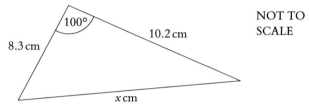

Find the value of x. [4]

15

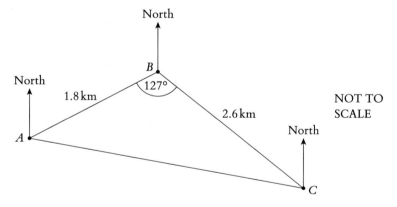

Robert sails from A to B, then from B to C and then returns to A.
$AB = 1.8$ km, $BC = 2.6$ km and angle $ABC = 127°$.

(a) **(i)** Find AC. [4]
   (ii) Find angle BCA. [3]

(b) The bearing of B from A is $062°$.
   (i) Find the bearing of A from B. [2]
   (ii) Find the bearing of A from C. [2]

16

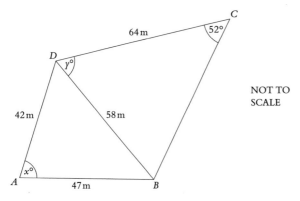

NOT TO SCALE

(a) Calculate the value of x. [4]

(b) Calculate the value of y. [4]

(c) Calculate the area of quadrilateral $ABCD$. [3]

17 The table shows information about the mass, m grams, of 100 eggs.

Mass (m grams)	$35 < m \leq 40$	$40 < m \leq 50$	$50 < m \leq 60$	$60 < m \leq 80$
Frequency	8	36	46	10

On the grid, complete the histogram to show this information.

[4]

18 The histogram shows information about the mass, x kilograms, of 40 babies in a hospital.

(a) Use the histogram to complete the grouped frequency table below.

Mass (x kilograms)	$1.8 < x \leq 2$	$2 < x \leq 2.5$	$2.5 < x \leq 3.5$	$3.5 < x \leq 5.1$
Frequency		12		

[3]

(b) Estimate the mean mass of the babies. [4]

19 In this question all lengths are in centimetres.

(a)

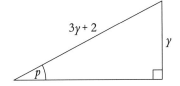

NOT TO SCALE

Given that $\sin p = 0.3$, find the value of y. [2]

(b)

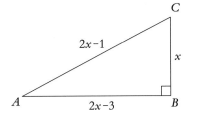

NOT TO SCALE

(i) Show that $x^2 - 8x + 8 = 0$. [6]

(ii) Solve the equation $x^2 - 8x + 8 = 0$.
Show all your working and give your answers correct to 2 decimal places. [4]

(iii) Find the two possible values for the perimeter of triangle ABC. [2]

20 Haroon and Farhat each cycle a distance of 50 km.
Haroon's average speed was x km/h.
Farhat's average speed was 2 km/h faster than Haroon's average speed.
Farhat took 6 minutes less than Haroon to cycle the 50 km.

(a) Write down an expression, in terms of x, for the time, in hours, it took for Haroon to cycle the 50 km. [1]

(b) Write down an expression, in terms of x, for the time, in hours, it took for Farhat to cycle the 50 km. [1]

(c) Show that $x^2 + 2x - 1000 = 0$. [4]

(d) Solve the equation $x^2 + 2x - 1000 = 0$.
Show all your working and give your answers correct to 2 decimal places. [4]

(e) Calculate the time taken by Farhat to cycle the 50 km.
Give your answer in hours and minutes, correct to the nearest minute. [3]

UNIT 8

Compound interest and exponential growth and decay

Compound interest

In Unit 6 Percentages 3 you learned how to find compound interest by two different methods. These two methods were:

- calculating in stages (year by year)
- calculating using a multiplying factor.

In this section you will learn how to apply the compound interest formula.

If $P is invested at a rate of $r\%$ compound interest per year, then the value of the investment after n years is given by the **compound interest formula**:

$$\text{Value of investment} = P\left(1+\frac{r}{100}\right)^{n}$$

EXAMPLE

Helen invests $720 in a bank account paying 2.1% compound interest per year.
Calculate the amount Helen has in her account after 8 years.
Give your answer in dollars correct to the nearest cent.

$$\text{Amount} = P\left(1+\frac{r}{100}\right)^{n}$$ *use P = 720, r = 2.1 and n = 8*

$$= 720\left(1+\frac{2.1}{100}\right)^{8}$$

$$= 720(1.021)^{8}$$

$$= \$850.2339\ldots$$

$$= \$850.23 \text{ correct to the nearest cent}$$

The next example shows you how to use the compound interest formula if you know the initial and final amounts and you want to find the interest rate.

EXAMPLE

Simone invests $600 for 12 years in an account paying $r\%$ compound interest per year.
At the end of the 12 years she has a total amount of $816.43 correct to the nearest cent.
Find the value of r.

$$\text{Amount} = P\left(1+\frac{r}{100}\right)^{n}$$ *use amount = 816.43, P = 600 and n = 12*

$$816.43 = 600\left(1+\frac{r}{100}\right)^{12}$$ *divide both sides by 600*

$$1.3607 = \left(1+\frac{r}{100}\right)^{12}$$ *take the 12th root of both sides*

$$\sqrt[12]{1.3706} = 1 + \frac{r}{100}$$

$$1.02599 \ldots = 1 + \frac{r}{100} \qquad \text{subtract 1 from both sides}$$

$$0.02599 \ldots = \frac{r}{100} \qquad \text{multiply both sides by 100}$$

$$r = 2.60\% \text{ correct to 3 sf}$$

EXERCISE 9.1

1   Flynn invests $800 in a bank account paying 1.8% compound interest per year.
    Calculate the amount he has after 6 years.

2   Bianca invests $480 in a bank account paying 2% compound interest per year.
    Show that at the end of 6 years, she has an amount of $541, correct to the nearest dollar.

3   Wei invests $4000 in a bank account paying 2.5% compound interest per year.
    Calculate the interest he receives after 15 years.
    Give your answer correct to the nearest dollar.

4   Velimir invests $1800 in an account paying 1.7% compound interest per year.
    Calculate how much interest he will receive after 10 years.
    Give your answer correct to the nearest dollar.

5   Jane invests $4000 in an account paying 2.5% compound interest per year.
    Carol invests $4000 in an account paying 3% simple interest per year.
    Calculate the difference between these two investments after 20 years.
    Give your answer in dollars correct to the nearest cent.

6   Chris invested some money at a rate of 4% compound interest per year.
    After 5 years the value of the investment totalled $669.16.
    Calculate how much Chris had invested.

7   Ali invests x at a rate of 3% compound interest per year.
    After 20 years the value of the investment is $7495.36.
    Calculate the value of x.

8   Haroon invests $2000. At the end of 4 years, his account is worth $2295.
    Find the yearly compound interest rate.

9   Fiona invests $1200 for 10 years at a rate of x% compound interest per year.
    At the end of the 10 years she has a total amount of $1652.27 correct to the nearest cent.
    Find the value of x.

10 Sarah and Azhar both invest $10 000.
    Sarah invests her $10 000 at a rate of x% compound interest per year.
    Azhar invests his $10 000 in a bank that pays 2% simple interest per year.
    After 7 years their investments are worth the same amount.
    Calculate the value of x.

Exponential growth and decay

An example of an exponential function is $y = 2^x$. You learned about exponential graphs and their applications in Unit 7.

When the growth rate of an exponential function is positive, it is called **exponential growth**. Some examples of exponential growth are:

- the value of an investment
- population growth
- bacteria growth

When the growth rate of an exponential function is negative, it is called **exponential decay**. Some examples of exponential decay are:

- population decrease
- the value of a car
- radioactive decay
- temperature cooling

The formula that is used for solving exponential growth and decay problems is:

$$\text{Final value} = x_0 \left(1 + \frac{r}{100}\right)^n$$

where x_0 is the initial value, r is the rate of growth or decay, and n is the time interval.

Note   For exponential growth: $r > 0$
For exponential decay: $r < 0$

EXAMPLE

At the start of an experiment there are 5000 bacteria.
The number of bacteria increases at a rate of 25% per hour.
Work out the number of bacteria after 10 hours.

$$\text{Number of bacteria} = x_0 \left(1 + \frac{r}{100}\right)^n \qquad \textit{use } x_0 = 5000, r = 25 \textit{ and } n = 10$$

$$= 5000 \left(1 + \frac{25}{100}\right)^{10}$$

$$= 500(1.25)^{10}$$

$$= 46\,566.128\ldots$$

$$= 46\,600 \text{ correct to 3 s.f.}$$

EXAMPLE

Farhat buys a boat for $2500.
Each year the value of the boat decreases by 10% of its value at the beginning of that year.
Find the value of the boat after 4 years.

$$\text{Value after 4 years} = P \left(1 + \frac{r}{100}\right)^n \qquad \textit{use } P = 2500, r = -10 \textit{ and } n = 4$$

$$= 2500 \left(1 + \frac{-10}{100}\right)^4$$

$$= 2500(0.9)^4$$

$$= \$1640.25$$

EXERCISE 9.2

1 Francesca buys a moped for $4000.
Each year the value of the moped decreases by 15% of its value at the beginning of that year.
Find the value of the moped after 5 years.

2 Each year the value of a car decreases by 10% of its value at the beginning of that year.
Paul buys a car for $30 000.
Calculate the value of Paul's car after 4 years.

3 Priya buys a jet ski for $12 000.
The value of the jet ski decreases each year by 12% of its value at the beginning of that year.
Calculate the value of the jet ski after 5 years.
Give your answer correct to the nearest dollar.

4 It is estimated that the population of an endangered species of bird is
decreasing at a rate of 3.5% per year.
On January 1st, 2010 the population was 5600.
Find the expected population on January 1st, 2060.

5 It is estimated that the population of a country is growing at a rate of 0.8% per year.
On January 1st, 2010 the population was 4.44 million.
Find the expected population on January 1st, 2040.

6 At the start of an experiment there are 20 000 radioactive particles.
The number of radioactive particles decreases at a rate of 20% per day.
Work out the number of radioactive particles after 5 days.

7 At the start of an experiment there are 5000 bacteria.
The number of bacteria increases at a rate of 35% per hour.
After how many hours will the number of bacteria be greater than five million?

8 The population of a city increases exponentially at a rate of x% per year.
In 2005 the population was 40 000.
In 2015 the population was 74 000.
Find the value of x.

9 Two months ago Ricardo had 4 mice.
He now has 8 mice.
Assuming that the number of mice increases exponentially at a rate of x% per month, find
a the value of x
b the number of mice that he will have in 2 months
c the number of mice that he will have in 1 year.

Simultaneous equations 2

> ## THIS SECTION WILL SHOW YOU HOW TO
> • Solve simultaneous equations using the substitution method

Substitution method

In the substitution method you make x or y the subject of one of the equations and then substitute into the other equation.

EXAMPLE

Solve these simultaneous equations. $\quad y = 3x - 10$
$\qquad\qquad\qquad\qquad\qquad\qquad\qquad x + y = -2$

$y = 3x - 10 \quad (1)$
$x + y = -2 \quad (2)$
Substitute for y from equation (1) into equation (2).

$x + (3x - 10) = -2$	remove brackets and collect like terms
$4x - 10 = -2$	add 10 to both sides
$4x = 8$	divide both sides by 4
$x = 2$	

Substitute $x = 2$ in equation (1) and then solve to find y.
$$y = 3 \times 2 - 10 = -4$$
The solution is $x = 2$, $y = -4$
➡ CHECK: $-4 = 3 \times 2 - 10$ ✓
$\qquad\qquad 2 + -4 = -2$ ✓

EXAMPLE

Solve these simultaneous equations. $\quad 2x + 3y = 0$
$\qquad\qquad\qquad\qquad\qquad\qquad\qquad\quad x + 6y = 3$

$2x + 3y = 0 \quad (1)$
$x + 6y = 3 \quad (2)$
There is only one x in equation (2) so make x the subject of equation (2).
$$x = 3 - 6y$$
Substitute for x into equation (1).

$2(3 - 6y) + 3y = 0$	remove brackets
$6 - 12y + 3y = 0$	collect like terms
$6 - 9y = 0$	add $9y$ to both sides
$6 = 9y$	divide both sides by 9
$y = \dfrac{6}{9} = \dfrac{2}{3}$	

Substitute $y = \dfrac{2}{3}$ in the equation $x = 3 - 6y$ to find x.
$$x = 3 - \left(6 \times \frac{2}{3}\right) = 3 - 4 = -1$$
The solution is $x = -1$, $y = \dfrac{2}{3}$

➡ CHECK: $(2 \times -1) + \left(3 \times \dfrac{2}{3}\right) = -2 + 2 = 0$ ✓

$\qquad\qquad -1 + \left(6 \times \dfrac{2}{3}\right) = -1 + 4 = 3$ ✓

EXERCISE 9.3

Solve these simultaneous equations

1   a $x + 2y = 4$
        $x = 3y - 11$

    b $x + 3y = 21$
        $y = 2x - 14$

    c $5x + 2y = 1$
        $x = 3y + 7$

    d $x + 2y = 11$
        $x = 2y + 5$

    e $y = 6 + 2x$
        $4x + 2y = 16$

    f $x = 3 - y$
        $2x - 3y = -19$

    g $x = 2y + 10$
        $5x + 4y = 8$

    h $y = 4x - 6$
        $2x - 3y = -7$

    i $4x + 2y - 14 = 0$
        $x = y - 8$

    j $5x - 3y = -17$
        $x = 3y - 25$

    k $x = 18 + 7y$
        $x - 4y = 9$

    l $y = 10x + 47$
        $2y - 5x = 34$

2   a $y = 2x - 7$
        $y = x - 3$

    b $x = 5y + 1$
        $x = 25 - 3y$

    c $y = 3x - 9$
        $y = 4x + 14$

    d $x = 3y + 5$
        $x = 2y - 4$

3   a $2x + 3y = 0$
        $x - 2y = 14$

    b $3x + y = 15$
        $5x - 3y = -3$

    c $2x + y = -3$
        $3x - 2y = -8$

    d $x - 5y = 18$
        $x + 3y = 2$

    e $2x + 3y + 10 = 0$
        $x + 4y + 15 = 0$

    f $x + 2y = 1$
        $3x - 2y = 19$

    g $5x + 3y = -18$
        $2x + y = -7$

    h $x + 2y = 11$
        $4y - x = -2$

    i $3x + y = -1$
        $6x - 2y = -2$

    j $x + 2y = 8$
        $3x + 4y - 6 = 0$

    k $3x + 2y = 18$
        $x - 2y = -6$

    l $3x + y = 0$
        $6x - 5y = 14$

4   Find the coordinates of the point where the lines $y = x + 2$ and $3x + 2y = 14$ intersect.

5   Find the coordinates of the point where the lines $y = 3x - 1$ and $2x - 5y = 18$ intersect.

6   A bag contains one-dollar coins and 50-cent coins. There are twice as many one-dollar coins as 50-cent coins and the total value of the coins is $42.50. How many one-dollar coins are there?

7   A magazine costs $2.50 more than a newspaper. The total cost of the magazine and the newspaper is $4.80. Find the cost of the magazine.

8   Adam is three times the age of Billy. The sum of their ages is 56 years. How old is Adam?

9   Sheena has some $10 and $5 notes. She has four times as many $10 notes as $5 notes and the total value of all the notes is $585. How many $5 notes does she have?

10 Theatre tickets cost either $30 or $42. One evening twice as many $30 tickets are sold as $42 tickets and the total money taken is $18 564. Find the total number of tickets that are sold.

> **KEY WORDS**
> substitution method

UNIT 9

Linear programming

EXAMPLE

A company plans to make two types of chair.
The machine time and craftsman's time needed for each type of chair are shown in the table.

	Chair A	Chair B
Machine time (hours)	2	3
Craftsman's time (hours)	4	2

The company has 30 hours of machine time and 32 hours of craftsman's time available.
The company wants to make at least 2 of chair A and at least 6 of chair B.
Let x be the number of chair A and y be the number of chair B.
Write down four inequalities in x and y.
Represent these four inequalities on a graph.
What is the largest number of type A chair that can be made?

Machine time gives $2x + 3y \leq 30$
Craftsman's time gives $4x + 2y \leq 32$ (this simplifies to $2x + y \leq 16$)
Number of chair A gives $x \geq 2$
Number of chair B gives $y \geq 6$
The boundary lines $2x + 3y = 30$, $2x + y = 16$, $x = 2$ and $y = 6$ need to be drawn.

- The boundary lines are all **solid** lines in this example.
- Remember to shade the **unwanted** region.
- The unshaded region represents the required region.
- The red dots represent all the possible combinations of chairs in the required region (these are also shown in the table below).

Chair A (x)	2	2	2	3	3	3	4	4	5
Chair B (y)	6	7	8	6	7	8	6	7	6

➡ NOTE: the maximum or minimum numbers always occur at/near one of the corners of the required region.

The largest number of type A chair that can be made is 5.

EXERCISE 9.4

1   A car park has space for x cars and y motorcycles.
    The car park has an area of $900\,m^2$.
    Each car needs $15\,m^2$ of space and each motorcycle needs $3\,m^2$ of space.
    There must be space for at least 40 cars.
    There must be space for at least 20 motorcycles.
    a   Explain why $5x + y \leq 300$
    b   Write down two more inequalities in x and y.
    c   Represent these three inequalities on a graph.
    d   What is the largest possible number of cars in the car park?

2   Petra works in a hotel during the school holidays.
    In one week she spends x hours cleaning rooms and y hours waitressing.
    She spends no more than 15 hours working.
    She spends at least 6 hours waitressing.
    She spends at least twice as much time waitressing as she does cleaning.
    a   Write down three inequalities in x and y.
    b   Represent these three inequalities on a graph.
    c   What is the largest possible number of hours she can spend cleaning rooms?

3   A builder plans to build some executive homes and some standard homes.
    He has $9000\,m^2$ of land available.
    He builds x executive homes and y standard homes.
    Each executive home requires $400\,m^2$ of land and each standard home requires $200\,m^2$ of land.
    The number of standard homes is to be less than the number
    of executive homes.
    There must be at least 10 standard homes.
    a   Explain why $2x + y \leq 45$
    b   Write down two more inequalities in x and y.
    c   Represent these three inequalities on a graph.
    d   What is the largest possible number of executive homes
        that can be built?

4   A school trip is planned for 100 students.
    The school uses x type A minibuses and y type B minibuses to transport the students.
    The type A minibus can carry 16 students and the type B minibus can carry 10 students.
    The school wishes to use no more than eight minibuses.
    The school wishes to use at least one type A minibus.
    The school wishes to use at least three type B minibuses.
    a   Explain why $8x + 5y \geq 50$
    b   Write down three more inequalities in x and y.
    c   Represent these four inequalities on a graph.
    d   What is the largest possible number of type A minibus that can be used?

An aircraft has 30 first class seats available and 220 economy class seats available.
A first class seat costs $240 and an economy class seat costs $120.
A flight will be cancelled if the money taken for the seats is less than $28 800.
Let x = the number of first class seats sold and y = the number of economy class seats sold.

a Write down three inequalities in x and y.

b Represent these three inequalities on a graph.

c What is the minimum number of seats to be sold for the flight not to be cancelled?

---

a First class seats $x \leq 30$
Economy class seats $y \leq 220$
Money taken $240x + 120y \geq 28\,800$ divide by 120 to simplify the inequality
                             $2x + y \geq 240$

The three inequalities are $x \leq 30$, $y \leq 220$ and $2x + y \geq 240$.

b The boundary lines $x = 30$, $y = 220$ and $2x + y = 240$ need to be drawn.
To draw the line $2x + y = 240$ substitute $x = 0$ and $y = 0$ into the equation to find the axis crossing points.

x	0	120
y	240	0

- The boundary lines are all **solid** lines in this example.
- Remember to shade the **unwanted** region.
- The unshaded region represents the required region.

c The maximum or minimum occur at/near one of the corners of the required region.
The three corners of the required region are A(30, 220), B(30, 180) and C(10, 220).

At A number of seats = 30 + 220 = 250
At B number of seats = 30 + 180 = 210
At C number of seats = 10 + 220 = 230

The minimum number of seats sold for the flight not to be cancelled is 210.

EXERCISE 9.5

1 A company makes model animals out of wood. They make giraffes and elephants.
The carving time and sanding time needed for each model animal are shown below.

	Giraffe	Elephant
Carving time (hours)	4	3
Sanding time (hours)	1	1

The company has 48 hours of carving time and 14 hours of sanding time available.
The company wants to make at least 5 giraffes and at least 5 elephants.
Let x be the number of giraffes and y be the number of elephants.
  a Write down four inequalities in x and y.
  b Represent these four inequalities on a graph.
  c The company makes a profit of \$10 for each giraffe sold and a profit of \$20 for each elephant sold.
     Calculate the greatest possible profit.

2 4500 DVDs need to be packed into storage units.
There are two sizes of storage units available.
A large unit can hold 500 DVDs and a small unit can hold 300 DVDs.
No more than 11 storage units are to be used.
At least 2 of the storage units must be small.
Let x be the number of large units used and y be the number of small units used.
  a Write down three inequalities in x and y.
  b Represent these three inequalities on a graph.
  c A large storage unit costs \$10 and a small storage unit costs \$8.
     Calculate the least possible cost of the storage units.

3 Lara is making some small cakes and biscuits to raise money for charity.
She only has 600 g of flour and 580 g of sugar available.
She has plenty of all the other ingredients.
The amount of flour and sugar needed for each cake and biscuit are shown below.

	Small cake	Biscuit
Flour (g)	6	3
Sugar (g)	4	5

Lara wants to make at least 50 small cakes and at least 40 biscuits.
Let x be the number of small cakes and y be the number of biscuits made.
  a Write down four inequalities in x and y.
  b Represent these four inequalities on a graph.
  c Lara sells each cake for \$1.50 and each biscuit for \$1.
     Calculate the largest possible amount of money that Lara can make if she sells all her cakes and biscuits.

KEY WORDS
linear programming

UNIT 9

Solving quadratic equations by completing the square

THIS SECTION WILL SHOW YOU HOW TO
- Complete the square
- Solve quadratic equations by completing the square

Completing the square

If you expand the expressions $(x + b)^2$ and $(x - b)^2$ you will obtain the results:

$$(x + b)^2 = x^2 + 2bx + b^2 \quad \text{and} \quad (x - b)^2 = x^2 - 2bx + b^2$$

Rearranging these give you the following important results:

$$x^2 + 2bx = (x + b)^2 - b^2$$
$$x^2 - 2bx = (x - b)^2 - b^2$$

This is known as **completing the square**.

To complete the square for $x^2 + 6x$:

$$6 \div 2 = 3$$

$$x^2 + 6x = (x + 3)^2 - 3^2$$
$$= (x + 3)^2 - 9$$

➡ CHECK: $(x + 3)(x + 3) - 9 = x^2 + 3x + 3x + 9 - 9 = x^2 + 6x$ ✓

EXAMPLE

Complete the square for the expressions

a $x^2 - 12x$ **b** $x^2 - 7x$

a $x^2 - 12x$:

$$12 \div 2 = 6$$

$$x^2 - 12x = (x - 6)^2 - 6^2$$
$$= (x - 6)^2 - 36$$

➡ CHECK: $(x - 6)(x - 6) - 36$
$$= x^2 - 6x - 6x + 36 - 36$$
$$= x^2 - 12x$ ✓

b $x^2 - 7x$:

$$7 \div 2 = 3.5$$

$$x^2 - 7x = (x - 3.5)^2 - 3.5^2$$
$$= (x - 3.5)^2 - 12.25$$

➡ CHECK: $(x - 3.5)(x - 3.5) - 12.25$
$$= x^2 - 3.5x - 3.5x + 12.25 - 12.25$$
$$= x^2 - 7x$ ✓

EXERCISE 9.6

1 Complete the square for these expressions.

   a $x^2 - 2x$ b $x^2 + 4x$ c $x^2 - 10x$ d $x^2 + 20x$

   e $x^2 - 16x$ f $x^2 - 12x$ g $x^2 + 18x$ h $x^2 + 36x$

   i $x^2 + 22x$ j $x^2 + 24x$ k $x^2 - 3x$ l $x^2 + 5x$

   m $x^2 + 7x$ n $x^2 + 9x$ o $x^2 - 20x$ p $x^2 + x$

> You may need to take out a numerical factor before completing the square.
>
> $$5x^2 - 20x \longrightarrow 5[x^2 - 4x] \longrightarrow 5[(x - 2)^2 - 4] \longrightarrow 5(x - 2)^2 - 20$$
>
>   take 5 outside   complete the   multiply both
>   square   terms by 5

2 Complete the square for these expressions.

   a $5x^2 - 20x$ b $3x^2 + 12x$ c $4x^2 + 20x$ d $3x^2 - 21x$

   e $2x^2 + 12x$ f $2x^2 - 5x$ g $3x^2 - 4x$ h $2x^2 + 9x$

> You may also have a constant term in your quadratic expression.
>
> $$x^2 + 12x - 3 \longrightarrow (x + 6)^2 - 6^2 - 3 \longrightarrow (x + 6)^2 - 39$$
>
>   complete the square   combine the
>   for $x^2 + 12x$ numbers
> $x^2 + 12x = (x + 6)^2 - 6^2$ $- 6^2 - 3 = -39$

3 Write these expressions in the form $(x + p)^2 + q$.

   a $x^2 - 8x + 15$ b $x^2 - 4x - 12$ c $x^2 - 6x - 4$ d $x^2 + 4x - 3$

   e $x^2 + 12x - 5$ f $x^2 - 8x + 1$ g $x^2 + 10x - 3$ h $x^2 + 9x - 22$

4 $x^2 - 10x + 4 = (x - a)^2 + b$. Find the values of a and b.

5 $x^2 + 8x - 3 = (x + p)^2 + q$. Find the values of p and q.

6 $2x^2 - 8x + 3 = 2(x - p)^2 + q$. Find the values of p and q.

7

> You can make x the subject of the equation $x^2 + 8x = a$ by completing the square.
>
> $$x^2 + 8x = a \longrightarrow (x + 4)^2 - 4^2 = a \longrightarrow (x + 4)^2 = a + 16 \longrightarrow x + 4 = \pm\sqrt{a + 16} \longrightarrow x = -4 \pm \sqrt{a + 16}$$

  Make x the subject of these equations. (You will need to complete the square first.)

   a $x^2 - 6x = b$ b $x^2 + 10x = a + b$

You can solve quadratic equations by completing the square.

Solve the equation $x^2 + 4x - 3 = 0$, giving your answers to two decimal places.

$$x^2 + 4x - 3 = 0 \qquad \text{add 3 to both sides}$$
$$x^2 + 4x = 3 \qquad \text{complete the square for } x^2 + 4x$$
$$(x + 2)^2 - 2^2 = 3$$
$$(x + 2)^2 - 4 = 3 \qquad \text{add 4 to both sides}$$
$$(x + 2)^2 = 7 \qquad \text{square root both sides}$$
$$x + 2 = \pm\sqrt{7} \qquad \text{subtract 2 from both sides}$$
$$x = -2 \pm \sqrt{7}$$
$$x = -2 + \sqrt{7} \quad \text{or} \quad x = -2 - \sqrt{7}$$
$$x = 0.65 \quad \text{or} \quad x = -4.65 \quad \text{(to 2 d.p.)}$$

The next example shows you what to do if the coefficient of x^2 is not 1.

Solve the equation $2x^2 - 8x + 5 = 0$, giving your answers to two decimal places.

$$2x^2 - 8x + 5 = 0 \qquad \text{divide both sides by 2 so that the coefficient of } x^2 \text{ is 1}$$
$$x^2 - 4x + 2\tfrac{1}{2} = 0 \qquad \text{subtract } 2\tfrac{1}{2} \text{ from both sides}$$
$$x^2 - 4x = -2\tfrac{1}{2} \qquad \text{complete the square for } x^2 - 4x$$
$$(x - 2)^2 - 2^2 = -2\tfrac{1}{2}$$
$$(x - 2)^2 - 4 = -2\tfrac{1}{2} \qquad \text{add 4 to both sides}$$
$$(x - 2)^2 = 1\tfrac{1}{2} \qquad \text{square root both sides}$$
$$x - 2 = \pm\sqrt{1\tfrac{1}{2}} \qquad \text{add 2 to both sides}$$
$$x = 2 \pm \sqrt{1\tfrac{1}{2}}$$
$$x = 2 + \sqrt{1\tfrac{1}{2}} \quad \text{or} \quad x = 2 - \sqrt{1\tfrac{1}{2}}$$
$$x = 3.22 \quad \text{or} \quad x = 0.78 \text{ (to 2 d.p.)}$$

You can use completing the square to find the **minimum** value of a quadratic expression.

$$x^2 + 4x + 5 = \boxed{(x + 2)^2} + 1$$

➡ NOTE: this part of the expression is a square so it will always be ≥ 0 (positive). The smallest value it can be is 0.

The minimum value of $x^2 + 4x + 5$ is $0 + 1 = 1$.

EXERCISE 9.7

In this exercise give your answers where appropriate correct to 2 decimal places.

1 Use completing the square to solve these equations.

a $x^2 + 6x + 8 = 0$
b $x^2 + 4x + 4 = 0$
c $x^2 + 2x - 8 = 0$
d $x^2 - 12x + 34 = 0$
e $x^2 - 6x + 7 = 0$
f $x^2 + 14x - 3 = 0$
g $x^2 - 20x - 33 = 0$
h $x^2 - 10x + 15 = 0$
i $x^2 - 2x - 6 = 0$

2 Use completing the square to solve these equations.

a $x^2 + 3x + 2 = 0$
b $x^2 - 7x + 12 = 0$
c $x^2 + x - 6 = 0$
d $x^2 - 5x + 5 = 0$
e $x^2 + x - 10 = 0$
f $x^2 - 11x + 3 = 0$

3 Use completing the square to solve these equations.

a $3x^2 - 5x - 2 = 0$
b $2x^2 + 7x + 3 = 0$
c $2x^2 + 16x + 30 = 0$
d $2x^2 - 16x + 4 = 0$
e $3x^2 + 6x + 2 = 0$
f $2x^2 + 8x - 6 = 0$

4 Anna is trying to solve the equations $12 = \dfrac{3}{x} - x$ and $x(x - 2) = 12$.

Copy the equations and correct her working.

a

$12 = \dfrac{3}{x} - x$

$12x = 3 - x$

$13x = 3$

$x = \dfrac{3}{13}$

b

$x(x - 2) = 12$

$x = 12 \quad \text{or} \quad x - 2 = 12$

$x = 12 \quad \text{or} \quad x = 14$

5 Solve these equations.

a $x(x - 4) = 20$
b $x^2 - 7 = 2x$
c $10 + 3x = 2x^2$
d $x = 3 + \dfrac{1}{x}$
e $8 = \dfrac{2}{x} + 5x$
f $x = \dfrac{6}{x + 2}$

6 Use completing the square to find the minimum value of $x^2 - 4x + 11$.

7 Use completing the square to show that $x^2 + 6x + 14$ is never less than 5.

8 Use completing the square to find the minimum value of $2x^2 - 4x + 5$.

CHALLENGE:

Try solving the equation $ax^2 + bx + c = 0$
by completing the square.

If you do it correctly you should obtain the answer

$x = \dfrac{-b \pm \sqrt{b^2 - 4ac}}{2a}$.

> **KEY WORDS**
> completing the square
> minimum

Finding turning points of quadratics by completing the square

> **THIS SECTION WILL SHOW YOU HOW TO**
> - Find the turning point of a quadratic by completing the square

 The shape of the graph of $y = ax^2 + bx + c$ is called a **parabola.**
The orientation of the parabola depends on the value of a; the coefficient of x^2.

If $a > 0$, the curve has a **minimum point** which occurs
at the lowest point of the curve.

If $a < 0$, the curve has a **maximum point** which occurs
at the highest point of the curve.

In the case of a parabola, we also call this point the **vertex** of the parabola.
Every parabola has a line of symmetry that passes through the vertex.

When you sketch the graph of a quadratic function, the key properties are:
- the general shape of the graph
- the axis intercepts
- the coordinates of the vertex.

EXAMPLE

a Find the axis crossing points for the graph of $y = x^2 - 4x - 5$.
b Sketch the graph of $y = x^2 - 4x - 5$ and find the coordinates of the vertex.

a $y = x^2 - 4x - 5$
When $x = 0$, $y = -5$.
When $y = 0$, $x^2 - 4x - 5 = 0$
$$(x + 1)(x - 5) = 0$$
$$x = -1 \quad \text{or} \quad x = 5$$
Axes crossing points are: $(0, -5)$, $(-1, 0)$ and $(5, 0)$.

b **Method 1** Using the symmetry of the curve:
The line of symmetry cuts the x-axis
midway between -1 and 5.
Hence the line of symmetry is $x = 2$.
When $x = 2$, $y = 2^2 - 4(2) - 5$
$$y = -9$$
Minimum point $= (2, -9)$

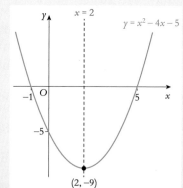

Method 2 By completing the square:
$$x^2 - 4x - 5 = (x - 2)^2 - 2^2 - 5$$
$$= \underbrace{(x - 2)^2}_{\text{min value} = 0} - 9$$

The minimum value of $(x - 2)^2 - 9$ is $0 - 9 = -9$ and this minimum occurs when $x = 2$.
So the graph of $y = x^2 - 4x - 5$ has a minimum point at $(2, -9)$.

a Write $6 - 5x - x^2$ in the form $a - (x + b)^2$ where a and b are constants.

b Write down the coordinates of the turning point of the curve $y = 6 - 5x - x^2$, stating whether it is a maximum or minimum point.

a $6 - 5x - x^2 = -(x^2 + 5x - 6)$

$$= -\left[\left(x + 2\frac{1}{2}\right)^2 - \left(2\frac{1}{2}\right)^2 - 6\right]$$

$$= -\left[\left(x + 2\frac{1}{2}\right)^2 - 12\frac{1}{4}\right]$$

$$= 12\frac{1}{4} - \left(x + 2\frac{1}{2}\right)^2$$

b $y = 6 - 5x - x^2$

$$= 12\frac{1}{4} - \underbrace{\left(x + 2\frac{1}{2}\right)^2}_{\text{min value} = 0}$$

The maximum value of $12\frac{1}{4} - \left(x + 2\frac{1}{2}\right)^2$ is $12\frac{1}{4} - 0 = 12\frac{1}{4}$ and this occurs when $x = -2\frac{1}{2}$.

Hence the turning point is $\left(-2\frac{1}{2}, 12\frac{1}{4}\right)$ and it is a maximum point.

EXERCISE 9.8

1 Use the symmetry of each quadratic function to find the maximum or minimum points. Sketch each graph, showing all axis crossing points.

   a $y = x^2 - 8x + 12$ **b** $y = x^2 + 6x - 7$

   c $y = 8 - 2x - x^2$ **d** $y = 2x^2 + 7x - 30$

2 a Express $x^2 - 8x + 7$ in the form $(x + a)^2 + b$, where a and b are integers.

   b Write down the coordinates of the turning point of the curve $y = x^2 - 8x + 7$, stating whether it is a maximum or minimum point.

   c Sketch the graph of $y = x^2 - 8x + 7$ showing all axis crossing points.

3 a Express $15 - 2x - x^2$ in the form $a - (x + b)^2$, where a and b are integers.

   b Find the coordinates of the turning point of the curve $y = 15 - 2x - x^2$, stating whether it is a maximum or minimum point.

   c Sketch the graph of $y = 15 - 2x - x^2$ showing all axis crossing points.

4 a Express $2x^2 + 8x + 7$ in the form $a(x + b)^2 + c$, where a, b and c are integers.

   b Write down the coordinates of the vertex of the curve $y = 2x^2 + 8x + 7$, and state whether this is a maximum or a minimum point.

5 a Write $10 - 12x - 2x^2$ in the form $p - 2(x + q)^2$.

b Write down the coordinates of the vertex of the curve $y = 10 - 12x - 2x^2$, and state whether this is a maximum or a minimum point.

6

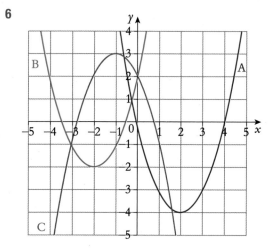

Find the equations of parabolas A, B and C.

Using graphs to solve equations

You can use graphs to find approximate solutions to equations that may be difficult to solve by other methods.

EXAMPLE

Draw the graph of $y = x^2 - 5x + 4$ for $0 \leq x \leq 5$.

Use your graph to solve the equations   **a** $x^2 - 5x + 4 = 2$ **b** $x^2 - 6x + 6 = 0$

a $x^2 - 5x + 4 = 2$

$y = x^2 - 5x + 4$ $y = 2$

To solve the equation $x^2 - 5x + 4 = 2$ draw the curve $y = x^2 - 5x + 4$ and the line $y = 2$ and find the x coordinates of the points where $y = x^2 - 5x + 4$ and $y = 2$ intersect.

The answers to $x^2 - 5x + 4 = 2$ are

$x \approx 0.4$ and $x \approx 4.6$

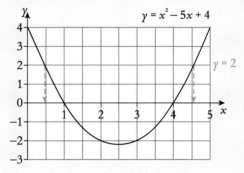

b   To use the graph of $y = x^2 - 5x + 4$ to solve the equation $x^2 - 6x + 6 = 0$ you must first rearrange the equation into the form '$x^2 - 5x + 4 = ...$'

$x^2 - 6x + 6 = 0$ *add x to both sides*

$x^2 - 5x + 6 = x$ *take 2 from both sides*

$x^2 - 5x + 4 = x - 2$

$y = x^2 - 5x + 4$ $y = x - 2$

To solve the equation $x^2 - 6x + 6 = 0$ draw the curve $y = x^2 - 5x + 4$ and the line $y = x - 2$ and find the x coordinates of the points where $y = x^2 - 5x + 4$ and $y = x - 2$ intersect.

The answers to $x^2 - 6x + 6 = 0$ are

$x \approx 1.3$ and $x \approx 4.7$

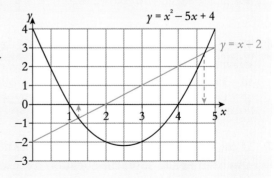

EXERCISE 9.9

1   $y = x^3 - 5x^2 + 10$ and $y = 2x$ are
    shown on the graph.
    Use the graph to solve the equation
    $x^3 - 5x^2 + 10x = 2x$

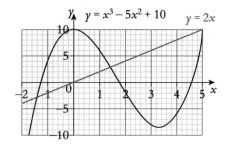

2   $y = \dfrac{4}{x}$ and $y = x - 2$ are shown
    on the graph.

    Use the graph to solve the equation
    $\dfrac{4}{x} = x - 2$

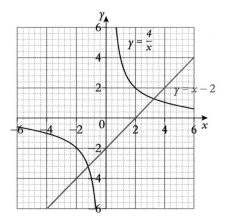

3   Draw the graph of $y = x^2$ for $-3 \leq x \leq 3$.
    Use your graph to solve these equations.
    a $x^2 = 6$ b $x^2 = x + 3$ c $x^2 - 2 = 2x$

4   Draw the graph of $f(x) = x^2 - 3x$ for $-2 \leq x \leq 5$
    Use your graph to solve these equations.
    a $x^2 - 3x = 0$ b $x^2 - 3x = x + 2$
    c $x^2 - x - 4 = 0$

5   Draw the graph of $y = x^3 + 1$ for $-3 \leq x \leq 3$
    Use your graph to solve these equations.
    a $x^3 + 1 = 20$ b $x^3 + 1 = 5x$ c $x^3 + 10x - 9 = 0$

6   If the graph of $f(x) = 3^x$ has been drawn, what graph must also be
    drawn to solve these equations.
    a $3^x = 4$ b $3^x = 0.5$ c $3^x = 4x$ d $3^x - 2 = x$
    e $3^x - x^2 + 2 = 0$ f $x3^x = 1 + 3x$ g $1 - 3^x = 2x$ h $x^2 3^x = 1$

7   If the graph of $y = 3x^2 - \dfrac{1}{x}$ has been drawn, what graph must
    also be drawn to solve the equation $3x^3 - x^2 - 5x - 1 = 0$?

- - - - - - - - - - - - - - - - - - -

TOP TIP

You must rearrange
$3x^3 - x^2 - 5x - 1 = 0$ to the form
'$3x^2 - \dfrac{1}{x} = ...$'

- - - - - - - - - - - - - - - - - - -

8   If the graph of $f(x) = \dfrac{2}{x^2}$ has been drawn, what graph
    must also be drawn to solve the equation $5x^3 - 5x^2 - 2 = 0$?

UNIT 9

The roots of the equation f(x) = k

The graph of $f(x) = \dfrac{x^2}{2} - \dfrac{8}{x}$ is shown below.

The equation $\dfrac{x^2}{2} - \dfrac{8}{x} = k$ will have 1, 2 or 3 roots.

The number of roots depends on the value of k.

To solve the equation $\dfrac{x^2}{2} - \dfrac{8}{x} = 12$ the line $y = 12$ needs to be drawn.

To solve the equation $\dfrac{x^2}{2} - \dfrac{8}{x} = 6$ the line $y = 6$ needs to be drawn.

To solve the equation $\dfrac{x^2}{2} - \dfrac{8}{x} = -9$ the line $y = -9$ needs to be drawn.

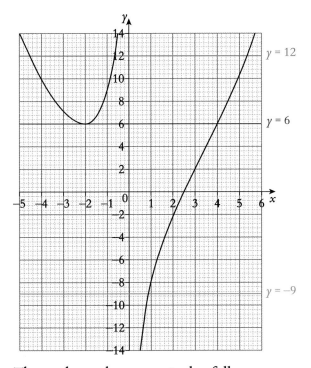

There are **three** roots to the equation $\dfrac{x^2}{2} - \dfrac{8}{x} = 12$
They are $x \approx -4.5$, $x \approx -0.7$ and $x \approx 5.2$

There are **two** roots to the equation $\dfrac{x^2}{2} - \dfrac{8}{x} = 6$
They are $x = -2$ and $x = 4$

There is **one** root to the equation $\dfrac{x^2}{2} - \dfrac{8}{x} = -9$
The root is $x \approx 0.9$

The results can be summarised as follows.

$$\boxed{\dfrac{x^2}{2} - \dfrac{8}{x} = k}$$

$k > 6$ means there will be **three** roots
$k = 6$ means there will be **two** roots
$k < 6$ means there will be **one** root

EXERCISE 9.10

1   The graph of $f(x) = \dfrac{(x-2)^2}{2} + 1$ is shown.

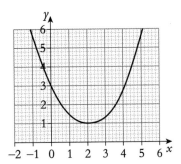

a   Use the graph to find the **two** roots of the equation $\dfrac{(x-2)^2}{2} + 1 = 5$

b   For what value of k is there only one root of the equation $\dfrac{(x-2)^2}{2} + 1 = k$

c   For what values of k are there no roots of the equation $\dfrac{(x-2)^2}{2} + 1 = k$

2   The graph of $f(x) = x + \dfrac{1}{2x} + 3$ is shown.

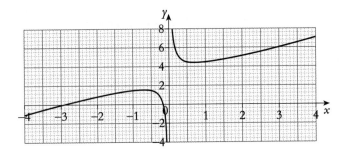

a   Use the graph to find the **two** roots of the equation $x + \dfrac{1}{2x} + 3 = 6$

b   There are three integer values of k for which the equation $x + \dfrac{1}{2x} + 3 = k$ has no roots.
Write down these three values of k.

3   The graph of $f(x) = x^2 + \dfrac{2}{x}$ is shown.

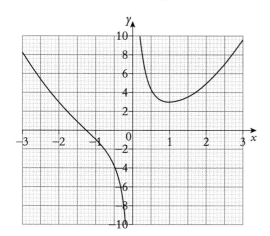

a   Use the graph to find the **three** roots of the equation $x^2 + \dfrac{2}{x} = 5$

b   There is one value of k for which the equation $x^2 + \dfrac{2}{x} = k$ has two roots.

Write down this value of k.

c   For what values of k is there only one root of the equation $x^2 + \dfrac{2}{x} = k$

4   The graph of $y = x^3 - 3x + 1$ is shown.

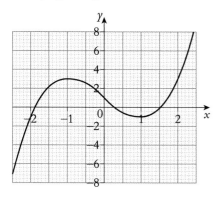

a   Use the graph to find the **three** roots of the equation $x^3 - 3x + 1 = 0$
b   There are two values of k for which the equation $x^3 - 3x + 1 = k$ has two roots.

Write down these two values of k.

c   For what values of k is there only one root of the equation $x^3 - 3x + 1 = k$

UNIT 9

Vectors and vector geometry

 A **vector** has both size and direction.
Examples of vectors are:
- displacement (5 km on a bearing of 300°)
- velocity (5 m/s due east)
- weight (20 N vertically downwards)

Vector notation

$\overrightarrow{AB}$ means the displacement from the point A to the point B.
A translation is described using a column vector.
A column vector describes the movement in both the x and y directions.

The vector $\begin{pmatrix} 4 \\ 3 \end{pmatrix}$ moves 4 to the right and 3 up

For the diagram, $\overrightarrow{AB} = \begin{pmatrix} 4 \\ 3 \end{pmatrix}$

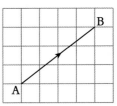

In textbooks, vectors are often written in bold, lower case letters.

In handwriting, vectors are written with a straight line or a wavy line underneath.

Magnitude of a vector

'The **magnitude** of the vector **a**' means 'the length of the vector **a**' and is denoted by |**a**|.
|**a**| is called the **modulus** of the vector **a**.

EXAMPLE

If $\mathbf{a} = \begin{pmatrix} -4 \\ 3 \end{pmatrix}$ find the magnitude of the vector **a**.

Using Pythagoras' theorem,
$$|\mathbf{a}| = \sqrt{3^2 + (-4)^2}$$
$$= \sqrt{25}$$
$$= 5$$

The magnitude of vector **a** is 5.

Two vectors are said to be equal if they are the same length and are in the same direction.

The vector −**a** is the same length as the vector **a** but is in the opposite direction.

EXERCISE 9.11

1 Draw these vectors on graph paper.

a $\begin{pmatrix} 5 \\ 1 \end{pmatrix}$ b $\begin{pmatrix} 4 \\ -2 \end{pmatrix}$ c $\begin{pmatrix} 0 \\ -4 \end{pmatrix}$ d $\begin{pmatrix} -5 \\ -3 \end{pmatrix}$ e $\begin{pmatrix} 6 \\ 0 \end{pmatrix}$

2 Write these vectors in column vector form.

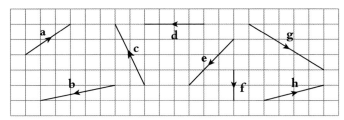

3 Draw the vectors $\begin{pmatrix} -4 \\ 2 \end{pmatrix}$ and $\begin{pmatrix} -8 \\ 4 \end{pmatrix}$.

What can you say about these two vectors?

4 Draw the vectors $\begin{pmatrix} 3 \\ 1 \end{pmatrix}$ and $\begin{pmatrix} -1 \\ 3 \end{pmatrix}$.

What can you say about these two vectors?

5 Find the magnitude of each of these vectors.

a $\begin{pmatrix} 6 \\ 8 \end{pmatrix}$ b $\begin{pmatrix} 5 \\ -12 \end{pmatrix}$ c $\begin{pmatrix} 0 \\ -4 \end{pmatrix}$ d $\begin{pmatrix} -15 \\ -8 \end{pmatrix}$ e $\begin{pmatrix} -20 \\ 21 \end{pmatrix}$

6 PQRSTU is a regular hexagon.
O is the centre of the hexagon.
$\overrightarrow{OP}$ = **p** and $\overrightarrow{OQ}$ = **q**.
($\overrightarrow{TU}$ = $\overrightarrow{OP}$ = **p** because they are the same length and in the same direction.)

a Write down all the vectors that are equal to **p**.
b Write down all the vectors that are equal to **q**.
c Write down all the vectors that are equal to −**p**.
d Write down all the vectors that are equal to −**q**.

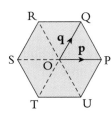

UNIT 9

Adding and subtracting vectors

The vector **a** + **b** means the vector **a** followed by the vector **b**.
The vector **a** − **b** means the vector **a** followed by the vector −**b**.
The **resultant vector** is usually shown with a double arrow.
It is drawn from the starting point to the finishing point.

If $\mathbf{a} = \begin{pmatrix} 2 \\ 4 \end{pmatrix}$ and $\mathbf{b} = \begin{pmatrix} 5 \\ 1 \end{pmatrix}$. Draw a diagram to find the column vector **a** + **b**.

First draw the vector **a**.
Follow vector **a** by the vector **b**.
Counting the squares on the grid:

$\mathbf{a} + \mathbf{b} = \begin{pmatrix} 7 \\ 5 \end{pmatrix}$

NOTE: $\begin{pmatrix} 2 \\ 4 \end{pmatrix} + \begin{pmatrix} 5 \\ 1 \end{pmatrix} = \begin{pmatrix} 2+5 \\ 4+1 \end{pmatrix}$

$= \begin{pmatrix} 7 \\ 5 \end{pmatrix}$

If $\mathbf{a} = \begin{pmatrix} 2 \\ 4 \end{pmatrix}$ and $\mathbf{b} = \begin{pmatrix} 5 \\ 1 \end{pmatrix}$. Draw a diagram to find the column vector **a** − **b**.

First draw the vector **a**.
Follow vector **a** by the vector −**b**.
Counting the squares on the grid:

$\mathbf{a} - \mathbf{b} = \begin{pmatrix} -3 \\ 3 \end{pmatrix}$

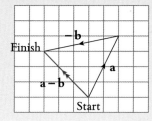

➡ NOTE: $\begin{pmatrix} 2 \\ 4 \end{pmatrix} - \begin{pmatrix} 5 \\ 1 \end{pmatrix} = \begin{pmatrix} 2-5 \\ 4-1 \end{pmatrix}$

$= \begin{pmatrix} -3 \\ 3 \end{pmatrix}$

Multiplication by a scalar

This vector can be
written as 3**a**.

3**a**

In the vector 3**a**, the number 3 is called a scalar.
(A scalar is a number.)

➡ NOTE: all these vectors are
parallel.

Parallel vectors

Two vectors are parallel if one vector can be written as a multiple of the other vector.
For example:

$\begin{pmatrix} 3 \\ -2 \end{pmatrix}$ and $\begin{pmatrix} 9 \\ -6 \end{pmatrix}$ are parallel and in the same direction because $\begin{pmatrix} 9 \\ -6 \end{pmatrix} = 3\begin{pmatrix} 3 \\ -2 \end{pmatrix}$

$\begin{pmatrix} 4 \\ -2 \end{pmatrix}$ and $\begin{pmatrix} -2 \\ 1 \end{pmatrix}$ are parallel and in opposite directions because $\begin{pmatrix} 4 \\ -2 \end{pmatrix} = -2\begin{pmatrix} -2 \\ 1 \end{pmatrix}$

Position vectors

The position vector of a point P means the displacement from
the origin to the point P.
For this diagram, the position vector of A = $\overrightarrow{OA}$ = $\begin{pmatrix} 2 \\ 3 \end{pmatrix}$

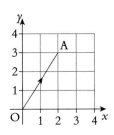

EXERCISE 9.12

1 $\mathbf{p} = \begin{pmatrix} 6 \\ 4 \end{pmatrix}$ Draw these vectors on squared paper.

   a $2\mathbf{p}$ b $\frac{1}{2}\mathbf{p}$ c $-\mathbf{p}$

   d $\frac{3}{2}\mathbf{p}$ e $-2\mathbf{p}$ f $3\mathbf{p}$

2 $\mathbf{p} = \begin{pmatrix} 6 \\ -3 \end{pmatrix}$ $\mathbf{q} = \begin{pmatrix} -2 \\ 4 \end{pmatrix}$ $\mathbf{r} = \begin{pmatrix} -1 \\ -2 \end{pmatrix}$

   Write these vectors as column vectors.

   a $3\mathbf{q}$ b $5\mathbf{r}$ c $-4\mathbf{r}$

   d $-\frac{1}{2}\mathbf{q}$ e $\frac{1}{3}\mathbf{p}$ f $2\frac{1}{2}\mathbf{q}$

3 $\mathbf{p} = \begin{pmatrix} -2 \\ 1 \end{pmatrix}$ $\mathbf{q} = \begin{pmatrix} 6 \\ 2 \end{pmatrix}$ $\mathbf{r} = \begin{pmatrix} 0 \\ -4 \end{pmatrix}$

   Write these as column vectors.

   a $\mathbf{p} + \mathbf{q}$ b $\mathbf{q} + \mathbf{r}$ c $\mathbf{r} - \mathbf{p}$ d $\mathbf{p} + \mathbf{q} - \mathbf{r}$
   e $2\mathbf{p} + 2\mathbf{q}$ f $7\mathbf{r} + \mathbf{p}$ g $\mathbf{q} - 3\mathbf{r}$ h $5\mathbf{p} + 4\mathbf{q} - 3\mathbf{r}$
   i $2\mathbf{p} + 3\mathbf{q}$ j $5\mathbf{q} - 2\mathbf{r}$ k $\mathbf{r} - 2\mathbf{p}$ l $3\mathbf{r} - \frac{1}{2}\mathbf{q}$

4 Which of these column vectors are parallel?

A $\begin{pmatrix} 5 \\ -10 \end{pmatrix}$ B $\begin{pmatrix} -4 \\ -7 \end{pmatrix}$ C $\begin{pmatrix} 5 \\ 1 \end{pmatrix}$ D $\begin{pmatrix} -1 \\ -3 \end{pmatrix}$

E $\begin{pmatrix} 20 \\ 4 \end{pmatrix}$ F $\begin{pmatrix} -10 \\ 20 \end{pmatrix}$ G $\begin{pmatrix} 3 \\ 9 \end{pmatrix}$ H $\begin{pmatrix} 12 \\ 21 \end{pmatrix}$

5 Write down the position vectors of the points:
A, B, C, D, E, F, G and H.

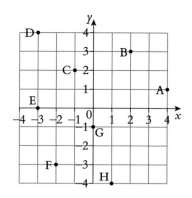

6 **a** Write as column vectors $\overrightarrow{AB}$, $\overrightarrow{BC}$, $\overrightarrow{CD}$, $\overrightarrow{DE}$ and $\overrightarrow{EA}$.

    b Write $\overrightarrow{AB} + \overrightarrow{BC} + \overrightarrow{CD} + \overrightarrow{DE} + \overrightarrow{EA}$ as a single column vector.
Explain your answer.

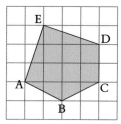

7 $\mathbf{p} = \begin{pmatrix} 5 \\ 6 \end{pmatrix}$ and $\mathbf{q} = \begin{pmatrix} 3 \\ 1 \end{pmatrix}$

    a Find as a single column vector, $3\mathbf{p} + 2\mathbf{q}$.

    b Calculate the value of $|3\mathbf{p} + 2\mathbf{q}|$.

8 $\mathbf{p} = \begin{pmatrix} 1 \\ 2 \end{pmatrix}$ and $\mathbf{q} = \begin{pmatrix} 5 \\ 21 \end{pmatrix}$

    a Find as a single column vector, $7\mathbf{p} + \mathbf{q}$.

    b Calculate the value of $|7\mathbf{p} + \mathbf{q}|$.

9 The diagram shows the position of two points A and B.

$\overrightarrow{AB} = \begin{pmatrix} p \\ q \end{pmatrix}$ where p and q are measured in kilometres.

    a Show that $p = 10.9$ correct to 3 s.f.

    b Calculate the value of q.

10 The diagram shows the position of two points A and B.

$\overrightarrow{AB} = \begin{pmatrix} p \\ q \end{pmatrix}$ where p and q are measured in kilometres.

Calculate the values of p and q.

11 The diagram shows the position of two points A and B.

$\overrightarrow{AB} = \begin{pmatrix} p \\ q \end{pmatrix}$ where p and q are measured in kilometres.

Calculate the values of p and q.

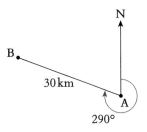

12 $\mathbf{p} = \begin{pmatrix} x \\ 4 \end{pmatrix}$ $\mathbf{q} = \begin{pmatrix} -2 \\ y \end{pmatrix}$ and $\mathbf{p} + \mathbf{q} = \begin{pmatrix} 5 \\ 3 \end{pmatrix}$

Find the values of x and y.

13 $x\begin{pmatrix} 5 \\ 4 \end{pmatrix} + y\begin{pmatrix} 3 \\ -2 \end{pmatrix} = \begin{pmatrix} 3 \\ 20 \end{pmatrix}$

Find the values of x and y.

• • • • • • • • • • • • • •

TOP TIP

Write down two simultaneous equations and solve.

• • • • • • • • • • • • • •

14 ABCD is a parallelogram.

A(1, 3), B(9, 4) and C(10, 7).

a   Write $\overrightarrow{AB}$ as a column vector.

b   Write $\overrightarrow{BC}$ as a column vector.

c   Write $\overrightarrow{AD}$ as a column vector.

d   Write down the position vector of the point D.

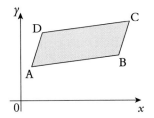

15 ABCD is a trapezium.

A(4, 5), B(3, 2) and D(7, 7).

$\overrightarrow{BC} = 2\overrightarrow{AD}$.

a   Write $\overrightarrow{AD}$ as a column vector.

b   Write $\overrightarrow{BC}$ as a column vector.

c   Find the coordinates of C.

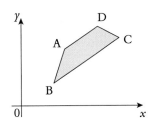

16 The position vector $\mathbf{r}$ is given by $\mathbf{r} = \begin{pmatrix} 3 \\ 5 \end{pmatrix} + t\begin{pmatrix} 2 \\ -1 \end{pmatrix}$.

a   Copy and complete the table below for the given values of t.

t	0	1	2	3	4
$\mathbf{r}$				$\begin{pmatrix} 9 \\ 2 \end{pmatrix}$	

b   On a square grid, plot the five points given by the position vectors in the table.

c   What can you say about the five points?

UNIT 9

Vector geometry

OPQR is a parallelogram.

$\overrightarrow{OP} = \mathbf{p}$ and $\overrightarrow{OR} = \mathbf{r}$.

Find the following in terms of $\mathbf{p}$ and $\mathbf{r}$.

a $\overrightarrow{RQ}$ b $\overrightarrow{QP}$ c $\overrightarrow{OQ}$ d $\overrightarrow{PR}$

---

a $\overrightarrow{RQ} = \mathbf{p}$

b $\overrightarrow{QP} = -\mathbf{r}$

c $\overrightarrow{OQ} = \overrightarrow{OP} + \overrightarrow{PQ} = \mathbf{p} + \mathbf{r}$

d $\overrightarrow{PR} = \overrightarrow{PQ} + \overrightarrow{QR} = \mathbf{r} - \mathbf{p}$

➡ **NOTE:** the journey from O to Q is the 'same as' the journey from O to P, followed by the journey from P to Q.

Vectors are often used to prove geometric properties.
The next two examples illustrate this technique.

ABCD is a trapezium.

$\overrightarrow{DC} = 2\mathbf{p}$, $\overrightarrow{AB} = 6\mathbf{p}$ and $\overrightarrow{AD} = 2\mathbf{q}$.

E, F, G and H are the midpoints of the sides.

Find in terms of $\mathbf{p}$ and $\mathbf{q}$

a $\overrightarrow{CB}$ b $\overrightarrow{CF}$ c $\overrightarrow{HE}$

d $\overrightarrow{GF}$ e $\overrightarrow{EF}$ f $\overrightarrow{HG}$

What can you say about quadrilateral EFGH?

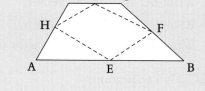

---

a $\overrightarrow{CB} = \overrightarrow{CD} + \overrightarrow{DA} + \overrightarrow{AB}$
$= -2\mathbf{p} - 2\mathbf{q} + 6\mathbf{p}$
$= 4\mathbf{p} - 2\mathbf{q}$

b $\overrightarrow{CF} = \frac{1}{2}\overrightarrow{CB}$
$= \frac{1}{2}(4\mathbf{p} - 2\mathbf{q})$
$= 2\mathbf{p} - \mathbf{q}$

c $\overrightarrow{HE} = \overrightarrow{HA} + \overrightarrow{AE}$
$= -\mathbf{q} + 3\mathbf{p}$
$= 3\mathbf{p} - \mathbf{q}$

d $\overrightarrow{GF} = \overrightarrow{GC} + \overrightarrow{CF}$
$= \mathbf{p} + (2\mathbf{p} - \mathbf{q})$
$= 3\mathbf{p} - \mathbf{q}$

e $\overrightarrow{EF} = \overrightarrow{EB} + \overrightarrow{BF}$
$= 3\mathbf{p} + (\mathbf{q} - 2\mathbf{p})$
$= \mathbf{p} + \mathbf{q}$

f $\overrightarrow{HG} = \overrightarrow{HD} + \overrightarrow{DG}$
$= \mathbf{q} + \mathbf{p}$
$= \mathbf{p} + \mathbf{q}$

So $\overrightarrow{HE} = \overrightarrow{GF}$ and $\overrightarrow{EF} = \overrightarrow{HG}$.

This means that HE and GF are parallel and the same length.

Also, EF and HG are parallel and the same length.

So EFGH is a parallelogram.

OPQ is a triangle.
X is the midpoint of OP.
Y is the midpoint of OQ.
$\overrightarrow{OP} = 2\mathbf{p}$ and $\overrightarrow{OQ} = 2\mathbf{q}$.
Find in terms of $\mathbf{p}$ and $\mathbf{q}$
a $\overrightarrow{PQ}$ **b** $\overrightarrow{XY}$
What can you say about the lines PQ and XY?

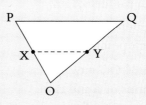

a $\overrightarrow{PQ} = \overrightarrow{PO} + \overrightarrow{OQ} = -2\mathbf{p} + 2\mathbf{q}$
b $\overrightarrow{XY} = \overrightarrow{XO} + \overrightarrow{OY} = -\mathbf{p} + \mathbf{q}$
So $\overrightarrow{PQ} = 2\overrightarrow{XY}$
This means that PQ and XY are parallel and that
PQ is twice the length of XY.

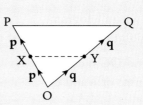

EXERCISE 9.13

1 ABC is a triangle. D is the midpoint of AC.
$\overrightarrow{AB} = \mathbf{p}$ and $\overrightarrow{AD} = \overrightarrow{DC} = \mathbf{q}$.
Find in terms of $\mathbf{p}$ and $\mathbf{q}$
  a $\overrightarrow{DA}$ **b** $\overrightarrow{AC}$ **c** $\overrightarrow{BD}$ **d** $\overrightarrow{CB}$

2 ABC is a triangle. M is the midpoint of AB.
$\overrightarrow{CA} = \mathbf{p}$ and $\overrightarrow{CB} = \mathbf{q}$.
Find in terms of $\mathbf{p}$ and $\mathbf{q}$
  a $\overrightarrow{AB}$ **b** $\overrightarrow{AM}$ **c** $\overrightarrow{BM}$ **d** $\overrightarrow{CM}$

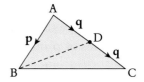

3 OPQR is a square. M is the midpoint of PQ.
$\overrightarrow{OP} = \mathbf{p}$ and $\overrightarrow{OR} = \mathbf{r}$.
Find in terms of $\mathbf{p}$ and $\mathbf{r}$
  a $\overrightarrow{OQ}$ **b** $\overrightarrow{MP}$ **c** $\overrightarrow{OM}$ **d** $\overrightarrow{MR}$

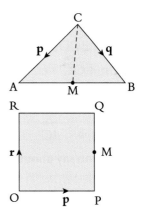

4 ABCD is a trapezium.
$\overrightarrow{AB} = 2\mathbf{p}$, $\overrightarrow{DC} = \mathbf{p}$ and $\overrightarrow{DA} = \mathbf{q}$.
Find in terms of $\mathbf{p}$ and $\mathbf{q}$
  a $\overrightarrow{BA}$ **b** $\overrightarrow{DB}$ **c** $\overrightarrow{CA}$ **d** $\overrightarrow{CB}$

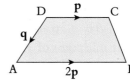

5 ABCDEF is a regular hexagon.
O is the centre of the hexagon.
$\overrightarrow{AF} = \mathbf{p}$ and $\overrightarrow{AB} = \mathbf{q}$.
Find the following in terms of $\mathbf{p}$ and $\mathbf{q}$.
  a $\overrightarrow{CD}$ **b** $\overrightarrow{DE}$ **c** $\overrightarrow{AO}$
  d $\overrightarrow{CE}$ **e** $\overrightarrow{FD}$ **f** $\overrightarrow{DB}$

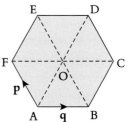

UNIT 9

6 OABC is a parallelogram.

   M is the midpoint of AB.
   N is the midpoint of CB.
   $\overrightarrow{OA}$ = **a** and $\overrightarrow{OC}$ = **c**.
   Find in terms of **a** and **c**

   a $\overrightarrow{NB}$ b $\overrightarrow{BM}$ c $\overrightarrow{AC}$ d $\overrightarrow{MN}$

   What can you say about the lines AC and MN?

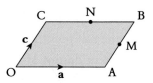

7 OABC is a parallelogram.
   M is the point of intersection of the two diagonals.
   $\overrightarrow{OA}$ = **a** and $\overrightarrow{OC}$ = **c**.
   Find in terms of **a** and **c**

   a $\overrightarrow{OB}$ b $\overrightarrow{CA}$ c $\overrightarrow{OM}$ d $\overrightarrow{CM}$

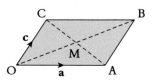

8 ABCD is a parallelogram.
   $\overrightarrow{AB}$ = **p** and $\overrightarrow{AD}$ = **q**.
   E, F, G and H are the midpoints of the sides.
   Find in terms of **p** and **q**

   a $\overrightarrow{FG}$ b $\overrightarrow{EH}$ c $\overrightarrow{EF}$ d $\overrightarrow{HG}$

   What can you say about quadrilateral EFGH?

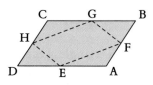

9 OABC and BCDE are two congruent parallelograms.
   $\overrightarrow{OA}$ = **a** and $\overrightarrow{OC}$ = **c**.
   M is the midpoint of BE and N is the midpoint of DE.
   Find in terms of **a** and **c**

   a $\overrightarrow{AM}$ b $\overrightarrow{AC}$ c $\overrightarrow{DM}$ d $\overrightarrow{MN}$

   What can you say about AC and MN?

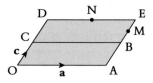

10 ABCD is a trapezium.

   BCDE is a parallelogram.
   $\overrightarrow{EB}$ = **p**, $\overrightarrow{AE}$ = 3**p** and $\overrightarrow{ED}$ = **q**.
   M is the midpoint of AD.
   Find in terms of **p** and **q**

   a $\overrightarrow{EC}$ b $\overrightarrow{EM}$ c $\overrightarrow{MC}$ d $\overrightarrow{AM}$

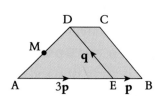

Further vector geometry

Vector geometry can be used to prove that points are **collinear** (lie on a straight line).

If $\overrightarrow{AB} = k\overrightarrow{AC}$, then the points A, B and C are collinear.

(This is because the lines AB and AC must be parallel and the point A lies on both lines.)

Ratios can also be used in vector geometry.

If X is a point on the line AB such that AX : XB = 2 : 3

then $\overrightarrow{AX} = \dfrac{2}{5}\overrightarrow{AB}$ and $\overrightarrow{XB} = \dfrac{3}{5}\overrightarrow{AB}$.

The next example illustrates these techniques.

EXAMPLE

OPQR is a trapezium.

$\overrightarrow{OP} = 3\mathbf{p}$ and $\overrightarrow{OR} = \mathbf{r}$

$\overrightarrow{RQ} = \dfrac{1}{3}\overrightarrow{OP}$

X lies on RP such that RX : XP = 1 : 3

a Find in terms of **p** and **r**

   i $\overrightarrow{OQ}$ **ii** $\overrightarrow{RP}$ **iii** $\overrightarrow{RX}$ **iv** $\overrightarrow{OX}$

b What do your answers for $\overrightarrow{OQ}$ and $\overrightarrow{OX}$ tell you about the points O, X and Q?

---

a **i** $\overrightarrow{OQ} = \overrightarrow{OR} + \overrightarrow{RQ}$

         $= \mathbf{r} + \mathbf{p}$

  ii $\overrightarrow{RP} = \overrightarrow{RO} + \overrightarrow{OP}$

         $= -\mathbf{r} + 3\mathbf{p}$

 iii $\overrightarrow{RX} = \dfrac{1}{4}\overrightarrow{RP}$ ➡ **NOTE:** $RX : XP = 1 : 3$ means that $\overrightarrow{RX} = \dfrac{1}{4}\overrightarrow{RP}$.

         $= \dfrac{1}{4}(-\mathbf{r} + 3\mathbf{p})$

         $= \dfrac{3}{4}\mathbf{p} - \dfrac{1}{4}\mathbf{r}$

  iv $\overrightarrow{OX} = \overrightarrow{OR} + \overrightarrow{RX} = \mathbf{r} + \dfrac{3}{4}\mathbf{p} - \dfrac{1}{4}\mathbf{r}$

         $= \dfrac{3}{4}\mathbf{r} + \dfrac{3}{4}\mathbf{p}$

         $= \dfrac{3}{4}(\mathbf{r} + \mathbf{p})$

b $\overrightarrow{OQ} = \mathbf{r} + \mathbf{p}$ and $\overrightarrow{OX} = \dfrac{3}{4}(\mathbf{r} + \mathbf{p})$

   So $\overrightarrow{OX} = \dfrac{3}{4}\overrightarrow{OQ}$

   This means that OX and OQ are parallel.

   The point O lies on both of these line segments.

   So the points O, X and Q are collinear.

EXERCISE 9.14

1 OPQ is a triangle and O is the origin.
$\overrightarrow{OP}$ = **p** and $\overrightarrow{OQ}$ = **q**.
X is a point on PQ such that PX : XQ = 1 : 2
Find in terms of **p** and **q**
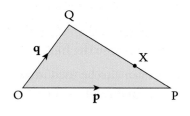

   a $\overrightarrow{PQ}$ b $\overrightarrow{PX}$ c the position vector of X.

2 OPQ is a triangle and O is the origin.
$\overrightarrow{OP}$ = **p** and $\overrightarrow{OQ}$ = **q**.
A is the midpoint on OQ.
B is a point on PQ such that PB : BQ = 3 : 1
Find in terms of **p** and **q**

   a $\overrightarrow{PQ}$ b $\overrightarrow{PB}$ c $\overrightarrow{AB}$ d the position vector of B.

3 OPQ is a triangle and O is the origin.
$\overrightarrow{OP}$ = **p** and $\overrightarrow{OQ}$ = **q**.
R is the midpoint on OQ.
S is a point on OP such that OS : SP = 1 : 2
T is a point on QP such that QT : TP = 3 : 2
Find in terms of **p** and **q**
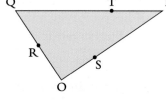

   a $\overrightarrow{OR}$ b $\overrightarrow{SR}$ c $\overrightarrow{PQ}$ d $\overrightarrow{PT}$

4 OPQR is a parallelogram and O is the origin.
$\overrightarrow{OP}$ = **p** and $\overrightarrow{OR}$ = **r**.
X is a point on PQ such that PX : XQ = 1 : 2
Y is a point on RQ such that RY : YQ = 1 : 3
Find in terms of **p** and **r**
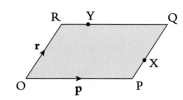

   a $\overrightarrow{PX}$ b $\overrightarrow{RY}$ c $\overrightarrow{XY}$

   d the position vector of Y.

5 OABC is a trapezium.
$\overrightarrow{OA}$ = 3**a**, $\overrightarrow{CB}$ = 2**a** and $\overrightarrow{OC}$ = **c**.
X is a point on AC such that AX : XC = 3 : 2
Find in terms of **a** and **c**
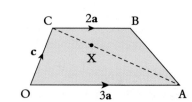

   a $\overrightarrow{AC}$ b $\overrightarrow{AX}$ c $\overrightarrow{OX}$ d $\overrightarrow{OB}$

   What do your answers for $\overrightarrow{OX}$ and $\overrightarrow{OB}$ tell you
   about the points O, X and B?

6   OPQR is a parallelogram and O is the origin.

$\overrightarrow{OP}$ = **p** and $\overrightarrow{OR}$ = **r**.

X is a point on PR such that PX : XR = 1 : 3

Find in terms of **p** and **r**

a $\overrightarrow{PR}$ b $\overrightarrow{PX}$ c $\overrightarrow{XQ}$

d the position vector of X.

7   OPQR is a parallelogram and O is the origin.

$\overrightarrow{OP}$ = **p** and $\overrightarrow{OR}$ = **r**.

Y is a point on PQ such that PY : YQ = 2 : 3

The line RY is extended to the point X so that

$\overrightarrow{RX} = \dfrac{5}{3}\overrightarrow{RY}$.

Find in terms of **p** and **r**

a $\overrightarrow{PY}$ b $\overrightarrow{RY}$ c $\overrightarrow{RX}$ d $\overrightarrow{OX}$

Explain why O, P and X are collinear.

8   The position vector of A is $\begin{pmatrix}1\\5\end{pmatrix}$. The position vector of B is $\begin{pmatrix}4\\3\end{pmatrix}$.

The position vector of C is $\begin{pmatrix}p\\-3\end{pmatrix}$. The position vector of D is $\begin{pmatrix}-7\\q\end{pmatrix}$.

The points A, B, C and D are collinear. Find the values of p and q.

9   $\overrightarrow{OP}$ = **p** and $\overrightarrow{OQ}$ = **q**.

OA : AP = 1 : 2   and   OB : BQ = 1 : 2

Prove that $\overrightarrow{PQ} = 3\overrightarrow{AB}$.

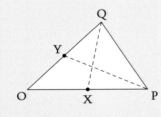

CHALLENGE:

OPQ is a triangle and O is the origin.

$\overrightarrow{OP}$ = **p** and $\overrightarrow{OQ}$ = **q**.

X is the midpoint of OP and Y is the midpoint of OQ.

V is a point on XQ such that

XV : VQ = 1 : 2.

a Find the position vector of V.

W is a point on YP such that YW : WP = 1 : 2.

b Find the position vector of W.

   What can you say about the points V and W?

UNIT 9

Probability 3

THIS SECTION WILL SHOW YOU HOW TO
• Use Venn diagrams to answer probability questions

🌐 Calculating probabilities from Venn diagrams

Probabilities can be calculated using information given on a Venn diagram.

EXAMPLE

In a survey, 100 adults are asked whether they like coffee (C) and whether they like tea (T).
The Venn diagram shows the results of the survey.

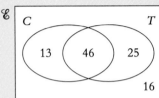

a A person is chosen at random.
 Find the probability that the person does not like coffee.
b A person who likes tea is chosen at random.
 Find the probability that this person also likes coffee.
c Two people are chosen at random.
 Find the probability that they both like coffee.

---

a The number of people who do not like coffee = 25 + 16 = 41
 You are choosing out of 100 people.

 So, the probability that the person does not like coffee $= \dfrac{41}{100}$

b The number of people who like tea = 46 + 25 = 71
 You are choosing out of 71 people and 46 of these also like coffee.

 So, the probability that the person also likes coffee $= \dfrac{46}{71}$

c The probability the first person likes coffee $= \dfrac{13+46}{100} = \dfrac{59}{100}$

 One person has been chosen so there are now only 99 to choose from.
 Of these 99 people there are now only 58 that like coffee.
 The probability the second person likes coffee $= \dfrac{58}{99}$

 So, the probability that they both like coffee $= \dfrac{59}{100} \times \dfrac{58}{99} = \dfrac{1711}{4950} \approx 0.346 \text{ (to 3 s.f.)}$

EXERCISE 9.15

1   In a survey, 60 people are asked if they own a mobile phone (M) or a computer (C).
    The Venn diagram shows the results of the survey.

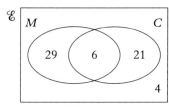

   a   A person is chosen at random.
       i   Find the probability that the person owns a mobile phone.
       ii   Find the probability that the person owns both a computer and a mobile phone.
       iii Find the probability that the person does not own a computer.
   b   A person who owns a computer is chosen at random.
        Find the probability that this person does not own a mobile phone.
   c   Two people are chosen at random. Find the probability that they both own a computer.

2   There are 100 students in a year group.
    50 study art (A), 29 study biology (B) and 13 study both subjects.
   a   Show this information on a Venn diagram.
   b   A student is chosen at random.
       i   Find the probability that the student studies biology but not art.
       ii   Find the probability that the student studies neither biology nor art.
   c   A student who studies art is chosen at random.
        Find the probability that this student does not study biology.
   d   Two students are chosen at random. Find the probability that they both study art.

3   In a survey, 150 members of a youth club are asked whether they like
    singing (S) and whether they like dancing (D).
    The Venn diagram shows the results of the survey.

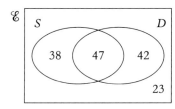

   a   A member of the youth club is chosen at random.
       i   Find the probability that this person likes dancing.
       ii   Find the probability that this person does not like singing.
       iii Find the probability that this person likes neither dancing nor singing.
   b   A member of the youth club who likes dancing is chosen at random.
        Find the probability that this person likes singing.
   c   Two members of the youth club are chosen at random.
        Find the probability that exactly one of the two members likes dancing.

4   In a survey, 100 students are asked if they like rock climbing (R), windsurfing (W)
    or swimming (S). The Venn diagram shows the results of the survey.

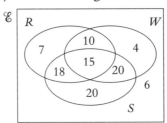

a   One student is chosen at random.
    i   Find the probability that the student likes swimming.
    ii   Find the probability that the student likes rock climbing but not windsurfing.
    iii Find the probability that the student likes all three sports.
b   A student who likes rock climbing is chosen at random.
    Find the probability that this student does not like swimming.
c   Two students are chosen at random from those who like windsurfing.
    Find the probability that they both like exactly one other sport.

5   There are 35 students in a class.
    18 study geography (G), 22 study history and 5 study neither geography nor history.
    a   Show this information on a Venn diagram.
    b   A student is chosen at random.
        i   Find the probability that the student studies both history and geography.
        ii   Find the probability that the student studies history but not geography.
    c   A student who studies history is chosen at random.
        Find the probability that this student studies geography.
    d   Two students are chosen at random.
        Find the probability that only one of them studies history.

6   The brakes, steering and lights are tested on 200 cars.
    The Venn diagram shows the results of the survey.
    B = {cars with faulty brakes} S = {cars with faulty steering} L = {cars with faulty lights}

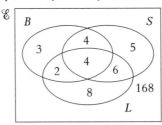

a   One of the 200 cars is chosen at random.
    i   Find the probability that the car has exactly one of the faults.
    ii   Find the probability that the car has exactly two of the faults.
    iii Find the probability that the car has all three of the faults.
b   A car with faulty steering is chosen at random.
    Find the probability that this car also has faulty brakes.
c   Two cars are chosen at random. Find the probability that they both have faulty lights.

7   $\mathscr{E} = \{1, 2, 3, 4, 5, 6, 7, 8, 9, 10, 11, 12, 13, 14, 15, 16\}$
    $A = \{\text{even numbers}\}$ and $B = \{\text{multiples of 3}\}$
    a   Show these sets on a Venn diagram.
    b   A number is chosen at random from the set $\mathscr{E}$.
        Find the probability that this number is in the set
        i B ii A' iii $A \cap B$ iv $A \cup B$ v $(A \cup B)'$

8   In a survey, 50 people are asked if they recycle glass (G), paper (P) or aluminium (A).
    The Venn diagram shows the results of the survey.

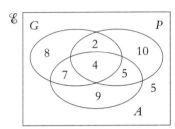

    a   One of the 50 people is chosen at random.
        i   Find the probability that they recycle exactly one of the materials.
        ii   Find the probability that they recycle exactly two of the materials.
        iii Find the probability that they recycle all three of the materials.
    b   A person who recycles aluminium is chosen at random.
        Find the probability that this person also recycles paper.
    c   Two people are chosen at random.
        Find the probability that exactly one of them recycles glass.

9   In a survey, a group of 50 students are asked whether they go to
    a gym (G) or whether they go swimming (S).
    16 students go to a gym.
    21 students go swimming.
    19 students neither go to a gym nor go swimming.
    a   Show this information on a Venn diagram.
    b   A student is chosen at random.
        Find the probability that the student goes to the gym and goes swimming.
    c   A student who goes swimming is chosen at random.
        Find the probability that this student does not go to the gym.
    d   Three students are chosen at random.
        Find the probability that all three students go to the gym.

Unit 9 Examination-style questions

1. At the start of an experiment there are 500 radioactive particles.
    The number of radioactive particles decreases exponentially at a rate of 8.5% per day.

    Work out the number of radioactive particles at the end of 12 days. [2]

2. At the start of an experiment there are 3 000 bacteria.
    The number of bacteria increases exponentially at a rate of 27% per hour.

    Find the number of complete hours it takes for the number
    of bacteria to be greater than one million. [2]

3. The population of a town increases exponentially at a rate of x % per year.
    On 1st January 2000 the population was 50 000.
    On 1st January 2015 the population was 63 000.
    Find the value of x.
    Give your answer correct to 3 significant figures.

4. $P = 45\,000 \times 0.985^t$
    A scientist uses this formula to predict the population, P, of an endangered species t years after 2010.
    (a) Write down the population in 2020. [1]
    (b) Write down the percentage that the population is predicted to decrease each year. [1]
    (c) Find the value of P when $t = 30$. Write your answer correct to the nearest hundred. [2]

5. Solve the simultaneous equations.
    You must show all your working.
    $$3x - 4y = 8$$
    $$x = 2y - 5$$
    [3]

6. Prya buys x apples and y oranges.
    She must buy
    - at least 5 apples
    - at least 7 oranges
    - more apples than oranges
    - a total of at least 18 apples and oranges.
    (a) Write down four inequalities in x and/or y. [4]

(b) On the grid, show the region R that represents these 4 inequalities.

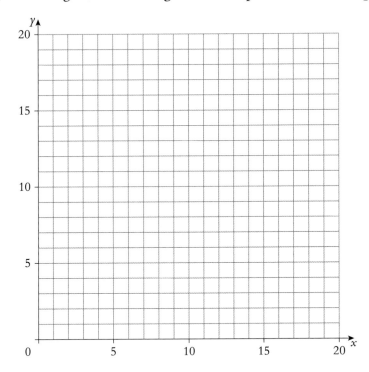

[5]

(c) An apple costs 60 cents and an orange costs 80 cents.

Find the smallest amount of money that Prya must spend. [2]

7 $x^2 - 8x + 10 = (x + a)^2 + b$

Find the value of a and the value of b. [2]

8 $3x^2 + 12x + 19 = 3(x + p)^2 + q$

Find the value of p and the value of q. [2]

9 $2x^2 - 9x + 3 = 2(x + e)^2 + f$

(a) Find the value of e and the value of f. [2]

(b) Write down the smallest value of $2x^2 - 9x + 3$. [1]

UNIT 9

10

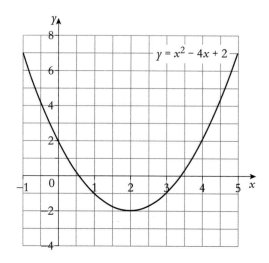

The graph of $y = x^2 - 4x + 2$ is shown on the grid.

(a) Use the graph to solve the equation $x^2 - 4x - 1 = 0$. [3]

(b) A straight line is to be drawn on the graph to solve the equation $x^2 - 5x + 5 = 0$.

    (i) Write down the equation of this straight line. [1]

    (ii) Draw this line on the graph and solve the equation. [2]

11

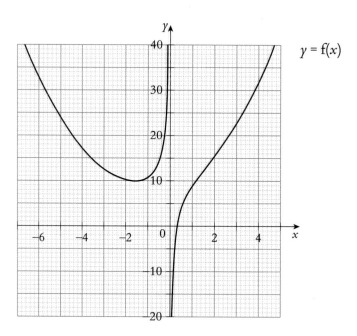

The graph of $y = f(x)$ is shown on the grid.

(a) Use the graph to find the **three** solutions of the equation $f(x) = 23$. [2]

(b) There is one value of k for which the equation $f(x) = k$ has two solutions.
Write down this value of k. [1]

(c) For what values of k is there only one solution of the equation $f(x) = k$. [1]

12 $\overrightarrow{AB} = \begin{pmatrix} 7 \\ -2 \end{pmatrix}$ $\qquad \overrightarrow{BC} = \begin{pmatrix} -4 \\ -3 \end{pmatrix}$

(a) Find $2\overrightarrow{AB}$. [1]

(b) Find $\overrightarrow{BA}$. [1]

(c) Find $\overrightarrow{AC}$. [1]

(d) Find $|\overrightarrow{BC}|$. [2]

13

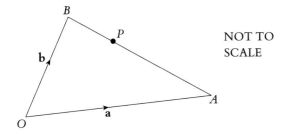

O is the origin, $\overrightarrow{OA} = \mathbf{a}$ and $\overrightarrow{OB} = \mathbf{b}$.
P is a point on AB such that $BP : PA = 1 : 2$.

Find, in terms of $\mathbf{a}$ and $\mathbf{b}$, the position vector of P.
Give your answer in its simplest terms. [3]

14

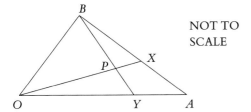

In the diagram, $\overrightarrow{OA} = \mathbf{a}$, $\overrightarrow{OB} = \mathbf{b}$, $\overrightarrow{BX} = \dfrac{3}{5} \overrightarrow{BA}$ and $\overrightarrow{OY} = \dfrac{3}{4} = \overrightarrow{OA}$.

(a) Find in terms of $\mathbf{a}$ and $\mathbf{b}$

    (i) $\overrightarrow{BA}$ [1]

    (ii) $\overrightarrow{BX}$ [2]

    (iii) $\overrightarrow{OX}$ [2]

    (iv) $\overrightarrow{BY}$ [2]

(b) Given that $\overrightarrow{OP} = k\overrightarrow{OX}$, find $\overrightarrow{OP}$ in terms of k, **a** and **b**. [1]

(c) Given that $\overrightarrow{BP} = m\overrightarrow{BY}$, find $\overrightarrow{OP}$ in terms of m, **a** and **b**. [2]

(d) Find the value of k and the value of m. [5]

15

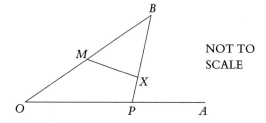

B

NOT TO
SCALE

In the diagram, $\overrightarrow{OA}$ = 3**a**, $\overrightarrow{OB}$ = 4**b** and M is the mid-point of OB.

$OP : PA = 4 : 3$ and $\overrightarrow{BX} = k\overrightarrow{BP}$.

(a) Find in terms of **a** and **b**.

    (i) $\overrightarrow{AB}$ [2]

    (ii) $\overrightarrow{MA}$ [2]

(b) Find in terms of k, **a** and **b**.

    (i) $\overrightarrow{BX}$ [2]

    (ii) $\overrightarrow{MX}$ [2]

(c) If M, X and A are collinear, find the value of k. [5]

16 $\mathscr{E}$

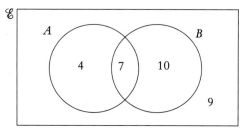

$\mathscr{E}$ = {students in a class}
A = {students who study art}
B = {students who study biology}

(a) A student who does not study art is chosen at random.
Find the probability that this student studies biology. [1]

(b) Two students are chosen at random.
Find the probability that they both study art. [2]

(c) Three students are chosen at random.
Find the probability that only two of these students study biology. [3]

17 In a survey, 50 house owners were asked if they liked cooking, decorating or gardening.

C = {people who like cooking}
D = {people who like decorating}
G = {people who like gardening}

The Venn diagram summarises the results of the survey.

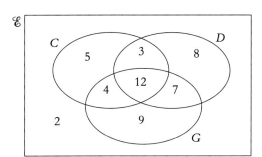

(a) One of the 50 people is chosen at random.
    (i) Find the probability that this person likes decorating and gardening. [1]
    (ii) Find the probability that this person does not like cooking. [1]

(b) A person who likes decorating is chosen at random.
    Find the probability that this person also likes cooking. [2]

(c) Two people are chosen at random.
    (i) Find the probability that both of these people like gardening. [3]
    (ii) Find the probability that only one of these people likes gardening. [3]

(d) Three people are chosen at random.
    Find the probability that only two of these people like decorating. [4]

Upper and lower bounds

 If the length of a nail is given as 6 cm correct to the nearest cm, you can find the **lower bound** and the **upper bound** for the length of the nail.

The lower bound   The upper bound

The lower bound is halfway between 5 cm and 6 cm. Lower bound = 5.5 cm.
The upper bound is halfway between 6 cm and 7 cm. Upper bound = 6.5 cm.
The range of possible values for the length of the nail can be written as:
$$5.5 \text{ cm} \le \text{length} < 6.5 \text{ cm}$$

EXAMPLE

The mass of a parcel is 3.2 kg, correct to one decimal place.
Write down the upper and lower bounds for the mass of the parcel.

You need to think of the numbers (to 1 d.p.) directly below 3.2 and directly above 3.2.
These numbers are 3.1 and 3.3.
The lower bound is halfway between 3.1 and 3.2.
The upper bound is halfway between 3.2 and 3.3.
Lower bound = 3.15 cm   Upper bound = 3.25 cm.

3.1   3.2   3.3

Lower bound   Upper bound
= 3.15 cm   = 3.25 cm

EXAMPLE

A rectangle has sides of length 5.7 cm and 3.4 cm, each correct to the nearest millimetre.
Calculate the upper and lower bounds for the area of the rectangle.

3.4 cm

5.7 cm

First write down the lower and upper bounds for the length and width of the rectangle.

Lower bound length = 5.65   Upper bound length = 5.75
Lower bound width = 3.35   Upper bound width = 3.45

So, the lower bound for the area = lower bound length × lower bound width
$$= 5.65 \times 3.35$$
$$= 18.9275 \text{ cm}^2$$
and the upper bound for the area = upper bound length × upper bound width
$$= 5.75 \times 3.45$$
$$= 19.8375 \text{ cm}^2$$

➡ NOTE: you must not round your answers when you are asked for a bound.
You must write the full calculator display.

$p = 8\,\text{cm}$ $q = 2\,\text{cm}$

The lengths of p and q have been given to the nearest centimetre.

Find the lower bound for each of the following calculations

a $p + q$ b $p - q$ c $p \times q$ d $p \div q$

---

a   First write down the lower and upper bounds for the lengths of p and q.

Lower bound of $p = 7.5$ Upper bound of $p = 8.5$
Lower bound of $q = 1.5$ Upper bound of $q = 2.5$

Lower bound of $(p + q)$ = lower bound of p + lower bound of q
$= 7.5 + 1.5$
$= 9\,\text{cm}$

b   Lower bound of $(p - q)$ = lower bound of p − upper bound of q
$= 7.5 - 2.5$
$= 5\,\text{cm}$

➡ **NOTE:** you must choose carefully which bounds to use in the calculation.

c   Lower bound of $(p \times q)$ = lower bound of p × lower bound of q
$= 7.5 \times 1.5$
$= 11.25$

d   Lower bound of $(p \div q)$ = lower bound of p ÷ upper bound of q
$= 7.5 \div 2.5$
$= 3$

EXERCISE 10.1

1   Write down the upper and lower bounds for each of these measurements.
   a   6 cm (to nearest cm)   b   32 min (to nearest minute)
   c   32 kg (to nearest kg)   d   9.2 cm (to nearest millimetre)
   e   7.7 cm (to 1 d.p.)   f   2.63 kg (to 3 s.f.)
   g   62.9 g (to 1 d.p.)   h   476 s (to nearest second)
   i   4.94 m (to 3 s.f.)   j   0.245 km (to nearest metre)

2   A bottle contains 250 ml of oil, correct to the nearest millilitre.
   Write down the range of possible values for the amount of oil,
   x millilitres, in the bottle.

3   A carton has a mass of 1.2 kg correct to 2 significant figures.
   Calculate the minimum possible total mass of 20 cartons.

4   The cost of making a necklace is $124 correct to the nearest dollar.
   Calculate the upper and lower bounds for the cost of making 150 necklaces.

5   When a bicycle wheel turns once, the bicycle travels 205 cm, correct to the nearest cm.
    Calculate the upper and lower bounds for the distance travelled by
    the bicycle when the wheel has turned 150 times.

6   The length of each side of an equilateral triangle is 46 mm,
    correct to the nearest millimetre.
    Calculate the upper and lower bounds for the perimeter
    of the triangle.

46 mm   46 mm

46 mm

7   The length of each side of a regular octagon is 8.2 cm,
    correct to one decimal place.
    Calculate the upper and lower bounds for the
    perimeter of the octagon.

8.2 cm

8   A rectangle has sides of length 5.3 cm and 7.4 cm, each
    correct to one decimal place.
    Calculate the upper and lower bounds for
    a   the perimeter of the rectangle,
    b   the area of the rectangle.

6.3 cm

7.4 cm

9   A rectangular photograph measures 22.4 cm by 18.6 cm,
    each correct to one decimal place.
    Calculate the upper and lower bounds for
    a   the perimeter of the photograph,
    b   the area of the photograph.

18.6 cm

22.4 cm

10 The diagram shows a quadrilateral.
    The lengths of the sides are given to the nearest cm.
    Calculate the upper and lower bounds for the
    perimeter of the quadrilateral.

8 cm

5 cm

6 cm

7 cm

11 A cube has sides of length 4.7 cm correct to the nearest millimetre.
    Calculate the upper and lower bounds for
    a   the volume of the cube,
    b   the surface area of the cube.

4.7 cm

4.7 cm

4.7 cm

12 A cuboid has sides of length 8.1 cm, 5.2 cm and 3.5 cm correct
    to the nearest millimetre.
    Calculate the upper and lower bounds for
    a   the volume of the cuboid,
    b   the surface area of the cuboid.

5.2 cm

3.5 cm

8.1 cm

13 The lengths of the edges of the triangular prism are correct to the nearest centimetre.
Calculate the upper and lower bounds for the volume of the prism.

6 cm   14 cm   10 cm

14 A truck can carry a maximum load of 8000 kg.
The truck is loaded with packages each with a mass of 35 kg correct to two significant figures.
Calculate the maximum number of packages that the truck can carry.

15 The area of a circle is 85 cm², correct to the nearest square centimetre.
Calculate the lower bound for the radius, r, of the circle.
(Write down all the numbers on your calculator display.)

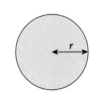

r

16 An equilateral triangle has sides of length 18 cm correct to the nearest centimetre.
Calculate the lower bound for the area of the triangle.
(Write down all the numbers on your calculator display.)

18 cm   18 cm   18 cm

17 The lengths of AB and AC are correct to the nearest millimetre.
Angle BAC is correct to the nearest degree.
a Calculate the lower bound for the length of BC.
b Calculate the upper bound for the area of the triangle.
(In each case write down all the numbers on your calculator display.)

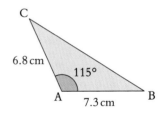

C   6.8 cm   115°   A   7.3 cm   B

18 The lengths of the two planks of wood, correct to the nearest centimetre, are 168 cm and 259 cm.
Calculate the upper and lower bounds for
a the total length of the two planks of wood.
b the difference in length of the two planks of wood.

168 cm

259 cm

19 The radius and height of the cylinder have been measured correct to the nearest centimetre.
Calculate the upper bound for the volume of the cylinder.
(Write down all the numbers on your calculator display.)

3.7 cm   4.8 cm

20 The formula $a = \dfrac{v - u}{t}$ is used to find the acceleration for an object that increases its speed from u to v in a time t.
If u = 4.5 m/s (to 1 d.p.), v = 10.2 m/s (to 1 d.p.) and t = 3.6 s (to 1 d.p.), calculate the upper bound for the acceleration.

Solving simultaneous 3

THIS SECTION WILL SHOW YOU HOW TO

- Solve simultaneous equations where one equation is linear and the second equation is quadratic

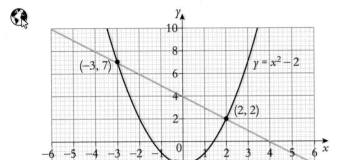

The diagram shows the parabola $y = x^2 - 2$ and the straight line $y = 4 - x$.

The coordinates of the points of intersection of the two graphs are $(-3, 7)$ and $(2, 2)$.

It follows that $x = -3$, $y = 7$ and $x = 2$, $y = 2$ are the solutions of the simultaneous equations $y = 4 - x$ and $y = x^2 - 2$.

The solutions can also be found algebraically:

$$y = 4 - x \qquad\qquad (1)$$
$$y = x^2 - 2 \qquad\qquad (2)$$

Substitute for y from equation (2) into equation (1):

$$x^2 - 2 = 4 - x \qquad \textit{rearrange}$$
$$x^2 + x - 6 = 0 \qquad \textit{factorise}$$
$$(x + 3)(x - 2) = 0$$
$$x + 3 = 0 \ \text{ or } \ x - 2 = 0$$
$$x = -3 \quad \text{ or } \quad x = 2$$

Substituting $x = -3$ into equation (1) gives $y = 4 - (-3) = 7$.

Substituting $x = 2$ into equation (1) gives $y = 4 - 2 = 2$.

The solutions are: $x = -3$, $y = 7$ and $x = 2$, $y = 2$.

A **general quadratic equation** is of the form $ax^2 + bxy + cy^2 + dx + ey + f = 0$ where at least one of a, b and c is non-zero. The same techniques can be used to solve general quadratic equations.

Solve the simultaneous equations.

$$y = 2x - 6$$
$$2x^2 + y^2 = 36$$

$y = 2x - 6$ ------(1)

$2x^2 + y^2 = 36$ -- (2)

Substitute for y from equation (1) into equation (2):

$2x^2 + (2x - 6)^2 = 36$	*expand brackets*
$2x^2 + 4x^2 - 24x + 36 = 36$	*simplify*
$6x^2 - 24x = 0$	*divide both sides by 6*
$x^2 - 4x = 0$	*factorise*
$x(x - 4) = 0$	

$x = 0$ or $x - 4 = 0$

$x = 0$ or $x - 4 = 4$

Substituting $x = 0$ in equation (1) gives $y = 2(0) - 6 = -6$.

Substituting $x = 4$ in equation (1) gives $y = 2(4) - 6 = 2$.

The solutions are: $x = 0, y = -6$ and $x = 4, y = 2$.

EXERCISE 10.2

1 Solve the simultaneous equations.

a $\quad y = x + 2$
$\quad\quad y = x^2$

b $\quad y = 3 - x$
$\quad\quad y = x^2 - 3$

c $\quad y = 2x + 4$
$\quad\quad y = x^2 - 3x + 4$

d $\quad y = 2x + 1$
$\quad\quad y = 4 - x^2$

e $\quad y = 3x - 7$
$\quad\quad y = 2x^2 - 5x + 1$

f $\quad x + y = 4$
$\quad\quad y = 1 + 5x - 3x^2$

2 Use graphing software to draw the graphs for **question 1e** and **question 1f**.
Explain the significance of your answers to these questions.

3 Solve the simultaneous equations.

a $\quad x + y = 0$
$\quad\quad y = x^2 + 2xy$

b $\quad 3y = x + 10$
$\quad\quad x^2 + y^2 = 100$

c $\quad 2x + y = 8$
$\quad\quad xy = 8$

d $\quad x - 4y = 2$
$\quad\quad xy = 12$

e $\quad y = 2x - 14$
$\quad\quad y^2 = 8x + 4$

f $\quad x + 2y = 5$
$\quad\quad x^2 + y^2 = 10$

4 a $\quad y = 3x - 1$
$\quad\quad 8x^2 - 2xy = 4$

b $\quad x + 4y = 6$
$\quad\quad x^2 + 2xy = 8$

c $\quad 4x - 3y = 5$
$\quad\quad x^2 + 3xy = 10$

5 a $\quad x + y = 7$
$\quad\quad x^2 + xy - 2y^2 = 10$

b $\quad x + 2y = 6$
$\quad\quad x^2 + y^2 + 4xy = 24$

c $\quad 5x - 2y = 23$
$\quad\quad x^2 - 5xy + y^2 = 1$

6 The line $y = x + 2$ cuts the curve $y = 8 - x^2$ at the points P and Q.
  a Find the coordinates of the points P and Q.
  b Find the length of the line PQ.

7 The line $y = 2x - 10$ cuts the curve $x^2 + y^2 = 100$ at the points A and B.
  a Find the coordinates of the points A and B.
  b Find the coordinates of the midpoint of the line AB.
  c Find the equation of the perpendicular bisector of the line AB.

8 The line $2x + 3y = 13$ cuts the curve $5y^2 = 4x^2 - 2xy + 41$ at the points C and D.
  Find the gradient of the line CD.

You may need to derive and solve simultaneous equations from given information.

EXAMPLE

The diagram shows a right-angled triangle with sides
x cm, $(2x - 1)$ cm and y cm.
  a Show that $y^2 = 5x^2 - 4x + 1$.
  b Given that the perimeter of the triangle is 40 cm, find the value of x and the value of y.

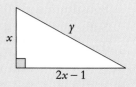

a Using Pythagoras:
$$y^2 = x^2 + (2x - 1)^2$$ *replace $(2x - 1)^2$ with $(2x - 1)(2x - 1)$*
$$y^2 = x^2 + (2x - 1)(2x - 1)$$ *expand brackets*
$$y^2 = x^2 + 4x^2 - 4x + 1$$ *simplify*
$$y^2 = 5x^2 - 4x + 1 \text{ -------------- (1)}$$

b Perimeter = 40:
$$y + x + 2x - 1 = 40$$ *simplify*
$$y + 3x - 1 = 40$$ *rearrange to make y the subject*
$$y = 41 - 3x \text{ --------- (2)}$$
Substitute for y from (2) in (1):
$$(41 - 3x)^2 = 5x^2 - 4x + 1$$ *replace $(41 - 3x)^2$ with $(41 - 3x)(41 - 3x)$*
$$(41 - 3x)(41 - 3x) = 5x^2 - 4x + 1$$ *expand brackets*
$$1681 - 123x - 123x + 9x^2 = 5x^2 - 4x + 1$$ *simplify*
$$1681 - 246x + 9x^2 = 5x^2 - 4x + 1$$ *rearrange to the form $ax^2 + bx + c = 0$*
$$4x^2 - 242x + 1680 = 0$$ *divide both sides by 2*
$$2x^2 - 121x + 840 = 0$$ *factorise*
$$(2x - 105)(x - 8) = 0$$
$$2x - 105 = 0 \quad \text{or} \quad x - 8 = 0$$
$$x = 52.5 \quad \text{or} \quad x = 8$$ *$x = 52.5$ is not possible as this would be greater than the perimeter*

When $x = 8$, $y = 41 - 3(8) = 17$
Hence $x = 8$ and $y = 17$.

➡ CHECK:

$8^2 + 15^2 = 17^2$ ✓

$8 + 15 + 17 = 40$ ✓

EXERCISE 10.3

1   The sum of two numbers, x and y, is 30.
    The product of x and y is 144.
    a   Write down two equations in terms of x and y.
    b   Use algebra to solve your two equations.

2   The perimeter of a rectangle is 16.2 cm and its area is 16.1 cm².
    Find the lengths of the sides of the rectangle.

3   The sum of the perimeters of two squares is 82 cm and the sum of the areas of the same
    squares is 220.25 cm².
    Find the side length of each square.

4   The sum of the circumferences of two circles is 42π cm and the sum of the areas of the same
    circles is 225π cm².
    Find the radius of each circle.

5   A cuboid has sides of length x cm, y cm and 8 cm and volume 330 cm³.
    Given that $x + y = 13$, find the possible values of x and y.

6   Given that $x = 4$ and $y = 2$ is a solution of the simultaneous equations $ax + by = 8$ and
    $b^2x + a^2y = 34$, find the possible values of a and b.

7   The diagram shows a solid formed by joining a hemisphere of radius r cm to a cylinder of radius r cm and height h cm.

The total height of the solid is 21 cm and the volume is 1458π cm³.

Find the value of r and the value of h.

[The volume, V, of a sphere with radius r is $V = \dfrac{4}{3}\pi r^3$.]

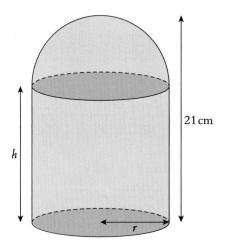

Differentiation

Finding the gradient of a curve

In Unit 4 (page 170) you learnt how to estimate the gradient of a curve at a point by drawing a suitable tangent and then finding the gradient of the tangent.

For example, to find the gradient of the curve $y = x^2$ at the point $P(2, 4)$, you have to
- plot the curve on graph paper
- draw the tangent to the curve at the point $P(2, 4)$
- use two points on the tangent to calculate the gradient of the tangent.

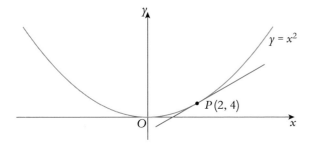

This method only gives an approximate answer because of the inaccuracy of plotting the points of a curve and in drawing the tangent. It is also time consuming.

Another method that can be used is to find the gradients of chords on the curve. These will also only give approximate answers for the gradient but they will be based on calculation and not on your drawing skills.

Consider the curve $y = x^2$ and the points $P(2, 4)$ and $A(2.2, 4.84)$ on the curve:

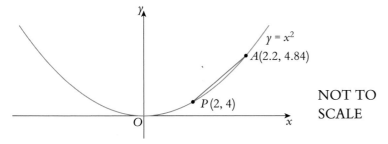

NOT TO SCALE

$$\text{Gradient of } AP = \frac{y_2 - y_1}{x_2 - x_1} = \frac{4.84 - 4}{2.2 - 2} = 4.2$$

The point $B(2.1, 4.41)$ also lies on the curve $y = x^2$.

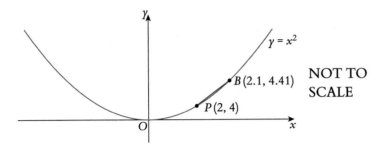

Gradient of $BP = \dfrac{y_2 - y_1}{x_2 - x_1} = \dfrac{4.41 - 4}{2.1 - 2} = 4.1$

The point $C(2.01, 4.0401)$ also lies on the curve $y = x^2$.

Gradient of $CP = \dfrac{y_2 - y_1}{x_2 - x_1} = \dfrac{4.0401 - 4}{2.01 - 2} = 4.01$

The results are getting closer to the gradient of the tangent to the curve $y = x^2$ at the point $P(2, 4)$.

The gradient of the curve $y = x^2$ at the point $P(2, 4)$ appears to be approaching the value 4.

EXERCISE 10.4

1   Consider the quadratic function $y = x^2$ and the point $P(3,9)$ on the curve.
    The points $A(3.2, 10.24)$, $B(3.1, 9.61)$ and $C(3.01, 9.0601)$ also lie on the curve and are close to the point $P(3,9)$.
    a   Calculate the gradient of
        i   the chord PA,   ii   the chord PB,   iii   the chord PC.
    b   Using your results to **part a**, suggest a value for the gradient of the curve $y = x^2$ at the point $(3, 9)$.

2   Use graphing software to investigate the value of the gradient at other points on the curve $y = x^2$.
    Use this table to record your results.

x-coordinate of P	−4	−3	−2	−1	0	1	2	3	4
Gradient of curve at P							4		

Can you suggest a formula for the gradient of the curve $y = x^2$ at the point (x, x^2)?

3   Use your formula from **question 2** to find the gradient of the curve $y = x^2$ at the points
    a $(7, 49)$ b $(-8, 64)$ c $(-1.8, 3.24)$

4 Use graphing software to investigate the value of the gradient at points on the curve $y = x^3$. Use this table to record your results.

x-coordinate of P		-4	-3	-2	-1	0	1	2	3	4
Gradient of curve at P										

Can you suggest a formula for the gradient of the curve $y = x^3$ at the point (x, x^3)?

5 Use your formula from **question 4** to find the gradient of the curve $y = x^3$ at the points
  a (5, 125)   **b** (−10, 1000)   **c** (0.2, 0.008)

Derivatives and gradient functions

In this section you will learn a quick and accurate method for finding the gradient of a curve, which does not involve drawing tangents or chords. This accurate method is called **differentiation.**

In Exercise 10.4, question 2 you discovered that if $y = x^2$, then the gradient of the curve at the point (x, x^2) is $2x$.

There are three different notations that can be used to describe this rule:

1. If $y = x^2$, then $\dfrac{dy}{dx} = 2x$.

2. If $f(x) = x^2$, then $f'(x) = 2x$.

3. $\dfrac{d}{dx}(x^2) = 2x$.

$\dfrac{dy}{dx}$ is called the **derivative** of y with respect to x.

$f'(x)$ is called the **gradient function** of the curve $y = f(x)$.

$\dfrac{d}{dx}(x^2) = 2x$ means 'if you differentiate x^2 with respect to x, the result is $2x$'.

In Exercise 10.4, question 4 you also discovered that if $y = x^3$, then the gradient of the curve at the point (x, x^3) is $3x^2$.

Hence you know that $\dfrac{d}{dx}(x^2) = 2x$ and $\dfrac{d}{dx}(x^3) = 3x^2$.

Investigating the gradient of the curves $y = x^4$, $y = x^5$ and $y = x^6$ would give the following results:

$$\dfrac{d}{dx}(x^4) = 4x^3 \qquad \dfrac{d}{dx}(x^5) = 5x^4 \qquad \dfrac{d}{dx}(x^6) = 6x^5$$

If you look carefully at these results you will see a general rule for differentiating power functions:

$$\dfrac{d}{dx}(x^n) = nx^{n-1}$$

In the Cambridge IGCSE examination you will only be expected to apply this rule if n is a positive integer or zero.

It is easier to remember this rule as

'multiply by the power n and then subtract one from the power'

So for the earlier example where $y = x^3$,

$$\frac{dy}{dx} = 3 \times x^{3-1}$$

$$= 3x^2$$

EXAMPLE

Find $\dfrac{dy}{dx}$ for each of the following.

a $y = x^8$ **b** $y = x^{10}$ **c** $y = x$ **d** $y = 5$

a $y = x^8$

$\dfrac{dy}{dx} = 8 \times x^{8-1}$ *multiply by the power 8 and then subtract one from the power*

$\dfrac{dy}{dx} = 8x^7$

b $y = x^{10}$

$\dfrac{dy}{dx} = 10 \times x^{10-1}$ *multiply by the power 10 and then subtract one from the power*

$\dfrac{dy}{dx} = 10x^9$

c $y = x = x^1$ *write x as x^1 ready for differentiating*

$\dfrac{dy}{dx} = 1 \times x^{1-1}$ *multiply by the power 1 and then subtract one from the power*

$\dfrac{dy}{dx} = 1x^0$ *use $x^0 = 1$ to simplify the expression*

$\dfrac{dy}{dx} = 1$

d $y = 5 = 5x^0$ *write 5 as $5x^0$ ready for differentiating*

$\dfrac{dy}{dx} = 0 \times x^{0-1}$ *multiply by the power and then subtract one from the power*

$= 0$

TOP TIP

When you differentiate a constant the answer is always 0.

Your rule for differentiating functions of the form x^n can be extended to

$$\frac{d}{dx}(ax^n) = nax^{n-1}$$

In the Cambridge IGCSE examination you will also be expected to differentiate simple sums of not more than three of these.

EXAMPLE

Differentiate $2x^3 - 5x^2 + 6x$ with respect to x.

$\frac{d}{dx}(2x^3 - 5x^2 + 6x) = \frac{d}{dx}(2x^3 - 5x^2 + 6x^1)$ *write ready for differentiating*

$\qquad\qquad = \frac{d}{dx}(2x^3) - \frac{d}{dx}(5x^2) + \frac{d}{dx}(6x^1)$

$\qquad\qquad = 3 \times 2x^2 - 2 \times 5x^1 + 1 \times 6x^0$

$\qquad\qquad = 6x^2 - 10x + 6$

TOP TIP

When you differentiate kx, where k is a constant, then the answer is k.

EXAMPLE

Given that $y = x(2x - 1)(x + 3)$, find $\frac{dy}{dx}$.

$y = x(2x - 1)(x + 3)$ *expand brackets and simplify*

$\quad = x(2x^2 + 6x - x - 3)$

$\quad = 2x^3 + 5x^2 - 3x^1$ *differentiate*

$\frac{dy}{dx} = 3 \times 2x^2 + 2 \times 5x^1 - 1 \times 3x^0$

$\quad = 6x^2 + 10x - 3$

EXAMPLE

Find the gradient of the tangent to the curve $y = x^3 + 3x^2 - 2$ at the point $(1, 2)$.

$y = x^3 + 3x^2 - 2$ *differentiate*

$\frac{dy}{dx} = 3x^2 + 6x$

When $x = 1$, $\frac{dy}{dx} = 3(1)^2 + 6(1)$

$\qquad\qquad = 9$

Gradient of curve at the point $(1, 2)$ is 9.

The curve $y = ax^4 + bx^2 + 3x$ has gradient 3 when $x = 1$ and gradient -9 when $x = -2$. Find the value of a and the value of b.

$y = ax^4 + bx^2 + 3x$

$\dfrac{dy}{dx} = 4ax^3 + 2bx + 3$

Since $\dfrac{dy}{dx} = 3$ when $x = 1$,

$4a(1)^3 + 2b(1) + 3 = 3$

$\qquad 4a + 2b = 0$

$\qquad\quad 2a + b = 0$ -------------------------------(1)

Since $\dfrac{dy}{dx} = -9$ when $x = -2$,

$4a(-2)^3 + 2b(-2) + 3 = -9$

$\qquad -32a - 4b = -12$

$\qquad\quad 8a + b = 3$ ------------------------------- (2)

Equation (2) − equation (1) gives $6a = 3$

$$a = \frac{1}{2}$$

Substituting $a = \dfrac{1}{2}$ into (1) gives $1 + b = 0$

$\qquad\qquad\qquad\qquad\qquad\quad b = -1$

Hence $a = \dfrac{1}{2}$ and $b = -1$.

EXERCISE 10.5

1 Differentiate with respect to x.

    a x^6 **b** x^9 **c** x^{10} **d** x^7

    e   8   **f** x **g** $\dfrac{1}{2}$ **h** -4

2 Find $f'(x)$ for each of these functions.

    a $f(x) = 3x^5$ **b** $f(x) = 2x^4$ **c** $f(x) = -5x^2$ **d** $f(x) = \dfrac{x^2}{2}$

    e $f(x) = -\dfrac{2}{3}x^6$ **f** $f(x) = -5x$ **g** $f(x) = \dfrac{5}{4}x^4$ **h** $f(x) = -\dfrac{x^8}{4}$

3 Find $\dfrac{dy}{dx}$ for each of the following.

   a $y = 5x^2 - 2x + 4$ **b** $y = x^3 + 5x - 2$ **c** $y = 1 - 2x + 3x^2$

   d $y = x(x + 2)$ **e** $y = 5x(3 - 2x^2)$ **f** $y = (x + 2)(x - 5)$

   g $y = \dfrac{(x-5)^2}{2}$ **h** $y = (2x^2 - 5)^2$ **i** $y = 5x(1 - x)^2$

4 Find the value of $\dfrac{dy}{dx}$ for each curve at the given point.

   a $y = x^2 + 5x - 2$ at the point $(1, 4)$ **b** $y = 2 + 3x - 2x^4$ at the point $(0, 2)$

   c $y = \dfrac{(x-2)^2}{4}$ at the point $\left(-1, 2\dfrac{1}{4}\right)$ **d** $y = (2x - 5)(x + 3)$ at the point $(2, -5)$

5 Find the coordinates of the two points on the curve $y = x^3 + 2$ where the gradient is 12.

6 Find the gradient of the curve $y = 3x^3 - 2x + 1$ at the point where the curve crosses the y-axis.

7 Find the coordinates of the two points on the curve $y = x^3 - 5x^2 + 3$ where the gradient is 8.

8 Find the gradient of the curve $y = (2x - 3)^2$ at the point $(2, 1)$.

9 **a** Sketch the graph of $y = (x - 4)(x - 2)$ showing clearly any axis crossing points.

     b Find the gradient of the curve $y = (x - 4)(x - 2)$ at the points where the curve crosses the x-axis.

10 **a** Find the coordinates of the points where the curve $y = x^3 - 4x$ crosses the x-axis.

      b Find the gradient of the curve $y = x^3 - 4x$ at each of the points where the curve crosses the x-axis.

11 The curve $y = x^2 - x + 1$ and the line $y = 2x + 5$ meet at the points A and B.

   a Find the coordinates of the points A and B.

   b Find the gradient of the curve at each of the points A and B.

12 The gradient of the curve $y = ax^2 + bx$ at the point $(3, 3)$ is 4. Find the value of a and the value of b.

13 The gradient of the curve $y = ax^3 + bx^2 - 3$ at the point $(1, -5)$ is -2. Find the value of a and the value of b.

14 The curve $y = ax^3 + bx$ has gradient -1 when $x = 1$ and gradient -7 when $x = 0$. Find the value of a and the value of b.

15 Given that the gradient of the curve $y = x^3 + ax^2 + bx$ is zero when $x = 1$ and when $x = 4$, find the value of a and the value of b.

16 Given that $y = 3x^2 - 12x + 1$, find the range of values of x for which $\dfrac{dy}{dx} > 0$.

17 A curve has equation $y = 3x^3 + 12x^2 + 16x$.
Show that the gradient of the curve is never negative.

Finding the equation of a tangent to a curve

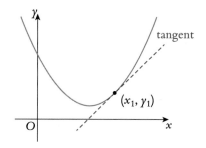

If the value of $\dfrac{dy}{dx}$ at the point (x_1, y_1) is m, then the equation of the tangent can be found using the equation $y = mx + c$.
The values x_1 and y_1 are substituted into $y = mx + c$ to find the value of c.
This is shown in the next worked example.

Find the equation of the tangent to the curve $y = x^3 - 9x + 1$ at the point where $x = 2$.

$y = x^3 - 9x + 1$
$\dfrac{dy}{dx} = 3x^2 - 9$

When $x = 2$, $y = (2)^3 - 9(2) + 1 = -9$

and $\dfrac{dy}{dx} = 3(2)^2 - 9 = 3$

The tangent passes through the point $(2, -9)$ and has gradient $= 3$.

$y = mx + c$ *use m = 3*
$y = 3x + c$ *use x = 2 when y = −9*
$-9 = 3(2) + c$
$c = -15$

The equation of the tangent is $y = 3x - 15$.

The tangents to the curve $y = x^2 - 5x + 4$ at the points $(1, 0)$ and $(3, -2)$ meet at the point P. Find the coordinates of P.

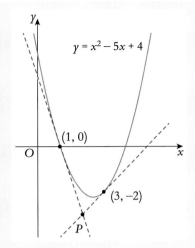

$$y = x^2 - 5x + 4$$
$$\frac{dy}{dx} = 2x - 5$$

When $x = 1$, $\frac{dy}{dx} = 2(1) - 5 = -3$

The tangent at the point $(1, 0)$ has gradient -3.

$\quad\quad y = mx + c$ *use m = −3*

$\quad\quad y = -3x + c$ *use x = 1 when y = 0*

$\quad\quad 0 = -3(1) + c$

$\quad\quad c = 3$

$\quad\quad y = -3x + 3$ ------------- (1)

When $x = 3$, $\frac{dy}{dx} = 2(3) - 5 = 1$

The tangent at the point $(3, -2)$ has gradient 1.

$\quad\quad y = mx + c$ *use m = 1*

$\quad\quad y = x + c$ *use x = 1 when y = −2*

$\quad\quad -2 = 3 + c$

$\quad\quad c = -5$

$\quad\quad y = x - 5$ ------------------ (2)

Equation (2) − equation (1) gives $0 = 4x - 8$

$\quad\quad\quad\quad\quad\quad\quad\quad\quad\quad x = 2$

Substituting $x = 2$ into (1) gives $y = -6 + 3$

$\quad\quad\quad\quad\quad\quad\quad\quad\quad\quad y = -3$

The coordinates of P are $(2, -3)$.

EXERCISE 10.6

1 Find the equation of the tangent to each curve at the given point.
   a $y = x^2 - 2x - 1$ at the point $(2, -1)$ b $y = x^3 - 5x - 3$ at the point $(1, -7)$
   c $y = 5 - 3x^2 - x^4$ at the point $(-1, 1)$ d $y = x(5 - x)^2$ at the point $(2, 18)$

2 A curve passes through the point $A(1, 1)$ and has equation $y = 3x^4 - 3x^2 + 1$.
  Find the equation of the tangent to the curve at the point A.

3 A curve has equation $y = 4x - 2x^2 - 2x^3$ and passes through the point $A(-1, -4)$.
   a Find the equation of the tangent to the curve at A.
   b Find the angle that this tangent makes with the x-axis.

4 The curve $y = x^3 + 8$ intersects the x-axis at C. The tangent to the curve at C intersects the
  y-axis at D. Find the distance CD.

5 The equation of a curve is $y = 2x^3 - x^2 + 4$.
   a Show that the equation of the tangent to the curve at the point $(1, 5)$ is $y = 4x + 1$.
   b Find the coordinates of the point at which the tangent meets the curve again.

6 The tangent to the curve $y = x^4 - 7x + 9$ at the point $(1, 3)$ intersects the x-axis at the point A
  and the y-axis at the point B.
   a Find the coordinates of A and B.
   b Find the area of triangle OAB, where O is the origin.

7 The tangent to the curve $y = x^3 - 4x + 4$ at the point $(-2, 4)$ meets the x-axis at A and the
  y-axis at B. Find the midpoint of AB.

8 A curve has equation $y = 2x^3 - 4x^2 + 5$ and passes through the point $P(2, 5)$.
   a Find the equation of the tangent to this curve at the point P.
   b Find the coordinates of the point where the tangent at P meets the curve again.
   The tangent at the point Q is parallel to the tangent at P.
   c Find the coordinates of Q.

9 The tangents to the curve $y = 2 - 3x - x^2$ at the points $(1, -2)$ and $(-3, 2)$ meet at
  the point P. Find the coordinates of P.

10 The tangents to the curve $y = 2x + 3x^2 - x^4$ at the points $(-2, -8)$ and $(2, 0)$ meet at
   the point R. Find the coordinates of R.

11 The curve $y = x(x - 1)(x - 5)$ crosses the x-axis at the points $O(0, 0)$, $A(1, 0)$ and $B(5, 0)$.
   The tangents to the curve at the points A and B meet at the point C.
   Find the coordinates of the point C.

Stationary points

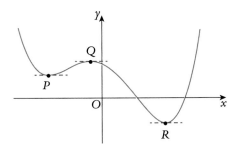

The gradient of the curve is zero at the points P, Q and R.
A point where the gradient is zero is called a **stationary point** or a **turning point**.

Stationary points occur when $\dfrac{dy}{dx} = 0$.

The stationary point Q is called a **maximum point**.
Q is called a maximum point because the value of y at this point is greater than the value of y at other points close to Q.

The stationary points P and R are called **minimum points**.
P is called a minimum point because the value of y at this point is less than the value of y at other points close to P. The same is true for R.

EXAMPLE

A curve has equation $y = x^3 - 3x^2 - 9x$.
Find the coordinates of the turning points on this curve.

$y = x^3 - 3x^2 - 9x$ *differentiate*

$\dfrac{dy}{dx} = 3x^2 - 6x - 9$

At stationary points $\dfrac{dy}{dx} = 0$.

$\qquad 3x^2 - 6x - 9 = 0$ *divide both sides by 3*
$\qquad\quad x^2 - 2x - 3 = 0$ *factorise*
$\qquad (x + 1)(x - 3) = 0$
$\quad x + 1 = 0$ or $x - 3 = 0$
$\qquad\quad x = -1$ or $x = 3$

When $x = -1$, $y = (-1)^3 - 3(-1)^2 - 9(-1) = 5$.
When $x = 3$, $y = (3)^3 - 3(3)^2 - 9(3) = -27$.
The turning points are $(-1, 5)$ and $(3, -27)$.

UNIT 10

EXERCISE 10.7

1   The curve with equation $y = x^2 - 6x$ has one turning point
    a   Use completing the square to find the coordinates of the turning point and sketch
        the graph of $y = x^2 - 6x$. State whether the turning point is a maximum or a
        minimum point.
    b   Use differentiation to find the coordinates of the turning point.

2

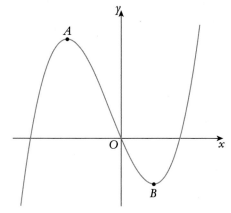

The diagram shows the graph of $y = x^3 + 3x^2 - 45x$.
The curve has a maximum point at A and a minimum point at B.
Find the coordinates of the points A and B.

3

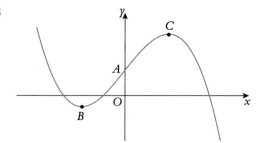

The diagram shows the graph of $y = 11 + 12x - x^3$.
The curve crosses the y-axis at the point A.
It has a minimum point at B and a maximum point at C.
    a   Find the gradient of the curve at the point A.
    b   Find the coordinates of the points B and C.

4   The curve with equation $y = x^4 - 4x$ has one turning point.
    Find the coordinates of this turning point.

5   A curve has equation $y = 24x - 3x^2 - x^3$.
    Find the coordinates of the turning points on this curve.

6

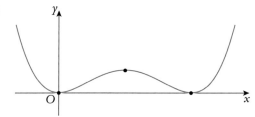

The diagram shows the graph of $y = x^4 - 4x^3 + 4x^2$.
Use differentiation to find the coordinates of the three turning points.

7 Find the coordinates of the stationary points on each of the following curves.
Use graphing software to check your answers

a $y = x^2 - 4x + 8$ b $y = x^3 - 12x + 6$

c $y = x^4 + 4x - 1$ d $y = x(x^2 - 3x - 9)$

e $y = (3 + x)(2 - x)$ f $y = (2x - 3)^3 - 6x$

8 The curve $y = x^3 + ax^2 - 9x$ has a minimum point at $x = 1$.
Find the value of a.

9 The curve $y = 2x^3 + ax^2 + bx$ has no turning points.
Show that $a^2 < 6b$.

First derivative test for maximum and minimum points

Consider the graph of the function shown below.

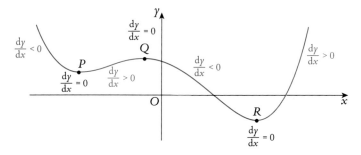

The gradient of the curve is zero at the points P, Q and R.
The red sections of the curve show where the gradient is negative.
The blue sections show where the gradient is positive.

The point Q is a maximum point.

At a maximum point:

- $\dfrac{dy}{dx} = 0$

- the gradient is positive to the left of the maximum and negative to the right

The points P and R are minimum points.

At a minimum point:

- $\dfrac{dy}{dx} = 0$

- the gradient is negative to the left of the minimum and positive to the right

EXAMPLE

Find the coordinates of the stationary points on the curve $y = x^3 - 12x + 10$ and determine the nature of these points. Sketch the graph of $y = x^3 - 12x + 10$.

$y = x^3 - 12x + 10$

$\dfrac{dy}{dx} = 3x^2 - 12$

For stationary points: $\dfrac{dy}{dx} = 0$

$\begin{aligned} 3x^2 - 12 &= 0 \qquad &\textit{divide both sides by 3} \\ x^2 - 4 &= 0 \qquad &\textit{factorise} \\ (x + 2)(x - 2) &= 0 \qquad &\textit{solve} \end{aligned}$

$x + 2 = 0 \quad$ or $\quad x - 2 = 0$

$x = -2 \quad$ or $\quad x = 2$

When $x = -2$, $y = (-2)^3 - 12(-2) + 10 = 26$

When $x = 2$, $y = (2)^3 - 12(2) + 10 = -6$

The stationary points are $(-2, 26)$ and $(2, -6)$.

Now consider the gradient on either side of the points (−2, 26) and (2, −6):

x	−2.1	−2	−1.9
$\dfrac{dy}{dx}$	$3(-2.1)^2 - 12$ = positive	0	$3(-1.9)^2 - 12$ = negative
direction of tangent	/	—	\
shape of curve		⌢	

x	1.9	2	2.1
$\dfrac{dy}{dx}$	$3(1.9)^2 - 12$ = negative	0	$3(2.1)^2 - 12$ = positive
direction of tangent	\	—	/
shape of curve		⌣	

So (−2, 26) is a maximum point and (2, −6) is a minimum point.
The sketch graph of $y = x^3 - 12x + 10$ is:

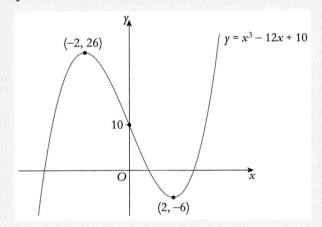

EXERCISE 10.8

1   The curve with equation $y = x^2 + 2x$ has one turning point
   a   Use differentiation to find the coordinates of the turning point.
   b   Use the first derivative test to determine whether this point is a maximum or a minimum point.

2   The curve with equation $y = 8 + 2x - x^2$ has one turning point
   a   Use differentiation to find the coordinates of the turning point.
   b   Use the first derivative test to determine whether this point is a maximum or a minimum point.

UNIT 10

3 Find the coordinates of the stationary points on each of the following curves and use the first derivative test to determine the nature of each stationary point. Sketch the graph of each function and use graphing software to check your graphs.

   a $y = x^2 - 10x + 4$ **b** $y = (3 + x)(2 - x)$

   c $y = 2x^3 - 15x^2$ **d** $y = 2x^3 - 3x^2 - 36x$

   e $y = 4x^3 + 9x^2 - 12x$ **f** $y = 3x^2 - \dfrac{2}{3}x^3 - 4x$

Second derivatives

If you differentiate y with respect to x you obtain $\dfrac{dy}{dx}$.

$\dfrac{dy}{dx}$ is called the **first derivative** of y with respect to x.

If you then differentiate $\dfrac{dy}{dx}$ with respect to x you obtain $\dfrac{d}{dx}\left(\dfrac{dy}{dx}\right)$ which can also be written as $\dfrac{d^2y}{dx^2}$.

$\dfrac{d^2y}{dx^2}$ is called the **second derivative** of y with respect to x.

So for $y = x^3 + 4x^2 - 2x + 1$ or $f(x) = x^3 + 4x^2 - 2x + 1$

       $\dfrac{dy}{dx} = 3x^2 + 8x - 2$ or $f'(x) = 3x^2 + 8x - 2$

       $\dfrac{d^2y}{dx^2} = 6x + 8$ or $f''(x) = 6x + 8$

A curve has equation $y = x^3 - 4x + 3$

a Find $\dfrac{dy}{dx}$ and $\dfrac{d^2y}{dx^2}$.

b Show that $\dfrac{d^2y}{dx^2} \neq \left(\dfrac{dy}{dx}\right)^2$.

---

a $y = x^3 - 4x + 3$

      $\dfrac{dy}{dx} = 3x^2 - 4$

      $\dfrac{d^2y}{dx^2} = 6x$

b $\dfrac{d^2y}{dx^2} = 6x$ and $\left(\dfrac{dy}{dx}\right)^2 = (3x^2 - 4)^2 = 9x^4 - 24x + 16$

   Hence, $\dfrac{d^2y}{dx^2} \neq \left(\dfrac{dy}{dx}\right)^2$.

TOP TIP

It is important to remember that $\dfrac{d^2y}{dx^2}$ is not the same as $\left(\dfrac{dy}{dx}\right)^2$.

EXERCISE 10.9

1 Find $\dfrac{d^2y}{dx^2}$ for each of the following functions.

   a $y = x^2 - 4x - 3$
           b $y = 2x^3 + 3x^2 - 5x$
           c $y = x^4 - x^3$

   d $y = 5 - x - 2x^2$
           e $y = 1 - 2x + 4x^3$
           f $y = 2x^5 - 3x^4 + 2$

   g $y = x(3 - x^2)$
           h $y = (x - 1)(x^2 + 2)$
           i $y = 2x^2(5 - 3x + x^2)$

2 Given that $y = 3x^3 - 5x^2 - 1$, find the value of $\dfrac{d^2y}{dx^2}$ when $x = 2$.

3 Find $f''(x)$ for each of the following functions.

   a $f(x) = 6x^4 - 2x^3$
           b $f(x) = 5x^2 - x^5$
           c $f(x) = (x - 3)^2 - 5$

4 Given that $f(x) = x^3 - x^2 + 5x$, find

   a $f(1)$,
           b $f'(1)$,
           c $f''(1)$.

5 Given that $f(x) = (x^2 - 2)^2$, find the value of $f''(-1)$.

6 A curve has equation $y = x^3 - 6x^2 + 9x$.

   a Show that $\dfrac{dy}{dx} = 0$ when $x = 1$ and when $x = 3$.

   b Find the value of $\dfrac{d^2y}{dx^2}$ when $x = 1$ and when $x = 3$.

7 A curve has equation $y = x^3 + ax^2 + bx$. Given that $\dfrac{dy}{dx} = 0$ and $\dfrac{d^2y}{dx^2} = 12$ when $x = 1$, find the value of a and the value of b.

8 A curve has equation $y = x^3 - 3x^2 - 9x$.

   a Find $\dfrac{dy}{dx}$ and $\dfrac{d^2y}{dx^2}$.

   b Copy and complete the table to show whether $\dfrac{dy}{dx}$ and $\dfrac{d^2y}{dx^2}$ are positive (+), negative (−) or zero (0) for the given values of x.

x	−3	−2	−1	0	1	2	3	4	5
$\dfrac{dy}{dx}$						−			
$\dfrac{d^2y}{dx^2}$						+			

c The graph of $y = x^3 - 3x^2 - 9x$ is shown below, together with the coordinates of its maximum and minimum points.

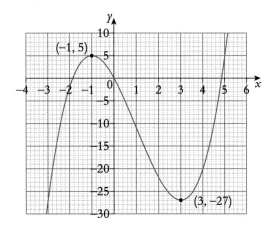

Use the word *positive* or the word *negative* to complete each of these statements.

i At the maximum point $\dfrac{dy}{dx} = 0$ and $\dfrac{d^2y}{dx^2}$ is ....

ii At the minimum point $\dfrac{dy}{dx} = 0$ and $\dfrac{d^2y}{dx^2}$ is ....

Second derivative test for maximum and minimum points

Consider moving from left to right along a curve, passing through a maximum point:

The gradient, $\dfrac{dy}{dx}$, starts as a positive value, decreases to zero at the maximum point and then decreases to a negative value.

Since $\dfrac{dy}{dx}$ decreases as x increases, then the rate of change of $\dfrac{dy}{dx}$ is negative.

The rate of change of $\dfrac{dy}{dx}$ is written as $\dfrac{d}{dx}\left(\dfrac{dy}{dx}\right) = \dfrac{d^2y}{dx^2}$.

This leads to the rule:

> If $\dfrac{dy}{dx} = 0$ and $\dfrac{d^2y}{dx^2} < 0$, then the point is a maximum point.

Now, consider moving from left to right along a curve, passing through a minimum point:

The gradient, $\frac{dy}{dx}$ starts as a negative value, increases to zero at the minimum point and then increases to a positive value.

Since $\frac{dy}{dx}$ increases as x increases, then the rate of change of $\frac{dy}{dx}$ is positive.

This leads to the rule:

> If $\frac{dy}{dx} = 0$ and $\frac{d^2y}{dx^2} > 0$, then the point is a minimum point.

If $\frac{dy}{dx} = 0$ and $\frac{d^2y}{dx^2} = 0$, then the nature of the stationary point can be found using the First Derivative Test.

EXAMPLE

Find the coordinates of the stationary points on the curve $y = x^3 - 3x + 2$ and use the second derivative test to determine the nature of these points.

$y = x^3 - 3x + 2$ *differentiate*
$\frac{dy}{dx} = 3x^2 - 3$

For stationary points: $\frac{dy}{dx} = 0$

$3x^2 - 3 = 0$ *divide both sides by 3*
$x^2 - 1 = 0$
$x^2 = 1$
$x = -1$ or $x = 1$

When $x = -1$, $y = (-1)^3 - 3(-1) + 2 = 4$.
When $x = 1$, $y = (1)^3 - 3(1) + 2 = 0$.
The stationary points are $(-1, 4)$ and $(1, 0)$.
Find the second derivative:

$$\frac{d^2y}{dx^2} = 6x$$

When $x = -1$, $\frac{d^2y}{dx^2} = 6(-1) < 0$ $\Rightarrow$ maximum point

When $x = 1$, $\frac{d^2y}{dx^2} = 6(1) > 0$ $\Rightarrow$ minimum point

$\therefore$ $(-1, 4)$ is a maximum point and $(1, 0)$ is a minimum point.

UNIT 10

EXERCISE 10.10

1 The curve with equation $y = 10x - x^2$ has one turning point
   a Use differentiation to find the coordinates of the turning point.
   b Use the second derivative test to determine whether this point is a maximum or a minimum point.

2 The curve with equation $y = x^2 - 2x - 8$ has one turning point
   a Use differentiation to find the coordinates of the turning point.
   b Use the second derivative test to determine whether this point is a maximum or a minimum point.

3 Find the coordinates of the stationary points on each of the following curves and use the second derivative test to determine the nature of each stationary point. Sketch the graph of each function and use graphing software to check your graphs.
   a $y = 2x^2 + 8x + 5$ b $y = 1 - (2x + 1)^2$
   c $y = x^4 + 4x - 1$ d $y = 4x^3 - 3x^2 - 36x$
   e $y = x^3 - 12x + 6$ f $y = 9x^2 - 15x - x^3$

4 The curve $y = 2x^3 + ax^2 + bx$ has a stationary point when $x = 2$.
   The curve passes through the point (1, 23).
   a Find the value of a and the value of b.
   b Find the coordinates of the other stationary point on the curve and determine the nature of this point.

5 The curve $y = x^3 + ax^2 + b$ has a stationary point at the point (4, −27).
   a Find the value of a and the value of b.
   b Determine the nature of the stationary point (4, −27).
   c Find the coordinates of the other stationary point on the curve and determine the nature of this stationary point.

6 The curve $y = 2x^3 + ax^2 + bx$ has a stationary point at the point (−1, 7).
   a Find the value of a and the value of b.
   b Find the coordinates of the second stationary point on the curve.
   c Determine the nature of the two stationary points.

KEY WORDS
differentiation
derivative
gradient function
stationary point
turning point
maximum point
minimum point
first derivative
second derivative

Expanding more than two brackets

To expand three brackets, you must first expand a pair of brackets to create a 'new' bracket and then you must expand the third bracket with your 'new' bracket.

It does not matter which pair of brackets that you multiply first. (The examples in this section all start by multiplying the 2nd and 3rd brackets first.)

Consider the expansion of $(2x + 3)(x + 2)(x + 4)$:

$(2x + 3)(x + 2)(x + 4)$	expand the second and third brackets
$= (2x + 3)(x^2 + 4x + 2x + 8)$	simplify
$= (2x + 3)(x^2 + 6x + 8)$	expand by multiplying each term in the new bracket first by $2x$ and then by 3
$= 2x^3 + 12x^2 + 16x + 3x^2 + 18x + 24$	simplify
$= 2x^3 + 15x^2 + 34x + 24$	

Alternatively, the expansions could be shown in table form:

	x	$+4$
x	$+x^2$	$+4x$
$+2$	$+2x$	$+8$
	$x^2 + 6x + 8$	

	x^2	$+6x$	$+8$
$2x$	$+2x^3$	$+12x^2$	$+16x$
$+3$	$+3x^2$	$+18x$	$+24$
	$2x^3 + 15x^2 + 34x + 24$		

Expand and simplify $(2x - 5)(x + 1)(x - 2)$.

$(2x - 5)(x + 1)(x - 2)$	expand the second and third brackets
$= (2x - 5)(x^2 - 2x + x - 2)$	simplify
$= (2x - 5)(x^2 - x - 2)$	expand the first bracket with the new bracket
$= 2x(x^2 - x - 2) - 5(x^2 - x - 2)$	
$= 2x^3 - 2x^2 - 4x - 5x^2 + 5x + 10$	simplify
$= 2x^3 - 7x^2 + x + 10$	

Alternative method:

	x	-2
x	$+x^2$	$-2x$
$+1$	$+x$	-2
	$x^2 - x - 2$	

	x^2	$-x$	-2
$2x$	$+2x^3$	$-2x^2$	$-4x$
-5	$-5x^2$	$+5x$	$+10$
	$2x^3 - 7x^2 + x + 10$		

Expand and simplify $(x + 4)^3$.

$(x + 4)^3 = (x + 4)(x + 4)(x + 4)$ *expand the second and third brackets*

$\qquad\quad = (x + 4)(x^2 + 4x + 4x + 16)$ *simplify*

$\qquad\quad = (x + 4)(x^2 + 8x + 16)$ *expand the first bracket with the new bracket*

$\qquad\quad = x(x^2 + 8x + 16) + 4(x^2 + 8x + 16)$

$\qquad\quad = x^3 + 8x^2 + 16x + 4x^2 + 32x + 64$ *simplify*

$\qquad\quad = x^3 + 12x^2 + 48x + 64$

EXERCISE 10.11

1 Expand and simplify.
   a $x(x + 2)(x + 4)$
   b $2x(x + 1)(x - 5)$
   c $3x^2(2x - 5)(x - 2)$
   d $7x(2x - 1)(5 - 7x)$
   e $3xy(x - 2)(y + 4)$
   f $2xy^2(1 - 3x)(2 - 5y)$

2 Expand and simplify.
   a $(x + 2)(x + 1)(x + 5)$
   b $(x + 4)(x + 3)(x + 2)$
   c $(2x + 1)(x + 2)(x + 1)$
   d $(2x + 3)(3x + 2)(x + 5)$

3 Expand and simplify.
   a $(x + 2)(x - 1)(x + 4)$
   b $(x - 1)(x - 3)(x + 2)$
   c $(2x - 5)(x - 3)(x - 1)$
   d $(5x + 1)(3x - 1)(x + 3)$

4 Expand and simplify.
   a $(3 - x)(2x - 1)(1 - 3x)$
   b $(x + 5)(1 - 2x)(3 - 2x)$
   c $(x^2 + 1)(4 - x)(3x + 2)$
   d $(3 - x^2)(2 - 5x)(2x + 1)$

5 Expand and simplify.
   a $(x + 1)(x + 3)^2$
   b $(x - 2)(2x + 1)^2$
   c $(3x + 2)(x - 5)^2$
   d $(x + 2)^3$
   e $(x - 1)^3$
   f $(2x - 5)^3$

6 $3x^3 - 21x^2 + 21x + 45 = a(x + 1)(x - 3)(x + b)$
   Find the value of a and the value of b.

7 $2x^3 + 13x^2 + 25x + 14 = (ax + b)(x + 2)(x + 1)$
   Find the value of a and the value of b.

8 $8x^3 + 12x^2 - 236x - 118 = a(x + b)(2x + 1)(x - 5) + 2$
   Find the value of a and the value of b.

9 Expand and simplify.
   a $(x + 1)(x + 2)(x + 3)(x + 4)$
   b $(x - 1)(x + 1)(x + 2)^2$
   c $(2x + 1)(x - 1)(x + 5)(x + 2)$
   d $(1 - x)(2x - 1)(3x + 1)(2 - x)$
   e $(x + 1)^4$
   f $(3 - 2x)^4$

Solve $(2x + 7)(x - 2)(x - 6) = 0$.

$(2x + 7)(x - 2)(x - 6) = 0$

$2x + 7 = 0$	or	$x - 2 = 0$	or	$x - 6 = 0$
$2x = -7$	or	$x = 2$	or	$x = 6$
$x = -3\dfrac{1}{2}$	or	$x = 2$	or	$x = 6$

Solve $(x + 1)(x + 2)(x - 2) = (x - 2)(x - 1)(x - 5)$.

First, expand each side of the equation.

$(x + 1)(x + 2)(x - 2)$ *expand second and third brackets*

$\quad = (x + 1)(x^2 - 2x + 2x - 4)$ *simplify*

$\quad = (x + 1)(x^2 - 4)$ *expand brackets*

$\quad = x^3 - 4x + x^2 - 4$

$\quad = x^3 + x^2 - 4x - 4$

TOP TIP

Do not divide both sides of the original equation by $(x - 2)$. If you do, you will lose one of the solutions.

$(x - 2)(x - 1)(x - 5)$ *expand second and third brackets*

$\quad = (x - 2)(x^2 - 5x - x + 5)$ *simplify*

$\quad = (x - 2)(x^2 - 6x + 5)$ *expand brackets*

$\quad = x^3 - 6x^2 + 5x - 2x^2 + 12x - 10$ *simplify*

$\quad = x^3 - 8x^2 + 17x - 10$

$x^3 + x^2 - 4x - 4 = x^3 - 8x^2 + 17x - 10$	*simplify*
$9x^2 - 21x + 6 = 0$	*divide both sides by 3*
$3x^2 - 7x + 2 = 0$	*factorise*
$(3x - 1)(x - 2) = 0$	*solve*

$3x - 1 = 0$	or	$x - 2 = 0$
$3x = 1$	or	$x = 2$
$x = \dfrac{1}{3}$	or	$x = 2$

EXERCISE 10.12

1 A cube has sides of length $(x + 5)$ cm and volume V cm³.
Show that $V = x^3 + 15x^2 + 75x + 125$.

2 In this question all lengths are in centimetres.

$x + 2$

$x - 2$

$x + 5$

The diagram shows a cuboid with volume V cm³.
Show that $V = x^3 + 5x^2 - 4x - 20$.

3   In this question all lengths are in centimetres.

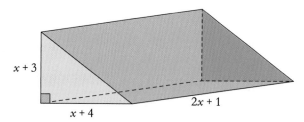

$x + 3$

$2x + 1$

$x + 4$

The diagram shows a triangular prism with volume V cm³.

Show that $V = x^3 + \dfrac{15}{2}x^2 + \dfrac{31}{2}x + 6$.

4   $3x^3 + x^2 - 62x + 40 = (3x + a)(x + 5)(x + b)$

   a   Show that $a + 3b = -14$ and $ab = 8$.

   b   Solve the simultaneous equations in **part a** to find the possible values of a and b.

5   Solve these equations.

   a $(x - 1)(x + 2)(x + 4) = (x + 1)(x - 3)(x + 5)$

   b $(x - 1)(x + 1)(x + 3) = (x - 2)(x + 2)(x - 1)$

6   Solve these equations, giving your answers correct to 2 decimal places.

   a $(x - 1)(x - 2)(x - 3) = (x + 1)(x + 2)(x - 5)$

   b $(x - 3)^2(x + 1) = (x + 3)^2(x - 1)$

7   Solve these equations.

   a $(x - 2)(x + 5)(x + 8) = 0$ b $(x + 1)(x + 7)(x - 3) = 0$

   c $(2x - 1)(x + 5)(x - 3) = 0$ d $(3x - 2)(2x + 5)(x - 2) = 0$

8   a   Show that $(x - 2)(x + 5)(x + 1) = x^3 + 4x^2 - 7x - 10$.

   b   Hence solve the equation $x^3 + 4x^2 - 7x - 10 = 0$.

9   Write these as a single fraction in its simplest terms.

   a $\dfrac{x+1}{x+2} + \dfrac{3x-1}{(x+1)(x+3)}$ b $\dfrac{x-1}{x+2} + \dfrac{x+2}{x+3} + \dfrac{x-5}{x-1}$

10   In this question all lengths are in centimetres.

The diagram shows two solid cuboids.
The volumes of the cuboids differ
by 474 cm³.
Find the value of x.

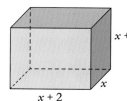

$x + 1$

x

$x + 2$

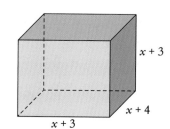

$x + 3$

$x + 4$

$x + 3$

11 In this question all lengths are in centimetres.

The diagram shows a solid hemisphere and a solid cone.
The two solids have the same volume.
Find the value of x.
[The volume, V, of a sphere with radius r is $V = \frac{4}{3}\pi r^3$.]

[The volume, V, of a cone with radius r and height h is $V = \frac{1}{3}\pi r^2 h$.]

12 A bag contains ten balls, of which x balls are red.
Four balls are picked at random from the bag without replacement.
Given that $x > 4$, show that the probability the four balls are all red is $\dfrac{x^4 - 6x^3 + 11x^2 - 6x}{5040}$.

Sketch graphs of cubic functions

EXAMPLE

Sketch the graph of $y = (x + 2)(x - 1)(x - 3)$ showing all axis crossing points.

If $(x + 2)(x - 1)(x - 3)$ was expanded, then the coefficient of x^3 would be positive.
Hence the graph of $y = (x + 2)(x - 1)(x - 3)$ will be of the form $\mathcal{N}$
Find the axis crossing points:
When $x = 0$, $\qquad\qquad y = (2) \times (-1) \times (-3) = 6$
So the curve crosses the y-axis at the point $(0, 6)$.
When $y = 0$, $\qquad\qquad (x + 2)(x - 1)(x - 3) = 0$ $\qquad\qquad$ *solve*
$\qquad\quad x + 2 = 0 \quad$ or $\quad x - 1 = 0 \quad$ or $\quad x - 3 = 0$
$\qquad\qquad x = -2 \quad$ or $\qquad x = 1 \quad$ or $\qquad x = 3$
So the curve crosses the x-axis at the point $(-2, 0)$, $(1, 0)$ and $(3, 0)$.
The sketch graph is:

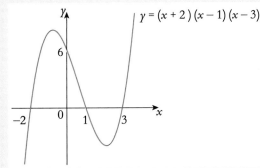

EXERCISE 10.13

1   a   Show that $(x + 2)(x - 1)(x - 5) = x^3 - 4x^2 - 7x + 10$.
    b   Solve the equation $(x + 2)(x - 1)(x - 5) = 0$.
    c   Sketch the graph of $y = x^3 - 4x^2 - 7x + 10$ showing all axis crossing points.

2   a   Show that $(2x + 5)(x + 1)(3 - x) = 15 + 16x - x^2 - 2x^3$.
    b   Solve the equation $(2x + 5)(x + 1)(3 - x) = 0$.
    c   Sketch the graph of $y = 15 + 16x - x^2 - 2x^3$ showing all axis crossing points.

3   Sketch the graph of each function showing all axis crossing points.
    a $y = (x - 1)(x - 2)(x - 3)$ b $y = (x + 2)(x - 2)(x - 6)$
    c $y = (2 - x)(x + 3)(x - 1)$ d $y = (x - 1)^2(x + 1)$
    e $y = (2x - 1)(x - 2)(x + 1)$ f $y = (2x - 7)(1 - x)(x + 3)$

4

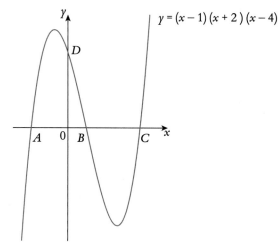

$y = (x - 1)(x + 2)(x - 4)$

The diagram shows the graph of $y = (x - 1)(x + 2)(x - 4)$.
The curve crosses the x-axis at the points A, B and C and crosses the y-axis at the point D.
Write down the coordinates of each of the points A, B, C and D.

Trigonometric equations and graphs

The graphs of $y = \sin x$ and $y = \cos x$

In the diagram the line OP is of length 1 unit and OP makes an angle x with the positive horizontal axis.

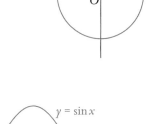

Using trigonometry:

> height of right-angled triangle = $\sin x$
> base length of right-angled triangle = $\cos x$

Now consider the point P as it moves around the unit circle, through one complete revolution.

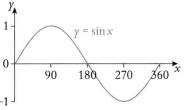

The height of P above the horizontal axis changes from $0 \rightarrow 1 \rightarrow 0 \rightarrow -1 \rightarrow 0$.
The graph of $y = \sin x$ for $0° \le x \le 360°$ is shown to the right.

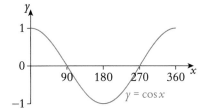

The displacement of P from the vertical axis changes from $1 \rightarrow 0 \rightarrow -1 \rightarrow 0 \rightarrow 1$.
The graph of $y = \cos x$ for $0° \le x \le 360°$ is shown to the right.

The graphs of $y = \sin x$ and $y = \cos x$ can be extended beyond $0° \le x \le 360°$, as shown in the diagrams below.

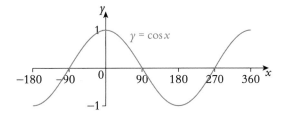

The sine and cosine functions are called **periodic functions** because they repeat themselves over and over again.
The **period** of a periodic function is defined as the length of one complete repetition or cycle.

The basic sine and cosine functions repeat every 360°.
We say they have a **period** of 360°.

The **amplitude** of a periodic function is defined as the distance between a maximum (or minimum) point and the principal axis.
The basic sine and cosine functions have amplitude 1.

The graph of $y = \tan x$

The tangent function behaves very differently to the sine and cosine functions.

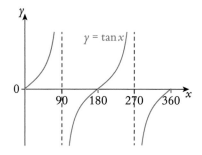

The red dashed lines at $x = 90°$ and $x = 270°$ are **asymptotes**.
The branches of the graph get closer and closer to the asymptotes without ever reaching them.

The tangent function repeats its cycle every 180° so its period is 180°.
The tangent function does not have an amplitude.

The graph of $y = \tan x$ can also be extended beyond $0° \le x \le 360°$:

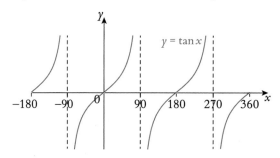

Solving trigonometric equations for values between 0° and 360°

Consider solving the equation: $\sin x = 0.5$
$$x = \sin^{-1}(0.5)$$
A calculator will give the answer: $x = 30°$
There is, however, a second value of x for which $\sin x = 0.5$

This can be found by considering the symmetry of the curve $y = \sin x$:

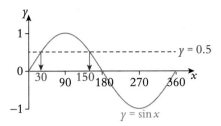

The second value = $180° - 30° = 150°$
Hence the solution of the equation $\sin x = 0.5$ for $0° \le x \le 360°$ is
$$x = 30° \text{ or } 150°$$

EXAMPLE

Solve $\cos x = -0.6$ for $0° \le x \le 360°$.

$\cos x = -0.6$ *use a calculator to find $\cos^{-1}(-0.6)$ correct to 1 decimal place*
    $x = 126.9°$
A sketch graph of $y = \cos x$ is used to find any other values:

Using the symmetry of the curve, the second value is $x = 360° - 126.9° = 233.1°$
Hence the solution of $\cos x = -0.6$ for $0° \le x \le 360°$ is
$$x = 126.9° \text{ or } 233.1°$$

EXAMPLE

Solve $\sin x = -\dfrac{3}{4}$ for $0° \le x \le 360°$.

$\sin x = -\dfrac{3}{4}$ *use a calculator to find $\sin^{-1}\left(-\dfrac{3}{4}\right)$*
  $x = -48.6°$ *this angle is out of range*
A sketch graph of $y = \sin x$ is used to find any other values:

The other values are:
$$x = 180° + 48.6° = 228.6°$$
$$x = 360° - 48.6° = 311.4°$$
Hence the solution of $\sin x = -\dfrac{3}{4}$ for $0° \le x \le 360°$ is
$$x = 228.6° \text{ or } 311.4°$$

Solve $\tan x = \sqrt{5}$ for $0° \le x \le 360°$.

$\tan x = \sqrt{5}$ *use a calculator to find* $\tan^{-1}\left(\sqrt{5}\right)$
   $x = 65.9°$

A sketch graph of $y = \tan x$ is used to find any other values:

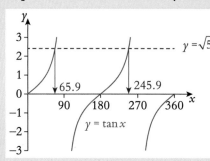

The other value is:
$$x = 180° + 65.9° = 245.9°$$
Hence the solution of $\tan x = \sqrt{5}$ for $0° \le x \le 360°$ is
$$x = 65.9° \text{ or } 245.9°$$

EXERCISE 10.14

1   Sketch the graph of each of the following functions for $0° \le x \le 360°$.
    You must show clearly all axis crossing points, all turning points and all asymptotes.
       a $y = \cos x$ b $y = \tan x$ c $y = \sin x$

2   Solve each of these equations for $0° \le x \le 360°$.
       a $\sin x = 0.3$ b $\sin x = 0.8$ c $\sin x = \dfrac{3}{5}$ d $\sin x = -0.7$

       e $\sin x = 1$ f $\sin x = -1$ g $\sin x = 0$ h $\sin x = \dfrac{\sqrt{3}}{2}$

       i $\sin x = \dfrac{1}{\sqrt{2}}$ j $\sin x = -\dfrac{1}{3}$ k $6\sin x = 4$ l $5\sin x + 3 = 1$

3   Explain why it is not possible to solve the equation $\sin x = -3$.

4 Solve each of these equations for $0° \leq x \leq 360°$.

  a $\cos x = 0.1$
  b $\cos x = 0.7$
  c $\cos x = -\dfrac{2}{5}$
  d $\cos x = -0.8$

  e $\cos x = -1$
  f $\cos x = 0$
  g $\cos x = 1$
  h $\cos x = \dfrac{\sqrt{3}}{2}$

  i $\cos x = -\dfrac{1}{\sqrt{2}}$
  j $\cos x = -\dfrac{1}{4}$
  k $7\cos x = 3$
  l $3\cos x + 2 = 1$

5 Solve each of these equations for $0° \leq x \leq 360°$.

  a $\tan x = 2$
  b $\tan x = 3.4$
  c $\tan x = -3$
  d $\tan x = -0.8$

  e $\tan x = 1$
  f $\tan x = 0$
  g $\tan x = -1$
  h $\tan x = \sqrt{3}$

  i $\tan x = -\sqrt{3}$
  j $2\tan x = 5$
  k $1 - 2\tan x = 4$
  l $5\tan x - 6 = 2$

CHALLENGE QUESTION

6 Solve these equations for $0° \leq x \leq 360°$.

  a $2\cos^2 x - \cos x = 0$
  b $4\tan^2 x - \tan x = 0$

  c $2\sin^2 x - 3\sin x + 1 = 0$
  d $6\cos^2 x - 7\cos x + 2 = 0$

  e $3\sin^2 x - 7\sin x + 2 = 0$
  f $5\tan^2 x + 3\tan x - 2 = 0$

TOP TIP

$\cos^2 x$ means $(\cos x)^2$

CHALLENGE QUESTION

7 Solve each of these equations for $0° \leq x \leq 360°$.

  a $\sin 2x = 0.5$

  b $\cos 2x = -0.8$

  c $\tan 2x = 1$

KEY WORDS

periodic function

period

amplitude

asymptote

Circle theorems 2

In Unit 6 you learnt about some of the circle theorems. In this section you will learn about another circle theorem, which is called the **alternate segment theorem**.

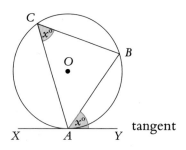

tangent

> **The alternate segment theorem states that:**
> The angle between the tangent and the chord at the point of contact is equal to the angle in the **alternate segment**.

Proof

Draw the radii OA and OB.

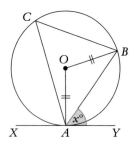

Triangle AOB is isosceles: $\angle OAB = \angle OBA$

Angles in a triangle: $\angle AOB = 180° - 2\angle OAB$ .... (1)

XY is a tangent: $\angle OAY = 90°$

$\therefore x° = 90° - \angle OAB$ .... (2)

From equations (1) and (2) it follows that

$$\angle AOB = 2x°$$

Angle at centre is twice angle at circumference:

$$\therefore \angle ACB = x°$$

Using the alternate segment theorem, we can see that there is
another pair of equivalent angles on the diagram:

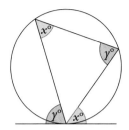

EXAMPLE

A, B and C are points on the circumference of a circle.
The line PQ is a tangent to the circle at A.
Find the value of x and the value of y.

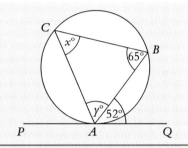

Angle ACB = angle BAQ *alternate segment theorem*
$$x = 52$$

$x + y + 65 = 180$ *angles in a triangle add up to 180°*
$$y = 180 - 65 - 52$$
$$y = 63$$

EXAMPLE

A, B, C and D are points on the circumference of a circle, centre O.
The line XY is a tangent to the circle at A.
a Find the value of a and the value of b.
b Find angle CAY.

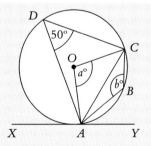

a   Angle $AOC = 2 \times$ angle ADC *angle at centre = 2 × angle at circumference*
$$a = 2 \times 50$$
$$a = 100$$
Angle ABC + angle $ADC = 180°$ *opposite angles of a cyclic quadrilateral add up to 180°*
$$b + 50 = 180$$
$$b = 130$$

b   Angle CAY = angle ADC *alternate segment theorem*
Angle $CAY = 50°$

UNIT 10

EXERCISE 10.15

1 Copy each diagram. Shade and label the matching angles in the alternate segments.

a

b

c

d

e

f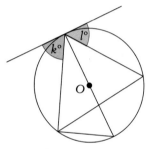

2 Find the value of the letters in each of the following diagrams.

a

b

c

d

e

f

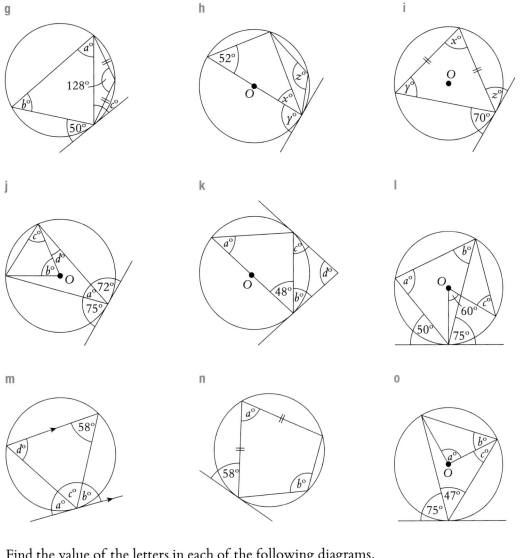

g

h

i

j

k

l

m

n

o

3   Find the value of the letters in each of the following diagrams.
    Give reasons for each of your answers.

a

b

c

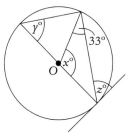

Distance from a point to a line

THIS SECTION WILL SHOW YOU HOW TO
- Find the shortest distance between a point and a line

 The diagram to the right shows a point P and a line L.

The distance from the point, P, to any point on the line L is found by drawing a straight line from P to that point on L.

The perpendicular distance from P to the line L is the shortest distance from from P to L.

If you are asked to find the distance from a point to a line, then you will need to find the *shortest* distance from the point to the line.

EXAMPLE

Find the shortest distance from the point B to the line AC.

First draw a perpendicular from B to the line AC.
Shortest distance = x cm.

$\sin 35° = \dfrac{x}{8}$

$\quad x = 8 \times \sin 35°$

$\quad x = 4.59$

Shortest distance is 4.59 cm.

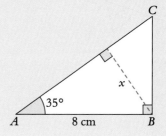

EXAMPLE

Find the shortest distance from the point $(-4, 1)$ to the line $y = 2x - 6$.

Step 1: Find the equation of the perpendicular line that passes through the point $(-4, 1)$.
Gradient of the line $y = 2x - 6$ is 2, hence gradient of perpendicular is $-\dfrac{1}{2}$.

$m = -\dfrac{1}{2} \quad \Rightarrow \quad y = -\dfrac{1}{2}x + c$

$(-4, 1) \quad \Rightarrow \quad 1 = -\dfrac{1}{2}(-4) + c$

$\qquad\qquad\qquad\qquad c = -1$

Equation of perpendicular line is $y = -\dfrac{1}{2}x - 1$

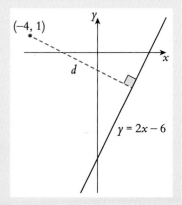

Step 2: Find the point of intersection of $y = 2x - 6$ and $y = -\frac{1}{2}x - 1$.

$$2x - 6 = -\frac{1}{2}x - 1$$

$$2\frac{1}{2}x = 5$$

$$x = 2$$

When $x = 2$, $y = 2(2) - 6 = -2$

Point of intersection is $(2, -2)$.

Step 3: Find the distance between $(-4, 1)$ and $(2, -2)$.

$$d^2 = (-2 - 1)^2 + (2 - -4)^2$$

$$d^2 = 9 + 36$$

$$d^2 = 45$$

$$d = 3\sqrt{5} = 6.71 \text{ to 3 sf}$$

The shortest distance from the point $(-4, 1)$ to the line $y = 2x - 6$ is 6.71 units.

EXERCISE 10.16

1   Find the shortest distance from the point B to the line AC for each triangle.

a

b

2

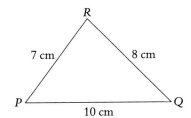

a   Find angle QPR.

b   Find the shortest distance from the point Q to the line PR.

3   A boat sails from a port on a bearing of 155°.
A lighthouse is 5 km due east of the port.
Calculate the shortest distance between the boat and the lighthouse.

UNIT 10

4 At 12 00 hours a ship departs from a port with a speed of 20 km/h.
The ship travels on a bearing of 140°.
An island is 30 km from the port on a bearing of 080°.
Find the time when the ship is closest to the island.

5 Find the shortest distance from the point to the line.
Give your answers correct to 3 significant figures.

  a $(6, 5)$ to $y = 2x + 3$ $\qquad$ **b** $(10, 5)$ to $y = 3x - 5$

  c $(-1, 6)$ to $y = \frac{1}{3}x - 7$ $\qquad$ **d** $(1, -3)$ to $y = \frac{2}{3}x + 5$

  e $(-2, -4)$ to $y = -\frac{1}{3}x + 2$ $\qquad$ **f** $(-4, 2)$ to $y = 3x - 10$

6 Find the shortest distance from the point to the line.
Give your answers correct to 3 significant figures.

  a $(-4, -8)$ to $x + 3y = 2$ $\qquad$ **b** $6\frac{1}{2}, 7$ to $2x - 5y = 7$

  c $(6, 7)$ to $2x - 3y = 4$ $\qquad$ **d** $(-6, 7)$ to $6x - 5y + 10 = 0$

7 A is the point $(3, 1)$ and B is the point $(8, 11)$.
Find the distance from the point $(9, 7)$ to the line AB.

Stem-and-leaf diagrams

THIS SECTION WILL SHOW YOU HOW TO
- Construct and interpret stem-and-leaf diagrams

Consider the following data that shows the test scores for each of 20 students.

45	2	21	25	13	36	27	37	5	28
23	13	35	30	25	6	19	27	36	13

A **stem-and-leaf diagram** can be used to group the data without losing any of the original detail.

To do this, each number is split into two parts. In this case, the tens digits form the 'stem' and the units digits form the 'leaves'. The stem is written to the left of a vertical line and the leaves are written to the right of the line. For example, the first value, 45, is written as 4|5. The leaves belonging to each value in the stem are all written in the same row. Lastly, the leaves are arranged in ascending order in each row.

The stem-and-leaf diagram for the data above is:

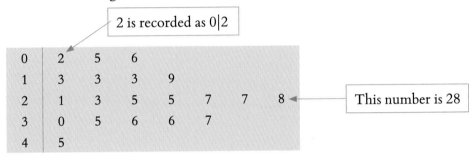

2 is recorded as 0|2

0	2	5	6				
1	3	3	3	9			
2	1	3	5	5	7	7	8
3	0	5	6	6	7		
4	5						

This number is 28

Key: 4|5 represents a score of 45

The **key** shows what the stems and leaves mean.

EXAMPLE

Raju records the mass, in kilograms, of each of 16 newborn babies. His results are shown below.

3.1	1.2	2.5	4.2	3.6	2.3	3.7	1.8
2.4	3.7	3.1	3.9	1.5	4.4	2.0	3.2

Draw a stem-and-leaf diagram to show this information.

Using 3|1 to represent 3.1 kg, the un-ordered stem-and-leaf diagram is:

1	2	8	5			
2	5	3	4	0		
3	1	6	7	7	1	9	2
4	2	4				

Ordering the numbers in each row then gives the final stem-and-leaf diagram:

1	2	5	8			
2	0	3	4	5		
3	1	1	2	6	7	7	9
4	2	4				

Key: 3|1 represents 3.1 kg

EXAMPLE

Lesley records the number of letters she receives each day for 15 days.
Her results are shown below.

13	25	16	35	28	24	13	6
27	38	20	2	13	25	31	

a Draw a stem-and-leaf diagram to show this information.
b Find
   i the range, **ii** the mode, **iii** the median.
c Find the probability that, on one of these 15 days chosen at random, Lesley receives more than 20 letters.

a Un-ordered stem-and-leaf diagram:

0	6	2				
1	3	6	3	3		
2	5	8	4	7	0	5
3	5	8	1			

Ordered stem-and-leaf diagram:

0	2	6				
1	3	3	3	6		
2	0	4	5	5	7	8
3	1	5	8			

Key: 1|3 represents 13 letters

b i

least value = 2

```
0 | 2  6
1 | 3  3  3  6
2 | 0  4  5  5  7  8
3 | 1  5  8
```
greatest value = 38

Range = greatest value − least value = 38 − 2 = 36

ii

```
0 | 2  6
1 | 3  3  3  6
2 | 0  4  5  5  7  8
3 | 1  5  8
```

Mode = most common value = 13

iii

```
0 | 2  6
1 | 3  3  3  6
2 | 0  4  5  5  7  8
3 | 1  5  8
```

Median = $\dfrac{15+1}{2}$ th value = 8th value = 24

c

```
0 | 2  6
1 | 3  3  3  6
2 | 0  4  5  5  7  8
3 | 1  5  8
```

Probability of more than 20 letters = $\dfrac{8}{15}$

EXERCISE 10.17

1   Jonny recorded the number of emails he received each day for 14 days.
His results are shown below.

29	12	25	23	7	16	18
18	22	2	13	17	27	11

Draw a stem-and-leaf diagram to show this information.

UNIT 10

2 Farhat measures the height, in millimetres, of each of 24 plants.
Her results are shown below.

128	142	138	155	124	145	135	139
155	132	144	166	133	168	127	157
130	154	123	168	144	137	148	128

Draw a stem-and-leaf diagram to show this information.

3 Prya records the speed, in metres per second, of each of 20 model cars.
Her results are shown below.

2.0	0.5	1.3	2.3	3.4	0.5	1.7	0.2	2.6	1.8
1.3	3.2	1.9	1.6	0.1	2.4	3.7	3.5	1.8	2.8

Draw a stem-and-leaf diagram to show this information.

4 The test scores of 20 students are shown below.

20	15	38	18	41	49	16	23	28	32
17	32	22	27	16	20	38	45	25	16

a Draw a stem-and-leaf diagram to show this information.
b Find
  i the range,   **ii** the modal score,   **iii** the median score.
c A student is picked at random from the 20 students. Find the probability that this student has a test score greater than 30.

5 Harroon records the number of cars parked in a car park at midday every day for 21 days.
The results are shown below.

64	84	70	87	81	69	77
79	80	96	67	52	76	93
86	59	94	71	80	88	68

a Draw a stem-and-leaf diagram to show this information.
b Find
  i the range,   **ii** the mode,   **iii** the median.
c Find the probability that, on one of these 21 days chosen at random, there are between 60 and 75 cars in the car park.

6 The stem-and-leaf diagram below shows the times, correct to the nearest second, that each of 16 people took to solve a puzzle.

5	3	4	7				
6	2	5	5	8			
7	0	2	3	5	7	7	8
8	1	6					

Key: 5|3 represents 53 s

Kieran says that the range is 86 − 53 = 33 seconds.
Explain why Kieran may be wrong.

7 15 students were asked how many text messages they sent in one weekend.
The stem-and-leaf diagram shows the results.

2	3	7	9		
3	1	2	5	7	
4	1	2	5	5	5
5	0	3	4		

Key: 2|3 represents 23 text messages

a Find
   i the range,   ii the mode,   iii the median,   iv the mean.
c Two students are picked at random from the 15 students.
   Find the probability that both students sent less than 30 text messages.

8 16 students took a statistics test. The stem-and-leaf diagram shows their scores. Three scores are missing from the diagram.

0	5	6	7			
1	0	1	1	3	.....	7
2	0	0	.....	6	9	
3	3	.....				

Key: 1|0 represents a score of 10

a The range of the scores was 31. The median was 16 and the mode was 20. Complete the stem-and-leaf diagram by filling in the missing scores.
b Calculate the mean score.

9 30 students took a mathematics examination and a science examination.

The back-to-back stem-and-leaf diagram shows their scores.

Mathematics score							Stem	Science score							
					7	5	2	1	5	7	7	7	8		
				8	3	2	3	1	3	6	6	8	9	9	9
		7	5	2	2	0	4	0	3	4	4	7	8		
	8	8	6	5	2	1	5	1	1	3	5	6			
9	6	5	4	3	3	2	6	4	7	9					
		7	4	4	0		7	0	3						
				5	3		8								
					4		9								

Key: 5|2|1 represents 25 in mathematics and 21 in science

a Use the information in the stem-and-leaf diagram to complete the following table.

	Mathematics	Science
Range	....	....
Median score	....	....

b Use your answers to **part a** to compare the scores in mathematics and in science.

KEY WORDS

stem-and-leaf diagram
key

Box-and-whisker plots

A **box-and-whisker plot** shows the median, the upper and lower quartiles, the smallest data item and the greatest data item for a particular data set.

In a survey of customer waiting times in a restaurant, the following information was obtained.

	Time (minutes)
Shortest time	5
Lower quartile	13
Median	24
Upper quartile	28
Longest time	43

The box-and-whisker plot below shows this information.

Time (minutes)

When drawing a box-and-whisker plot it is important to remember that

- the ends of the whiskers are placed at the smallest and greatest data values
- the ends of the box are drawn at the lower and upper quartiles
- the median is drawn inside the box
- the width of the box gives the interquartile range
- the scale must be linear and labelled.

Box-and-whisker plots give a visual summary of the data and they are particularly useful for comparing the distributions of two (or more) sets of data.

When comparing two (or more) sets of data, the two main items of information from the box-and-whisker plots that are compared are

- the medians
- the interquartile ranges.

Comparing the medians tells you which set of data has the greatest average.

Comparing the interquartile ranges tells you which set of data is more spread out (more varied).

➡ **NOTE:** The interquartile range is a more useful measure of spread than the range as it is not affected by extreme values (outliers).

The box-and-whisker plot shows information about the daily earnings of a group of workers at factory A and a group of workers at factory B.

Daily earnings ($)

a Find the median daily earnings for the group of workers at
  i factory A, **ii** factory B.
b Find the interquartile range in daily earnings for the group of workers at
  i factory A, **ii** factory B.
c Compare the two distributions of the daily earnings for the group of workers at factory A and the group of workers at factory B.

---

a i The median daily earnings for factory A = $440
  ii The median daily earnings for factory B = $410

b i The interquartile range for factory A = UQ – LQ
$$= \$460 - \$400$$
$$= \$60$$

  ii The interquartile range for factory B = UQ – LQ
$$= \$480 - \$350$$
$$= \$130$$

c The median for factory A ($440) was greater than the median for factory B ($410). This means that, in general, the workers at factory A earn more than the workers at factory B.
The interquartile range for factory A ($60) is less than the interquartile range for factory B ($130). This means that, in general, the weekly earnings at factory A are less spread out than the weekly earnings at factory B.

EXERCISE 10.18

1 The box-and-whisker plot shows information about the speeds, in kilometres per hour, of some cars.

Speed (km/h)

Write down
a the highest speed,   b the lowest speed,   c the median speed,
d the lower quartile,   e the upper quartile,   f the interquartile range.

2 Khadisha records the times, in minutes, that some boys took to solve a puzzle.
The table shows information about her results.

	Time (minutes)
Shortest time	5
Lower quartile	44
Median	65
Upper quartile	74
Longest time	92

Construct a box-and-whisker plot to show this information.

3 The table shows some information about the scores in a test for a group of students.

Lowest score	Highest score	Median	Upper quartile	Interquartile range
15	84	48	58	26

Construct a box-and-whisker plot to show this information.

UNIT 10

4   The box-and-whisker plots show information about the masses, in kilograms, of a group of 12-year-old boys and a group of 12-year-old girls.

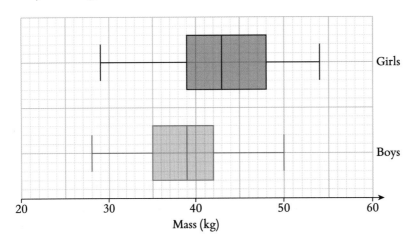

a   Find the median mass for
       i the boys,   ii the girls.
b   Find the interquartile range for
       i the boys,   ii the girls.
c   Compare the distributions of the girls' masses and the boys' masses.

5   The cumulative frequency diagram shows information about the heights of 60 adult females.
   a   Find an estimate for the
         i   median height,
         ii   the lower quartile,
         iii the upper quartile,
         iv   the interquartile range.
   b   The height of the smallest female was 152 cm.
         The height of the tallest female was 196 cm.
         Draw a box-and-whisker plot to show the distribution of the heights of the adult females sampled.

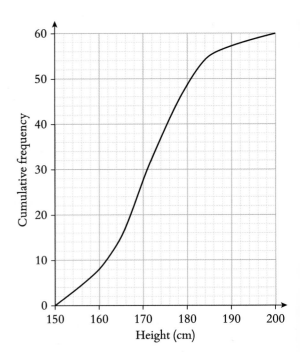

c Information about the heights of 60 adult males is shown in the box-and-whisker plot below.

Compare the distribution of the male heights with the distribution of the female heights.

6 Danusia records the time, in minutes, that the same number of patients waited to see two dentists: dentist A and dentist B. Her results are shown in the cumulative frequency diagram.

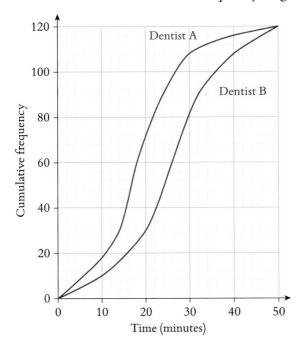

a The shortest waiting time for dentist A was 2 minutes.
The shortest waiting time for dentist B was 5 minutes.
The greatest waiting time for dentist A was 49 minutes.
The greatest waiting time for dentist B was 48 minutes.
Draw two box-and-whisker plots to show the distribution of the waiting times for dentist A and distribution of the waiting times for dentist B.

b Compare the two distributions.

┌ ─ ─ ─ ─ ─ ─ ─ ┐
│   **KEY WORDS**   │
│ box-and-whisker plot │
└ ─ ─ ─ ─ ─ ─ ─ ┘

1 A regular hexagon has sides of length 43 mm, correct to the nearest millimetre.
Calculate the lower bound and the upper bound for the perimeter of this hexagon. [2]

2 A rectangle has sides of length 5.3 cm and 7.5 cm, each correct to 1 decimal place.
Calculate the lower bound and the upper bound for the area of this rectangle. [3]

3 Jack walks a distance of 16.68 km, correct to 2 decimal places.
The time taken to walk this distance is 3.6 hours, correct to 1 decimal place.
Calculate the upper bound for his average speed.
Give your answer in kilometres per hour. [3]

4 Expand and simplify $(x + 2)(x + 3)(x + 5)$. [4]

5 Expand and simplify $(2y + 1)(3y - 2)(y + 5)$. [4]

6 Expand and simplify $(y + 3)(y - 1)^2$. [4]

7 Expand and simplify $(3x - 4)^3$. [4]

8 $3x^3 - 8x^2 - 5x + 6 = (ax + b)(x - 3)(x + 1)$
Find the value of a and the value of b. [2]

9 $6x^3 - 27x^2 - 18x + 11 = a(x + b)(2x - 1)(x + 1) - 4$
Find the value of a and the value of b. [2]

10 $2x^3 - 7x^2 - 7x + 30 = (2x + a)(x - 3)(x + b)$
   a Show that $a + 2b = -1$ and $ab = -10$. [4]
   b Solve the equations in **part a** to find the possible values of a and b. [5]

11 In this question all lengths are in centimetres.

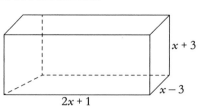

The diagram shows two solid cuboids that have the same volume.
   a Show that $x^2 - 14x + 49 = 0$. [7]
   b Factorise $x^2 - 14x + 49$. [2]
   c Find the value of x. [1]

12

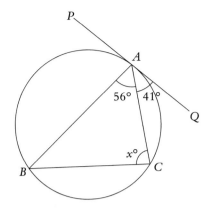

A, B and C are points on the circumference of a circle.
The line PQ is a tangent to the circle at the point A.
Find the value of x. [2]

13

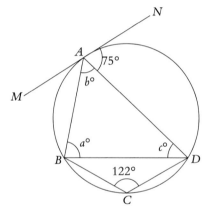

A, B, C and D are points on the circumference of a circle.
The line MN is a tangent to the circle at the point A.
Find the value of a, the value of b and the value of c. [3]

14

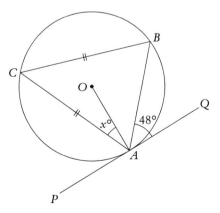

A, B and C are points on the circumference of a circle, centre O.
The line PQ is a tangent to the circle at the point A.
Find the value of x. [4]

15
$$x + 2y = 5$$
$$5x^2 + 4y^2 + 12x = 29$$
Solve the simultaneous equations [6]

16 The line $2x + y = 3$ intersects the curve $x^2 + y^2 + xy = 3$ at the points A and B.
   a Find the coordinates of A and B. [6]
   b Find the equation of the perpendicular bisector of the line AB. [4]

17 Differentiate $5x^4 - 3x + 1$ with respect to x. [2]

18 Find the gradient of the curve $y = 5 - 2x^2 - x^3$ at the point where $x = 1$. [4]

19 A curve has equation $y = 4x^3 - 6x^2 + 3x$.
Show that the gradient of the curve is never negative. [5]

20 The equation of a curve is $y = 5 - 3x - 2x^4$

   a Find $\dfrac{dy}{dx}$. [2]

   b Find $\dfrac{d^2y}{dx^2}$. [2]

21 The equation of a curve is $y = 5x - 2x^2$.

   a Find $\dfrac{dy}{dx}$. [1]

   b Show that the tangent to the curve at the point $(2, 2)$ meets the y-axis at the point $(0, 8)$. [3]

22 The tangent to the curve $y = 2 + 5x - x^2$ at the point $(1, 6)$ meets the x-axis at P and the y-axis at Q. Find the length of PQ. [6]

23 **a** $y = x(x - 3)^2$
     i Show that $y = x^3 - 6x^2 + 9x$. [3]

     ii Find $\dfrac{dy}{dx}$. [2]

   b The curve with equation $y = x(x - 3)^2$ has two turning points.
     i Find the coordinates of these turning points. [5]
     ii Determine the nature of these turning points. [3]

24 On the grid, sketch the graph of $y = \cos x$ for $0° \leq x \leq 360°$.

[2]

25 Solve the equation $4\cos x = 3$ for $0° \leq x \leq 360°$. [4]

26 Solve the equation $5\sin x + 1 = 0$ for $0° \leq x \leq 360°$. [4]

27 The masses, in kilograms, of each of 16 parcels are shown below.

1.1	1.9	2.8	1.6	2.5	0.7	3.6	1.2
2.0	0.4	1.2	0.8	3.2	2.8	1.4	2.3

Draw a stem-and-leaf diagram to show this information. [3]

28 Farhat counted the number of letters in each of 30 sentences in a book.
The stem-and-leaf diagram shows her results.

```
0 | 5   8   9
1 | 1   2   4   4   5   6   8
2 | 0   2   6   6   7   9   9
3 | 1   1   2   4   4   4   7   8
4 | 0   2   2   4   6
```

Key: $3|1$ represents 31 letters

a Write down the number of sentences with 34 letters. [1]
b Work out the range. [1]
c Work out the median. [1]

29 Mustafa records the number of words in each sentence in a book.
    The table shows information about his results.

	Number of words
Lowest value	4
Lower quartile	18
Median	23
Interquartile range	16
Greatest value	46

Construct a box-and-whisker plot to show this information.   [3]

30 Danusia grows two different types of apples, type A and type B.
    She records the mass, in grams, of 80 apples of each type.
    Her results are shown in the cumulative frequency diagram.

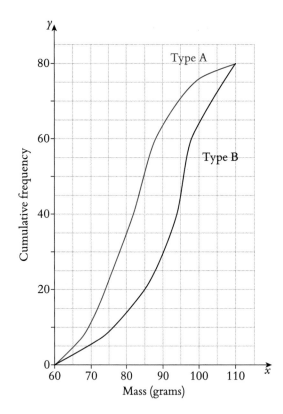

a Find an estimate for the median mass of an apple of
   i type A,   **ii** type B.   [2]

b Find an estimate for the interquartile range for
   i type A,   **ii** type B.   [4]

c The lowest mass for type A was 62 g.
The lowest mass for type B was 64 g.
The greatest mass for type A was 104 g.
The greatest mass for type B was 106 g.
Draw two box-and-whisker plots to show the distribution of the
masses for type A apples and for type B apples.   [6]

d Compare the two distributions.   [2]

Answers

Unit 1

Exercise 1.1

1	17	**2**	8	**3**	2
4	26	**5**	6	**6**	4
7	19	**8**	46	**9**	3
10	14	**11**	48	**12**	10
13	50	**14**	7	**15**	44
16	40	**17**	196	**18**	22
19	34	**20**	85		

Exercise 1.2

1 $(2 + 3) \times 4 + 5 = 25$
2 $2 \times 3 + 4 \times 5 = 26$
3 $2 + 3 \times (4 + 5) = 29$
4 $(2 + 3) \times 4^2 = 80$
5 $2 \times (3 + 4 \times 5) = 46$
6 $5 + 4 \times 3 - 2 = 15$
7 $(2 \times 3 + 4) \times 5 = 50$
8 $2 \times (3 + 4) \times 5 = 70$
9 $(2 + 3) \times (4 + 5) = 45$
10 $2 + 3 \times 4^2 = 50$

Exercise 1.3

1	−8	**2**	10	**3**	−2
4	−3	**5**	−6	**6**	−18
7	28	**8**	28	**9**	−14
10	−57	**11**	−18	**12**	0
13	−52	**14**	25	**15**	55
16	−15	**17**	7	**18**	−47
19	−15	**20**	−5	**21**	6
22	9	**23**	−5	**24**	53

Exercise 1.4

1	60	**2**	−32	**3**	−32
4	4	**5**	−11	**6**	29
7	−10	**8**	5	**9**	121
10	−60	**11**	64	**12**	126
13	60	**14**	81	**15**	225
16	−125	**17**	−216 000		
18	64	**19**	−3200	**20**	−1

21	−1	**22**	2	**23**	2
24	−3	**25**	Answers as above.		
26	±4	**27**	−6	**28**	−36

Exercise 1.5

1
a   1, 2, 5, 10
b   1, 3, 5, 15
c   1, 3, 9   d   1, 17
e   1, 2, 3, 4, 5, 6, 10, 12, 15, 20, 30, 60
f   1, 2, 4, 5, 8, 10, 16, 20, 40, 80
g   1, 2, 4, 5, 10, 20, 25, 50, 100
h   1, 2, 4, 8, 16, 32, 64
i   1, 5, 25, 125
j   1, 2, 3, 5, 6, 9, 10, 15, 18, 30, 45, 90

2
a   1, 2   b   1, 5
c   1, 3, 9
d   1, 2, 4 e   1, 5
f   1, 2, 3, 6
g   1, 2, 4, 5, 10, 20
h   1, 2, 3, 6 i   1, 2, 3, 6

3
a   2 b   5 c   18
d   9 e   23
f   4 g   15 h   6 i   4

4
a   10, 20, 30, 40, 50, 60
b   6, 12, 18, 24, 30, 36
c   9, 18, 27, 36, 45, 54
d   18, 36, 54, 72, 90, 108
e   25, 50, 75, 100, 125, 150
f   40, 80, 120, 160, 200, 240
g   100, 200, 300, 400, 500, 600
h   12, 24, 36, 48, 60, 72
i   27, 54, 81, 108, 135, 162
j   121, 242, 363, 484, 605, 726

5
a   24 b   15 c   18
d   56 e   12 f   24
g   42 h   55 i   120

6   24 m

7   3.30 am
8   5 minutes

Exercise 1.6

1   11, 17, 47
2   3, 13, 23, 43, 53, 73
3
a   50 b   66 c   189
d   70 e   234 f   132
g   4725 h   15840
4
a 2×5 b $2 \times 3 \times 5^2$
c 3^4 d $2^2 \times 3 \times 5$
e 2×37 f $2^2 \times 5^2$
g 2×7^2 h 2×5^3
i $2 \times 3 \times 5 \times 37$ j $5^2 \times 11$
k $2^2 \times 3 \times 167$
l $2 \times 5 \times 13 \times 17$
5
a   3, 7, 19
b   3, 15, 21
c   10, 15, 35
d   3, 10, 15
e   10, 19
6   83, 89, 97
7 $713 = 23 \times 31$
8
a $3 + 7$ b $3 + 11$
c $2 + 23$ d $2 + 47$
e $13 + 17$ f $3 + 17$
g $7 + 31$ h $3 + 79$
i $17 + 19$ j $7 + 41$
9
a   6, 168 b   15, 315
c   14, 210 d   5, 600
10
a   6, 1260
b   7, 280
c   30, 1260

Exercise 1.7

1 3^2
2
a   1, 9, 49, 64, 289
b   1, 27, 64, 343, 512
3   729

Exercise 1.8

1 $\frac{1}{2}$ **2** $\frac{5}{7}$ **3** $\frac{3}{4}$

4 $\frac{2}{5}$ **5** $\frac{5}{8}$ **6** $\frac{6}{7}$

7 $\frac{4}{7}$ **8** $\frac{4}{5}$ **9** $\frac{7}{8}$

10 $\frac{3}{11}$ **11** $\frac{17}{20}$ **12** $\frac{7}{12}$

13 $1\frac{3}{5}$ **14** $2\frac{1}{3}$ **15** $2\frac{1}{7}$

16 $1\frac{3}{17}$ **17** $6\frac{1}{2}$ **18** $4\frac{3}{4}$

19 $1\frac{5}{12}$ **20** $3\frac{2}{15}$ **21** $1\frac{7}{8}$

22 $1\frac{1}{21}$ **23** $3\frac{2}{5}$ **24** $3\frac{1}{3}$

Exercise 1.9

1 $3\frac{5}{6}$ **2** $5\frac{9}{20}$ **3** $7\frac{25}{42}$

4 $7\frac{7}{15}$ **5** $4\frac{7}{12}$ **6** $4\frac{7}{30}$

7 $4\frac{7}{40}$ **8** $15\frac{4}{9}$ **9** $2\frac{3}{10}$

10 $\frac{7}{24}$ **11** $3\frac{22}{63}$ **12** $2\frac{11}{40}$

13 $3\frac{11}{40}$ **14** $\frac{17}{30}$ **15** $3\frac{5}{12}$

16 $3\frac{29}{35}$ **17** $-2\frac{3}{10}$ **18** $6\frac{13}{15}$

19 $4\frac{1}{12}$ **20** -1 **21** $-1\frac{4}{15}$

22 $1\frac{7}{15}$ **23** Answers as above.

24 $\frac{13}{35}$ **25** $\frac{13}{20}$ **26** $1\frac{9}{10}$

27 $6\frac{31}{35}$ **28** $-\frac{1}{12}$

29 a $\frac{13}{30}, \frac{3}{5}, \frac{2}{3}$ **b** $\frac{5}{9}, \frac{7}{12}, \frac{11}{36}$

c $\frac{7}{10}, \frac{3}{4}, \frac{4}{5}$ **d** $\frac{5}{6}, \frac{8}{9}, \frac{11}{12}$

Exercise 1.10

1 $3\frac{2}{3}$ **2** $5\frac{1}{16}$ **3** $3\frac{29}{30}$

4 $19\frac{23}{28}$ **5** $11\frac{5}{18}$ **6** $20\frac{11}{25}$

7 $\frac{9}{14}$ **8** $2\frac{1}{2}$ **9** $1\frac{7}{10}$

10 $3\frac{29}{32}$ **11** $\frac{10}{27}$ **12** $1\frac{1}{20}$

13 $\frac{9}{25}$ **14** $6\frac{1}{4}$ **15** $\frac{27}{8000}$

---

16 $1\frac{7}{9}$ **17** $\frac{2}{5}$ **18** $1\frac{5}{8}$

19 Answers as above.

20 $1\frac{2}{3}$ **21** $1\frac{1}{2}$ **22** $\frac{15}{56}$

23 $2\frac{3}{11}$ **24** $3\frac{3}{4}$ litres

25 a $\frac{1}{3}$ **b** $\frac{1}{7}$ **c** 2

d 8 **e** $\frac{5}{3}$ **f** $\frac{7}{6}$

g $\frac{3}{7}$ **h** $\frac{4}{7}$

Exercise 1.11

1 a 5.3 **b** 8.8 **c** 6.0

d 30.0 **e** 0.1 **f** 8.9

g 4.2 **h** 16.3 **i** 644.0

j 7.0

2 a 6.35 **b** 8.39 **c** 16.16

d 4.21 **e** 5.70 **f** 0.04

g 0.07 **h** 2.99 **i** 3.06

j 7.10

3 a 7.222 **b** 6.162

c 35.686 **d** 82.009

e 24.789 **f** 3.000

g 6.009 **h** 6.667

i 102.103 **j** 5.010

4 a 3 **b** 8 **c** 10

d 50 **e** 400 **f** 30 000

g 50 000 **h** 0.002 **i** 0.09

j 0.3

5 a 1.7 **b** 3.1 **c** 5700

d 61 000 **e** 16 **f** 20

g 100 **h** 0.0063

i 0.058 **j** 0.00040

6 a 27.3 **b** 6.51 **c** 2590

d 149 **e** 16.7 **f** 0.349

g 0.0718 **h** 0.00808

i 10.1 **j** 40 000

7 a 7 000 000 000

8 a 100 000 000

b 110 000 000

c 106 000 000

9 a 9000 **b** 8800 **c** 8850

10 a 0.06 **b** 0.064 **c** 0.0640

d 0.1 **e** 0.06 **f** 0.064

---

11 a 40 000 **b** 40 000

c 40 000 **d** 40 010

e 40 008.6 **f** 40 008.63

Exercise 1.12

1 a 60 (62.72) **b** 16 (16.83)

c 3000 (3555)

d 2500 (2569)

e 80 000 (81290)

f 6 (5.695) **g** 5 (5.861)

h 5 (4.404) **i** 16 (16.54)

2 a 10 (10.10) **b** 2 (2.081)

c 3 (2.564)

3 Accurate answers given in brackets above.

4 $8 **5** $9500

Exercise 1.13

1 $-x$ **2** $-3y$ **3** $6xy$

4 $-3xy$ **5** $7x - 9y$

6 $5p + 5q$ **7** $5xy - 3x$

8 $7x^2 - 15x$ **9** $7 + 4x$

10 $-7xy$ **11** $-3x^2 + 9$

12 $-6y^2 - 2y$ **13** $8xy - x$

14 $a - 4ab$ **15** $10ab - 6bc$

16 $x^4 + 5x^2 - 5$ **17** $5x^3 - x^2 + x$

18 $-2fg - 4gh$ **19** $4a^2b - 16ab^2$

20 $5cd^2 - 9c^2d$ **21** $6x + \frac{10}{x}$

22 $\frac{9}{x} - \frac{7}{y}$

23 $-2xy^2 + 12xy - 10x^2y + x^2 - y^2$

24 3

Exercise 1.14

1 $7(2x + 3) = 14x + 21$

2 a $4x + 12$ **b** $6y + 12$

c $4x + 20$ **d** $6 - 2a$

e $7y - 28$ **f** $8x - 72$

g $10x + 15$ **h** $18y + 24$

i $35a + 42$ **j** $6x + 6y - 3$

k $20a + 25b - 15$

l $24p - 32q - 56r$ **m** $4x - 1$

n $3x + 2$ **o** $5y - 2$

3 a $-3x - 12$ **b** $-2x + 12$

c $-30 + 20x$ **d** $-16x - 40$

e $-21x + 56$ **f** $-8x + 72$

g $-5x - 4$ h $-2x + 7$
i $-3x - 8$ j $-18x + 18y - 30$
k $-12p - 16q + 20$
l $-27x^2 - 9x + 6$

4 a $x^2 + 3x$ b $y^2 - 5y$
c $7a - a^2$ d $10x - 6x^2$
e $5y^2 + 40y$ f $6x^2 + 12xy$

5 a $5x + 30$ b $11x + 32$
c $9y$ d $11x - 74$
e $36x - 4y$ f $2x^2 - 11x$
g $2x^2 + 6x$ h $2x^2 + 4x$
i $38x - 9x^2$
j $12xy - 8x - 15y$
k $-4x^2 + 11xy + 21y^2$

6 $5(2x - 3) - 4(x - 6) =$
$10x - 15 - 4x + 24 = 6x + 11$

7 a x b $2y - 11$
c $23a - 10$ d $36x - 20$
e $2x + 17$ f $11 - 8y$
g $-h - 6g$ h $x^2 - 5x$
i $11p^2 - 44p$
j $63a + 6ab - 51a^2$

8 a $2x + 16$ b $27 - 3x$
c $8 - 6x + 8y$ d $-1 - 5y$
e $22 - 7y$ f $14x - 15$
g $8y + x$ h $11x - 2x^2$

Exercise 1.15
1 a 6   b 9   c 7
d $1\frac{1}{6}$ e $1\frac{1}{2}$ f $13\frac{1}{4}$
g 3   h $-\frac{2}{3}$ i $\frac{3}{4}$
j $1\frac{7}{8}$ k $-2\frac{1}{2}$ l $-2\frac{4}{5}$
m $7\frac{2}{3}$ n $8\frac{1}{2}$ o $\frac{1}{2}$
p $1\frac{5}{6}$ q 7   r $-2\frac{2}{5}$
s 2   t $2\frac{4}{5}$

2 a 2   b 5   c 7
d $3\frac{1}{2}$ e $\frac{1}{8}$ f $3\frac{4}{5}$
g $\frac{1}{5}$ h $-6\frac{1}{2}$ i -5
j 1   k $1\frac{1}{2}$ l 1

3 a 4   b 3   c 4
d 5   e $6\frac{1}{2}$ f -4
g $-\frac{1}{3}$ h $4\frac{1}{2}$ i $1\frac{2}{3}$

4 56, 57, 58   5 20
6 2   7 1.5 cm
8 5

Exercise 1.16
1 a 20   b 60   c 75
d $6\frac{2}{3}$ e 45   f -28
g 25   h $9\frac{1}{3}$ i -14
j 22   k 24   l 20

2 a 7   b 11   c $3\frac{1}{4}$
d $1\frac{1}{2}$ e $-2\frac{1}{2}$ f 5
g $4\frac{1}{2}$ h $1\frac{7}{15}$

3 a 3   b $\frac{1}{2}$ c $1\frac{3}{4}$
d $\frac{3}{10}$ e $\frac{1}{2}$ f 2
g 5   h -2 i $1\frac{1}{2}$
j -2 k $2\frac{1}{2}$ l -4
m 3   n 3   o 1
p 0

4 a 0   b 3   c 4   d 1
e $-\frac{8}{11}$ f -7 g 3
h $-3\frac{7}{8}$

5 $12x + 4 = 12x - 5$ means that
$4 = -5$ which is not possible
6 6

Exercise 1.17
1 $P = 1350 + 13n$
2 $Q = 100 - 9n$
3 $C = 4b + 7c$
4 $T = \dfrac{5r}{100} + \dfrac{6p}{100} + 4f$
5 $T = 30 + 4n$
6 $T = 45m + 20$

Exercise 1.18
1 -8 2 -23 3 -36
4 11   5 20   6 3
7 4   8 210   9 -2
10 16   11 -48 12 -480
13 -40 14 128   15 12
16 28   17 6   18 8
19 -1 20 -9 21 $-2\frac{1}{2}$
22 3   23 $3\frac{1}{2}$ 24 $-15\frac{2}{3}$
25 0   26 $-5\frac{4}{5}$ 27 -3
28 26

Exercise 1.19
1 a -10 b 5
c -20 d 100
2 a 25   b 9   c 10
3 a 6   b 2.1   c 0.912
4 a 1   b 1.2   c 1.8
5 a 435   b 16
6 a 5   b 8
7 a 7   b 10
8 a 9   b 8

Exercise 1.20
1 a 1   b 4   c $-\frac{1}{3}$
d $\frac{1}{4}$ e -2 f $\frac{2}{3}$
g 0   h $-\frac{3}{2}$ i -1
j 2

2 a 1   b $-\frac{9}{8}$ c $\frac{3}{2}$
d $\frac{1}{3}$ e -4 f $\frac{9}{7}$
g 0   h -11 i 4
j -1 k $\frac{2}{5}$ l $1\frac{1}{4}$

3 a 1 b 2   c $\frac{1}{2}$
d 2 e $-\frac{1}{2}$ f infinite(∞)
g 1 h 0
4 6   5 8   6 7
7 8   8 5   9 -3
10 2   11 11.25

Exercise 1.21
1 a $y = 2$ b $y = x$
c $x = 4$ d $y = -x$

2 a

x	0	1	2
y	2	3	4

b

x	0	1	2
y	-5	-4	-3

c

x	0	1	2
y	-2	0	2

d

x	0	1	2
y	-4	-1	2

e

x	-2	0	2
y	-2	-1	0

f

x	-3	0	3
y	-5	-4	-3

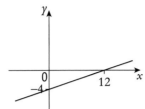

g

x	0	1	2
y	3	1	-1

h

x	0	1	2
y	5	2	-1

3

Parallel

4

5

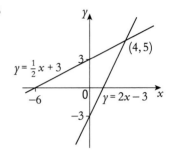

6 2

7 $-4\frac{1}{2}$

8 -14

Exercise 1.22

1

x	0	2
y	4	0

2

x	0	2
y	3	0

Answers

3

x	0	5
y	2	0

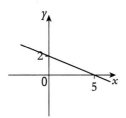

4

x	0	3
y	9	0

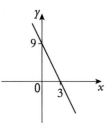

5

x	0	-6
y	-4	0

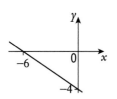

6

x	0	-5
y	-6	0

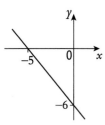

7

x	0	6
y	-3	0

8

x	0	5
y	-4	0

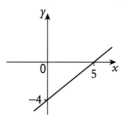

9

x	0	6
y	-4	0

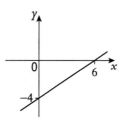

10

x	0	-5
y	15	0

11

x	0	-6
y	10	0

12

x	0	-2
y	12	0

Exercise 1.23

1 $a = 138°$ $b = 42°$ $c = 138°$

2 $a = 150°$

3 $a = 55°$

4 $a = 36°$

5 $a = 49°$

6 $a = 25°$

7 $a = 68°$ $b = 44°$

8 $a = 18°$

9 $a = 50°$ $b = 65°$

10 $a = 40°$

11 $a = 40°$ $b = 35°$

12 $a = 30°$

13 $a = 40°$

14 $a = 120°$

15 $a = 55°$

16 $a = 50°$

17 $a = 40°$ $b = 40°$

18 $a = 45°$

19 $a = 100°$ $b = 130°$

20 $a = 65°$

21 $a = 60°$

22 $a = 60°$ $b = 70°$

23 $a = 73°$ $b = 45°$

24 $a = 109°$

25 33°, 66°, 99°, 162°

26 Several possible proofs, for example

$E\hat{F}B = F\hat{G}D$ (Corresponding angles)

$E\hat{F}B = 180° - B\hat{F}G$

$F\hat{G}D = 180° - F\hat{G}D$ (Angles on a straight line)

$B\hat{F}G + F\hat{G}D = 180°$

Exercise 1.24

1 a 4, 4   **b** 2, 2   **c** 0, 2

d 0, 1   **e** 2, 2   **f** 1, 1

2 a 1, 1   **b** ∞, ∞   **c** 0, 1

     d 2, 2   **e** 2, 2   **f** 8, 8

     g 0, 2   **h** 0, 4   **i** 0, 2

     j 6, 6   **k** 4, 4   **l** 0, 2

3 a 0, 2   **b** 2, 2   **c** 0, 4

4 a

There are other possible answers.

b

There are other possible answers.

c

There are other possible answers.

5 a 1, 1   **b** 0, 2

     c 2, 2   **d** 0, 2

6 The four properties allow you to distinguish all quadrilaterals except a kite and an arrowhead.

Exercise 1.25

1

2 a 9   **b** ∞   **c** ∞

     d ∞   **e** 7

3 a 2   **b** 1

     c 0   **d** 5

4

Exercise 1.26

1 No

     Sum of interior angles =

     4 × 180° = 720°

2 124°   **3** 140°

4 12   **5** 20°

6 1440°

7 a 117°   **b** 58°   **c** 41°

     d 94°   **e** 125°   **f** 55°

8 a 108°   **b** 135°   **c** 67.5°

     d 22.5°   **e** 36°   **f** 81°

     g 117°   **h** 36°

9 18

Exercise 1.27

1 He is incorrect   Median = 5

2 a mean = 9   median = 10

       mode = 10   range = 5

     b mean = −2   median = −2

       no mode   range = 15

     c mean = 58   median = 58.5

       no mode   range = 15

     d mean = 3   median = 3

       mode = 3   range = 5

     e mean = $1\frac{1}{12}$ median = $1\frac{1}{12}$

       no mode   range = $1\frac{1}{6}$

3 mean = 12   median = 13

     mode = 13   range = 9

4 mean = 10.336s

     median = 10.305s

     mode = 10.28s   range = 0.6s

5 a Use mediam = 5 or mean = 4.5; mode = 0 or 8 which are extremal.

     b Use mode = 7 or median = 7; mean = 11.4 is sensitive to single large value.

c Use median = 8 or mean = 8, though there are no data values near these averages. Mode not defined.

d Use mean = 0 or median = 2 Mode = 3 is extremal.

6 a 659.2 kg   **b** 7.14 m

7 1.75 m

8 a 69 **b** 7   **c** 13 **d** 56

9 68.2   **10** 61   **11** 37.1 cm

Exercise 1.28

1 a Incorrect   Mode = 1

     b Incorrect   Median = 1

2 a 1 **b** 1   **c** 1.6

3 mode = 1   median = 1

     mean = 1.2

4 mode = 1   median = 1

     mean = 1.43

5 mode = 7   median = 7

     mean = 7.025

6 a $x = 25, n = 41$ **b** 5

Examination-style questions

1 15 − (2 × 3 + 4) ÷ 2 = 2.5

2 100 °C

3 48

4 a $2^2 × 5 × 7$

     b 420

5 53, 59

6 $1\frac{19}{42}$ **7** $2\frac{1}{8}$

8 a 302.66   **b** 300

9 100   **10** $4x − 11$

11 −20

12 a 1.2   **b** $\frac{6}{7}$

13 a $\frac{8}{17}$ **b** $\frac{7}{13}$

14 $T = 170 + 40n$

15 a $80x + 910 = 1790$

     b 11

16 −617

17 a −1.5   **b** (0, 3)

18 −0.5   **19** −3

20 $q = 2p + 23$ **21** −2

22 $x = 107, y = 60$

23 a 4 **b** 4
24 a 6 **b** 7
25 20 **26** 16
27 150
28 a i 7 **ii** 28
iii 25.5 **iv** 25.625
b $\dfrac{26n+205}{n+8}$
29 a 1 **b** 4
c 3.525 **d** 3.5
30 8

Unit 2

Exercise 2.1

1 a $\dfrac{6}{25}$ **b** $\dfrac{4}{5}$ **c** $\dfrac{29}{50}$
d $\dfrac{13}{20}$ **e** $\dfrac{3}{10}$
2 a 60% **b** 35% **c** 72%
d 74% **e** 87.5%
3 a 0.18 **b** 0.7 **c** 0.06
d 0.47 **e** 0.025
4 a 28% **b** 80% **c** 8%
d 120% **e** 75.5%
5 a \$12 **b** 312 km
c 135 kg
6 30% of \$60
7 a \$64.96 **b** \$89.28
c \$190.40 **d** \$271.40
d \$451 **f** \$198
8 a \$54.40 **b** \$272
c \$230 **d** \$112
e \$482.50 **f** \$359.28
9 \$735
10 \$883.50
11 \$1277.50
12 \$3510
13 \$18

Exercise 2.2

1 a 2:3 **b** 3:4 **c** 1:5
d 8:5 **e** 29:36 **f** 5:3
g 8:7 **h** 7:11
2 a 1:5 **b** 1:20 **c** 1:4
d 1:5 000 000 **e** 25:1

f 1:50 **g** 1:25 **h** 5:8
i 1:4
3 a 7:3 **b** 4:3 **c** 3:1
d 1:5 **e** 2:5 **f** 26:11
g 7:1 **h** 150:1
4 a 2:1 **b** 2:5 **c** 9:8
d 3:5 **e** 1:4 **f** 9:10
g 3:2 **h** 3:2
5 a 1:4:5 **b** 3:5:4
c 1:3:5 **d** 8:3:7
e 21:45:77 **f** 1:4:7
g 8:12:1 **h** 10:15:4
6 a 1:4 **b** $1:\dfrac{2}{3}$
c 1:0.16 **d** 1:0.625
e 1:500 000 **f** 1:400
g 1:750 000 **h** $1:333333\dfrac{1}{3}$
7 3:1
8 6:15:11
9 3:7
10 1:1.6, 1:1.625, 1:1.615,
1:1.619, 1:1.617, 1:1.618
Tends to a constant
ratio 1:1.61803399....

Exercise 2.3

1 a \$56, \$28 **b** 105 m, 175 m
c \$1200, \$900
d 187.2 km, 436.8 km
e 112 kg, 70 kg
f \$23.20, \$29
2 a \$70, \$140, \$ 210
b 225 m, 45 m, 90 m
c \$140, \$60, \$20
d 900 km, 750 km, 1200 km
e 8000 kg, 6000 kg, 10 000 kg
f \$269.60, \$377.44, \$431.36
3 \$31.35
4 84°
5 36°
6 $\dfrac{4}{9}$
7 4:3
8 85
9 315
10 1161

11 115 cm
12 15

Exercise 2.4

1 a i 3.5 cm **ii** 2.6 cm
iii 1.6 cm
b i 70 km **ii** 52 km
iii 32 km
2 40 km
3 a 15 km **b** 32.5 km
c 21 km **d** 4.5 km
4 a 8 km **b** 5 km
c 7.6 km **d** 1.4 km
5 a 2 cm **b** 10 cm
c 5 cm **d** 8.6 cm
6 3.2 km **7** 3 km
8 6 cm
9 27.2 km
10 4.8 cm
11 7.8 cm

Exercise 2.5

1 Incorrect $3^x \times 3^y = 3^{x+y}$
2 a x^9 **b** b^8 **c** y^{10}
d c^{12} **e** a^{11} **f** p^8
g y^9 **h** a^7
3 a $15x^6$ **b** $8b^4$ **c** $14y^{14}$
d $25c^6$ **e** $6a^3$ **f** $70p^8$
g $60y^6$ **h** $27a^6$
4 a $6x^6y^2$ **b** $30x^4y^3$
c $10x^2y^3$ **d** $6x^4y^2$
e $15x^3y^3$ **f** $35x^3y$
g $4x^4y^2$ **h** $6a^8b^4$
5 a x^5 **b** b **c** a^3
d x^5 **e** $6x^3$ **f** $2y^2$
g $5b^7$ **h** $3c$
6 a $5y^2$ **b** $12ab$ **c** $\dfrac{x}{4}$
d $\dfrac{y}{2}$ **e** $2a$ **f** $4abc$
g a^2b^2c **h** $5x^2$ **i** x^5
j y^7 **k** $6a^7$ **l** $3x^6$
7 a x^6 **b** a^{10} **c** b^{16}
d y^{21} **e** $3a^6$ **f** $5x^{20}$
g $8x^9$ **h** $81y^8$ **i** $8a^6$
j $9y^8$ **k** $18x^4y^2$ **l** $40x^7$

8 **a** $27x^3y^6$ **b** $32a^{10}b^{15}$
c $25x^8y^6$ **d** $1000x^{15}y^{21}$
9 **a** 4 **b** $13x^6$
c $36x^3$ **d** $\dfrac{ab^3}{9}$
e $4a^4bcd^2$ **f** $32x^{19}y^7$
g $8x^9$ **h** $16x^4y^8$

Exercise 2.6

1 **a** $\dfrac{1}{3}$ **b** 1 **c** $\dfrac{1}{8}$ **d** $\dfrac{1}{27}$
e 1 **f** $\dfrac{1}{1000}$ **g** $\dfrac{1}{16}$
h $\dfrac{1}{7}$ **i** $\dfrac{1}{10000}$ **j** $\dfrac{1}{125}$
k $\dfrac{1}{32}$ **l** $\dfrac{1}{81}$

2 **a** $\dfrac{1}{9}$ **b** $-\dfrac{1}{8}$ **c** $\dfrac{1}{36}$
d $-\dfrac{1}{9}$ **e** $\dfrac{1}{16}$ **f** $-\dfrac{1}{1000}$

3 **a** $1\dfrac{1}{2}$ **b** $2\dfrac{1}{2}$ **c** $1\dfrac{1}{3}$
d $1\dfrac{1}{5}$ **e** $3\dfrac{1}{2}$ **f** $1\dfrac{1}{4}$

4 **a** $2\dfrac{1}{4}$ **b** $6\dfrac{1}{4}$ **c** $1\dfrac{7}{9}$
d $1\dfrac{11}{25}$ **e** $12\dfrac{1}{4}$ **f** $1\dfrac{9}{16}$
g 8 **h** 1000

5 **a** a^4 **b** b^{-9} **c** c^{-2} **d** d^{-13}
e d^3 **f** x^3 **g** y^4 **h** d^3
i a^5 **j** b **k** 1 **l** d^{-4}

6 **a** x^{-2} **b** x^5 **c** $6x^9$ **d** x^{-5}

7 **a** $8x$ **b** $15x^{-3}$ **c** $6x^3$
d $28x^{-5}$

8 **a** x^{-2} **b** y^{-6} **c** a^{-20} **d** b^{-8}
e a^6 **f** y^2 **g** a^{10} **h** a

9 **a** $9a^{-2}$ **b** $125b^{-3}$ **c** $16c^{-8}$
d $16d^{-4}$ **e** $\dfrac{1}{4}x^{-4}$ **f** $\dfrac{1}{27}y^{-6}$
g $\dfrac{1}{25}x^{-6}$ **h** $\dfrac{1}{4}x^4$

10 **a** x **b** $\dfrac{1}{2}x^7$ **c** y^{-1}
d $7x^{-2}$

11 $2a^2 + 3b^{-3}$

Exercise 2.7

1 $x \geq 1$ **2** $x < 2$ **3** $-1 \leq x \leq 2$
4 $-2 \leq x < 3$ **5** $x \leq 6$
6 $x \geq 4$ **7** $x < 7$ **8** $x > 2$
9 $x \geq 1\dfrac{1}{2}$ **10** $x < 6$ **11** $x \leq -1$

12 $x < 7$ **13** $x \geq 1$ **14** $x < 7\dfrac{1}{2}$
15 $x \leq -6$ **16** $x < 2$ **17** $x \geq 7$
18 $x < -\dfrac{1}{5}$ **19** $x > -2\dfrac{1}{2}$
20 $x \leq -4$ **21** $x \leq 1$ **22** $y > 8$
23 $x \geq 2$ **24** $x < 7$ **25** $x < \dfrac{1}{2}$
26 $x \geq -3$ **27** $x \leq 4$ **28** $x > 2$
29 $x \geq 3$ **30** $x < -7$ **31** $x \geq 9$
32 $x < 2$ **33** $x \geq 7$ **34** $x \leq 3$
35 $x \leq 2$ **36** $x < 1\dfrac{1}{2}$ **37** $x \leq 1$
38 $x \geq 18$ **39** $x > 4\dfrac{1}{2}$
40 $x \leq -3\dfrac{1}{5}$ **41** $x > 4\dfrac{2}{5}$
42 $x > 3$ **43** $x \leq -7$
44 $x > -5\dfrac{1}{2}$ **45** $x \leq -5\dfrac{1}{2}$
46 $-3 \leq x \leq 5$
$-3, -2, -1, 0, 1, 2, 3, 4, 5$
47 $-3 \leq x < 4$ $-3, -2, -1, 0, 1, 2, 3$
48 $2 < x \leq 9$ $3, 4, 5, 6, 7, 8, 9$
49 $-2 < x \leq 4$ $-1, 0, 1, 2, 3, 4$
50 $2 < x < 4$ 3
51 $-2\dfrac{1}{2} \leq x < 5\dfrac{1}{2}$
$-2, -1, 0, 1, 2, 3, 4, 5$
52 $0 < x \leq 4$ $1, 2, 3, 4$
53 $3 \leq x \leq 7$ $3, 4, 5, 6, 7$
54 $3 < x \leq 9$ $4, 5, 6, 7, 8, 9$
55 4 **56** 4
57 $x = 1, y = 1$

Exercise 2.8

1 **a** $\dfrac{4x}{5}$ **b** $\dfrac{5x}{7}$ **c** $\dfrac{x}{2}$
d $\dfrac{x}{2}$ **e** $\dfrac{2x}{3}$ **f** $\dfrac{x}{2}$
g $\dfrac{2x}{5}$ **h** $\dfrac{2x}{5}$ **i** $\dfrac{5x}{7}$

2 $\dfrac{y}{3} + \dfrac{2y}{5} = \dfrac{5y}{15} + \dfrac{6y}{15} = \dfrac{11y}{15}$

3 **a** $\dfrac{3x}{4}$ **b** $\dfrac{7x}{12}$ **c** $\dfrac{11x}{15}$
d $\dfrac{17x}{20}$ **e** $\dfrac{x}{6}$ **f** $\dfrac{7x}{15}$
g $\dfrac{x}{2}$ **h** $\dfrac{5x}{36}$ **i** $\dfrac{3x}{5}$

4 **a** $\dfrac{7x+6}{12}$ **b** $\dfrac{11x-13}{30}$
c $\dfrac{17x+13}{35}$ **d** $\dfrac{37x+13}{35}$
e $\dfrac{17x+33}{12}$ **f** $\dfrac{46x+64}{33}$

5 **a** $\dfrac{21x-2}{12}$ **b** $\dfrac{19x-1}{40}$
c $\dfrac{9x-8}{30}$ **d** $\dfrac{21-37x}{36}$
e $\dfrac{12x+49}{15}$ **f** $\dfrac{19x-75}{36}$

6 $\dfrac{34x+127}{60}$ **7** $\dfrac{3x}{4} - \dfrac{2x}{3}$

Exercise 2.9

1 **a** 36 **b** 18 **c** 40
d 12 **e** 40 **f** -36
g 10 **h** 42

2 **a** 15 **b** 4 **c** 4 **d** 6
e -4 **f** $\dfrac{2}{3}$ **g** 6 **h** -2

3 **a** 2 **b** 7 **c** 5 **d** 3
e -3 **f** 6 **g** 4 **h** 8
i -3 **j** -2 **k** $2\dfrac{1}{2}$
l $\dfrac{1}{3}$

4 **a** 7 **b** 1 **c** 3 **d** 6
e 4 **f** 1 **g** 5 **h** 7
i -3 **j** -5 **k** $1\dfrac{1}{2}$
l $\dfrac{1}{3}$

5 2

6 **a** $2 \times \left(\dfrac{x+2}{3} + \dfrac{4x+7}{5} \right) = 20$
$5(x+2) + 3(4x+7) = 20 \times 3 \times 5 \div 2$
$17x + 31 = 150$
b $x = 7; 3, 7$

7 $5\dfrac{1}{2}$

Exercise 2.10

1 **a** $3, 2$ **b** $2, -5$ **c** $\dfrac{1}{2}, 3$
d $\dfrac{2}{3}, -1$ **e** $2, 3$ **f** $-5, 4$
g $-\dfrac{1}{2}, 7$ **h** $3, \dfrac{1}{2}$

2 **a** $1\dfrac{1}{2}, 2$ **b** $2, -\dfrac{2}{3}$ **c** $\dfrac{2}{5}, -\dfrac{3}{5}$
d $-\dfrac{2}{3}, 1\dfrac{2}{3}$ **e** $-1\dfrac{1}{2}, 3$
f $\dfrac{1}{3}, -2$ **g** $2, -1\dfrac{1}{2}$
h $-\dfrac{3}{7}, \dfrac{2}{7}$

3 **a** **i** $1\dfrac{1}{2}$ **ii** 3
iii $y = 1\dfrac{1}{2}x + 3$
b **i** $-\dfrac{1}{4}$ **ii** 4
iii $y = -\dfrac{1}{4}x + 4$

c **i** $\frac{1}{2}$ **ii** -1
    iii $y = \frac{1}{2}x - 1$
d **i** $-\frac{5}{3}$ **ii** 5
    iii $y = -\frac{5}{3}x + 5$

4 **a** $y = -2$ **b** $y = 2x$
   c $y = 3x - 2$ **d** $y = \frac{1}{2}x + 6$
   e $3x + 4y = 26$ **f** $2y - x = 8$

5 **a**

b

c

d

e

f

g

h

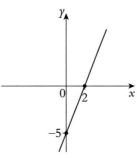

6 **a** E   **b** A, E   **c** B, C
   d D   **e** B, D

Exercise 2.11

1 **a** $y = \frac{1}{2}x + 6$ **b** $y = -2x - 3$
   c $y = x + 1$ **d** $y = 4x - 4$
   e $y = -2x - 2$ **f** $y = \frac{2}{3}x + 5$
   g $y = -\frac{3}{5}x - 10$ **h** $y = \frac{2}{5}x + 8$
   i $y = \frac{3}{4}x + 5$

2 **a** $y = \frac{1}{2}x + 2$ **b** $y = -3x - 4$
   c $y = x + 5$ **d** $y = -2x + 2$
   e $y = x - 5$ **f** $y = \frac{2}{3}x - \frac{1}{3}$
   g $y = -\frac{1}{5}x + 3\frac{1}{5}$ **h** $y = \frac{1}{4}x - 5$
   i $y = \frac{1}{2}x - 1\frac{1}{2}$

Exercise 2.12

1 **a** $(-3, 2)$ **b** $(4\frac{1}{2}, \frac{1}{2})$
   c $(2\frac{1}{2}, -1\frac{1}{2})$ **d** $(1\frac{1}{2}, 1\frac{1}{4})$
   e $(-2\frac{1}{4}, -1\frac{1}{4})$

2 **a** $(4, 3\frac{1}{2})$ **b** $(-2, 0)$
   c $(2\frac{1}{2}, -1)$ **d** $(-4, 5)$
   e $(-1\frac{1}{2}, 3\frac{1}{2})$ **f** $(4\frac{1}{2}, -4)$
   g $(-3\frac{1}{2}, -4\frac{1}{2})$
   h $(-3\frac{3}{4}, -2\frac{1}{4})$ **i** $(2\frac{1}{2}, \frac{3}{4})$

Exercise 2.13

1 **a** $y \le 1$ **b** $x < -2$
   c $-1 \le y < 3$ **d** $y \ge x$
   e $y > x - 2$ **f** $x + y \le 2$
   g $y \ge -\frac{1}{2}x + 1$ **h** $y > 2x - 3$
   i $y < -3x + 3$

2 **a**

b

c

d

e

f

g

h

i

j

k

l

3 a

b

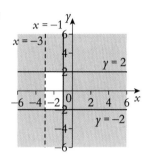

4 a $y \geq 2$, $\quad y \leq 2x$
   b $y \leq 2$, $\quad y \leq 2x$
   c $y \leq 2$, $\quad y \geq 2x$

5 P and A, Q and C, R and B

6 a $x > -1$, $\quad y > -1$, $\quad x + y \leq 2$
   b $x > -1$, $\quad y > 1$, $\quad x + y \leq 3$
   c $x < -1$, $\quad y > -1$, $\quad y < x + 3$
   d $x > -1$, $\quad x + y < 2$, $\quad y \geq x - 2$
   e $x > -2$, $\quad y \geq -3$, $\quad y < \frac{1}{2}x + 1$
   f $y < 2$, $\quad y > x$, $\quad y < -2x - 2$
   g $x > -2$, $\quad y \geq x$, $\quad x + y < 3$
   h $y \leq 4$, $\quad y > 2x$, $\quad x + y > 0$
   i $x + 2y < 4$, $\quad y \geq x - 2$,
      $y < 3x + 4$

7

8

9

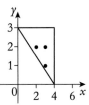

10 a

b $x < 4$, $y < 3$, $3x + 4y > 12$

c (2, 2), (3, 1), (3, 2)

Exercise 2.14

1 a 36 cm, 62 cm²
   b 24 cm, 30 cm²
   c 36 cm, 84 cm²
   d 42 cm, 84 cm²

2 a 45 cm² **b** 40 cm
   c 72 cm²

3 a 18 cm² **b** 22.5 cm²
   c 45 cm² **d** 66.5 cm²

4 a 28 cm² **b** 30 cm²
   c 160 cm² **d** 49.5 cm²

5 8 cm

6 8.5

Exercise 2.15

1 a 8.06 cm **b** 10.4 cm
   c 8.25 cm **d** 6.62 m
   e 6.80 m **f** 6.96 cm

2 $x^2 + 4^2 = 6^2$, $x^2 = 20$, $x = 4.47$ cm

3 a 6.93 cm **b** 5.66 cm
   c 13.3 cm **d** 8.08 cm
   e 19.0 cm **f** 14.4 cm

4 38.1 km

5 4.77 m

6 a 3.54 cm **b** 8.94 cm
   c 2.83 cm

7 7.81 cm

8 8.94 cm

9 10.6 cm

10 a 5 cm **b** 22 cm
   c 26 cm² **d** 10 cm²

11 a 4.33 cm **b** 10.8 cm²

12 6.63 cm

13 He is incorrect. $4^2 + 5^2 \neq 6^2$

14 Yes. $48^2 + 55^2 = 73^2$

15 5 miles

16 5.29 cm

17 17 cm

18 4.85 cm

19 0.828 cm

Exercise 2.16

1 a 5.39 **b** 3.61 **c** 5
   d 7.07

2 a 8.06 **b** 15.3 **c** 15.6
   d 8.54 **e** 11.7 **f** 13.9
   g 9.49 **h** 3.16 **i** 4.12

Exercise 2.17

1 a 5.39 m **b** 8.31 m
   c 12.3 m **d** 12.1 m

2 14.8 cm

3 11.1 cm

Exercise 2.18

1 a 18.8 cm, 28.3 cm²
   b 47.1 cm, 177 cm²
   c 15.1 cm, 18.1 cm²
   d 23.9 cm, 45.4 cm²
   e 126 cm, 1260 cm²
   f 29.5 cm, 69.4 cm²

2 a 163 cm **b** 8.17 km

3 a 0.631 cm **b** 3.96 m

4 a 30.9 cm² **b** 30.9 cm²
   c 30.9 cm² **d** same

5 50.3 cm²

6 114 cm²

Exercise 2.19

1 15.4 cm, 14.1 cm²

2 25.0 cm, 38.5 cm²

3 13.4 cm, 9.42 cm²

4 22.9 cm, 34.8 cm²

5 23.4 cm, 28.1 cm²

6 30.3 cm, 44.6 cm²

7 24.6 cm, 11.4 cm²

8 40.6 cm, 51.8 cm²

9 31.4 cm, 21.5 cm²

10 25.1 cm, 25.1 cm²

11 14.9 cm, 15.8 cm²

12 28.6 cm

13 a 1.9544 cm, 10.04878 cm
   b 3.9088 cm, 20.09756 cm
   c When the area quadruples, the lengths double.

14 a 2.523 cm, 9.010 cm
   b 7.569 cm, 27.03 cm
   c When the area is multiplied by 9, the lengths treble.

15 35.5 cm²

16 7.78 cm

17 4 cm

Exercise 2.20

1 a 3.67 cm **b** 19.5 cm
   c 6.14 cm **d** 32.1 cm

2 a 6.68 cm² **b** 22.3 cm²
   c 127 cm² **d** 159 cm²

3 a 9.59 cm, 5.59 cm²
   b 65.1 cm, 61.1 cm²
   c 40.3 cm, 64.5 cm²
   d 39.2 cm, 49.7 cm²

4 76.4°

5 4.09 cm

6 a 40.9 cm **b** 77.4 cm²

7 0.161 cm²

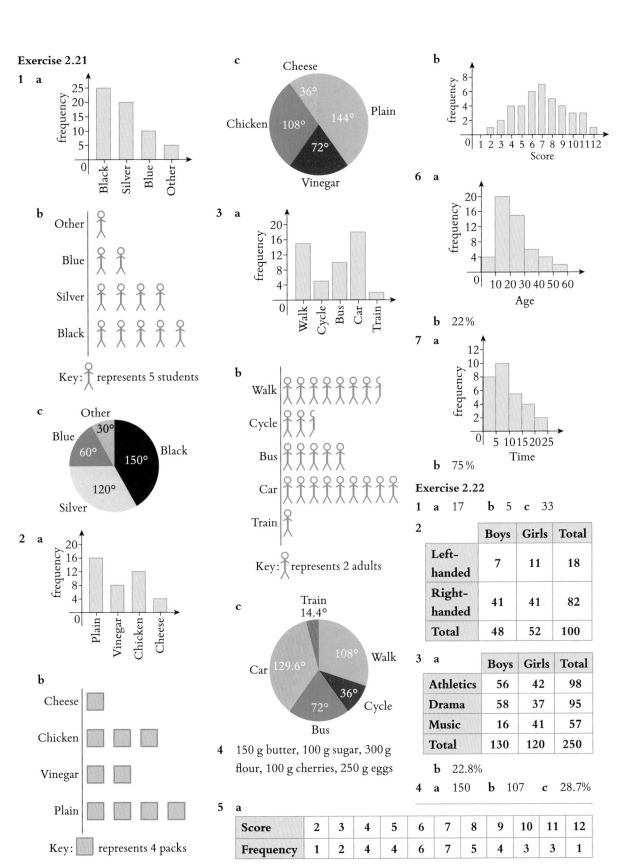

Exercise 2.21

1 a [bar chart: frequency vs Black, Silver, Blue, Other]

b [pictogram of car colours] Key: represents 5 students

c [pie chart] Other 30°, Blue 60°, Silver 120°, Black 150°

2 a [bar chart: frequency vs Plain, Vinegar, Chicken, Cheese]

b [pictogram of crisps] Key: represents 4 packs

c [pie chart] Cheese 36°, Plain 144°, Vinegar 72°, Chicken 108°

3 a [bar chart: frequency vs Walk, Cycle, Bus, Car, Train]

b [pictogram] Key: represents 2 adults

c [pie chart] Train 14.4°, Walk 108°, Cycle 36°, Bus 72°, Car 129.6°

4 150 g butter, 100 g sugar, 300 g flour, 100 g cherries, 250 g eggs

5 a

Score	2	3	4	5	6	7	8	9	10	11	12
Frequency	1	2	4	4	6	7	5	4	3	3	1

b [bar chart: frequency vs Score 1–12]

6 a [frequency diagram: frequency vs Age 10–60]

b 22%

7 a [frequency diagram: frequency vs Time 5–25]

b 75%

Exercise 2.22

1 a 17 **b** 5 **c** 33

2

	Boys	Girls	Total
Left-handed	7	11	18
Right-handed	41	41	82
Total	48	52	100

3 a

	Boys	Girls	Total
Athletics	56	42	98
Drama	58	37	95
Music	16	41	57
Total	130	120	250

b 22.8%

4 a 150 **b** 107 **c** 28.7%

UNIT 2

Answers 509

Examination-style questions

1 $15 480   **2** 27 540

3 3.5   **4** $325, $175

5 $1635   **6** 3.2 km

7 a $x^5 \div x^2$ **b** x^{12}

8 a $2\frac{3}{8}$

  b i 7   **ii** $32x^2$

9 -4 **10** $x < -2.5$

11 a $x \le 4\frac{3}{7}$ **b** 1, 2, 3 and 4

12 $\dfrac{13x}{24}$ **13** $10\frac{1}{4}$

14 $y = 2x - 3$

15 a $(1, 3)$

  b 13.4 or $6\sqrt{5}$

  c $y = -2x + 5$

  d $y = -2x - 1$

16 $9.25\,\text{m}^2$

17 9.5

18

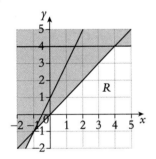

19 7.07 cm

20 13.2 cm

21 a $78.5\,\text{cm}^2$ **b** 62.8 cm

22 16.58 cm

23 a Grade B   **b** 99°

24 a

	Walked	Cycled	Bus	Total
Boys	8	10	7	25
Girls	17	7	5	29
Total	25	17	12	54

  b $33\frac{1}{3}\%$

Unit 3

Exercise 3.1

1 a, c, f, g

2 a 5×10^4 **b** 2×10^2

  c 7×10^5 **d** 5.33×10^3

  e 8.2×10^7 **f** 3.02×10^3

  g 6.66×10^5 **h** 3.636×10^1

3 a 480 000   **b** 370

  c 564 000 000   **d** 70 600 000

  e 20 000   **f** 1 100 000

  g 300.1   **h** 9 500 000 000

4 a 6×10^3 **b** 4.5×10^5

  c 3×10^4 **d** 4.1×10^6

  e 3.2×10^9 **f** 6.3×10^7

  g 4×10^3 **h** 2.5×10^7

  i 1.6×10^{13} **j** 5×10^4

  k 4.2×10^2 **l** 4.87×10^2

5 Answers as for question **4**.

6 a 6.2×10^9 **b** 5.8×10^9

  c 1.1×10^{10} **d** 1.2×10^{18}

  e 3×10^1 **f** 3.6×10^{19}

  g 3.1×10^1 **h** 9×10^{10}

7 a 30 : 1   **b** 1 : 40   **c** 500 : 1

8 a 9.6×10^4 **b** 2.1×10^4

  c 1.46×10^6

9 a 2×10^4 **b** 3×10^2

  c 6×10^3 **d** 7×10^4

10 2.13×10^4, 5.8×10^{13},
  2.04×10^{14}, 2.2×10^{14}

11 1.49×10^8 **12** 5 : 12

13 1.2995×10^9

Exercise 3.2

1 a 1.5×10^{-2} **b** 6.7×10^{-4}

  c 9×10^{-4} **d** 6.06×10^{-4}

  e 3.2×10^6 **f** 5.2×10^{-4}

  g 4.4×10^{-1} **h** 5.308×10^7

  i 5.7×10^{-8} **j** 6.13×10^{-4}

  k 7.002×10^5 **l** 8.9×10^{-4}

2 a 0.000088   **b** 0.00000023

  c 0.006   **d** 0.0511

  e 99 000   **f** 0.00000104

  g 0.00068   **h** 600 000 000

  i 0.38   **j** 22

  k 408 000   **l** 0.0000095

3 a 6×10^{-2} **b** 7.2×10^{-5}

  c 5×10^{-8} **d** 6×10^{-4}

  e 3×10^{-9} **f** 6.4×10^{-7}

  g 3×10^{12} **h** 2.4×10^{-2}

  i 9×10^{-10} **j** 2×10^6

  k 2.7×10^3 **l** 2×10^{-8}

4 Answer as for question **3**.

5 a 3×10^{-3} **b** 2×10^{-5}

  c 8×10^{-3} **d** 9×10^{-7}

6 a 6.3×10^{-8} **b** 5.7×10^{-8}

  c 1.86×10^{-7} **d** 1.8×10^{-16}

  e 2×10^1 **f** 3.6×10^{-15}

  g 9×10^{-18} **h** 1.5×10^{-6}

7 8.35×10^{-22} grams

8 1.87×10^{23}

9 1.5×10^{-5} seconds

10 2.625×10^{-5} kg

Exercise 3.3

1

x	0	2	4
y	2	4	6

x	0	2	4
y	4	2	0

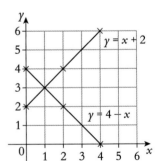

$x = 1, y = 3$

2

x	0	2	4
y	1	2	3

x	0	4
y	5	0

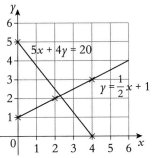

$x = 2\frac{2}{7}, y = 2\frac{1}{7}$

Exercise 3.4

1
  a $x = 3, y = 4$
  b $x = 5, y = 2$
  c $x = 10.5, y = -2$
  d $x = 4, y = 4$
  e $x = 2, y = -1$
  f $x = -3, y = 4$
  g $x = -6, y = -2$
  h $x = 5, y = -2$

2
  a $x = 2, y = 4$
  b $x = 9, y = 5$
  c $x = 2, y = 10$
  d $x = 7, y = 3$
  e $x = 5, y = -2$
  f $x = -3, y = 4$
  g $x = 7, y = -5$
  h $x = -2\frac{1}{2}, y = -6$

3
  a $x = 6, y = 2$
  b $x = 3, y = 3$
  c $x = 5, y = -2$
  d $x = 1\frac{1}{2}, y = 3$
  e $x = -4, y = 2\frac{1}{2}$
  f $x = 2, y = 1\frac{1}{3}$
  g $x = -1, y = -2\frac{1}{4}$
  h $x = -4, y = 3\frac{1}{2}$

4 $x + y = 15, x - y = 4$;
  $x = 9\frac{1}{2}, y = 5\frac{1}{2}$

5 a 39, 15 **b** 15, -7

6 $x = 11, y = 2$
7 $x = 2.92, y = 1.8$
8 \$0.85, \$0.32
9 $1 = -2m + c, 4 = 4m + c$;
  $m = \frac{1}{2}, c = 2$
10 \$39.68

Exercise 3.5

1
  a $x = 3, y = 5$
  b $x = 4, y = 1$
  c $x = 6, y = 4$
  d $x = 3, y = 7$
  e $x = 5, y = -2$
  f $x = 10, y = -3$
  g $x = 1.625, y = 7.75$
  h $x = 3, y = -2.5$

2
  a $x = 4, y = 7$
  b $x = 3, y = 2$
  c $x = 5, y = 3$
  d $x = 2, y = 2$
  e $x = 8, y = 6$
  f $x = 11, y = 4$
  g $x = 3, y = 9$
  h $x = 1, y = 7$

3
  a $x = -\frac{1}{2}, y = 4$
  b $x = 3, y = -5$
  c $x = -2, y = 7$
  d $x = -3, y = -2$
  e $x = 2\frac{1}{2}, y = 3$
  f $x = 6, y = 1\frac{1}{2}$
  g $x = 3\frac{1}{2}, y = -5$
  h $x = -9, y = 4$

4
  a $x = 4, y = 2$
  b $x = 2, y = 1$
  c $x = 4, y = 2$
  d $x = \frac{5}{7}, y = 4\frac{3}{7}$
  e $x = 2, y = -3$
  f $x = -1, y = 2$
  g $x = -2, y = 1$
  h $x = 1, y = 2$

5
  a $x = 12, y = 15$
  b $x = 20, y = -16$
  c $x = -18, y = 10$
  d $x = 24, y = -6$

6 $x = 3, y = 7$
7 $x = 4, y = 2.5$
8 17 **9** 153
10 \$1.85 **11** \$0.19
12 $a = 3, b = 5$ **13** $a = 2, b = -3$
14 a $x = 3, y = -1$ **b** 28
  c 40
15 a $x = 1\frac{1}{2}, y = 4$ **b** 20
  c 25
16 a $x = 4, y = 3$ **b** 24
  c 27.7

Exercise 3.6

1
  a $6(x + y)$ **b** $5xy(1 - 2y)$
  c $2(2x + 3y)$

2
  a $4(x + 2)$ **b** $3(x - 2)$
  c $2(4x + 1)$ **d** $5(2x - 3)$
  e $7(y - 2)$ **f** $3(3y + 4)$
  g $4(5 - 2x)$ **h** $12(3 - y)$
  i $7(6 - x)$ **j** $2(9y - 2)$
  k $8(3x + 2)$ **l** $11(2y - 5)$

3
  a $x(x + 5)$ **b** $x(x - 8)$
  c $y(y - 4)$ **d** $a(a + 9)$
  e $4x(x - 2)$ **f** $3y(y - 3)$
  g $2x(5x - 2)$ **h** $2y(4 - y)$
  i $5y(3y + 1)$ **j** $7x(2 - x)$
  k $2x(3 - 2x)$ **l** $3y(4y - 3)$

4
  a $4(2\pi + 1)$ **b** $3(5 - 3\pi)$
  c $\pi r(r + l)$ **d** $2\pi r(r + h)$

5
  a $3xy(2x - 1)$
  b $5x^4 y(2y - 1)$
  c $8xy(y^2 - 4x^2)$
  d $3x^2 y^2(5x - 4y^2)$
  e $3xy(4x - 5)$
  f $7pq(4q - 5p)$
  g $3ab(2a + 3)$
  h $7x^2 y(3x^3 - 4)$
  i $7ab^5(8a^3 b^2 - 5)$

6
  a $3(a + b - c)$
  b $5(x + y + x^2)$
  c $a(2x - y - 3y^2)$
  d $x(x^2 + 4x - 2)$
  e $y^2(y^2 + 6y - 6)$

f $pqr(pq - 1 + q)$

g $4ab(5abc^2 - 2ab + 4c^2)$

h $3x^2y(5xy - 9 + 7y)$

i $2p^3q^3r^2(4p^4q^2r + 3p - 2r)$

7 a $(x + 3)(y + 2)$

b $(a + 2)(b - 4)$

c $(p - 5)(q + 3)$

d $(x - 3)(y - 5)$

e $(x + y)^3$

f $(a + b)^2(a + b - 1)$

g $(x - y)^2(1 - x + y)$

h $(x + y)(5 + x + y)$

i $(x - y)^2(x - y - 4)$

8 a $(y + 3)(x + 1)$

b $(5 + x)(y - 2)$

c $(4 + c)(a + b)$

d $(p + 3)(q + 2r)$

e $(3 - y)(x + 4)$

f $(x - 4)(y - 3)$

Exercise 3.7

1 a $x - 2$ **b** $\dfrac{x+2}{4}$

c $\dfrac{3x+4}{5}$

2 a $x + 2$ **b** $4y + 2$

c $x + 2$ **d** $3y + 2$

e $\dfrac{3x-6}{4}$ **f** $\dfrac{3x+2}{4}$

g $\dfrac{3-4y}{2}$ **h** $\dfrac{6-4a}{5}$

3 a $x + 9$ **b** $y - 8$

c $\dfrac{x-3}{x}$ **d** $1 - x^2$

e $\dfrac{2x+y}{z}$ **f** $\dfrac{x+y}{z}$

g $\dfrac{x+y}{y}$ **h** $\dfrac{x-2}{y}$

4 a 3 **b** 5 **c** $\dfrac{1}{6}$ **d** $\dfrac{1}{5}$

e $\dfrac{2}{5}$ **f** $\dfrac{3x}{7}$ **g** $\dfrac{x}{z}$ **h** $\dfrac{2}{3}$

5 a x **b** $\dfrac{5}{x-5}$ **c** $\dfrac{x}{5}$

d $\dfrac{2y}{5}$ **e** $\dfrac{x}{x-1}$ **f** $\dfrac{3}{(y-2)^2}$

g x **h** $\dfrac{xy}{2}$

6 a $3\dfrac{1}{3}$ **b** $4\dfrac{2}{3}$

c $\dfrac{x^2}{y^2}$ **d** $\dfrac{x+1}{y+1}$

e $\dfrac{7(x+y)}{y}$ **f** $\dfrac{2f}{g}$

7 a $\dfrac{5xy}{12}$ **b** $\dfrac{9}{10}$

Exercise 3.8

1 a $x = \dfrac{p+q}{3}$ **b** $x = \dfrac{8b-a}{2}$

c $x = (y - b)^2$

2 a $x = y - 3$ **b** $x = 5y + 6$

c $x = 4 - y$ **d** $x = a + b$

e $x = y + 8$ **f** $x = 5 - 2y$

g $x = 6y - 8$ **h** $x = y - 10$

3 a $x = \dfrac{y}{6}$ **b** $x = \dfrac{y}{3}$

c $x = \dfrac{y-4}{3}$ **d** $x = \dfrac{7-5y}{a}$

e $x = 2p$ **f** $x = 15 + 5d$

g $x = 2y - 16$

h $x = 10a - 4ay$

i $x = \dfrac{3y}{2}$ **j** $x = \dfrac{15y}{4}$

k $x = \dfrac{7(a+b)}{3}$

l $x = \dfrac{b(c+d)}{a}$

4 a $x = \dfrac{d-c}{2}$ **b** $x = \dfrac{y+2z}{5}$

c $x = \dfrac{6-3y}{4}$ **d** $x = \dfrac{3b+c+d}{8}$

e $x = \dfrac{d-b}{a}$ **f** $x = \dfrac{c+cd}{b}$

g $x = \dfrac{a+b+q}{p}$ **h** $x = \dfrac{y-8}{y}$

5 a $x = \dfrac{2}{y+z}$ **b** $x = \dfrac{p}{2q+3}$

c $x = \dfrac{a-3y}{6}$ **d** $x = \dfrac{p+qr}{q}$

6 a $x = bc - a$ **b** $x = 3gh + 2f$

c $x = \dfrac{cd-by}{a}$ **d** $x = \dfrac{p-mr}{q}$

e $x = \dfrac{p}{q}$ **f** $x = \dfrac{g}{h}$

g $x = \dfrac{p+q}{r}$ **h** $x = \dfrac{p-q}{5}$

7 a $x = \pm\sqrt{\dfrac{b}{a}}$ **b** $x = \pm\sqrt{\dfrac{q}{p}}$

c $x = \pm\sqrt{\dfrac{c}{ab}}$ **d** $x = \pm\sqrt{\dfrac{bc}{a}}$

e $x = \pm\sqrt{b-a}$

f $x = \pm\sqrt{d+e}$

g $x = \pm\sqrt{\dfrac{c-b}{a}}$

h $x = \pm\sqrt{\dfrac{4r+5q}{p}}$

i $x = \pm\sqrt{4(b+a)}$

j $x = \pm\sqrt{a(d-bc)}$

k $x = \pm\sqrt{g(f-3h)}$

l $x = \pm\sqrt{2(3fg-g)}$

8 a $x = b^2 - a$ **b** $x = q^2r^2 + p$

c $x = \dfrac{y+16}{2}$ **d** $x = \dfrac{z^2+4y}{4}$

9 They are both correct.

Exercise 3.9

1 a not congruent

b congruent

c congruent

d not congruent

e not congruent

f congruent

2 a SAS **b** RHS **c** ASA

d SAS **e** SSS **f** RHS

For questions **3** to **5** other answers are possible.

3 SSS **5** SSS **6** RHS

Exercise 3.10

1 B and C

2 B and C

3 a $x = 12$, $y = 4$

b $x = 3.6$, $y = 12.5$

c $x = 15$, $y = 16.5$

d $x = 4$, $y = 4$

e $x = 8.75$

f $x = 15$, $y = 17.5$

Exercise 3.11

1 **a** $x = 5, y = 12$
  b $x = 8.4, y = 2.3$

2 $w = 33\frac{1}{3}$

3 **a** 4 **b** 12 **c** 2 **d** $3\frac{1}{3}$

4 54.5 m

5 **a** $x = 8, y = 20$
  b $x = 12, y = 5.5$

6 **a** D = (5, 4), E = (14, 7)
  b $(9\frac{1}{2}, 5\frac{1}{2})$

7 **a** $(-3, -1)$ **b** $(0, -3)$
  c $(-7\frac{1}{2}, 2)$

8 **a** $x = 4\frac{1}{2}, y = 7\frac{1}{2}$
  b $x = 30.45, y = 20.05$

9 **a** $x = 12, y = 10$
  b $x = 15, y = 7.5$

Exercise 3.12

1 **a**

b

c

d

e

f

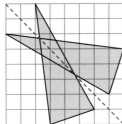

2 **a** $x = 6$ **b** $x = 10.5$
  c $x = 13$ **d** $x = 4$
  e $x = 6$ **f** $x = 11$
  g $x = 11$ **h** $x = 13$

3 **a** $y = 4.5$ **b** $y = 2$
  c $y = 1$ **d** $y = -1$
  e $y = 4$ **f** $y = -1$

4 **a** $x = 0$ **b** $y = 0$
  c $y = 1$

5 **a** $y = x$ **b** $x = 1$
  c $y = x$ **d** $y = 1$
  e $x = 0$

6 **a** $x = -1$ **b** $x = -1$
  c $y = 1$ **d** $y = 1$
  e $y = -x$ **f** $y = x$
  g $y = x$ **h** $y = -x$
  i $y = -x$ **j** $y = -x$

7

8

9

10

11

12

d $x = 6\frac{1}{2}$

13

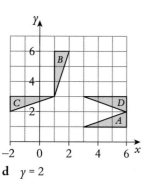

d $y = 2$

Exercise 3.13

1 a

b

c

d

e

f

2

3

4

5

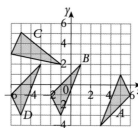

Exercise 3.14

1 a rotation, 90° clockwise about (0, 0)

b rotation, 180° about (0, 0)

c rotation, 90° anticlockwise about (0, 3)

d rotation, 90° clockwise about (2, −1)

e rotation, 90° anticlockwise about (2, 3)

f rotation, 180° about $(0, -\frac{1}{2})$

2 a rotation, 180° about (3, 3)

b rotation, 180° about (0, 0)

c rotation, 90° anticlockwise about (−1, 2)

d rotation, 90° clockwise about (−1, −1)

e rotation, 90° anticlockwise about (1, −2)

f rotation, 180° about (−1, 2)

g rotation, 90° clockwise about (2, 1)

h rotation, 90° anticlockwise about (1, −1)

i rotation, 90° anticlockwise about (−2, −1)

j rotation, 180° about (0.5, 0.5)

k rotation, 90° anticlockwise about (−1, 2)

l rotation, 90° clockwise about (2, 2)

Exercise 3.15

1 a $\begin{pmatrix} 2 \\ 4 \end{pmatrix}$ **b** $\begin{pmatrix} 3 \\ 3 \end{pmatrix}$ **c** $\begin{pmatrix} 5 \\ -1 \end{pmatrix}$

d $\begin{pmatrix} 3 \\ 0 \end{pmatrix}$ **e** $\begin{pmatrix} 0 \\ -3 \end{pmatrix}$ **f** $\begin{pmatrix} -2 \\ 4 \end{pmatrix}$

UNIT 3

2 a

b

c

d

e

f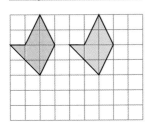

3 a (8, 8)   **b** (5, −2)
  c (−4, −1)   **d** (−9, 6)
  e (−4, −12) **f** (7, −8)

4 a translation $\begin{pmatrix} -4 \\ 1 \end{pmatrix}$

b translation $\begin{pmatrix} -8 \\ -1 \end{pmatrix}$

c translation $\begin{pmatrix} -9 \\ -4 \end{pmatrix}$

d translation $\begin{pmatrix} -5 \\ -5 \end{pmatrix}$

e translation $\begin{pmatrix} 2 \\ -5 \end{pmatrix}$

f translation $\begin{pmatrix} 5 \\ -2 \end{pmatrix}$

g translation $\begin{pmatrix} 5 \\ 1 \end{pmatrix}$

h translation $\begin{pmatrix} 0 \\ -3 \end{pmatrix}$

i translation $\begin{pmatrix} -7 \\ 0 \end{pmatrix}$

j translation $\begin{pmatrix} 9 \\ 0 \end{pmatrix}$

k translation $\begin{pmatrix} 10 \\ -4 \end{pmatrix}$

l translation $\begin{pmatrix} 14 \\ -2 \end{pmatrix}$

5 a b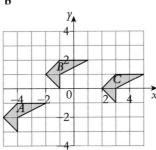

c translation $\begin{pmatrix} 7 \\ 2 \end{pmatrix}$

6 a b

c translation $\begin{pmatrix} 4 \\ -2 \end{pmatrix}$

7 $C = (1, 4)$ $B' = (6, -3)$

8 $A = (4, 1)$ $C = (-1, 3)$
   $D' = (-1, -2)$

Exercise 3.16

1 a reflection in $x = 3$
  b reflection in $y = x$
  c reflection in x-axis
  d rotation, 180°
      about (0, 0)
  e reflection in $y = -x$
  f translation $\begin{pmatrix} -6 \\ -1 \end{pmatrix}$
  g rotation, 90° anticlockwise
      about (1, 1)
  h reflection in $y = x$
  i rotation, 90° clockwise
      about (0, 0)
  j reflection in $y = -1$
  k reflection in y-axis
  l reflection in $x = 1$

2 a translation $\begin{pmatrix} 1 \\ 6 \end{pmatrix}$
  b rotation, 180°
      about (3.5, 2)
  c reflection in $x = 4$
  d rotation, 180°
      about (3, 7)
  e rotation, 90° clockwise
      about (5, 4)
  f translation $\begin{pmatrix} 5 \\ 3 \end{pmatrix}$
  g translation $\begin{pmatrix} 6 \\ -3 \end{pmatrix}$

h reflection in $y = 5$

i reflection in $x + y = 15$

j translation $\begin{pmatrix} -3 \\ 4 \end{pmatrix}$

k rotation, 90° clockwise about (8, 7)

l rotation, 90° anticlockwise about (4, 1)

Exercise 3.17

1 a b c

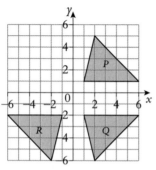

d rotation, 180° about (0, 0)

2 a b c

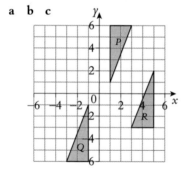

d rotation 180° about (3, 1.5)

3 a b c

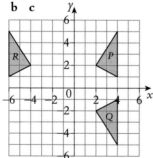

d reflection in $x = -1$

4 a b c

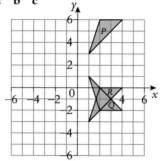

d translation $\begin{pmatrix} 0 \\ -6 \end{pmatrix}$

5 a b c

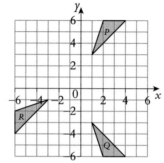

d reflection in $y = -x$

6 a b c

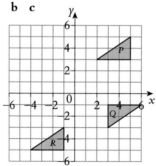

d translation $\begin{pmatrix} -6 \\ -8 \end{pmatrix}$

7 a translation $\begin{pmatrix} 6 \\ 10 \end{pmatrix}$

b translation $\begin{pmatrix} 3 \\ 10 \end{pmatrix}$

8 a rotation, 180° about (3, 2)

b translation $\begin{pmatrix} 0 \\ 6 \end{pmatrix}$

9 a translation $\begin{pmatrix} 4 \\ 2 \end{pmatrix}$

b translation $\begin{pmatrix} -6 \\ 10 \end{pmatrix}$

Exercise 3.18

1 translation $\begin{pmatrix} -2 \\ 4 \end{pmatrix}$

2 translation $\begin{pmatrix} 0 \\ -6 \end{pmatrix}$

3 translation $\begin{pmatrix} 5 \\ -7 \end{pmatrix}$

4 translation $\begin{pmatrix} 8 \\ 0 \end{pmatrix}$

5 reflection in x-axis

6 reflection in y-axis

7 reflection in $y = 3$

8 reflection in $x = -5$

9 reflection in $x + y = 4$

10 rotation, 90° anticlockwise about (0, 0)

11 rotation, 90° clockwise about (0, 0)

12 rotation, 180° about (0, 0)

13 rotation anticlockwise about (5, −2)

14 rotation 90° clockwise about (−4, 7)

Exercise 3.19

1 a SF 2, (6, 4)

b SF 2, (2, 8)

c SF 3, (2, 1)

d SF 2, (0, 0)

e SF 2, (6, 2)

f SF 3, (−0.5, 7)

2 a enlargement, SF 2, centre (8, 3)

b enlargement, SF 2, centre (12, 6)

c enlargement, SF 2, centre (0, 7)

d enlargement, SF 3, centre (13, 4)

e enlargement, SF 2, centre (18, 3)

f enlargement, SF 2, centre (22, 6)

Exercise 3.20

1 a

b

c

2 a

b

c

3 a

b

c

4 a

b

c

d

e

f

5

6

7

8

9

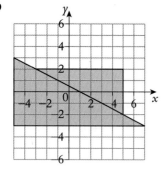

Exercise 3.21

1 a b c

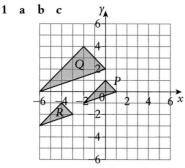

   d translation $\begin{pmatrix} -4 \\ -2 \end{pmatrix}$

2 a b c

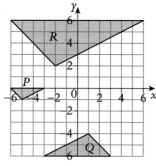

   d enlargement, SF 4, centre (−6, −2)

3 a b c

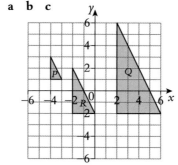

   d enlargement, SF 2, centre (−6, 4)

Exercise 3.22

1 **a** 125 cm³   **b** 96 cm³
    c 120 000 cm³
2 **a** 180 cm³   **b** 192 cm³
    c 16 cm³
3 **a** 24 cm³   **b** 128 cm³
    c 2240 cm³   **d** 90 cm³
    e 450 cm³   **f** 540 cm³
4 **a** 3.14 m³   **b** 226 cm³
    c 236 cm³
5 **a** 151 cm³   **b** 490 cm³
    c 25100 cm³
6 20 cm
7 **a** 7.875 m³
    b 7 875 000 cm³
    c 7875 litres
8 257 cm³
9 5.64 cm
10 306 cm

11 109.3 cm³
12 **a** 166 cm²   **b** 4157 cm³
    c 2.7 kg

Exercise 3.23

1 **a** 216 cm²   **b** 184 cm²
    c 928 cm²
2 **a** 240 cm²   **b** 88 cm²
    c 172 cm²
3 **a** 510 cm²   **b** 216 cm²
4 **a** 101 cm²   **b** 254 cm²
    c 176 cm²
5 **a** 75.4 cm²   **b** 89.5 cm²
    c 50.3 cm²
6 234 cm²

Exercise 3.24

1 **a** $\frac{1}{8}$ **b** $\frac{1}{2}$ **c** $\frac{1}{4}$ **d** $\frac{1}{2}$
    e $\frac{1}{4}$ **f** 1
2 **a** $\frac{2}{5}$ **b** $\frac{2}{5}$ **c** $\frac{4}{5}$ **d** $\frac{1}{5}$
    e $\frac{4}{5}$ **f** 1
3 **a** $\frac{1}{10}$ **b** $\frac{1}{2}$ **c** $\frac{2}{5}$ **d** $\frac{9}{10}$
    e $\frac{3}{5}$ **f** $\frac{1}{2}$ **g** 0 **h** 1
4 **a** $\frac{1}{3}$ **b** $\frac{2}{3}$ **c** $\frac{4}{9}$ **d** $\frac{1}{9}$
5 **a** $\frac{17}{30}$ **b** $\frac{12}{25}$

Exercise 3.25

1 **a**

Number	1	2	3
Probability	$\frac{1}{4}$	$\frac{1}{8}$	$\frac{5}{8}$

    b **i** $\frac{3}{8}$ **ii** $\frac{7}{8}$ **iii** $\frac{3}{4}$ **iv** 0
2 **a** **i** $\frac{5}{8}$ **ii** $\frac{3}{8}$
    b **i** $\frac{4}{7}$ **ii** $\frac{3}{7}$
    c **i** $\frac{5}{7}$ **ii** $\frac{2}{7}$

3 a $\frac{1}{4}$ **b** green **c** $\frac{5}{6}$

4 a 0.2 **b** 5 **c** 0.75

Exercise 3.26

1 a

	1	2	3	4	5
1	2	3	4	5	6
2	3	4	5	6	7
3	4	5	6	7	8
4	5	6	7	8	9
5	6	7	8	9	10

b i $\frac{2}{25}$ **ii** $\frac{2}{25}$ **iii** 0

iv $\frac{12}{25}$ **v** $\frac{1}{5}$ **vi** $\frac{11}{25}$

2 a

	1	2	3	4
1	2	3	4	5
2	3	4	5	6
3	4	5	6	7
4	5	6	7	8

b i $\frac{1}{8}$ **ii** $\frac{1}{4}$ **iii** $\frac{1}{2}$ **iv** $\frac{3}{8}$

3 a

	2	4	6	8
1	2	4	6	8
2	4	8	12	16
3	6	12	18	24

b i $\frac{1}{6}$ **ii** 0

iii 1 **iv** $\frac{5}{12}$

Exercise 3.27

1 288 **2** 145

3 150 **4** 30

5 492

6 a 0.255, 0.42, 0.325

b 234

7 a 0.18, 0.36, 0.27, 0.19

b 162, 324, 243, 171

Examination-style questions

1 a 5.62×10^8 **b** 2.53×10^5

2 a 0.000 000 8

b 1.8×10^{-7}

3 $x = 2$, $y = -1$

4 $x = 1$, $y = 3$

5 $x = -3.5$, $y = -2$

6 $x(x - 7)$

7 a $5x^2y(xy - 2)$

b $(2x + 3)(y - 4)$

8 $\dfrac{5x}{1 - 3x}$ **9** $a = 5c + 5b$

10 $x = 5y + 2$ **11** $h = \dfrac{A - \pi r^2}{2\pi r}$

12 $h = \sqrt{\dfrac{2p - q}{5}}$

13 $P = \dfrac{9R^2}{4Q}$

14 a 12.5 cm **b** 7.2 cm

15 47.5 m³

16 a 50 cm² **b** 350 cm³

17 a 8.74 **b** 1304 cm²

18 a Rotation, 90° anticlockwise, centre (6, 5)

b Image at (5, 3), (5, 5), (9, 3)

c Image at (10, 8), (18, 8), (18, 4)

19 a Image at (1, 3), (1, 7), (3, 5), (3, 4)

b Image at (2, 8), (6, 8), (5, 6), (4, 6)

c Reflection in $x + y = 9$

20 a $\frac{1}{2}$ **b** $\frac{5}{6}$ **c** 0

21 a 0.1 **b** 5 **c** 0.55

22 a

	1	2	3	4	5	6
1	1	2	3	4	5	6
2	2	4	6	8	10	12
3	3	6	9	12	15	18
4	4	8	12	16	20	24
5	5	10	15	20	25	30
6	6	12	18	24	30	36

b i $\frac{1}{9}$ **ii** $\frac{7}{18}$

23 90

Unit 4

Exercise 4.1

1 57.5 % **2** 37 % **3** 3.55 %

4 10 % **5** 60 % **6** 5 %

7 1.32 % **8** 3.09 % **9** 5 %

10 21.4 % **11** 3.125 %

12 7.42 % **13** 16 %

Exercise 4.2

1 $x^2 + 13x + 30$ **2** $x^2 + 7x + 12$

3 $x^2 + 10x + 21$ **4** $x^2 + 6x + 8$

5 $x^2 + 6x + 5$ **6** $x^2 + 15x + 56$

7 $x^2 + 8x + 12$ **8** $x^2 + 13x + 42$

9 $x^2 + 8x + 16$ **10** $x^2 + 19x + 60$

11 $x^2 + 18x + 72$ **12** $2x^2 + 13x + 15$

13 $6x^2 + 19x + 10$

Exercise 4.3

1 a $x^2 + 4x + 3x + 12$

$= x^2 + 7x + 12$

b $x^2 - 6x + 4x - 24$

$= x^2 - 2x - 24$

c $x^2 - 4x - 5x + 20$

$= x^2 - 9x + 20$

d $x^2 + 4x + 4x + 16 = x^2 + 8x + 16$

2 a $x^2 + 3x + 2$

b $x^2 + 12x + 35$

c $x^2 + 11x + 24$ **d** $x^2 + 6x + 8$

e $x^2 + 9x + 20$ **f** $x^2 + 4x + 3$

g $x^2 + 12x + 27$

h $x^2 + 11x + 30$

i $x^2 + 7x + 12$ **j** $x^2 + 5x + 6$

k $x^2 + 10x + 16$ **l** $x^2 + 5x + 4$

3 a $x^2 + x - 2$ **b** $x^2 + 4x - 12$

c $x^2 + 3x - 18$ **d** $x^2 + 3x - 4$

e $x^2 - 2x - 63$

f $x^2 + 6x - 16$

g $x^2 - 4x - 32$

h $x^2 - 5x - 14$

i $x^2 - 3x - 10$

j $x^2 + 5x - 24$

k $x^2 - 2x - 3$

l $36 - 5x - x^2$

4 a $x^2 - 9$ **b** $x^2 - 64$
   c $x^2 - 36$ **d** $x^2 - 100$
   e $x^2 - 16$ **f** $x^2 - 81$
   g $x^2 - 1$ **h** $144 - x^2$

5 a $x^2 - 7x + 10$
   b $x^2 - 5x + 4$
   c $x^2 - 11x + 24$
   d $x^2 - 8x + 12$
   e $x^2 - 14x + 49$
   f $x^2 - 9x + 18$
   g $x^2 - 9x + 20$
   h $x^2 - 11x + 28$
   i $x^2 - 13x + 36$
   j $x^2 - 2x + 1$
   k $x^2 - 6x + 5$
   l $4 - 4x + x^2$

6 a $x^2 + 6x + 9$
   b $y^2 + 10y + 25$
   c $x^2 - 8x + 16$
   d $x^2 + 14x + 49$
   e $x^2 + 16y + 64$
   f $a^2 - 20a + 100$
   g $36 - 12x + x^2$
   h $4 + 4x + x^2$

7 a $2y^2 - 5y - 3$
   b $4x^2 + 5x - 6$
   c $5x^2 + 22x + 8$
   d $7y^2 + 33y - 10$
   e $8y^2 - 22y - 21$
   f $10x^2 - 49x - 33$
   g $15x^2 - 38x + 24$
   h $27y^2 - 96y + 20$
   i $24y^2 - 47y + 20$
   j $6a^2 - 5a - 21$
   k $3 - 13a + 12a^2$
   l $30x^2 - 3x - 9$

8 a $4x^2 - 1$ **b** $9x^2 - 4$
   c $25x^2 - 49$ **d** $25x^2 - 4$

9 a $4x^2 - 4x + 1$
   b $25x^2 + 20x + 4$
   c $9x^2 + 12xy + 4y^2$
   d $9y^2 - 48y + 64$

10 a $2x^2 + 3x + 19$
   b $8x^2 + 12x - 38$

c $x^2 - 13x - 3$
   d $14x^2 - 12x + 3$
   e $13x^2 - 14x + 26$
   f $8x^2 - 8x + 10$
   g $32x^2 + 72x + 16$
   h $6x^2 - 48x - 73$

Exercise 4.4

1 a −5.5 **b** 2 **c** −2
2 a 35 **b** 23
3 a A and B **b** D and E
   c B and E **d** B and C
   e B and D **f** A and C
   g A and D **h** A and E
4 10
5 a $3x^2 + 9x - 30$
   b $2x^2 + 18x - 2$
6 answer given
7 a c^2 **b** $(a + b)^2$
   c $2ab$ **d** answer given

Exercise 4.5

1 a

x	−3	−2	−1	0	1	2	3
y	10	5	2	1	2	5	10

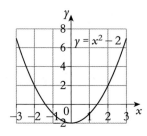

b

x	−3	−2	−1	0	1	2	3
y	7	2	−1	−2	−1	2	7

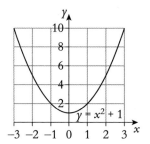

c

x	−3	−2	−1	0	1	2	3
y	−9	−4	−1	0	−1	−4	−9

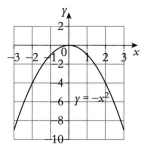

d

x	−3	−2	−1	0	1	2	3
y	13	3	−3	−5	−3	3	13

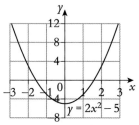

e

x	−3	−2	−1	0	1	2	3
y	2.5	0	−1.5	−2	−1.5	0	2.5

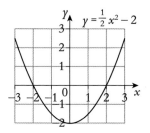

f

x	−4	−3	−2	−1	0	1	2
y	8	3	0	−1	0	3	8

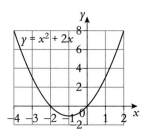

g

x	−1	0	1	2	3	4
y	4	0	−2	−2	0	4

$y = x^2 - 3x$

h

x	−1	0	1	2	3	4
y	−4	0	2	2	0	−4

$y = 3x - x^2$

2 a

x	−1	0	1	2	3	4	5
y	8	3	0	−1	0	3	8

b

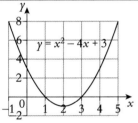

$y = x^2 - 4x + 3$

c −0.8, 4.8

3 a

x	−2	−1	0	1	2	3
y	4	0	−2	−2	0	4

b

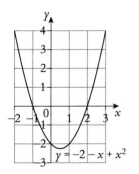

$y = -2 - x + x^2$

c −1.6, 2.6

4 a

x	−2	−1	0	1	2	3
y	−4	0	2	2	0	−4

b

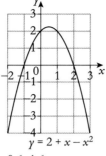

$y = 2 + x - x^2$

c −0.6, 1.6

5 a

x	−1	0	1	2	3	4
y	8	1	−2	−1	4	13

b

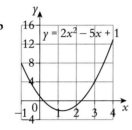

$y = 2x^2 - 5x + 1$

c 0.2, 2.3

Exercise 4.6

1 a C **b** D **c** B **d** F
e E **f** A

2 a 1.5 **b** 1 **c** 0.5 **d** 0
e −0.5 **f** −1 **g** −1.5

3 a −4 **b** −2 **c** 0
d 2 **e** 4

Exercise 4.7

1 a answer given

b

x	0	0.2	0.4	0.6	0.8	1
V	0	0.24	0.56	0.96	1.44	2

c

$V = x^2 + x$

d 0.75

2 a

t	0	1	2	3	4	5
h	0	20	30	30	20	0

b

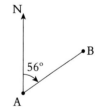

$h = 25t - 5t^2$

c 31.25 m **d** 1.5, 3.5

3 a

x	0	10	20	30	40	50
y	0	8	12	12	8	0

b

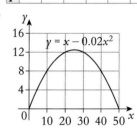

$y = x - 0.02x^2$

c 12.5 m

d 13.8 m < x < 36.2 m

Exercise 4.8

1 a

b

c

UNIT 4

d
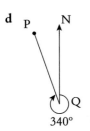

2 a 135° **b** 180°
  c 270° **d** 225°
  e 450° **f** 315°

3 a 085° **b** 135°
  c 010° **d** 300°

4

5 a

  b 111°
  c 25.4 km

6 a 115° **b** 050° **c** 110°
  d 255° **e** 065° **f** 320°
  g 039° **h** 153°

7 200°

8 a 232° **b** 302° **c** 067°
  d 115°

9 a 060° **b** 240° **c** 090°
  d 270° **e** 075° **f** 255°

10 a 300° **b** 305°

11 a 8 km **b** 035° **c** 215°

12 13 km

13

110°
P
45°
Locus of points
L

14 $x = 80$, $y = 60$, $z = 40$

15 $x = 83$, $y = 45$, $z = 52$

Exercise 4.9

All answers in cm to 3 s.f.

1 a 3.46 **b** 7.20 **c** 7.00
  d 9.63 **e** 13.7 **f** 7.85
  g 4.08 **h** 4.36 **i** 19.0
  j 14.3 **k** 12.6 **l** 8.31
  m 5.36 **n** 9.38 **o** 11.3

2 a $x = 8.66$, $y = 5.32$
  b $x = 10.9$, $y = 4.58$
  c $x = 4.69$, $y = 5.70$
  d $x = 6.71$, $y = 3.88$
  e $x = 6.40$, $y = 9.14$
  f $x = 13.2$, $y = 13.6$

Exercise 4.10

All answers to 3 s.f.

1 a 20.6° **b** 38.7° **c** 21.8°
  d 21.8° **e** 18.4° **f** 54.5°
  g 18.4° **h** 16.7° **i** 56.3°

2 a 54.5° **b** 234°

3 $x = 18.4°$, $y = 36.9°$

4 a 65.2° **b** 50.8° **c** 43.8°

5 a $x = 36.9°$, $y = 29.2°$
  b $x = 38.7°$, $y = 19.3°$
  c $x = 23.6°$, $y = 10.9°$

Exercise 4.11

All answers in cm, unless stated otherwise, to 3 s.f.

1 a 6.51 **b** 3.35 **c** 5.73
  d 4 **e** 9.58 **f** 7.55

  g 14.5 **h** 8.67 **i** 1.75
  j 13.1 **k** 7.71 **l** 15.8

2 a 7.62 **b** 30.8 **c** 8.44

3 a 5.52, 12.9 cm²
  b 9.38, 113 cm²
  c 6.93, 27.7 cm²

4 3.47, 34.0 cm²

Exercise 4.12

All answers to 3 s.f.

1 44.4° **2** 60° **3** 44.4°
4 23.6° **5** 19.5° **6** 48.2°
7 65.4° **8** 17.5° **9** 52.0°
10 25.4° **11** 33.7° **12** 50.6°
13 67.1° **14** 56.0° **15** 51.8°

Exercise 4.13

All answers to 3 s.f.

All lengths in cm.

1 a 6.90 **b** 38.6° **c** 31.1
  d 10.3 **e** 53.1 **f** 10.1
  g 5.20 **h** 10.5 **i** 60°
  j 11.8 **k** 14.8 **l** 9.97
  m 6.40 **n** 7.81 **o** 5.12
  p 37.9° **q** 66.4° **r** 22.0°

2 a $x = 8.58$, $y = 30.1°$
  b $x = 4.52$, $y = 28.2°$
  c $x = 5.96$, $y = 13.3°$

3 a $x = 4.77$, $y = 57.8°$, $z = 5.63$
  b $x = 4.50$, $y = 5.41$, $z = 33.7°$
  c $x = 15.0$, $y = 26.6°$, $z = 8.94$

4 60°

5 a $x = 4.31$, $y = 6.30$
  b $x = 11.0$, $y = 37.6°$

6 $x = 56.3°$, $y = 7.48$, $z = 15.5°$

7 a 41.6 cm²
  b 61.9 cm² **c** 309 cm²

8 a 1020 cm² **b** 2202 cm³

Exercise 4.14

All answers to 3 s.f.

1 114 m

2 a 2.41 m **b** 3.29 m
  c 2.13 m

UNIT 4

3 **a** 56.4° **b** 45.6°
  c 41.1 m
4 111 m
5 **a** 72.1 m **b** 52.0 m
  c 102° **d** 78°
  e 2450 m²
6 **a** 11.8 cm **b** 76.4 cm²
7 **a** 56.8 m **b** 0.123 m
8 **a** 8.68 km **b** 49.2 km
9 **a** 1270 km **b** 2720 km
10 **a** 826 km **b** 929 km
  c 1240 km **d** 048°
  e 228°

Exercise 4.15

All answers to 3 s.f.
1 **a** 7.07 **b** 8.66 **c** 35.3°
2 **a** 9.85 **b** 11.0 **c** 26.9°
3 **a** 12.8 **b** 13.4 **c** 17.3°
4 **a** 5.66, 4.12, 4.58 **b** 55.6°
  c 51.8°
5 **a** 7.5, 9.60, 8.48
  b 38.7°
  c 90°
6 15.9°

Exercise 4.16

All answers to 3 s.f.
All lengths in m.
1 145
2 9.99
3 553
4 828
5 275
6 3730
7 45.3
8 43.0
9 4.06
10 **a** 7.03, 64.4
  b 9.96°
  c 6.26°

Exercise 4.17

1 **a** negative
  b zero
  c positive
  d zero
2 **a**

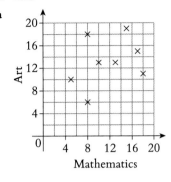

  b zero correlation
3 **a**

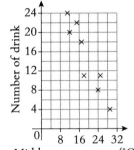

  b negative correlation
4 **a**

  b positive correlation
5 **a**

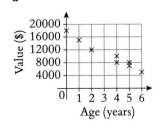

  b negative correlation

6 **a** positive
  b negative
  c positive
  d zero
  e positive

Exercise 4.18

1 **a** 68 %
  b 25 %
2 **a** 8.3
  b 6.8
  c

  d negative **e** 9.5
3 **a** 21.05 **b** 176.2
  c

  d positive **e** 174

Examination-style questions

1 2.5%
2 12%
3 1.54%
4 $x^2 - 3x - 40$
5 $6a^2 - 19ab + 15b^2$
6 $25 + 120y - 48y^2$

7 a

x	−1	0	1	2	3	4	5	6
y	9	3	−1	−3	−3	−1	3	9

b

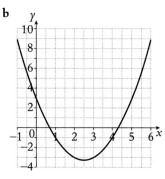

c 0.8 to 1.2

8 048°

9 a 9.22 cm **b** 40.6

10 a 9.63 cm **b** 33.7 cm²

11 18.6

12 31.6°

13 a 53.5° **b** 44.1°

c 47.8°

14 6.26 m

15 a, b

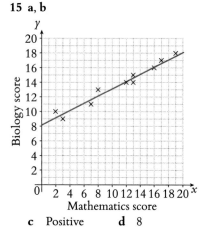

c Positive **d** 8

Unit 5

Exercise 5.1

1 $13.15 **2** $30

3 $145

4 a 150 km **b** 52.5 litres

5 1500 g flour, 3600 ml milk,
15 g salt, 15 eggs

6 16 seconds

7 2 hours 24 mins

8 7.5 days **9** 6

10 a 18 hours **b** 12

11 8

12 a 4 days **b** 25

Exercise 5.2

1 a i 320 Rf **ii** 690 Rf
iii 1040 Rf **iv** 2560 Rf
b i $47 **ii** $86
iii $19 **iv** $156

2 a i 199 ARS **ii** 1194 ARS
iii 286.56 ARS
iv 7960 ARS
b i $10.05 **ii** $20.60
iii $125.63 **iv** $9.15

3 a i 250.78 MYR
ii 62.70 MYR
iii 231.97 MYR
iv 1567.40 MYR
b i $19.14 **ii** $5.74
iii $95.70 **iv** $149.93

4 $75

Exercise 5.3

1 a 100 **b** 105
c 65 **d** 82.5

2 a 20 **b** 33
c 30 **d** 36

3 6250 kg

4 1 minute 57 seconds

5 560

6 105 kg

7 $1656

8 a 7.5 cm, 10 cm
b i 75 cm² **ii** 48 cm²
c 25 : 16

9 a 8 cm, 20 cm, 28 cm
b i 4480 cm³
ii 1890 cm³
c 64 : 27

Exercise 5.4

1 a 11 **b** −9
c 4 **d** 3

2 a −19 **b** 17
c 3.5 **d** 6.5

3 a 10 **b** 0
c 0 **d** 1.75

4 a 16 **b** −4
c −4 **d** −5

5 a 66 **b** −6
c 2.125 **d** 2

6 a 12.25 **b** 27.25
c $\frac{7}{16}$ **d** 0.25

7 3 **8** ±6

9 −1.75 **10** −2.75

11 −3 **12** 0.5

13 ±3 **14** −7

Exercise 5.5

1 a −6 **b** 2

2 a −29 **b** −37

3 a 1 **b** 25

4 a 3 **b** 7

5 a undefined **b** −0.5

6 a 9 **b** −6
c 2.25 **d** 9 **e** 4

7 a −6 **b** 14
c −7 **d** 14.5
e 0.75

8 a D **b** A
c B **d** C

9 a $x + 5$ **b** $x + 5$
c $x − 6$

10 a $2x − 4$ **b** $2x − 9$
c $4x + 3$

11 a $5x^2 + 15$ **b** $25x^2 + 3$
c $25x$

12 a $\frac{3}{x−1}$
b $\frac{3}{x−2} + 1$ or $\frac{x+1}{x−2}$

13 7

14 16.5

15 ±0.5

Exercise 5.6

1 a $x - 2$ **b** $x + 7$
  c $x - 22$ **d** $x + 0.5$
  e $\dfrac{x}{3}$ **f** $\dfrac{x}{8}$
  g $4x$ **h** $6x$

2 a $\dfrac{x+5}{2}$ **b** $\dfrac{x-8}{3}$
  c $\dfrac{x+2}{5}$ **d** $\dfrac{x-3}{4}$
  e $\dfrac{x-6}{3}$ **f** $\dfrac{x+28}{4}$
  g $\dfrac{x+20}{2}$ **h** $\dfrac{x-10}{2}$
  i $\dfrac{x-8}{10}$ **j** $\dfrac{15-x}{6}$
  k $\dfrac{28-x}{12}$ **l** $\dfrac{x+27}{6}$
  m $4x + 2$ **n** $5x - 6$
  o $\dfrac{4x+3}{2}$ **p** $\dfrac{5-6x}{3}$

3 a $\dfrac{5}{x+3}$ **b** $\dfrac{3}{x-2}$
  c $\dfrac{6}{x+7}$ **d** $\dfrac{5}{4-x}$
  e $\dfrac{2-3x}{x}$ **f** $\dfrac{4-x}{2x}$
  g $\dfrac{3+5x}{2x}$ **h** $\dfrac{3x-6}{2x}$
  i $\dfrac{1+3x}{x-2}$ **j** $\dfrac{5x+7}{1-2x}$
  k $\dfrac{8x+6}{x-1}$ **l** $\dfrac{3x-1}{4x-2}$

4 a $\sqrt[3]{x} - 3$ **b** $\sqrt[3]{x} + 5$
  c $\dfrac{\sqrt[3]{x}-7}{2}$ **d** $\dfrac{5-\sqrt[3]{x}}{3}$

5 a -1.5 **b** 2
  c -2.5

6 a 0.4 **b** 1.6
  c 0

7 1 **8** -1

9 a 3 **b** 2.5
  c -29

Exercise 5.7

1 a $x(x + 5)$ **b** $x(x - 7)$
  c $3x(x - 5)$ **d** $6x(2 - 3x)$

2 a $(x + 3)(x + 1)$
  b $(x + 5)(x + 2)$
  c $(x + 1)(x + 1)$
  d $(x + 6)(x + 3)$
  e $(x + 4)(x + 2)$
  f $(x + 5)(x + 1)$
  g $(x + 2)(x + 3)$
  h $(x + 18)(x + 2)$
  i $(x + 5)(x + 5)$
  j $(x + 9)(x + 4)$
  k $(x + 4)(x + 5)$
  l $(x + 7)(x + 2)$
  m $(x + 7)(x + 3)$
  n $(x + 4)(x + 7)$
  o $(x + 21)(x + 1)$
  p $(x + 3)(x + 5)$

3 a $(x + 3)(x - 2)$
  b $(x - 6)(x + 1)$
  c $(x + 7)(x - 3)$
  d $(x - 8)(x + 2)$
  e $(x + 8)(x - 2)$
  f $(x - 16)(x + 1)$
  g $(x + 7)(x - 1)$
  h $(x - 8)(x + 5)$
  i $(x + 19)(x - 2)$
  j $(x - 11)(x + 3)$
  k $(x + 10)(x - 3)$
  l $(x - 5)(x + 3)$
  m $(x + 5)(x - 4)$
  n $(x - 20)(x + 1)$
  o $(x + 21)(x - 1)$
  p $(x - 7)(x + 1)$

4 a $(x - 5)(x - 2)$
  b $(x - 15)(x - 1)$
  c $(x - 3)(x - 7)$
  d $(x - 6)(x - 2)$
  e $(x - 10)(x - 1)$
  f $(x - 3)(x - 4)$
  g $(x - 7)(x - 1)$
  h $(x - 3)(x - 3)$
  i $(x - 5)(x - 6)$
  j $(x - 4)(x - 7)$
  k $(x - 21)(x - 1)$
  l $(x - 3)(x - 5)$
  m $(x - 7)(x - 2)$
  n $(x - 6)(x - 4)$
  o $(x - 13)(x - 1)$
  p $(x - 13)(x - 2)$

5 a $2(x + 4)(x + 2)$
  b $3(x - 4)(x + 3)$
  c $2(x - 5)(x + 1)$
  d $3(x - 11)(x - 1)$
  e $4(x + 3)(x + 1)$
  f $2(x + 9)(x + 1)$
  g $2(x - 3)(x - 3)$
  h $3(x - 9)(x + 4)$
  i $5(x - 5)(x + 1)$
  j $4(x + 3)(x + 5)$
  k $7(x + 2)(x + 1)$
  l $2(x + 7)(x - 5)$

6 a $x + 3$ **b** $x + 3$
  c $x + 9$ **d** $x + 11$
  e $x - 1$ **f** $x + 4$
  g $\dfrac{1}{x+24}$ **h** $\dfrac{x+3}{x-4}$
  i $\dfrac{x-8}{x-3}$ **j** $\dfrac{x+7}{x-5}$
  k $\dfrac{x}{x+6}$ **l** $\dfrac{x-1}{x}$

Exercise 5.8

1 a $(x - 9)(x + 9)$
  b $(y - 1)(y + 1)$
  c $(x - 8)(x + 8)$
  d $(a - 6)(a + 6)$
  e $(y - 10)(y + 10)$
  f $(4 - a)(4 + a)$
  g $(x - y)(x + y)$
  h $(12 - x)(12 + x)$
  i $(2x - 3)(2x + 3)$
  j $(4y - 1)(4y + 1)$
  k $(5x - 6)(5x + 6)$
  l $(3 - 4x)(3 + 4x)$
  m $(10x - 9y)(10x + 9y)$
  n $(5a - 7b)(5a + 7b)$
  o $(9x - 7y)(9x + 7y)$
  p $(11x - 10)(11x + 10)$

2 a $2(x + 5)(x - 5)$
  b $2(y + 2)(y - 2)$
  c $3(x + 1)(x - 1)$
  d $5(y + 4)(y - 4)$
  e $3(y + 8)(y - 8)$
  f $4(x + y)(x - y)$

g $2(x + 11)(x - 11)$

h $6(n + 10)(n - 10)$

i $3(5y + 6)(5y - 6)$

3 $(x^2 + y^2)(x + y)(x - y)$

4 **a** $(2x + 1)(x + 5)$

b $(2x + 3)(x + 1)$

c $(2x + 1)(x + 7)$

d $(2x + 11)(x + 1)$

e $(3x + 2)(x + 1)$

f $(3x + 1)(x + 5)$

g $(3x + 1)(x + 3)$

h $(3x + 7)(x + 1)$

i $(2x - 1)(x + 3)$

j $(3x + 5)(x - 1)$

k $(3x - 1)(x - 7)$

l $(5x + 3)(x - 1)$

m $(7x - 2)(x - 1)$

n $(5x - 2)(x + 1)$

o $(11x + 1)(x - 2)$

p $(2x - 13)(x - 1)$

5 **a** $(2x + 3)(x + 4)$

b $(2x + 5)(x + 2)$

c $(3x + 2)(x + 4)$

d $(7x + 3)(x + 5)$

e $(3x + 2)(2x + 1)$

f $(6x + 5)(x + 1)$

g $(4x + 1)(2x + 3)$

h $(10x + 1)(x + 7)$

i $(3x - 2)(x + 3)$

j $(5x + 2)(x + 4)$

k $(2x - 3)(x - 4)$

l $(7x - 2)(x + 4)$

m $(5x - 4)(x + 5)$

n $(3x - 5)(x + 2)$

o $(2x - 5)(x - 2)$

p $(3x + 8)(x + 2)$

6 **a** $2(2x + 7)(x - 3)$

b $3(2x + 1)(x + 3)$

c $2(3x + 2)(x + 2)$

d $4(3x + 1)(x + 2)$

e $2y(4x + 1)(2x - 3)$

f $2x(3x + 1)(x - 2)$

7 **a** $\dfrac{2x + 1}{x}$ **b** $\dfrac{3x - 1}{x - 2}$

c $\dfrac{2x - 5}{x + 2}$ **d** $\dfrac{2x + 3}{x + 1}$

e $\dfrac{x}{2x + 3}$ **f** $\dfrac{2(x - 5)}{3x - 8}$

8 $3x(3x + 4)(3x + 2)^2$

Exercise 5.9

1 a

x	−3	−2	−1	0	1	2	3
y	−26	−7	0	1	2	9	28

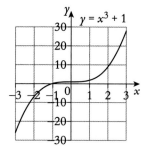

$y = x^3 + 1$

b

x	−3	−2	−1	0	1	2	3
y	29	10	3	2	1	−6	−25

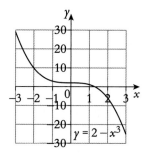

$y = 2 - x^3$

c

x	−3	−2	−1	0	1	2	3
y	27	8	1	0	−1	−8	−27

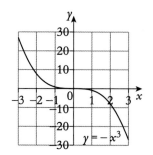

$y = -x^3$

d

x	−3	−2	−1	0	1	2	3
y	−33	−12	−3	0	3	12	33

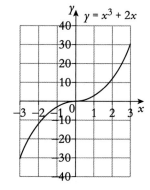

$y = x^3 + 2x$

e

x	−2	−1	0	1	2	3	4
y	20	4	0	2	4	0	−16

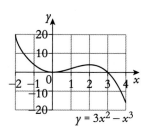

$y = 3x^2 - x^3$

f

x	−2	−1	0	1	2	3	4
y	−8	1	0	−5	−8	−3	16

$y = x^3 - 2x^2 - 4x$

g

x	−1	0	1	2	3	4
y	−3	2	−1	−6	−7	2

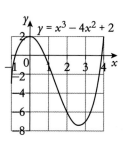

$y = x^3 - 4x^2 + 2$

h

x	-6	-5	-4	-3	-2	-1	0	1	2
y	2	14.5	18	15.5	10	4.5	2	5.5	18

$y = \frac{1}{2}x^3 + 3x^2 + 2$

2 a

x	-3	-2	-1	0	1	2	3
y	-25	-6	1	2	3	10	29

b

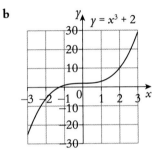

$y = x^3 + 2$

c 1.7

d 3

3 a

x	-2	-1	0	1	2	3	4
y	-6	3.5	6	4.5	2	1.5	6

b

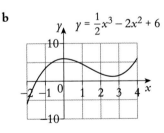

$y = \frac{1}{2}x^3 - 2x^2 + 6$

c −0.9, 1.2, 3.7

d −2

4

$y = \frac{1}{2}x^3$

$y = 2x$

$(-2, -4)\ (0, 0)\ (2, 4)$

5

$y = x^3 - 4x^2 + 3$

$x + y = 1$

$(-0.6, 1.6)\ (1, 0)\ (3.6, -2.6)$

6

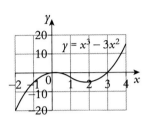

$y = x^3 - 3x^2$

$0 < x < 2$

Exercise 5.10

1 a answer given

b

x	0	0.2	0.4	0.6	0.8	1
v	0	0.096	0.448	1.152	2.304	4

c

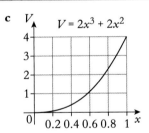

$V = 2x^3 + 2x^2$

d 0.75

2 a answer given

b

x	0	1	2	3	4	5	6	7	8
V	0	252	384	420	384	300	192	84	0

c

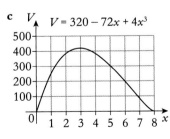

$V = 320 - 72x + 4x^3$

d 420 cm³, 2.9

Exercise 5.11

1 a 40 cm³   **b** 33 cm³

   c 56 cm³   **d** 20 cm³

2 128 cm³   **3** 140 cm³

4 14.4 cm³   **5** 6 cm

6 2.96 × 10⁶ m³

7 9.05 × 10³ m³

8 30.2 mm³

9 224 cm³

10 520 cm³

11 a 90 cm²   **b** 246 cm²

   c 11.2 cm²   **d** 154 cm²

   e 133 cm²   **f** 412 cm²

12 a 173 cm²   **b** 39.9 cm²

13 a 118 cm³   **b** 13.0 cm³

Exercise 5.12

1 a 117 cm³   **b** 56.5 cm³

   c 236 cm³

2 5.97 cm   **3** 4.46 cm

4 159 cm³   **5** 687 cm³

6 a 660 cm³   **b** 775 cm³

   c 1190 cm³

7 $\frac{7}{3}\pi r^2 h$

8 a 56.5 cm²   **b** 126 cm²

   c 113 cm²

9 a 333 cm²   **b** 163 cm²

   c 749 cm²

10 a 5.59 cm²   **b** 54.5 cm²

   c 79.9 cm²

11 a i 43.4 cm²   **ii** 2.3 cm

     iii 5.54 cm

   b i 282 cm²   **ii** 6.42 cm

     iii 12.4 cm

   c i 1320 cm²   **ii** 16.8 cm

     iii 18.5 cm

12 a 694 cm²   **b** 1230 cm²

   c 860 cm²

Exercise 5.13

1 a 113 cm³   **b** 2140 cm³

   c 776 cm³

2 a 113 cm²   **b** 804 cm²

   c 408 cm²

3 **a** 134 cm³ **b** 8580 cm³

   c 2090 cm³

4 **a** 151 cm² **b** 2410 cm²

   c 942 cm²

5 4.69 cm

6 6.31 cm

7 221 cm³

8 1.11 cm

9 4.96 cm

10 a 1360 cm³ **b** 7800 cm³

11 a 641 cm² **b** 1990 cm²

Exercise 5.14

1	20	**2**	90	**3**	27
4	30	**5**	11	**6**	75
7	27	**8**	20	**9**	6
10	6	**11**	2.5	**12**	3
13	5	**14**	2.83	**15**	4.34
16	22.5	**17**	3.12	**18**	12
19	28.4	**20**	56.32		

Exercise 5.15

1 **a** 27, 15

   b 72, 54

2 **a** 15 **b** 8

   c 117 **d** 12

Exercise 5.16

1	72	**2**	75	**3**	216
4	135	**5**	56	**6**	463
7	6	**8**	9	**9**	240

10 20 **11** 12.5 ml **12** 4050 g

13 0.633 l **14** 2.16 l **15** 7.15 cm

16 23.7 cm **17** 30 cm, 20 cm

18 a 240 cm³ **b** 540 cm²

19 675 g

20 a 3 : 4 **b** 27 : 64

21 a 96 cm² **b** 61.44 cm³

22 18.24, 89.92

23 9.3075, 3.02, 2.5

Exercise 5.17

1 **a** 45 **b** 4.25 **c** 12

   d 2.55 **e** 6 **f** 5.5

   g 4.05 **h** 21.5

2 **a** 40 < v ≤ 50

---

b

speed (v km/h)	f	(x)	($f \times x$)
30 < v ≤ 40	37	35	37 × 35 = 1295
40 < v ≤ 50	85	45	85 × 45 = 3825
50 < v ≤ 60	76	55	76 × 55 = 4180
60 < v ≤ 70	2	65	2 × 65 = 130
		Total = 200	Total = 9430

mean = 47.15

3 **a** 150 < h ≤ 160 **b** 152.8 cm

4 **a** 3 < t ≤ 3.5 **b** 3.53°C

5 **a** 10.5 < d ≤ 11 **b** 10.955 m

6 **a** 3 < m ≤ 4 **b** 3.12 kg

   c 8%

7 **a** 0 to 2 **b** 2.935

8 **a** 5.74 hrs **b** 0.59

9 **a** 1.74 miles **b** 2%

10 a 60 < t ≤ 90 **b** 93.6 mins

   c p = 8, q = 72 **d** 94.2 mins

Examination-style questions

1 98 **2** £21.09 **3** $115.68

4 **a** −19

   b $f^{-1}(x) = \dfrac{x+4}{3}$

   c 8

5 **a** −4 **b** 11

6 **a** −45 **b** $12x^2 - 26x + 14$

   c $g^{-1}(x) = \dfrac{3-x}{2}$

7 **a** 19 683 **b** $42x^2 - 20x + 28$

   c $3^{2x} + 3$

8 **a** $(2x - 5)(2x + 5)$

   b $(4x - 1)(x - 6)$

9 **a** $(y - 4)(y + 4)$

   b $(y + 8)(y - 2)$

10 $2(a - b)(5a - 5b - 3)$

11 $\dfrac{x-2}{x-8}$ **12** $\dfrac{x+8}{2x-1}$

13 a

x	−2.5	−2	−1.5	−1	−0.5	0	0.5	1	1.5	2	2.5
y	−1.8	**1**	2.3	**2.5**	1.9	1	**3**	0.06	−0.5	1	3.8

---

b

c 3.5 to 4.5

14 408 cm²

15 228 cm²

16 a 25.1 cm

   b i 4 cm

   ii 19.6 cm

   iii 328 cm³

17 89.8 cm³

18 a 328 cm³ **b** 3.456 cm

19 5100 cm² **20** 3.42 cm²

21 148 800 cm³

22 a 6.5 < t ≤ 7

   b 6.46 minutes

23 a 12 < t ≤ 15

   b 10.53 hours

   c a = 16, b = 43

   d 10.62 hours

Unit 6

Exercise 6.1

1 3×10^6 **2** $80

3 $20 **4** $300

5 38.2 minutes **6** $16 500

7 $2.32 **8** $3540

9 $8.50 **10** $130

11 $44.80 **12** 21.6°C

13 $5360

Exercise 6.2

1 $60 **2** $756

3 $295 **4** $481.50

5 $530.45   6 $2153.78

7 $757.70   8 $63.05

9 3   10 15

11 7 years   12 $12 000

13 3365

3	36 km/h	4	12 600 m
5	31.25 s	6	41.4 km/h

7 a 8400 km   b 1400 km/h

8 a 23.4 km   b $4\frac{1}{3}$ m/s

9 a 520 km   b 86.7 km/h

10 30 m/s   11 80

7 a TRUE   b FALSE
  c FALSE   d TRUE

8 a TRUE   b FALSE
  c TRUE   d TRUE
  e FALSE   f TRUE

Exercise 6.3

1 a $\frac{1}{3}$ hr   b $\frac{1}{2}$ hr   c $\frac{1}{6}$ hr

  d $\frac{1}{4}$ hr   e $\frac{5}{12}$ hr   f $\frac{8}{15}$ hr

  g $\frac{3}{4}$ hr   h $\frac{1}{15}$ hr   i $\frac{9}{10}$ hr

  j $\frac{2}{5}$ hr   k $\frac{2}{3}$ hr   l $\frac{4}{5}$ hr

2 a 30 min b 3 min   c 15 min

  d 21 min e 48 min f 42 min

  g 6 min   h 27 min i 24 min

  j 45 min k 25 min l 18 min

3 a 62.5 km/hr   b 38 km/hr

  c 13 km/hr   d 48 km/hr

  e 18 km/hr   f 10 km/hr

  g 48 km/hr   h 24 km/hr

  i 120 km/hr

4 a 20 m/s   b 25 m/s

  c 50 m/s   d 20 m/s

  e 30 m/s   f 6 m/s

5 a 20 m/s   b $3\frac{1}{3}$ m/s

  c 100 m/s d 72 km/h

  e 126 km/h

  f 147.6 km/h

6 20 m/s

7 3×10^8 m/s

8 343 m/s

Exercise 6.4

1 a 2 hours   b 2 hrs 30 mins

  c 30 mins

  d 2 hours 15 mins

  e 2 hours 50 mins

  f 2 hours 39 mins

2 a 56 km   b 216 km

  c 315 km   d 25 km

  e 10 km   f 5 km

Exercise 6.5

1 a {1, 4, 9, 16, 25, 36, 49}

  b {2, 3, 5, 7, 11, 13, 17, 19, 23}

  c {Jan, Feb, Mar, Apr, May,
     June, July, Aug, Sept, Oct,
     Nov, Dec}

  d {1, 2, 3, 4, 6, 12}

  e {5}

  f {2, 4, 6, 8, 12, 14}

  g {21, 23, 25, 27, 29}

  h {151, 157, 163, 167, 173,
     179, 181, 191, 193, 197, 199}

2 a {1, 7, 49} b {125}

  c {2, 5}

  d {1, 2, 4, 5, 10, 20}

  e {2, 3}

  f {Jan, June, July}

3 a {square numbers less than 17}

  b {odd numbers}

  c {months of the year
     beginning with M}

  d {multiples of 4}

  e {cube numbers}

  f {colours}

4 a {prime numbers}

  b {factors of 20}

  c {powers of 2 smaller than 33}

  d {Pythagorean triples}

5 a FALSE   b TRUE

  c FALSE   d FALSE

  e FALSE   f FALSE

6 a FALSE   b TRUE

  c FALSE   d TRUE

Exercise 6.6

1 a

  b

  c

  d

  e

  f

d

e

f

g

h

i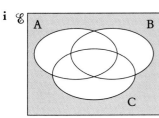

Exercise 6.7

1 **a** B **b** (A∪B)′
c A∪B **d** A∩B
e (A∩B)′ **f** A∪(A∪B)′

2 **a** A∪B∪C **b** A∩C
c A **d** (A∪B∪C)′
e A∩(B∪C)′ **f** A∩C∩B′
g A∩B′ **h** (A∪C)∩B′
i (A∪B∪C)∩(A∩B∩C)′

3 **a** B′∩C **b** A′∩B∩C′
c C∪(A∩B)

Exercise 6.8

1 **a** {3, 6, 9, 12,...}
b {1, 2, 4, 5, 10, 20}
c {1, 3, 5, 7,...}
d {2, 3, 5, 7, 11, 13, 17, 19}
e {2, 3} **f** {2}
g {−5, 5} **h** {3} **i** ∅

2 **a** {2, 3, 6, 7} **b** {3, 5, 7, 8, 9}
c {1, 4, 5, 8, 9, 10}
d {1, 2, 4, 6, 10}
e {2, 3, 5, 6, 7, 8, 9}
f {3, 7} **g** {1, 4, 10}
h {2, 6}

3 **a** {1, 3, 4, 8, 9, 10, 13, 14}
b {2, 3, 4, 5, 6, 8, 10, 14}
c {11}
d {1, 3, 4, 7, 9, 11, 12, 13, 14}
e {1, 2, 3, 4, 5, 6, 7, 8, 9, 10, 12, 13, 14}
f {1, 9, 13} **g** {8, 9, 10}
h {7, 9, 12}

4 **a** {1, 2, 4, 5, 10}
b {4, 8} **c** {2, 3, 5, 7}
d ∅ **e** {4} **f** {2, 5}
g ∅ **h** {6, 9}
i
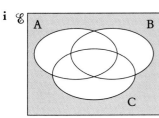

5 **a** {b, d, e, f} **b** {a, e, f, g}
c {c} **d** {a, b, c, d, g}
e {b, d} **f** {a, g}

g {a, b, d, e, f, g}
h {e, f}
i

6

7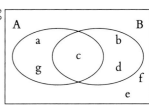

Exercise 6.9

1 **a** 14 **b** 19 **c** 8
d 8 **e** 24 **f** 3
g 11 **h** 5
2 28 **3** 19 **4** 55
5 7 **6** 8
7 **a** 17 **b** 10 **c** 8
8 **a** 10 **b** 15
9 **a** 36 **b** 14 **c** 10
10 **a** 17 **b** 22
11 23
12 25
13 35

Exercise 6.10

1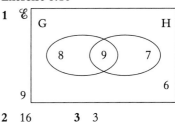

2 16 **3** 3
4 4 **5** 4
6 **a** 2 **b** 2
7 23

Exercise 6.11

1
a 3   b 8   c 3
d 9   e 4   f 2
g 10   h 3   i 12
j 13   k 20   l 20

2
a $\dfrac{1}{3}$ b $\dfrac{1}{2}$ c $\dfrac{1}{3}$
d $\dfrac{1}{5}$ e $\dfrac{1}{3}$ f $\dfrac{1}{5}$
g $\dfrac{1}{2}$ h $\dfrac{1}{4}$ i $\dfrac{1}{10}$
j $\dfrac{1}{6}$ k $\dfrac{1}{11}$ l $\dfrac{1}{2}$

3
a 125   b 16   c 8
d 27   e 100 000   f 1
g 4   h 243
i 100   j 2197   k 27
l 16

4
a $\dfrac{1}{125}$ b $\dfrac{1}{16}$ c $\dfrac{1}{64}$
d $\dfrac{1}{8}$ e $\dfrac{1}{1000}$ f $\dfrac{1}{4}$
g $\dfrac{1}{243}$ h $\dfrac{1}{32}$
i $\dfrac{1}{100000}$ j $\dfrac{1}{16}$
k $\dfrac{1}{27}$ l 1

5
a x^2 b x^2 c $x^{\frac{1}{2}}$
d x^{-2} e x f x^2
g x^{-1} h x^4 i x^3
j x k x^{-2} l x^2
m x^2 n 1   o $x^{\frac{5}{6}}$
p $x^{-\frac{1}{6}}$

6
a $15x$ b 16   c $6x^4$
d $3x^{\frac{1}{3}}$ e $6x^{1.5}$ f $3x^{-1}$
g $2x^{-4.5}$ h $4x^{5.5}$

7
a $5x^{-3}y^{-2}$ b $64x^{18}y^9$
c $5x^3y^{\frac{1}{4}}$ d $4x^5y$

Exercise 6.12

1
a 5   b 2   c 1
d 0   e 2   f 3
g 8   h 3   i 1
j 3   k 4   l 4

2
a −4   b −2   c −7
d −2   e −2   f −3
g −3   h −4   i −1
j −3   k −4   l −1

3
a 3   b 3   c 4
d 2   e 1.5   f 2
g 9   h 1   i 3
j 1   k 4   l 0.5

4
a −2   b −1   c −1.5
d −1   e −4   f −2.5
g −3   h −3

5
a $\dfrac{1}{5}$ b $\dfrac{1}{3}$ c $\dfrac{1}{2}$
d $\dfrac{1}{2}$ e $\dfrac{1}{4}$ f $\dfrac{1}{3}$
g $\dfrac{1}{3}$ h $\dfrac{1}{2}$ i −7
j −3   k −1   l −0.5

6
a $\dfrac{1}{6}$ b 2   c 0
d 1.5   e −1   f 3
g −3   h 2

Exercise 6.13

1
a ±4   b ±6   c ±10
d $\pm\dfrac{1}{2}$ e ±5   f ±3
g ±6   h ±11   i $\pm\dfrac{2}{3}$
j $\pm\dfrac{3}{4}$ k $\pm\dfrac{4}{5}$ l $\pm\dfrac{1}{3}$
m ±9   n ±1   o ±20
p $\pm\dfrac{3}{2}$

2 No. You cannot find the square root of a negative number.

3
a 0, −6   b 0, 8   c 0, 10
d 0, −2   e 0, 5   f 0, 12
g 0, −2.25   h 0, $\dfrac{1}{3}$
i 0, −6.5   j 0, 25   k 0, −40
l 0, −3   m 0, 4   n 0, 15
o 0, 11   p 0, 1

4
a −2, −3   b 6, −1   c 2, −3
d 5, 4   e 7, −2   f −3, −9
g 5, −4   h 8, 2   i 3, −10
j 8   k 5   l −1, −3
m 3, −7   n 3   o 8, 1
p 5, −9

5
a $3, -\dfrac{1}{2}$ b $1, \dfrac{2}{3}$
c 0.6, −1   d 0.5, −7
e 2.5, 0. 5   f $\dfrac{1}{3}, -2\dfrac{1}{2}$
g 0.8, 0.5   h $\dfrac{1}{6}, -5$
i $\dfrac{2}{3}, -2\dfrac{1}{2}$ j 2.5, 1.5
k $\dfrac{2}{7}, -5$ l $1\dfrac{1}{4}, -\dfrac{2}{3}$

6 10, 2

7
a 3, 2   b 6, 2   c 3, −6
d −2, −4   e 4   f 7, −1
g 7, 5   h 5, −3   i 3, −6

8
a 6, −1   b 4, −5
c 6, −12   d 4, −3

Exercise 6.14

1 a 7, −6   b 17, −18
2 a 9, −11   b 12, −10
3 15, −18
4 a $(2x + 1)^2 + (2x)^2 = 29^2$
    $8x^2 + 4x + 1 = 841$
    $2x^2 + x - 210 = 0$
  b 20, 21, 29
5 6
6 4
7 11 cm, 14 cm
8 10
9 2 s, 3 s
10 (5, 8), (−3, 0)

Exercise 6.15

1

−5	−4	−3	−2	−1
−1	−1.25	−1.67	−2.5	−5

0	1	2	3	4	5
−	5	2.5	1.67	1.25	1

$y = \dfrac{5}{x}$

2

−5	−4	−3	−2	−1	0
1	1.25	1.67	2.5	5	−

1	2	3	4	5
−5	−2.5	−1.67	−1.25	−1

$y = -\dfrac{5}{x}$

3

−5	−4	−3	−2	−1	0
1.2	1	0.67	0	−2	−

1	2	3	4	5
6	4	3.33	3	2.8

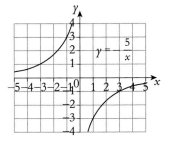

$y = \dfrac{4}{x} + 2$

4

−2	−1	0	1	2
−1	−1.25	−1.67	−2.5	−5

3	4	5	6	7	8
−	5	2.5	1.67	1.25	1

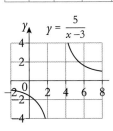

$y = \dfrac{5}{x-3}$

5

−6	−5	−4	−3	−2	−1
−6	−5.2	−4.5	−4	−4	−6

0	1	2	3	4	5	6
−	8	6	6	6.5	7.2	8

$y = \dfrac{6}{x} + x + 1$

6

−4	−3	−2	−1	0
14.5	7	1	−5	−

1	2	3	4	−4
7	7	11	17.5	14.5

$y = x^2 + \dfrac{6}{x}$

7

−6	−5	−4	−3	−2	−1
0.33	0.48	0.75	1.33	3	12

0	1	2	3	4	5	6
−	12	3	1.33	0.75	0.48	0.33

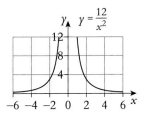

$y = \dfrac{12}{x^2}$

8

−6	−5	−4	−3	−2
−7.89	−6.84	−5.75	−4.56	−3

−1	0	1	2	3	4	5	6
1	−	3	1	1.44	2.25	3.16	4.11

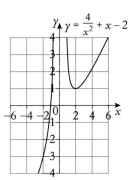

$y = \dfrac{4}{x^2} + x - 2$

9 **a** answer given

b $T = 2x + y$

c answer given

d

x	5	10	15	20	30	40	50
T	110	70	63.3	65	76.7	92.5	110

e

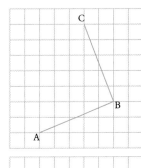

$T = 2x + \dfrac{500}{x}$

f minimum length = 63.2 m when x = 15.8

Exercise 6.16

1 **a**

b

c

2 a

b

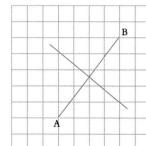

c

3 a $-\dfrac{1}{5}$ **b** -3 **c** $-\dfrac{5}{2}$

   d $\dfrac{3}{2}$ **e** $\dfrac{1}{4}$ **f** $-\dfrac{7}{5}$

4 a neither   **b** neither
   c neither   **d** perpendicular
   e perpendicular
   f perpendicular
   g perpendicular
   h neither   **i** parallel

---

5 a i A, D   **ii** C, E

   b $y = -\dfrac{2}{3}x + k$

6 $y = -\dfrac{1}{3}x + 5y$

7 a $y = -\dfrac{1}{2}x + 5$

   b $y = -\dfrac{1}{5}x + 7$

   c $y = -\dfrac{3}{2}x - 8$

   d $y = -\dfrac{1}{4}x$

8 a $\dfrac{1}{2}$ **b** -2

9 $\dfrac{1}{3} \times -3 = -1$

10 $-\dfrac{1}{2} \times 2 = -1$

11 a -4 **b** $(0, -4)$

12 $y = -2x$

13 P(−1.5, 0), Q(0, 2.25)

14 a (2, 3)   **b** $y = \dfrac{2}{3}x + \dfrac{5}{3}$

15 (−3, 2)

16 (7, 0)

17 (8, 7), (0, −5)

18 a (1, 5)   **b** -3

19 a $y = 2x - 4$ **b** (2, 0)

20 3 or −4

21 3 or −0.5

22 a i $2x + y = 7$
      ii $x - 7y = -4$
   b (3, 1)

Exercise 6.17

1 a 9.17 cm   **b** 18.8 cm
   c 63.6°   **d** 71.6°

2 a 6.63 cm   **b** 56.4°
   c 33.2 cm²   **d** 11.5 cm²

3 a 53.1°   **b** 106°
   c 48 cm²   **d** 33.4 cm²
   e 14.6 cm²

4 a 8 cm   **b** 24 cm
   c 13.9 cm   **d** 333 cm²
   e 131 cm²

Exercise 6.18

1 9.17 cm

2 5.29 cm

3 13 cm

4 a 9 cm   **b** 108 cm²

5 a 1.71 cm   **b** 4.70 cm
   c 9.40 cm   **d** 8.03 cm²
   e 30.5 cm²   **f** 22.5 cm²

6 16.0 cm

7 a 6 cm   **b** 16 cm
   c 128 cm²

Exercise 6.19

1 $x = 240°$, $y = 30°$

2 $x = 100°$, $y = 260°$

3 $x = 110°$, $y = 35°$

4 $x = 286°$, $y = 53°$

5 $x = 76°$, $y = 52°$

6 $x = 100°$, $y = 80°$, $z = 50°$

7 $x = 32°$, $y = 16°$, $z = 16°$

8 $x = 96°$, $y = 84°$, $z = 48°$

9 $x = 43°$, $y = 90°$

10 $x = 30°$, $y = 120°$

11 $x = 50°$, $y = 40°$

12 $x = 90°$, $y = 64°$

13 $x = 54°$, $y = 27°$

14 $x = 74°$

15 $x = 102°$

16 $x = 30°$

17 $x = 20°$, $y = 70°$, $z = 50°$

18 $x = 130°$, $y = 90°$, $z = 65°$

19 $x = 22.5°$

Exercise 6.20

1 $x = 90°$ **2** $x = 62°$

3 $x = 30°$ **4** $x = 84°$

5 $x = 48°$ **6** $x = 52.5°$

7 $x = 70°$ **8** $x = 200°$

9 $x = 170°$ **10** $x = 45°$

11 $x = 30°$ **12** $x = 80°$

13 $x = 16°$, $y = 74°$

14 $x = 115°$ **15** $x = 45°$

16 $x = 28°$, $y = 62°$

17 $x = 88°$, $y = 46°$

18 $x = 50°$, $y = 40°$

Exercise 6.21

1. $x = 50°$
2. $x = 56°$, $\quad y = 100°$
3. $x = 80°$, $\quad y = 105°$
4. $x = 123°$, $\quad y = 56°$
5. $x = 80°$, $\quad y = 110°$
6. $x = 85°$, $\quad y = 95°$
7. $x = 29°$
8. $x = 100°$, $\quad y = 55°$
9. $x = 78°$, $\quad y = 102°$
10. $x = 50°$
11. $x = 66°$
12. $x = 54°$, $\quad y = 126°$
13. $x = 30°$, $\quad y = 30°$
14. $x = 55°$, $\quad y = 45°$
15. $x = 27°$, $\quad y = 35°$

Exercise 6.22

1. $x = 28°$, $\quad y = 62°$
2. $x = 22°$
3. $x = 27°$
4. $x = 17°$
5. $x = 57.5°$
6. $x = 105°$
7. $x = 113°$
8. $x = 68°$, $\quad y = 93°$
9. $x = 9°$
10. $x = 26°$, $\quad y = 64°$
11. $x = 25°$
12. $x = 64°$, $\quad y = 32°$
13. $x = 142°$, $\quad y = 38°$
14. $x = 18°$
15. $x = 68°$, $\quad y = 44°$
16. $x = 130°$
17. $x = 100°$
18. $x = 28°$, $\quad y = 62°$
19. $x = 66°$, $\quad y = 71°$
20. $x = 196°$
21. $x = 130°$, $\quad y = 65°$
22. $x = 70°$, $\quad y = 35°$
23. $x = 40°$, $\quad y = 140°$
24. $x = 70°$, $\quad y = 110°$, $\quad z = 35°$
25. $x = 69°$, $\quad y = 21°$, $\quad z = 21°$
26. $x = 40°$, $\quad y = 43°$

27. $x = 60°$, $\quad y = 50°$, $\quad z = 30°$
28. $x = 60°$, $\quad y = 120°$
29. $x = 22°$
30. $x = 58°$, $\quad y = 52°$

For questions **31–36** explanations are also required.

31. $x = 28°$, $\quad y = 62°$
32. $x = 76°$, $\quad y = 38°$, $\quad z = 14°$
33. $x = 90°$, $\quad y = 60°$, $\quad z = 30°$
34. $x = 56°$
35. $x = 48°$, $\quad y = 24°$
36. $x = 130°$, $\quad y = 90°$

Exercise 6.23

1 a

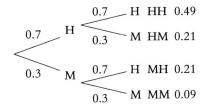

b **i** 0.49 **ii** 0.09
   iii 0.42 **iv** 0.91

2 a $\dfrac{9}{25}$ **b** $\dfrac{4}{25}$ **c** $\dfrac{6}{25}$

3 a $\dfrac{2}{5}$ **b** $\dfrac{2}{15}$ **c** $\dfrac{7}{15}$

4 a 0.0001 **b** 0.9801
   c 0.0198 **d** 0.0199

5 a

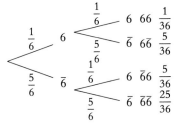

b **i** $\dfrac{1}{36}$ **ii** $\dfrac{25}{36}$
   iii $\dfrac{5}{18}$

6 a $\dfrac{25}{49}$ **b** $\dfrac{4}{49}$
   c $\dfrac{29}{49}$ **d** $\dfrac{45}{49}$

7 a

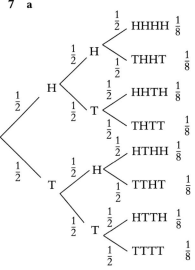

b **i** $\dfrac{1}{8}$ **ii** $\dfrac{1}{8}$
   iii $\dfrac{3}{8}$ **iv** $\dfrac{1}{2}$

8 a $\dfrac{8}{27}$ **b** $\dfrac{1}{27}$
   c $\dfrac{4}{9}$ **d** $\dfrac{26}{27}$

9 a $\dfrac{1}{216}$ **b** $\dfrac{125}{216}$
   c $\dfrac{25}{72}$ **d** $\dfrac{5}{72}$

10 a 0.512 **b** 0.008 **c** 0.096

11 a

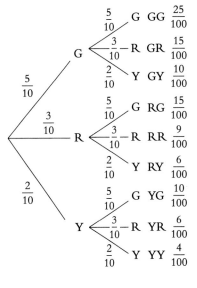

b **i** $\dfrac{1}{4}$ **ii** $\dfrac{9}{100}$ **iii** $\dfrac{1}{25}$

iv $\dfrac{19}{50}$ **v** $\dfrac{31}{50}$

12 a $\dfrac{1}{64}$ **b** $\dfrac{1}{27}$

c $\dfrac{125}{1728}$ **d** $\dfrac{5}{24}$

Exercise 6.24

1 a $\dfrac{10}{21}$ **b** $\dfrac{1}{21}$ **c** $\dfrac{11}{21}$

d $\dfrac{10}{21}$

2 a $\dfrac{1}{2}$ **b** 0 **c** 1

3 a $\dfrac{2}{5}$ **b** $\dfrac{1}{15}$ **c** $\dfrac{8}{15}$

d $\dfrac{3}{5}$

4 a $\dfrac{5}{12}$ **b** $\dfrac{1}{12}$ **c** $\dfrac{1}{2}$

d $\dfrac{11}{12}$

5 a $\dfrac{1}{6}$ **b** $\dfrac{1}{12}$ **c** $\dfrac{1}{36}$

d $\dfrac{5}{18}$ **e** $\dfrac{13}{18}$

6 a $\dfrac{1}{3}$ **b** $\dfrac{1}{4}$ **c** $\dfrac{5}{12}$

d $\dfrac{3}{4}$

7 a

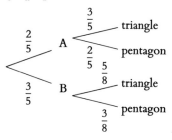

b i 0.26 **ii** 0.74

8 a i

ii $\dfrac{123}{200}$ **iii** $\dfrac{77}{200}$

b i $\dfrac{71}{210}$ **ii** $\dfrac{39}{70}$

Exercise 6.25

1 $\dfrac{343}{4096}$ **2** $\dfrac{1}{64}$ **3** $\dfrac{625}{7776}$

4 $\dfrac{1}{256}$ **5** $\dfrac{10}{63}$

Examination-style questions

1 \$645 **2** \$840

3 \$675.90 **4** \$155.03

5 3% **6** 2.08%

7 15 m/s **8** 38.1 km/h

9 30 m/s

10 a i 31 **ii** 14

b 20

c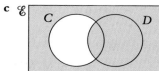

11 a $(A\cap B)'\cap C$

b $(A\cap B)\cap C'$

12 4

13 a

b $20 - x + x + 17 - x = 80$

c 4

14 2.5 **15** −12

16 a 1 **b** p^8

c $8q^{12}$ **d** $\dfrac{a^3}{216}$

17 a x^7 **b** $20x^3y^{11}$ **c** $9x^4$

18 $\dfrac{7}{9}$

19 a $(x-5)(x+8)$ **b** −8, 5

20 a $(3x+4)(x-2)$ **b** $-\dfrac{4}{3}$, 2

21 −1, 2.5

22 b $2(x+9)(2x-19)$ **c** 9.5 cm

23 a $y = \dfrac{48}{x}$

c

x	1	2	4	6	10	15	20
L	50	28	20	20	26.8	33.2	42.4

d

e 19.6 m

24 a $y = \dfrac{1}{4}x + \dfrac{23}{4}$

b $y = -4x + 10$

25 $y = \dfrac{3}{4}x - 2$

26 a $y = -\dfrac{1}{2}x - \dfrac{3}{2}$

b $y = 2x - 4$

c $(1, -2)$

27 $x = 46$, $y = 38$, $z = 54$

28 $x = 76$, $y = 52$

29 a 52° **b** 38°

c 76° **d** 38°

e 28°

30 0.49

31 a 0.14

b i 0.0225 **ii** 0.111

32 a i

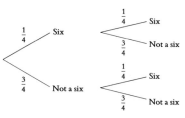

ii $\dfrac{7}{16}$ **b** $\dfrac{9}{64}$

33 $\dfrac{5}{9}$ **34** $\dfrac{8}{81}$

35 $\dfrac{3}{28}$

36 b $x = -2\dfrac{1}{2}$ or $x = 12$

 c 35 cm

37 b $x = -\dfrac{2}{3}$ or $x = 12$

 c 16 cm

38 a $\dfrac{1}{5}$

 b i

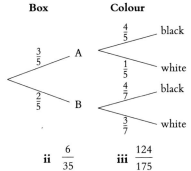

Box	Colour

 ii $\dfrac{6}{35}$ **iii** $\dfrac{124}{175}$

 c i $\dfrac{27}{56}$ **ii** $\dfrac{13}{28}$

Unit 7

Exercise 7.1

1 a i 0.8 km/min
 ii 48 km/h
 b i 1.7 km/min
 ii 102 km/h
 c i 0.4 km/min
 ii 24 km/h
 d 64 km/h

2 a 5 mins
 b i 0.08 km/min
 ii 4.8 km/h
 c i 0.0267 km/min
 ii 1.6 km/h
 d 2.4 km/h

3 a 1.25 m/s **b** 1.43 m/s
 c 1.33 m/s

4 a 6 km, 10 km
 b 5 min, 5 min
 c i 0.8 km/min
 ii 48 km/h
 d i 0.5 km/min
 ii 30 km/h

5 a 3   **b** 18 mins
 c between 15 and 20 mins
 d 50 km **e** 50 km/h

6 a answer given **b** 9:09 am
 c

 d 8:32 am (approx)

Exercise 7.2

1 a $2\dfrac{2}{3}$ m/s^2 **b** $\dfrac{2}{7}$ m/s^2
 c 75 m

2 a 1 m/s^2 **b** $\dfrac{2}{3}$ m/s^2
 c 700 m

3 a 0.5 m/s^2 **b** 0.25 m/s^2
 c 300 m   **d** 5 m/s

4 a 1.25 m/s^2 **b** 250 m
 c 1000 m   **d** 20 m/s

5 a 0.25 m/s^2 **b** $\dfrac{1}{3}$ m/s^2
 c 200 m   **d** 950 m

6 a 1.25 m/s^2 **b** -0.5 m/s^2
 c 950 m   **d** 15.8 m/s

7 a 0.5 m/s^2 **b** 2000 m
 c 225 m

8 a 0.8 m/s^2 **b** 0.4 m/s^2
 c 1120 m   **d** 2560 m
 e 2440 m

9 $9\dfrac{2}{3}$ km

10 a 32 m/s   **b** 16 m/s
11 a 19.6 m/s   **b** 1.96 m/s^2

Exercise 7.3

1 $x = \dfrac{r}{p-q}$ **2** $x = \dfrac{b}{a-c}$

3 $x = \dfrac{c}{a-b}$ **4** $x = \dfrac{a}{1-b}$

5 $x = \dfrac{c-a}{1-b}$ **6** $x = \dfrac{5+b}{a-c}$

7 $x = \dfrac{3-b}{a+2}$ **8** $x = \dfrac{-a^2}{a+b}$

9 $x = \dfrac{3a+4b}{a-b}$ **10** $x = \dfrac{7b+3d}{3c-7a}$

11 $x = \dfrac{3a+2}{1-a}$ **12** $x = \dfrac{b}{c-a}$

13 $x = \dfrac{2e-1}{d+3e}$ **14** $x = \dfrac{d-2b}{2a-c}$

15 $x = \dfrac{3a+4b}{b-a}$ **16** $x = \dfrac{a^2c^2}{1+b}$

17 $x = \dfrac{2}{a^2-1}$ **18** $x = \dfrac{4p}{4-q^2}$

19 $x = \pm\sqrt{\dfrac{a}{1-b}}$ **20** $x = \sqrt{\dfrac{c-b}{a+d}}$

21 $x = \dfrac{fy}{y-f}$ **22** $x = \dfrac{2a}{a-2}$

23 a $x = \dfrac{5}{b-a}$ **b** $x = \dfrac{b}{a-c}$

 c $x = \dfrac{p}{2r-5q}$ **d** $x = \dfrac{6f}{7h-g}$

 e $x = \dfrac{a-b}{3c-2}$ **f** $x = \dfrac{a+d}{b+c}$

Exercise 7.4

1 a 23, 27
 b 30, 35
 c 32, 64
 d 14, 15.5
 e 8, 5

f 78.125, 195.3125

g $1\frac{1}{3}, \frac{4}{9}$

h 2.5, −0.75

i 13, 21

j 63, 127

k 17, 27

l 100, 1000

2 a 7, 8, 9, 10, 11

b 2, 7, 12, 17, 22

c 6, 10, 14, 18, 22

d 1, 3, 5, 7, 9

e 8, 11, 14, 17, 20

f −2, 0, 2, 4, 6

g 48, 46, 44, 42, 40

h 15, 14, 13, 12, 11

i 22, 19, 16, 13, 10

j 2.5, 3, 3.5, 4, 4.5

k 29.5, 29, 28.5, 28, 27.5

l 3, −1, −5, −9, −13

3 nth term = $2n-1$. He is incorrect.

4 a 13 **b** 58

c $3n-2$

5 a $4n+3$ **b** $3n-3$

c $5n+3$ **d** $3n-7$

e $2.5n-0.5$ **f** $7n-15$

g $3n-2$ **h** $4n-5$

i $6n-8$ **j** $1.5n-7$

k $2.5n+5.5$ **l** $0.02n+6$

6 a $23-2n$ **b** $104-4n$

c $22-7n$ **d** $20-3n$

e $7-2n$ **f** $2.1-0.4n$

g $1-3n$ **h** $15-2n$

i $2.5-0.5n$

7 20th

8 38th

9 25th

10 63rd

Exercise 7.5

1 a 3, 6, 11, 18, 27

b −2, 1, 6, 13, 22

c 3, 12, 27, 48, 75

d −1, 0, 3, 8, 15

e 2, 9, 28, 65, 126

f −3, 4, 23, 60, 121

g $3, 2, 1\frac{2}{3}, 1\frac{1}{2}, 1\frac{2}{5}$

h 1, 4, 10, 20, 35

2 a n^2

b n^2-1

c $2n^2$

d n^2+2

e n^2+10

f $3n^2$

3 a n^3

b n^3-1

c n^3-2

d $2n^3$

e n^3+2

4 a 10^n **b** 2^n **c** 3^n

d 2^{n+1} **e** 3^{n-1} **f** 10^{n-2}

5 a $n(n+2)$

b $n(n+1)(n+2)$

c $\dfrac{n}{n+5}$

d $\dfrac{n+1}{(n+1)^2+1}$

6 a $8x^6$ **b** $18x^{11}$

c $7x^6$ **d** x^2y^6

7 a n^3 **b** $3n+1$

c n^3-3n-1

8 55, 91

9 a 10

b

c $10 = \dfrac{4\times5}{2}, 15 = \dfrac{5\times6}{2}$

d $\dfrac{n(n+1)}{2}$

e 120

10 a

b 5, 9, 14, 20

c 27 **d** 170 **e** $\dfrac{n(n-3)}{2}$

11 35th **12** 50th

13 a 1, 6, 15, 20, 15, 6, 1

b

Row	1	2	3
Sum	$1=2^0$	$2=2^1$	$4=2^2$

4	5	6	7
$8=2^3$	$16=2^4$	$32=2^5$	$64=2^6$

c 2^{n-1} **d** 16

14 a

b

Year	1	2	3	4	5
Flowers	1	2	4	8	16
Stems	1	3	7	15	31

c 32

d 2^{n-1}

e 63

f 2^n-1

15 12

Exercise 7.6

1 $b=3, c=4$

2 $b=5, c=2$

3 $b=-2, c=4$

4 $b=3, c=1$

5 $b=1, c=2$

UNIT 7

6 $a = 2, b = 5, c = 2$

7 $a = 2, b = -3, c = 5$

8 $a = 3, b = 1, c = -3$

9 $a = 0.5, b = 6, c = -2$

10 a 40

b 60

c $2n(n + 1)$ or $2n^2 + 2n$

11 a 25

b 41

c $(n - 1)^2 + n^2$ or $2n^2 - 2n + 1$

12 $\dfrac{2n(n+1)(n+2)}{3}$

13 a 30

b $k = 6$

14 $a = 2, b = -4$

Exercise 7.7

1 a $-1, 1, 3, 5$

b $6, 11, 16, 21$

c $5, 8, 11, 14$

d $1, 4, 9, 16$

e $3, 6, 11, 18$

f $0, 1, 4, 9$

g $1, 8, 27, 64$

h $0, 4, 18, 48$

i $8, 27, 64, 125$

j $2, 4, 8, 16$

k $\dfrac{1}{3}, 1, 3, 9$

l $10\,000, 100\,000, 1\,000\,000, 10\,000\,000$

m $\dfrac{1}{3}, \dfrac{1}{2}, \dfrac{3}{5}, \dfrac{2}{3}$

n $\dfrac{5}{6}, \dfrac{6}{7}, \dfrac{7}{8}, \dfrac{8}{9}$

o $\dfrac{1}{5}, \dfrac{4}{7}, 1, \dfrac{16}{11}$ or $1\dfrac{5}{11}$

2 a $U_n = 5n - 1$

b $U_n = 3n + 5$

c $U_n = 23 - 3n$

d $U_n = n^2 - 1$

e $U_n = 3^{n-1}$

f $U_n = \dfrac{n+3}{2n+5}$

Exercise 7.8

1

x	-3	-2	-1	0	1	2	3
y	0.04	0.11	0.33	1	3	9	27

2

x	-3	-2	-1	0	1	2	3
y	27	9	3	1	0.33	0.11	0.04

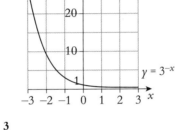

3

x	-3	-2	-1	0	1	2	3
y	1.04	1.11	1.33	2	4	10	28

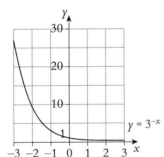

4

x	-3	-2	-1	0	1	2	3
y	-4.96	-4.89	-4.67	-4	-2	4	22

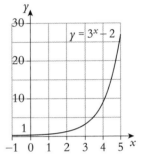

5

x	-1	0	1	2	3	4	5
y	0.04	0.11	0.33	1	3	9	27

6

x	-3	-2	-1	0	1	2	3
y	8	4	2	1	0.5	0.25	0.13

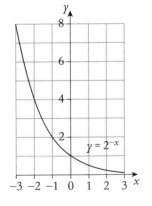

7

x	-3	-2	-1	0	1	2	3
y	1.13	1.25	1.5	2	3	5	9

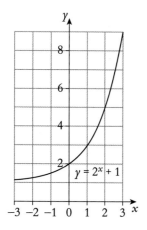

$y = 2^x + 1$

8

x	-4	-3	-2	-1	0	1	2
y	0.13	0.25	0.5	1	2	4	8

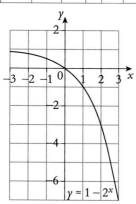

$y = 2^{x+1}$

9

x	-3	-2	-1	0	1	2	3
y	0.87	0.75	0.5	0	-1	-3	-7

$y = 1 - 2^x$

10

x	-3	-2	-1	0	1	2	3
y	8	4	2	1	0.5	0.25	0.13

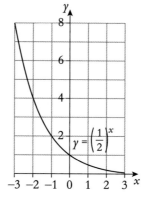

$y = \left(\dfrac{1}{2}\right)^x$

11 a i 2 **ii** -1.5

 b i 2 **ii** 3.6 **c** 2.8

Exercise 7.9

1 a 214, 314, 459, 673

 b

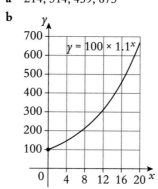

$y = 100 \times 1.1^x$

 c 17

2 a 26 200, 21 300, 17 200, 13 900

 b

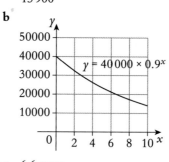

$y = 40\,000 \times 0.9^x$

 c 6.6 years

3 a 300, 360, 432, 518, 622, 746

 b

$P = 250 \times (1.2)^t$

 c 3.8 years

4 a 75, 56.3, 42.2, 31.6, 23.7, 17.8, 13.3, 10.0

 b

$P = 100 \times (0.75)^t$

 c 5.6 years

Exercise 7.10

1 78.5° **2** 45.6°

3 61.6°, 118.4° **4** 110.5°

5 11.5°, 168.5° **6** 90°

7 180° **8** 0°, 180°

9 no solution

10 no solution in range **11** 139.5°

12 54.1°, 125.9° **13** 73.4°

14 36.9°, 143.1° **15** 138.6°

16 53.1°, 126.9°

17 no solution in range

18 no solution **19** 60°

20 19.9°, 160.1° **21** 30°, 150°

22 60°, 120° **23** 41.8°, 138.2°

24 18.4°, 161.6°

Exercise 7.11

1 a 15.3 cm² **b** 44.5 cm²

 c 9.64 cm² **d** 6.68 cm²

 e 15.5 cm² **f** 32.7 cm²

2 a 21.2 cm² **b** 43.3 cm²

 c 29.1 cm²

UNIT 7

3 **a** 171 cm² **b** 25.7 cm²

c 59.4 cm²

4 **a** 25.0 cm² **b** 28.4 cm²

c 20.8 cm²

5 374 cm²

6 9.61

7 10.1

8 6.20

9 8.51

10 13.2

11 173 cm²

12 125 cm²

13 48.6, 131.4

Exercise 7.12

1 **a** 1.85 cm² **b** 7.34 cm²

c 9.83 cm² **d** 11.0 cm²

e 51.4 cm² **f** 1.33 cm²

2 22.0

Exercise 7.13

1 **a**

Time	cf
$t \leq 2$	15
$t \leq 4$	27
$t \leq 6$	37
$t \leq 8$	45
$t \leq 10$	50

b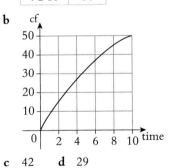

c 42   **d** 29

2 **a**

Height	cf
$h \leq 160$	7
$h \leq 165$	31
$h \leq 170$	66
$h \leq 175$	88
$h \leq 180$	100

b

c 17   **d** 21

3 **a**

Mark	cf
≤ 20	5
≤ 40	15
≤ 60	29
≤ 80	46
≤ 100	50

b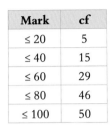

c 36   **d** 29

4 **a**

Mass	cf
≤ 2.5	6
≤ 3	16
≤ 3.5	33
≤ 4	46
≤ 4.5	54
≤ 5	60

b

c 23   **d** 22

5 **a**

b 20   **c** 26%

6

Speed	Frequency
$0 < v \leq 30$	6
$30 < v \leq 40$	18
$40 < v \leq 50$	26
$50 < v \leq 60$	10

7

Mark	Frequency
$0 < m \leq 20$	3
$20 < m \leq 40$	18
$40 < m \leq 60$	37
$60 < m \leq 80$	21
$80 < m \leq 100$	1

8 **a** 23

b 4

c

Time	cf
$t \leq 10$	4
$t \leq 20$	16
$t \leq 30$	32
$t \leq 40$	38
$t \leq 50$	40

Time	Frequency
$0 < t \leq 10$	4
$10 < t \leq 20$	12
$20 < t \leq 30$	16
$30 < t \leq 40$	6
$40 < t \leq 50$	2

d 22.5 minutes

9 **a** 5

b 13%

c

Time	cf		Time	Freq
≤ 700	2		600 < t ≤ 700	2
≤ 800	12		700 < t ≤ 800	10
≤ 900	30		800 < t ≤ 900	18
≤ 1000	38		900 < t ≤ 1000	8
≤ 1100	40		1000 < t ≤ 1100	2

d 845 hours

Exercise 7.14

1 a i 31 **ii** 22
   iii 40 **iv** 18
   v 28

 b i 57 **ii** 44
   iii 68 **iv** 24
   v 52

 c i 168 **ii** 165.5
   iii 171 **iv** 5.5
   v 167

 d i 47 **ii** 44
   iii 51 **iv** 7
   v 45

2 a

 b i 156 **ii** 145
   iii 168 **iv** 23
   v 164

3 a

 b i 16 **ii** 11 **iii** 22
   iv 11 **v** 25

4 a

 b i 400 **ii** 353
   iii 436 **iv** 83
   v 377

5 In general, the 10 to 20 year olds react quicker.

The 10 to 20 year olds are less varied.

6 a

	Median	LQ	UQ	IQR
Paper 1	46	30	62	32
Paper 2	58	47	67	20

 b In general, the marks on paper 2 are higher.
   The marks on paper 2 are less varied.

7 a

b

	Median	LQ	UQ	IQR
Super-maket A	75	58	92	34
Super-maket B	71	44	93	49

 c In general, shoppers spent more money in Supermarket A.

   The amounts spent in Supermarket A are less varied.

Examination-style questions

1 a $0.75\,\text{m/s}^2$ **b** 4575 m
2 a $0.5\,\text{m/s}^2$ **b** 4525 m
   c 22.625 m/s

3 $c = \dfrac{ab}{2b-a}$

4 $p = \dfrac{3}{5r+4q}$

5 $x = \sqrt{\dfrac{c-d}{a-b}}$

6 3, −1 **7** 45th
8 a $7n - 3$ **b** 2^{n+1}
9 a $11 - 3n$
  b $2n^2 - 3$
  c $\dfrac{n(n+1)}{2}$ x^{n+1}

10 17th
11 $a = 5$, $b = 3$
12 $p = 3$, $q = -7$, $r = 2$

13

Term	1	2	3	4	5		nth term
Sequence A	3	5	7	9	11		$2n + 1$
Sequence B	$\dfrac{2}{9}$	$\dfrac{3}{16}$	$\dfrac{4}{25}$	$\dfrac{5}{36}$	$\dfrac{6}{49}$		$\dfrac{n+1}{(n+2)^2}$
Sequence C	1	2	8	16	32		2^{n+1}
Sequence D	−2	1	6	13	22		$n^2 - 3$
Sequence E	3	1	2	3	10		$2^{n+1} - n^2 + 3$

14 a

x	−2	−1.5	−1	−0.5	0	0.5	1	1.5	2	2.5	3
y	2.69	2.59	2.44	2.25	2	1.66	1.2	0.59	−0.24	−1.35	−2.83

b

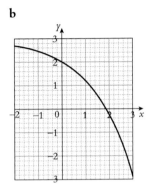

c $x = 1.2$ **d** −1.1 to −0.9

15 a

Time (t minutes)	$t \le 5.5$	$t \le 6$	$t \le 6.5$	$t \le 7$	$t \le 7.5$	$t \le 8$
Frequency	11	35	68	84	96	100

b

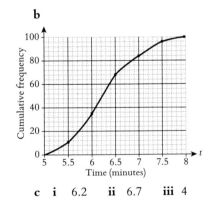

c i 6.2 **ii** 6.7 **iii** 4

16 30, 150

17 12.6 cm²

18 8.81 cm²

19 693 cm²

Unit 8

Exercise 8.1

1 a $0.\dot{3}$ **b** $0.\dot{5}$ **c** $0.1\dot{8}$
d $0.31\dot{8}$ **e** $0.6\dot{1}$ **f** $0.6\dot{5}$
g $0.1\dot{5}$ **h** $0.17\dot{1}$
i $0.\dot{2}8571\dot{4}$ **j** $0.\dot{3}8461\dot{5}$

2 a $\dfrac{1}{3}$ **b** $\dfrac{7}{9}$ **c** $\dfrac{4}{11}$
d $\dfrac{68}{99}$ **e** $\dfrac{14}{99}$ **f** $\dfrac{145}{999}$
g $\dfrac{238}{999}$ **h** $\dfrac{47}{90}$ **i** $\dfrac{11}{18}$
j $\dfrac{3}{22}$

3 a $\sqrt{36}$ **b** $\sqrt{40}$ **c** $\sqrt{64}$
d $\sqrt{49}$ **e** $\sqrt{\dfrac{4}{9}}$

4 $\pi, \sqrt{\dfrac{5}{8}}$

5 $\sqrt{2}, \sqrt{3}, \sqrt{5}, \sqrt{6}$

6 a irrational **b** rational

7 a 25π cm², irrational
 b 100 cm², rational
 c $100 - 25\pi$ cm², irrational

Exercise 8.2

1 The value of the square root was rounded too soon. Using $\sqrt{141} = 11.8743...$ gives the correct answers.

2 a 4, −6 **b** 0.56, −3.56
 c 3.19, −2.19
 d 2.73, −0.73
 e 5.65, 0.35
 f 2.53, −5.53
 g 1.32, −5.32 **h** 2.39, 0.28
 i 3.39, −0.89
 j 1.85, −0.18
 k 15.62, −25.62
 l 0.54, −2.29
 m 2.35, −0.85
 n 1.45, −3.45
 o 0.68, −3.68
 p −1.26, −8.74

3 Impossible to solve because of the square root of a negative number

4 $x = 2.5$. There is only one (repeated) root of the equation.

5 a 2.61, −4.61
 b 1.61, −5.61
 c 4.45, −0.45
 d −0.46, −6.54
 e −0.46, −6.54
 f $3, -\dfrac{1}{3}$
 g 0.72, −0.61
 h 7.52, −2.52

6 a 1.61, −5.61
b 4.46, −2.46

7 a 2.87, −4.87
b 3.48, −0.48
c 2.14, −5.14

Exercise 8.3

1 a 2 **b** 1 **c** 0 **d** 2
e 1 **f** 2 **g** 0 **h** 1
i 2 **j** 2

2 ±10   **3** $k < 2$

Exercise 8.4

1 2.65 **2** 2.61 **3** 5.23
4 2.72 **5** 2.86, 0.14
6 a $A = w(w + 20)$
b 74.26 m, 337 m
7 a answer given **b** 5
8 2.30
9 (0.414, −0.586), (−2.414, −3.414)
10 a answer given
b 10   **c** 12, 96

Exercise 8.5

1 a $\dfrac{5(x-3)}{x(x-5)}$ **b** $\dfrac{11x+27}{(x+3)(x+2)}$

c $\dfrac{5x+62}{(x-2)(x+7)}$ **d** $\dfrac{11x+4}{x(3x+1)}$

e $\dfrac{17x-24}{(2x+5)(3x-2)}$

f $\dfrac{-4x-19}{(1-2x)(x-4)}$

g $\dfrac{2x+5}{(x+2)(x+3)}$

h $\dfrac{9x+17}{(x+1)(x+3)}$

i $\dfrac{2+3x}{x(x+1)}$ **j** $\dfrac{x+3}{(x+2)(x+4)}$

k $\dfrac{-3x-1}{(x-3)(x+1)}$ **l** $\dfrac{x^2+y^2}{x+y}$

2 a −2.25 **b** −0.5 **c** $2, -\dfrac{1}{3}$

3 a $3, -1\dfrac{1}{4}$ **b** $2, -\dfrac{5}{6}$

c 11, −2 **d** 5, 4
e $-1, -2\dfrac{1}{16}$ **f** $4, 2\dfrac{5}{7}$

g 2 **h** $-1\dfrac{1}{2}, -5\dfrac{1}{2}$

i 6, 2

Exercise 8.6

1 a $y = 5x$ **b** 40 **c** 1.4
2 a $y = 8x$ **b** 24 **c** 0.75
3 a $y = 0.5x$ **b** 1.2 **c** 10
4 a $y = \dfrac{1}{3}x$ **b** $1\dfrac{1}{3}$ **c** 10.2
5 a $y = \dfrac{1}{10}x$ **b** 0.8 **c** 70

6
x	2	5	13
y	6	15	39

7 a $v = 9.8t$ **b** 29.4 m/s
c 2.5 s
8 a $e = 4.4\,m$ **b** 3.52 cm
c 0.4 kg
9 a $d = 1.5V$ **b** 1.8 m
c 0.38 m^3

Exercise 8.7

1 a $y = 2x^2$ **b** 50 **c** ±8
2 a $y = 0.5x^2$ **b** 40.5 **c** ±8
3 a $y = 4x^3$ **b** 32 **c** 4
4 a $y = 2(x + 3)^2$ **b** 98
c 2, −8
5 a $y = 5(x − 2)^2$ **b** 180
6 a $y = 6\sqrt{x}$ **b** 15 **c** 64

7
x	1	2	5
y	2	16	250

8 a $d = 0.015v^2$ **b** 24
9 a $E = 12e^2$ **b** 75
10 a $R = 2v^2$ **b** 2450

Exercise 8.8

1 a $y = \dfrac{6}{x}$ **b** 1 **c** 4

2 a $y = \dfrac{24}{x}$ **b** 6 **c** 3

3 a $y = \dfrac{10}{x}$ **b** 20 **c** 4

4 a $y = \dfrac{1}{2x}$ **b** 0.25 **c** 0.5

5
x	2	4	6
y	18	9	6

6
x	2.5	4	5
y	40	25	20

7 a $w = \dfrac{300000}{f}$ **b** 2000
c 1500

8 a $P = \dfrac{300}{V}$ **b** 2 **c** 120

9 a $t = \dfrac{24}{n}$ **b** 8 **c** 6

Exercise 8.9

1 a B **b** C **c** E
d A **e** D

2 a $y = \dfrac{36}{x^2}$ **b** 9 **c** ±6

3 a $y = \dfrac{20}{\sqrt{x}}$ **b** 1.25 **c** 25

4 a $y = \dfrac{15}{x+2}$ **b** 1.5 **c** 2

5 a $y = \dfrac{16}{(x+1)^2}$ **b** 1 **c** 1, −2

6
x	±1	2	5
y	50	12.5	2

7 a $F = \dfrac{20}{d^2}$ **b** 80 **c** 10

8 a $I = \dfrac{126000}{d^2}$ **b** 12.6
c 251

9 a D **b** A **c** B **d** C

Exercise 8.10

1 a 3.38 **b** 4.31 **c** 15.1
d 5.38 **e** 9.95 **f** 4.82
g 6.84 **h** 4.16 **i** 10.5
2 a 30.9 **b** 43.7 **c** 24.2
d 35.8 **e** 28.0 **f** 46.4
g 59.1 **h** 47.6 **i** 41.2
3 7.01
4 a 5.71 cm **b** 51.0°
5 25.4°
6 a 9.56 km
b i 110° **ii** 147°
7 13.1 km

Exercise 8.11

1 34.6, 145.4 **2** 62.4, 117.6

Exercise 8.12

1 a 3.81 cm **b** 5.74 cm
c 2.63 cm **d** 6.03 cm

UNIT 8

e   5.99 cm   f   5.35 cm
g   5.31 cm   h   9.27 cm
i   5.42 cm

2   a   34.8   b   16.1   c   45.5
d   34.1   e   97.2   f   35.6
g   112.9   h   22.3   i   120

Exercise 8.13

1   a   12.8 cm   b   7.90 cm
2   a   5 cm   b   92.1°
3   a   80°   b   7.86 km
4   29.0°
5   104.5°
6   8.61
7   a   85°
b   17.4 cm²
c   8.24
d   37.2
e   22.8°
8   32.4 cm
9   a   6.48 cm
b   45.2 cm²
10   a   37.6 cm
b   24.2 cm
c   604 cm²
11   1020 cm²
12   a   i   5   ii   10   iii   11.2
b   25
13   a   answer given   b   3.91
c   11.7 cm²
14   a   answer given   b   4.74
c   13.9 cm²

Exercise 8.14

1   a   1, 3.5, 4.5, 3
b

mass (*m* grams)

2   a   7, 13, 14, 2
b

Time (*t* hours)

3   a   5, 8, 7, 6, 4
b
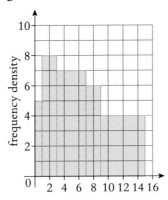
Time (*t* minutes)

4   a   2.4, 5.8, 12.6, 9, 0.5
b

Height (*h* cm)

5

Speed (*v* km/h)

6

Time (*t* minutes)

7

Time (*t* minutes)

8   a   6, 8, 7, 9, 5
b   5.84 min
9   a   2, 8, 6, 5, 4
b   3.17 kg
10   9 cm, 24 cm, 2 cm
11   8 cm, 10 cm, 2.4 cm
12   a   8, 20, 15, 14, 12
b   19
c   2.19 hours
d $\frac{41}{70}$
13   a   48, 24
b

Distance (km)

c   12.9 km

Examination-style questions

1 $\dfrac{5}{9}$

2 $\dfrac{16}{45}$

3 $\dfrac{263}{333}$

4 $\pi, \sqrt{7}$

5 $-3.61, 1.11$

6 $-0.53, 1.86$

7 **a** $r^2 + 5r - 75 = 0$
   b 6.51

8 $\dfrac{3x+17}{(x-1)(x+3)}$

9 $\dfrac{3x^2 - 2x - 13}{4(x-3)}$

10 $-4, 5$

11 6

12 $y = \dfrac{250}{x^2}$

13 58.6

14 14.2

15 **a** **i** 3.95 km
       ii 21.3°
   b **i** 242°
       ii 274°

16 **a** 81.1°
   b 67.6°
   c 2690 cm²

17

18 **a**

Mass (x kilograms)	$1.8 < x \le 2$	$2 < x \le 2.5$	$2.5 < x \le 3.5$	$3.5 < x \le 5.1$
Frequency	2	12	18	8

   b 2.98 kg

19 **a** $y = 6$
   b **ii** 1.17 or 6.83
       iii 1.85 cm or 30.15 cm

20 **a** $\dfrac{50}{x}$
   b $\dfrac{50}{x+2}$ or $\dfrac{50}{x} - 0.1$
   d $x = -32.64$ or $x = 30.64$
   e 1 hour 32 minutes

Unit 9

Exercise 9.1

1 $890.38

2 $540.56 → $541

3 $5793

4 $330.50

5 $154.47

6 $550

7 $4150

8 3.5%

9 3.25

10 1.89

Exercise 9.2

1 $1774.82

2 $19 683

3 $6333

4 943

5 5.64 million

6 6554

7 24 hours

8 6.35

9 3.25
   a $100(\sqrt{2} - 1)\%$
        $(= 4.44\%$ to 3 sf$)$
   b 16
   c 268 435 456

Exercise 9.3

1 **a** $x = -2, y = 3$
   b $x = 9, y = 4$
   c $x = 1, y = -2$
   d $x = 8, y = 1\dfrac{1}{2}$
   e $x = \dfrac{1}{2}, y = 7$
   f $x = -2, y = 5$
   g $x = 4, y = -3$
   h $x = 2\dfrac{1}{2}, y = 4$
   i $x = -\dfrac{1}{3}, y = 7\dfrac{2}{3}$
   j $x = 2, y = 9$
   k $x = -3, y = -3$
   l $x = -4, y = 7$

2 **a** $x = 4, y = 1$
   b $x = 16, y = 3$
   c $x = -23, y = -78$
   d $x = -22, y = -9$

3 **a** $x = 6, y = -4$
   b $x = 3, y = 6$
   c $x = -2, y = 1$
   d $x = 8, y = -2$
   e $x = 1, y = -4$
   f $x = 5, y = -2$
   g $x = -3, y = -1$
   h $x = 8, y = 1\dfrac{1}{2}$
   i $x = -\dfrac{1}{3}, y = 0$
   j $x = -10, y = 9$
   k $x = 3, y = 4\dfrac{1}{2}$
   l $x = \dfrac{2}{3}, y = -2$

4 $(2, 4)$ 5 $(-1, -4)$

6 34   7 $3.65

8 42   9 13   10 546

Exercise 9.4

1 a $15x + 3y \leq 900$

b $x \geq 40, y \geq 20$

c

d 56

2 a $x + y \leq 15, y \geq 6, y \geq 2x$

b

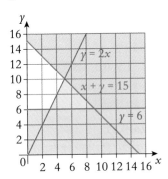

c 5

3 a $400x + 200y \leq 9000$

b $y < x, y \geq 10$

c

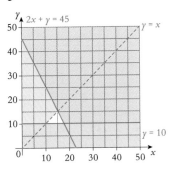

d 17

4 a $16x + 10y \geq 100$

b $x + y \leq 8 \quad x \geq 1 \quad y \geq 3$

---

c

d 5

Exercise 9.5

1 a $4x + 3y \leq 48, x + y \leq 14,$
  $x \geq 5, y \geq 5$

b

c $230

2 a $5x + 3y \geq 45, x + y \leq 11, y \geq 2$

b

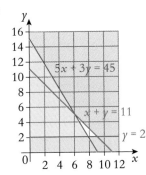

c $96

3 a $2x + y \leq 200, 4x + 5y \leq 580,$
  $x \geq 50, y \geq 40$

---

b

c $165

Exercise 9.6

1 a $(x - 1)^2 - 1$

b $(x + 2)^2 - 4$

c $(x - 5)^2 - 25$

d $(x + 10)^2 - 100$

e $(x - 8)^2 - 64$

f $(x - 6)^2 - 36$

g $(x + 9)^2 - 81$

h $(x + 18)^2 - 324$

i $(x + 11)^2 - 121$

j $(x + 12)^2 - 144$

k $(x - 1.5)^2 - 2.25$

l $(x + 2.5)^2 - 6.25$

m $(x + 3.5)^2 - 12.25$

n $(x + 4.5)^2 - 20.25$

o $(x - 10)^2 - 100$

p $(x + 0.5)^2 - 0.25$

2 a $5(x - 2)^2 - 20$

b $3(x + 2)^2 - 12$

c $4(x + 2.5)^2 - 25$

d $3(x - 3.5)^2 - 36.75$

e $2(x + 3)^2 - 18$

f $2(x - 1.25)^2 - 3.125$

g $3(x - \frac{2}{3})^2 - 1\frac{1}{3}$

h $2(x + 2.25)^2 - 10.125$

UNIT 9

3 **a** $(x-4)^2-1$
   b $(x-2)^2-16$
   c $(x-3)^2-13$
   d $(x+2)^2-7$
   e $(x+6)^2-41$
   f $(x-4)^2-15$
   g $(x+5)^2-28$
   h $(x+4.5)^2-22.25$

4 $a=5, b=-21$

5 $p=4, q=-19$

6 $p=2, q=-5$

7 **a** $x=3\pm\sqrt{b-9}$
   b $x=-5\pm\sqrt{a+b+25}$

Exercise 9.7

1 **a** $-2,-4$ **b** -2
   c $2,-4$ **d** $7.41, 4.59$
   e $4.41, 1.59$
   f $0.21, -14.21$
   g $21.5, -1.53$
   h $8.16, 1.84$
   i $3.65, -1.65$

2 **a** $-1,-2$ **b** $4, 3$
   c $2,-3$ **d** $3.62, 1.38$
   e $2.70, -3.70$
   f $10.72, 0.28$

3 **a** $2, -\dfrac{1}{3}$ **b** $-\dfrac{1}{2}, -3$
   c $-3,-5$ **d** $7.74, 0.26$
   e $-0.42, -1.58$
   f $0.65, -4.65$

4 **a** $0.24, -12.24$
   b $4.61, -2.61$

5 **a** $6.90, -2.90$
   b $3.83, -1.83$
   c $3.11, -1.61$
   d $3.30, -0.30$
   e $1.29, 0.31$
   f $1.65, -3.65$

6 7

7 answer given

8 3

Exercise 9.8

1 **a** $\cup$ shaped curve
      minimum point: $(4, -4)$
      axis crossing points:
      $(2, 0), (6, 0), (0, 12)$
   b $\cup$ shaped curve
      minimum point: $(-3, -16)$
      axis crossing points:
      $(-7, 0), (1, 0), (0, -7)$
   c $\cap$ shaped curve
      maximum point: $(-1, 9)$
      axis crossing points:
      $(-4, 0), (2, 0), (0, 8)$
   d $\cup$ shaped curve
      minimum point:
      $\left(-1\dfrac{3}{4}, -36\dfrac{1}{8}\right)$
      axis crossing points:
      $(-6, 0), \left(2\dfrac{1}{2}, 0\right), (0, -30)$

2 **a** $(x-4)^2-9$
   b $(4, -9)$, minimum
   c $\cup$ shaped curve
      axis crossing points:
      $(1, 0), (7, 0), (0, 7)$

3 **a** $16-(x+1)^2$
   b $(-1, 16)$, maximum
   c $\cap$ shaped curve
      axis crossing points:
      $(-5, 0), (3, 0), (0, 15)$

4 **a** $2(x+2)^2-1$
   b $(-2, -1)$, minimum

5 **a** $28-2(x+3)^2$
   b $(-3, 28)$, maximum point

6 A: $y=(x-2)^2-4$ or x^2-4x
   B: $y=(x+2)^2-2$ or x^2+4x+2
   C: $y=3-(x+1)^2$ or $2-2x-x^2$

Exercise 9.9

1 $-1.41, 1.41, 5$

2 $-1.2, 3.2$

3 **a** $-2.45, 2.45$ **b** $-1.3, 2.3$
   c $-0.7, 2.7$

4 **a** $0, 3$ **b** $-0.45, 4.45$
   c $-1.6, 2.6$

5 **a** 2.7 **b** $2.1, 0.2, -2.3$
   c 0.84

6 **a** $y=4$ **b** $y=0.5$
   c $y=4x$ **d** $y=x+2$
   e $y=x^2-2$
   f $y=\dfrac{1}{x}+3$
   g $y=1-2x$
   h $y=\dfrac{1}{x^2}$

7 $y=x+5$

8 $y=5x-5$

Exercise 9.10

1 **a** $-0.8, 4.8$ **b** $k=1$
   c $k<1$

2 **a** $0.2, 2.8$
   b $k=2, k=3, k=4$

3 **a** $-2.4, 0.4, 2$ **b** $k=3$
   c $k<3$

4 **a** $-1.9, 0.3, 1.5$
   b $k=-1$ and $k=3$
   c $k>3$ and $k<-1$

Exercise 9.11

1 **a**

   b

   c

   d

UNIT 9

e

2 a $\begin{pmatrix} 3 \\ 2 \end{pmatrix}$ **b** $\begin{pmatrix} -5 \\ -1 \end{pmatrix}$ **c** $\begin{pmatrix} -2 \\ 4 \end{pmatrix}$

d $\begin{pmatrix} -4 \\ 0 \end{pmatrix}$ **e** $\begin{pmatrix} -3 \\ -3 \end{pmatrix}$ **f** $\begin{pmatrix} 0 \\ -2 \end{pmatrix}$

g $\begin{pmatrix} 5 \\ -3 \end{pmatrix}$ **h** $\begin{pmatrix} 4 \\ 1 \end{pmatrix}$

3

Parallel

4

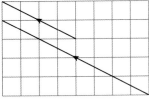

Perpendicular

5 a 10 **b** 13 **c** 4
d 17 **e** 29

6 a $\overrightarrow{TU}, \overrightarrow{SO}, \overrightarrow{RQ}, \overrightarrow{OP}$
b $\overrightarrow{UP}, \overrightarrow{TO}, \overrightarrow{SR}, \overrightarrow{OQ}$
c $\overrightarrow{OS}, \overrightarrow{UT}, \overrightarrow{QR}, \overrightarrow{PO}$
d $\overrightarrow{QO}, \overrightarrow{OT}, \overrightarrow{PU}, \overrightarrow{RS}$

Exercise 9.12

1 a

b

c

d

e

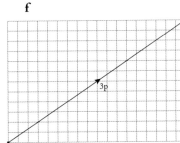

f

2 a $\begin{pmatrix} -6 \\ -10 \end{pmatrix}$ **b** $\begin{pmatrix} -5 \\ -10 \end{pmatrix}$ **c** $\begin{pmatrix} 4 \\ 8 \end{pmatrix}$

d $\begin{pmatrix} 1 \\ -2 \end{pmatrix}$ **e** $\begin{pmatrix} 2 \\ -1 \end{pmatrix}$ **f** $\begin{pmatrix} -5 \\ 10 \end{pmatrix}$

3 a $\begin{pmatrix} 4 \\ 3 \end{pmatrix}$ **b** $\begin{pmatrix} 6 \\ -2 \end{pmatrix}$ **c** $\begin{pmatrix} 2 \\ -5 \end{pmatrix}$

d $\begin{pmatrix} 4 \\ 7 \end{pmatrix}$ **e** $\begin{pmatrix} 8 \\ 6 \end{pmatrix}$

f $\begin{pmatrix} -2 \\ -27 \end{pmatrix}$ **g** $\begin{pmatrix} 6 \\ 14 \end{pmatrix}$ **h** $\begin{pmatrix} 14 \\ 25 \end{pmatrix}$

i $\begin{pmatrix} 14 \\ 8 \end{pmatrix}$ **j** $\begin{pmatrix} 30 \\ 18 \end{pmatrix}$ **k** $\begin{pmatrix} 4 \\ -6 \end{pmatrix}$

l $\begin{pmatrix} -3 \\ -13 \end{pmatrix}$

4 C and E, B and H, G and D,
A and F

5 a $\begin{pmatrix} 4 \\ 1 \end{pmatrix}$ **b** $\begin{pmatrix} 2 \\ 3 \end{pmatrix}$ **c** $\begin{pmatrix} -1 \\ 2 \end{pmatrix}$

d $\begin{pmatrix} -3 \\ 4 \end{pmatrix}$ **e** $\begin{pmatrix} -3 \\ 0 \end{pmatrix}$ **f** $\begin{pmatrix} -2 \\ -3 \end{pmatrix}$

g $\begin{pmatrix} 0 \\ -1 \end{pmatrix}$ **h** $\begin{pmatrix} 1 \\ -4 \end{pmatrix}$

6 a $\begin{pmatrix} 2 \\ -1 \end{pmatrix}, \begin{pmatrix} 2 \\ 1 \end{pmatrix}, \begin{pmatrix} 0 \\ 2 \end{pmatrix}, \begin{pmatrix} -3 \\ 1 \end{pmatrix}, \begin{pmatrix} -1 \\ -3 \end{pmatrix}$

b $\begin{pmatrix} 0 \\ 0 \end{pmatrix}$ Start and finish at the same place

7 a $\begin{pmatrix} 21 \\ 20 \end{pmatrix}$ **b** 29

8 a $\begin{pmatrix} 12 \\ 35 \end{pmatrix}$ **b** 37

9 a answer given
b 5.07
10 $p = 6.12$, $q = -5.14$
11 $p = -28.2$, $q = 10.3$
12 $x = 7$, $y = -1$
13 $x = 3$, $y = -4$

14 a $\begin{pmatrix} 8 \\ 1 \end{pmatrix}$ **b** $\begin{pmatrix} 1 \\ 3 \end{pmatrix}$ **c** $\begin{pmatrix} 1 \\ 3 \end{pmatrix}$

d $\begin{pmatrix} 2 \\ 6 \end{pmatrix}$

15 a $\begin{pmatrix} 3 \\ 2 \end{pmatrix}$ **b** $\begin{pmatrix} 6 \\ 4 \end{pmatrix}$ **c** $(9, 6)$

16 a

t	0	1	2	3	4
r	$\begin{pmatrix} 3 \\ 5 \end{pmatrix}$	$\begin{pmatrix} 5 \\ 4 \end{pmatrix}$	$\begin{pmatrix} 7 \\ 3 \end{pmatrix}$	$\begin{pmatrix} 9 \\ 2 \end{pmatrix}$	$\begin{pmatrix} 11 \\ 1 \end{pmatrix}$

b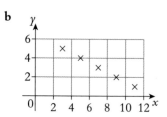

c The points lie in a straight line.

Exercise 9.13

1 a −q   b 2q
  c −p + q   d −2q + p
2 a −p + q   b $-\frac{1}{2}$p + $\frac{1}{2}$q
  c $\frac{1}{2}$p − $\frac{1}{2}$q   d $\frac{1}{2}$p + $\frac{1}{2}$q
3 a p + r   b $\frac{1}{2}$r
  c p + $\frac{1}{2}$r   d $\frac{1}{2}$r − p
4 a $\vec{BA}$ = −2p   b q + 2p
  c −p + q   d p + q
5 a p   b −q
  c p + q   d p − q
  e 2q + p   f −q − 2p
6 a $\frac{1}{2}$a   b $-\frac{1}{2}$c
  c −a + c   d $\frac{1}{2}$c − $\frac{1}{2}$a
  parallel and AC = 2 MN
7 a a + c   b −c + a
  c $\frac{1}{2}$a + $\frac{1}{2}$c   d $\frac{1}{2}$a − $\frac{1}{2}$c
8 a $\frac{1}{2}$p + $\frac{1}{2}$q   b $\frac{1}{2}$p + $\frac{1}{2}$q
  c $-\frac{1}{2}$q + $\frac{1}{2}$p   d $\frac{1}{2}$p − $\frac{1}{2}$q
  parallelogram
9 a $\frac{3}{2}$c   b −a + c
  c a − $\frac{1}{2}$c   d $\frac{1}{2}$c − $\frac{1}{2}$a
  parallel and AC = 2 MN
10 a p + q   b $-\frac{3}{2}$p + $\frac{1}{2}$q
  c $\frac{5}{2}$p + $\frac{1}{2}$q   d $\frac{1}{2}$(3p + q)

Exercise 9.14

1 a −p + q   b $-\frac{1}{3}$p + $\frac{1}{3}$q
  c $\frac{2}{3}$p + $\frac{1}{3}$q
2 a −p + q   b $-\frac{3}{4}$p + $\frac{3}{4}$q
  c $\frac{1}{4}$p + $\frac{1}{4}$q   d $\frac{1}{4}$p + $\frac{3}{4}$q
3 a $\frac{1}{2}$q   b $-\frac{1}{3}$p + $\frac{1}{2}$q
  c −p + q   d $-\frac{2}{5}$p + $\frac{2}{5}$q
4 a $\frac{1}{3}$r   b $\frac{1}{4}$p
  c $\frac{2}{3}$r − $\frac{3}{4}$p   d r + $\frac{1}{4}$p
5 a −3a + c   b $-\frac{9}{5}$a + $\frac{3}{5}$c
  c $\frac{6}{5}$a + $\frac{3}{5}$c   d 2a + c
  collinear
6 a r − p   b $\frac{1}{4}$r − $\frac{1}{4}$p
  c $\frac{1}{4}$p + $\frac{3}{4}$r   d $\frac{3}{4}$p + $\frac{1}{4}$r
7 a $\frac{2}{5}$r   b p − $\frac{3}{5}$r
  c $\frac{5}{3}$p − r   d $\frac{5}{3}$p
  $\vec{OX} = \frac{5}{3}\vec{OP}$
8 $p = 13, q = 10\frac{1}{3}$
9 answer given

Challenge
a $\frac{1}{3}p + \frac{1}{3}q$

b $\frac{1}{3}p + \frac{1}{3}q$

The points coincide.

Exercise 9.15

1 a i $\frac{7}{12}$ ii $\frac{1}{10}$ iii $\frac{11}{20}$
  b $\frac{7}{9}$ c $\frac{117}{590}$

2 a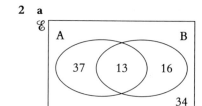
  b i $\frac{4}{25}$ ii $\frac{17}{50}$
  c $\frac{37}{50}$ d $\frac{49}{198}$
3 a i $\frac{89}{150}$ ii $\frac{13}{30}$ iii $\frac{23}{150}$
  b $\frac{47}{89}$ c 0.486
4 a i $\frac{73}{100}$ ii $\frac{1}{4}$ iii $\frac{3}{20}$
  b $\frac{17}{50}$ c $\frac{145}{392}$
5 a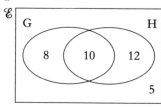
  b i $\frac{2}{7}$ ii $\frac{12}{35}$
  c $\frac{5}{11}$ d $\frac{286}{595}$
6 a i $\frac{2}{25}$ ii $\frac{3}{50}$ iii $\frac{1}{50}$
  b $\frac{8}{19}$ c $\frac{19}{1990}$
7 a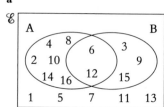
  b i $\frac{5}{16}$ ii $\frac{1}{2}$ iii $\frac{1}{8}$
  iv $\frac{11}{16}$ v $\frac{5}{16}$

UNIT 9

8 **a** **i** $\dfrac{27}{50}$ **ii** $\dfrac{7}{25}$ **iii** $\dfrac{2}{25}$

b $\dfrac{9}{25}$ **c** $\dfrac{87}{175}$

9 **a**

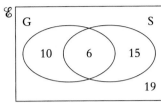

b $\dfrac{3}{25}$ **c** $\dfrac{5}{7}$ **d** $\dfrac{1}{35}$

Examination-style questions

1 172

2 25

3 1.55

4 **a** 38 700

b 1.5%

c 28 600

5 $x = 18,\ y = 11.5$

6 **a** $x \ge 5,\ y \ge 7,\ x > y,\ x + y \ge 18$

b

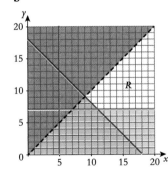

c $12.20

7 $a = -4,\ b = -6$

8 $p = 2,\ q = 7$

9 **a** $p = 2.25,\ q = -7.125$

b -7.125

10 **a** $x = -0.2,\ x = 4.2$

b **i** $y = x - 2$

ii $x = 1.4,\ x = 3.6$

11 **a** $-4.8,\ -0.2,\ 3.0$

b $k = 10$

c $k < 10$

12 **a** $\begin{pmatrix} 14 \\ -4 \end{pmatrix}$

b $\begin{pmatrix} -7 \\ 2 \end{pmatrix}$

c $\begin{pmatrix} 3 \\ -5 \end{pmatrix}$

d 5

13 $\dfrac{1}{3}\mathbf{a} + \dfrac{2}{3}\mathbf{b}$

14 **a** **i** $\mathbf{a} - \mathbf{b}$

ii $\dfrac{3}{5}(\mathbf{a} - \mathbf{b})$

iii $\dfrac{3}{5}\mathbf{a} + \dfrac{2}{5}\mathbf{b}$

iv $\dfrac{3}{4}\mathbf{a} - \mathbf{b}$

b $\dfrac{3k}{5}\mathbf{a} + \dfrac{2k}{5}\mathbf{b}$

c $\dfrac{3m}{4}\mathbf{a} + (1-m)\mathbf{b}$

d $k = \dfrac{5}{6},\ m = \dfrac{2}{3}$

15 **a** **i** $-3\mathbf{a} + 4\mathbf{b}$

ii $3\mathbf{a} - 2\mathbf{b}$

b **i** $\dfrac{12k}{7}\mathbf{a} - 4k\mathbf{b}$

ii $\dfrac{12\lambda}{7}\mathbf{a} + (2 - 4\lambda)\mathbf{b}$

c 0.7

16 **a** $\dfrac{10}{19}$

b $\dfrac{11}{87}$

c $\dfrac{442}{1015}$

17 **a** **i** $\dfrac{19}{50}$

ii $\dfrac{13}{25}$

b $\dfrac{1}{2}$

c **i** $\dfrac{496}{1225}$

ii $\dfrac{5763}{1225}$

d $\dfrac{87}{196}$

Unit 10

Exercise 10.1

1 **a** 5.5 cm, 6.5 cm

b 31.5 min, 32.5 min

c 31.5 kg, 32.5 kg

d 91.5 mm, 92.5 mm

e 7.65 cm, 7.75 cm

f 2.625 kg, 2.635 kg

g 62.85 g, 62.95 g

h 475.5 s, 476.5 s

i 4.935 m, 4.945 m

j 244.5 m, 245.5 m

2 $249.5 \le x < 250.5$

3 23 kg

4 $18 675, $18 525

5 30 825 cm, 30 675 cm

6 139.5 mm, 136.5 mm

7 66 cm, 65.2 cm

8 **a** 25.6 cm, 25.2 cm

b 39.8575 cm^2, 38.5875 cm^2

9 **a** 82.2 cm, 81.8 cm

b 418.6925 cm^2, 414.5925 cm^2

10 28 cm, 24 cm

11 **a** 107.171875 cm^3, 100.544625 cm^3

b 135.375 cm^2, 129.735 cm^2

12 **a** 151.895625 cm^3, 143.028375 cm^3

b 180.715 cm^2, 173.995 cm^2

13 494.8125 cm^3, 352.6875 cm^3

14 231

15 5.186249645 cm

16 132.61014 cm^2

17 **a** 11.77765262 cm

b 22.90713754 cm^2

18 **a** 428 cm, 426 cm

b 92 cm, 90 cm

19 214.2664365 cm^3

20 1.633802817 m/s^2

Exercise 10.2

1 a $(-1, 1), (2, 4)$
   b $(-3, 6), (2, 1)$
   c $(0, 4), (5, 14)$
   d $(-3, -5), (1, 3)$
   e $(2, -1)$ f $(1, 3)$

2 The line is a tangent to the parabola in both cases.

3 a $(0, 0), (1, -1)$
   b $(-10, 0), (8, 6)$
   c $(2, 4)$ d $(-6, -2), (8, 1\frac{1}{2})$
   e $(4, -6), (12, 10)$
   f $(-1, 3), (3, 1)$

4 a $(-2, -7), (1, 2)$
   b $(-8, 3.5), (2, 1)$
   c $(-1, -3), (2, 1)$

5 a $(4, 3), (13.5, -6.5)$
   b $(2, 2), (10, -2)$
   c $(-5, -24), (5, 1)$

6 a $(-3, -1)$ and $(2, 4)$
   b $5\sqrt{2}$ or 7.07

7 a $(0, -10)$ and $(8, 6)$
   b $(4, -2)$
   c $y = -\frac{1}{2}x$

8 $-\frac{2}{3}$

Exercise 10.3

1 a $x + y = 30, xy = 144$
   b 6 and 24

2 $3\frac{1}{2}$ cm and $4\frac{3}{5}$ cm

3 8 cm and $12\frac{1}{2}$ cm

4 9 cm and 12 cm

5 $x = 5\frac{1}{2}, y = 7\frac{1}{2}$
   or $x = 7\frac{1}{2}, y = 5\frac{1}{2}$

6 $a = 3, b = -2$ or $a = \frac{5}{9}, b = 2\frac{8}{9}$

7 $r = 9, h = 12$

Exercise 10.4

1 a i 6.2   ii 6.1
       iii 6.01
   b 6

2

x-coordinate of P	-4	-3	-2	-1	0	1	2	3	4
Gradient of curve at P	-8	-6	-4	-2	0	2	4	6	8

Gradient = $2x$

3 a 14   b -16   c -3.6

4

x-coordinate of P	-4	-3	-2	-1	0	1	2	3	4
Gradient of curve at P	48	27	12	3	0	3	12	27	48

Gradient = $3x^2$

5 a 75   b 300   c 0.12

Exercise 10.5

1 a $6x^5$ b $9x^8$ c $10x^9$
   d $7x^6$ e 0   f 1
   g 0   h 0

2 a $15x^4$ b $8x^3$ c $-10x$
   d x e $-4x^5$ f -5
   g $5x^3$ h $-2x^7$

3 a $10x - 2$ b $3x^2 + 5$
   c $6x - 2$ d $2x + 2$
   e $15 - 30x^2$ f $2x - 3$
   g $x - 5$ h $16x^3 - 40x$
   i $5 - 20x + 15x^2$

4 a 7 b 3 c -1.5 d 9

5 $(-2, -6), (2, 10)$

6 -2

7 $\left(-\frac{2}{3}, \frac{13}{27}\right), (4, -13)$

8 4

9 a
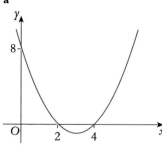

   b -2 and 2

10 a $(-2, 0), (0, 0), (2, 0)$
    b $8, -4, 8$

11 a $(-1, 3), (4, 13),$
    b $-3, 7$

12 $a = 1, b = -2$

13 $a = 2, b = -4$

14 $a = 2, b = -7$

---

15 $a = -7.5, b = 12$

16 $x > 2$

Exercise 10.6

1 a $y = 2x - 5$ b $y = -2x - 5$
   c $y = 10x + 11$
   d $y = -3x + 24$

2 $y = 6x - 5$

3 a $y = 2x - 2$ b $63.4°$

4 24.1

5 b $\left(-1\frac{1}{2}, -5\right)$

6 a $A(2, 0), B(0, 6)$
   b 6 units^2

7 $\left(-1\frac{1}{4}, 10\right)$

8 a $y = 8x - 11$
   b $(-2, -27)$
   c $\left(-\frac{2}{3}, 2\frac{17}{27}\right)$

9 $(-1, 8)$

10 $(0, 36)$

11 $\left(4\frac{1}{3}, -13\frac{1}{3}\right)$

Exercise 10.7

1 a $(3, -9)$, minimum
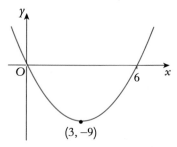

   b $(3, -9)$

2 $(-5, 175), (3, -81)$

3 **a** 12

   b $(-2, -5), (2, 27)$

4 $(1, -3)$

5 $(-4, -80), (2, 28)$

6 $(0, 0), (1, 1), (2, 0)$

7 **a** $(2, 4)$

   b $(-2, 22), (2, -10)$

   c $(-1, -4)$

   d $(-1, 5), (3, -27)$

   e $(-0.5, 6.25)$

   f $(1, -7), (2, -11)$

8 $a = 3$

Exercise 10.8

1 **a** $(-1, -1)$ **b** minimum

2 **a** $(1, 9)$ **b** maximum

3 **a** $(5, -21)$ minimum

   b $\left(-\dfrac{1}{2}, 6\dfrac{1}{4}\right)$ maximum

   c $(0, 0)$ maximum;

     $(5, -125)$ minimum

   d $(-2, 44)$ maximum;

     $(3, -81)$ minimum

   e $(-2, 28)$ maximum;

     $\left(\dfrac{1}{2}, -3\dfrac{1}{4}\right)$ minimum

   f $\left(1, -1\dfrac{2}{3}\right)$ minimum;

     $\left(2, -1\dfrac{1}{3}\right)$ maximum

Exercise 10.9

1 **a** 2   **b** $12x + 6$

   c $12x^2 - 6x$ **d** -4

   e $24x$ **f** $40x^3 - 36x^2$

   g $-6x$ **h** $6x - 2$

   i $20 - 36x + 24x^2$

2 26

3 **a** $72x^2 - 12x$

   b $10 - 20x^3$ **c** 2

4 **a** 5 **b** 6 **c** 4

5 4

6 **b** $-6, 6$

---

7 $a = 3, b = -9$

8 **a** $3x^2 - 6x - 9, 6x - 6$

   b

x	-3	-2	-1	0	1	2	3	4	5
$\dfrac{dy}{dx}$	$+$	$+$	0	$-$	$-$	$-$	0	$+$	$+$
$\dfrac{d^2y}{dx^2}$	$-$	$-$	$-$	$-$	0	$+$	$+$	$+$	$+$

   c **i** negative

      ii positive

Exercise 10.10

1 **a** $(5, 25)$ **b** maximum

2 **a** $(1, -9)$ **b** minimum

3 **a** $(-2, -3)$ minimum

   b $\left(-\dfrac{1}{2}, 1\right)$ maximum

   c $(-1, -4)$ minimum

   d $(-1.5, 33.75)$ maximum;

     $(2, -52)$ minimum

   e $(-2, 22)$ maximum;

     $(2, -10)$ minimum

   f $(1, -7)$ minimum;

     $(5, 25)$ maximum

4 **a** $a = -15, b = 36$

   b $(3, 27)$, minimum

5 **a** $a = -6, b = 5$

   b minimum

   c $(0, 5)$, maximum

6 **a** $a = -3, b = -12$

   b $(2, -20)$

   c $(-1, 7) = $ maximum,

     $(2, -20) = $ minimum

Exercise 10.11

1 **a** $x^3 + 6x^2 + 8x$

   b $2x^3 - 8x^2 - 10x$

   c $6x^4 - 27x^3 + 30x^2$

   d $-98x^3 + 119x^2 - 35x$

   e $3x^2y^2 + 12x^2y - 6xy^2 - 24xy$

   f $30x^2y^3 - 12x^2y^2 - 10xy^3 + 4xy^2$

2 **a** $x^3 + 8x^2 + 17x + 10$

   b $x^3 + 9x^2 + 26x + 24$

---

   c $2x^3 + 7x^2 + 7x + 2$

   d $6x^3 + 43x^2 + 71x + 30$

3 **a** $x^3 + 5x^2 + 2x - 8$

   b $x^3 - 2x^2 - 5x + 6$

   c $2x^3 - 13x^2 + 26x - 15$

   d $15x^3 + 43x^2 - 7x - 3$

4 **a** $6x^3 - 23x^2 + 16x - 3$

   b $4x^3 + 12x^2 - 37x + 15$

   c $-3x^4 + 10x^3 + 5x^2 + 10x + 8$

   d $10x^4 + x^3 - 32x^2 - 3x + 6$

5 **a** $x^3 + 7x^2 + 15x + 9$

   b $4x^3 - 4x^2 - 7x - 2$

   c $3x^3 - 28x^2 + 55x + 50$

   d $x^3 + 6x^2 + 12x + 8$

   e $x^3 - 3x^2 + 3x - 1$

   f $8x^3 - 60x^2 + 150x - 125$

6 $a = 3, b = -5$

7 $a = 2, b = 7$

8 $a = 4, b = 6$

9 **a** $x^4 + 10x^3 + 35x^2 + 50x + 24$

   b $x^4 + 4x^3 + 3x^2 - 4x - 4$

   c $2x^4 + 13x^3 + 12x^2 - 17x - 10$

   d $6x^4 - 19x^3 + 14x^2 + x - 2$

   e $x^4 + 4x^3 + 6x^2 + 4x + 1$

   f $16x^4 - 96x^3 + 216x^2 - 216x + 81$

Exercise 10.12

4 **b** $a = -2, b = -4$ or

     $a = -12, b = -\dfrac{2}{3}$

5 **a** $-7, -\dfrac{1}{2}$

   b $-\dfrac{7}{4}, 1$

6 **a** $-0.16, 6.16$

   b $-1.34, 1.34$

7 **a** $-8, -5, 2$ **b** $-7, -1, 3$

   c $-5, \dfrac{1}{2}, 3$ **d** $-\dfrac{5}{2}, \dfrac{2}{3}, 2$

8 **b** $-5, -1, 2$

9 **a** $\dfrac{x^3 + 8x^2 + 12x + 1}{(x+1)(x+2)(x+3)}$

   b $\dfrac{3x^3 + 4x^2 - 24x - 31}{(x-1)(x+2)(x+3)}$

10 6   **11** 2

Exercise 10.13

1 b $-2, 1, 5$

c

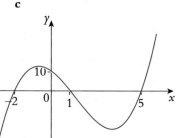

2 b $-2\frac{1}{2}, -1, 3$

c

3 a

b

c

d

e

f

4 $A(-2, 0), B(1, 0), C(4, 0), D(0, 8)$

Exercise 10.14

1 a

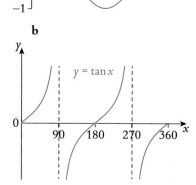

b

c

2 a 17.5°, 162.5°
  b 53.1°, 126.9°
  c 36.9°, 143.1°
  d 224.4°, 315.6°
  e 90° **f** 270°
  g 0°, 180°, 360°
  h 60°, 120°   **i** 45°, 135°
  j 199.5°, 340.5°
  k 41.8°, 138.2°
  l 203.6°, 336.4°

3 $-1 \le \sin x \le 1$

4 a 84.3°, 275.7°
  b 45.6°, 314.4°
  c 113.6°, 246.4°
  d 143.1°, 216.9°
  e 180° **f** 90°, 270°

g 0°, 360° **h** 30°, 330°
i 135°, 225°
j 104.5°, 255.5°
k 64.6°, 295.4°
l 109.5°, 250.5°
5 a 63.4°, 243.4°
 b 73.6°, 253.6°
 c 108.4°, 288.4°
 d 141.3°, 321.3°
 e 45°, 225°
 f 0°, 180°, 360°
 g 135°, 315°
 h 60°, 240°
 i 120°, 300°
 j 68.2°, 248.2°
 k 123.7°, 303.7°
 l 58.0°, 238.0°
6 a 60°, 90°, 270°, 300°
 b 0°, 14.0°, 180°, 194.0°, 360°
 c 30°, 90°, 150°
 d 48.2°, 60°, 300°, 311.8°
 e 19.5°, 160.5°
 f 21.8°, 135°, 201.8°, 315°
7 a 15°, 75°, 195°, 255°
 b 71.6°, 108.4°, 251.6°, 288.4°
 c 22.5°, 112.5°, 202.5°, 292.5°

Exercise 10.15

1 a

 b

c

d

e

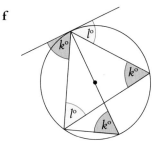

f

2 a $x = 56$, $y = 72$, $z = 52$
 b $x = 70$, $y = 75$
 c $x = 66$
 d $x = 56$, $y = 56$
 e $x = 65$, $y = 65$, $z = 50$
 f $x = 27$
 g $a = 50$, $b = 52$, $c = 26$
 h $x = 38$, $y = 90$, $z = 128$
 i $x = 70$, $y = 55$, $z = 55$
 j $a = 33$, $b = 66$, $c = 57$, $d = 18$

k $a = 42$, $b = 42$, $c = 42$, $d = 96$
l $a = 75$, $b = 50$, $c = 45$
m $a = 58$, $b = 58$, $c = 64$, $d = 58$
n $a = 64$, $b = 116$
o $a = 94$, $b = 43$, $c = 32$
3 a $a = 80°$ alternate segment
 theorem
 $b = 65°$ opposite angles in
 cyclic quadrilateral
 $c = 35°$ angles in a triangle
 add up to 180°
 b $p = 65°$ alternate segment
 theorem
 $q = 65°$ angles subtended
 by the same arc at the
 circumference are equal
 $r = 105°$ alternate segment
 theorem, tangent and radius
 at 90°, angles in a triangle
 add up to 180°
 c $x = 114°$ isosceles triangle,
 angles in a triangle add up to
 180°
 $y = 57°$ angle at centre twice
 angle at circumference
 $z = 57°$ alternate segment
 theorem

Exercise 10.16
1 a 4.01 cm
 b 9.46 cm
2 a 52.6°
 b 7.95 cm
3 4.53 km
4 12 45
5 a 4.47 **b** 6.32
 c 12.6 **d** 7.21
 e 6.32 **f** 7.59
6 a 9.49 **b** 5.39
 c 3.61 **d** 7.81
7 $\dfrac{6\sqrt{5}}{5}$ or 2.68

Exercise 10.17

1
```
0 | 2  7
1 | 1  2  3  6  7  8  8
2 | 2  3  5  7  9
```
Key: 3|4 represents 34 emails

2
```
12 | 3  4  7  8  8
13 | 0  2  3  5  7  8  9
14 | 2  4  4  5  8
15 | 4  5  5  7
16 | 6  8  8
```
Key: 12|3 represents 123 mm

3
```
0 | 1  2  5  5
1 | 3  3  6  7  8  8  9
2 | 0  3  4  6  8
3 | 2  4  5  7
```
Key: 1|3 represents 1.3 m/s

4 a
```
1 | 5  6  6  6  7  8
2 | 0  0  2  3  5  7  8
3 | 2  2  8  8
4 | 1  5  9
```
Key: 1|5 represents a score of 15

  b i 34 **ii** 16 **iii** 24
  c $\frac{7}{20}$

5 a
```
5 | 2  9
6 | 4  7  8  9
7 | 0  1  6  7  9
8 | 0  0  1  4  6  7  8
9 | 3  4  6
```
Key: 5|2 represents 52 cars

b i 44 cars **ii** 80 cars
  iii 79 cars
  c $\frac{6}{21} = \frac{2}{7}$

6 It is continuous data so the range could be
86.4 − 52.5 = 33.9 seconds.

7 a i 31 **ii** 45
  iii 41 **iv** 39.2$\dot{6}$
  b $\frac{1}{35}$

8 a
```
0 | 5  6  7
1 | 0  1  1  3  5  7
2 | 0  0  0  6  9
3 | 3  6
```
b 17.4

9 a

	Mathematics	Science
Range	69	52
Median score	58	41.5

b The scores in mathematics were more varied than the scores in science.

In general, students scored better in mathematics than in science.

Exercise 10.18

1 a 76 km/h
  b 28 km/h
  c 44 km/h
  d 38 km/h
  e 56 km/h
  f 18 km/h

2

3

4 a i 39 kg **ii** 43 kg
  b i 7 kg **ii** 9 kg

c By comparing the medians we can say that, in general, the girls are heavier than the boys. By comparing the interquartile ranges we can say that, in general, the girls' masses are more spread out.

5 a i 171 cm **ii** 165 cm
  iii 178 cm **iv** 13 cm

b

c By comparing the medians we can say that, in general, the males are taller. By comparing the interquartile ranges we can say that, in general, the heights of the males are more spread out.

6 a

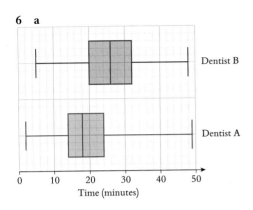

c The median for dentist A (18 minutes) was less than the median for dentist B (26 minutes). This means that, in general, the patients waited less time for dentist A than for dentist B. The interquartile range for dentist A (10 minutes) was less than the interquartile range for dentist B (12 minutes). This means that, in general, the waiting times for dentist A were less spread out than the waiting times for dentist B.

Examination-style questions

1 LB = 255 mm, UB = 261 mm

2 LB = 39.1125 cm², UB = 40.3925 cm²

3 4.7 km/h

4 $x^3 + 10x^2 + 31x + 30$

5 $6y^3 + 29y^2 - 7y - 10$

6 $y^3 + y^2 - 5y + 3$

7 $27x^3 - 108x^2 + 144x - 64$

8 $a = 3, b = -2$

9 $a = 3, b = -5$

10 $a = -5, b = 2$ or $a = 4, b = -\dfrac{5}{2}$

11 b $(x - 7)(x - 7)$ **c** 7

12 $x = 83$

13 $a = 75, b = 58, c = 47$

14 $x = 24$

15 $x = -1, y = 3$
or $x = \dfrac{2}{3}, y = 2\dfrac{1}{6}$

16 a $(1, 1), (2, -1)$

b $y = \dfrac{1}{2}x + \dfrac{3}{4}$

17 $20x^3 - 3$

18 -7

20 a $-3 - 8x^3$

b $-24x^2$

21 a $5 - 4x$

22 $\sqrt{10}$ or 3.16

23 a ii $3x^2 - 12x + 9$

b i $(1, 4), (3, 0)$

ii $(1, 4)$ = maximum, $(3, 0)$ = minimum

24

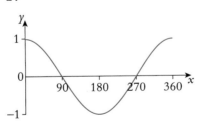

25 41.4°, 318.6°

26 191.5°, 348.5°

27

0	4	7	8		
1	1	2	2	4	6	9
2	0	3	5	8	8
3	2	6			

Key: 3|2 represents 3.2 kg

28 a 3   **b** 41   **c** 28

29

30 a i 82 g   **ii** 94 g

b i 14 g   **ii** 13 g

c

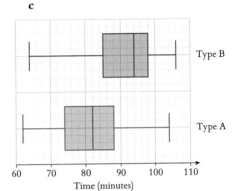

d The median for type A (82 g) was less than the median for type B (92 g). This means that, in general, the type B apples are heavier than the type A apples. The interquartile range for type A (14 g) was slightly more than the interquartile range for type B (13 g). This means that, in general, the spread of the masses for type A is slightly greater than the spread of the masses for type B.

Index

hemispheres 228
hexagons 39, 147
highest common factor (HCF) 5, 7
histograms 382
hypotenuse 78, 178

image 122, 137
   in enlargement 138, 140
improper fractions 10
increase
   percentage 162
   in price 50
   ratios in 206
independent events 296
indices 58
   and BIDMAS 2
   in equations 270
   fractional 268
   in standard form 98, 100
   see also powers
inequalities 62, 72–3
   in linear programming 396, 398
integers 3
interest 250
   compound 250, 390–1
interior angles 39
interquartile range (IQR) 348, 349
   on box-and-whisker plots 487–8
intersection of sets 258
intersections on graphs 274, 407, 438–9
   of tangents 451
invariant point 122
inverse functions 212, 213
inverse proportion 202, 370
inverse transformations 137
inverse variation 370, 372
IQR (interquartile range) 348, 349
   on box-and-whisker plots 487–8
irrational numbers 358
isosceles triangles 33

key 481
kites 76

large numbers 98
LCM (lowest common multiple) 5, 7
like terms 17
line of best fit 196
line segments, midpoint of 71
linear equations 20, 22
   see also lines
linear inequalities 62
   graphs of 72–3
   in linear programming 396, 398
linear programming 396, 398

linear relationships 366
linear sequences 324, 333
lines
   angles on 33, 34
   distance to points 478–9
   equations of 20, 22, 28, 30, 32
      gradient 28, 68
      joining points 70
      perpendicular 478–9
      tangents to curves 450–1
   graphs 28, 30, 32, 68, 70
      joining points 82
      midpoints from 71
   intersecting with quadratics 274, 407, 438–9
   joining points 28, 70, 82
   parallel 33, 68
   perpendicular 33, 278–9, 478–9
   see also chords; tangents
lines of symmetry 36, 168
loss, percentage 162
lower bounds 434–5
lower quartile (LQ) 348
   on box-and-whisker plots 487–8
lowest common multiple (LCM) 5, 7

magnitude of vectors 412
map scales 52, 56
mapping 208
maximum points 404–5, 453
   and first derivatives 455–7
   and second derivatives 460–1
mean 41–2
   on frequency tables 44
   and grouped frequency tables 238–9
   on scatter diagrams 196
median 41–2
   on box-and-whisker plots 487–8
   on cumulative frequency diagrams 348–9
   on frequency tables 44
   on stem-and-leaf diagrams 482–3
mid-value 238, 239
midpoint of lines 71
minimum points 404–5, 453
   and first derivatives 455–7
   and second derivatives 460–1
minimum value 402
mirror line 122
mixed numbers 10
modal class 238
mode 41–2
   on frequency tables 44
   on stem-and-leaf diagrams 482–3
modelling with exponential graphs 336
modulus of vectors 412
multiples 5